Business Research Methods & Statistics

Millersville University
BUAD 306
Dr. Don Brady

David L. Eldredge
Murray State University

Ken Black
University of Houston - Clear Lake

Printed in the United States of America

South-Western College Publishing
5191 Natorp Boulevard
Mason, OH 45040
USA

For information about our products, contact us:
Thomson Learning Academic Resource Center
1-800-423-0563
http://www.swcollege.com

International Headquarters
Thomson Learning
International Division
290 Harbor Drive, 2nd Floor
Stamford, CT 06902-7477
USA

UK/Europe/Middle East/South Africa
Thomson Learning
Berkshire House
168-173 High Holborn
London WCIV 7AA

Asia
Thomson Learning
60 Albert Street, #15-01
Albert Complex
Singapore 189969

Canada
Nelson Thomson Learning
1120 Birchmount Road
Toronto, Ontario MIK 5G4
Canada
United Kingdom

ISBN 0-324-26498-4

The Adaptable Courseware Program consists of products and additions to existing South-Western College Publishing products that are produced from camera-ready copy. Peer review, class testing, and accuracy are primarily the responsibility of the author(s).

Custom Contents

1

THE ROLE OF BUSINESS RESEARCH

What you will learn in this chapter

- To understand the importance of business research as a management decision-making tool.
- To define *business research.*
- To understand the difference between basic and applied research.
- To understand the managerial value of business research and the role it plays in the development and implementation of strategy.
- To define *total quality management* and show its relationship to business research.
- To understand when business research is needed and when it should not be conducted.
- To identify various topics for business research.
- To explain that business research is a global activity.

DuPont has 94,000 employees worldwide and 54,000 in the United States.[1] Its 2000 Work/Life Needs Assessment Survey of employees, conducted across all of DuPont's U.S. business units, is the fourth of its kind in 15 years. This business research provides the company with extensive trend data on employees' work/life behavior and their needs. A key finding of DuPont's latest survey is that, as the company's work force ages, employees' child care difficulties are diminishing, but they see elder care needs emerging on the horizon.

The survey found 88 percent of the respondents identified themselves as baby boomers. About 50 percent of respondents say they have—or expect to have—elder care responsibilities within the next 3 to 4 years, up from 40 percent in 1995.

Prior surveys uncovered that DuPont employees want very much to be able to balance work and family responsibilities, feeling deeply committed to both aspects of their lives. The latest research shows that the company's efforts along these lines have been successful. Employees perceive even greater support by management for work/life issues since the 1995 survey, and indicate that they feel less stress. Support from colleagues is rated high, and women indicated that they now have more role models. Work/life programs are clearly powerful tools that are good for employees and good for business.

The researchers concluded that the feeling of management support is directly connected to employees' discretionary efforts to make the company successful. Employees who use work/life programs reported that they are willing to "go the extra mile."

Other major findings indicate that

- DuPont's work/life programs are highly valued, even by those employees who don't personally use them.
- Flexibility, in particular, is highly valued and appears to work quite well (e.g., almost half of employees have used flexible work hours).
- Other highly valued aspects of work/life are tuition reimbursement, Dependent Care Spending Accounts (where employees can put away before-tax dollars to use on certain types of dependent care), and the company's resource and referral service.

Business research input like this has helped expand and revise work/life programs offerings at DuPont year after year. ■

In thousands of organizations, business research is an important managerial tool that exerts a major influence on decision making. The above example about DuPont's Work/Life Needs Assessment Survey illustrates how business research can provide insights into and solutions for organizational problems. The managerial value and diverse nature of business research can be illustrated by the following additional examples. As you read through these examples, imagine you are an executive considering the importance of business research in providing information essential for good decision making.

Harley-Davidson researchers had Harley owners, would-be owners, and owners of other brands create cut-and-paste collages to express their feelings about Harley-Davidson motorcycles. Whether the artwork was from longtime Harley loyalists or fresh prospects, common themes emerged: enjoyment, the great outdoors, and freedom. Subsequent surveys among customers identified seven core types: Adventure-Loving Traditionalists, Sensitive Pragmatists, Stylish Status-Seekers, Laid-Back Campers, Classy Capitalists, Cool-Headed Loners, and Cocky Misfits. While the groups differed in many aspects, they all appreciated Harley-Davidson products because they were associated with independence, freedom, and power.[2]

When Steelcase, an office furniture manufacturer, decided there was an opportunity for a new product specifically designed for work teams, researchers conducted an observation study. Steelcase placed video cameras at various companies so that they could observe firsthand how teams operate. After the recording period ended, the researchers exhaustively analyzed the tapes, looking for patterns of behavior and motion that workers don't even notice themselves. The main observation was that people in teams function best if they can do some work collaboratively and some privately. Designers used these findings to develop the Personal Harbor brand of modular office units. The units are similar in shape and size to a phone booth and can be arranged around a common space where a team works, fostering synergy but also allowing individuals to work alone when necessary.[3]

Most physicians connect to the Internet daily, and 42 percent work in practices that have Web sites, according to business research conducted in 2001.[4] The study from Harris Interactive found that doctors' use of the Internet has increased significantly since 1999. Only 7 percent of physicians do not use the Internet, compared with 11 percent in 1999. Over half (55 percent) of physicians now use e-mail to communicate with professional colleagues, while 34 percent communicate with support staff via e-mail.

Another study showed that despite the popularity of the Internet among the medical community, few physicians are using the Internet to perform work-related tasks such as communicating with patients and storing medical records.[5] Approximately one in five physicians e-mail their patients, while 4 percent prescribe medicine online. Overall, only 20 percent of doctors believe the Internet is essential to their professional practices. The study found that privacy and security concerns have deterred many physicians from using online services.

According to the Bureau of Labor Statistics (BLS), there were about 693,000 financial managers nationwide in 1998.[6] Although these managers were found in virtually every industry, more than a third were employed by services industries, including business, health, social, and management services. Nearly 3 out of 10 were employed by financial institutions, such as banks, savings institutions, finance companies, credit unions, insurance companies, securities dealers, and real estate firms. Median annual earnings of financial managers were $55,070 in 1998. The middle 50 percent earned between

Business research evidence has indicated that customer satisfaction and employee satisfaction are closely linked.[7] Separate research studies carried out by Ryder and Sears found a very high correlation between the way employees viewed an organization and the way its customers felt about it. Companies like these realize that business research is important to their success.

$38,240 and $83,800. The lowest 10 percent had earnings of less than $27,680, while the top 10 percent earned over $118,950. The BLS projects that the total employment for the American work force will increase by 14 percent between 1998 and 2008. The outlook for financial managers is good, as the need for financial expertise will keep the profession growing about as fast as the average for all occupations through 2008.

An academic researcher conducted an experiment to determine whether workers whose goals are set unattainably high will perform better than workers whose goals are relatively easy to achieve. The experimenter concluded that the higher the intended level of achievement, the higher the level of performance.

Campbell Soup Company's IntelligentQuisine brand of frozen meals designed to combat high blood pressure, high cholesterol, and diabetes, never made it to national distribution, despite the company's $30 million commitment in resources from its Center for Nutrition and Wellness. Tests in limited markets indicated that demand was not great enough to warrant national marketing.[8] On the other hand, Pepsi's Storm, a caffeinated lemon-lime drink, showed promise in test markets.[9] Equally useful, however, was Pepsi's finding that its replacement for the company's Slice brand would best be marketed nationally under the name Sierra Mist rather than Storm. Pepsi also tested two new flavors of Mountain Dew, cherry-colored Code Red and electric-blue Arctic.

Each of these examples illustrates a business research problem. All of the examples relate to business research, but each illustrates a different form of research. The DuPont example illustrates how survey findings can be directly translated into business strategy. The Steelcase example points out the value of an observation study. The other examples illustrate that researchers use more than surveys. Government and trade association statistics, internal records, psychological tests, and experiments are valuable tools for business research. Because these examples illustrate only a few applications of business research, it should not surprise you to learn that business research is widespread and growing in importance.

SCOPE OF BUSINESS RESEARCH

The scope of business research is limited by one's definition of "business." Certainly research in the production, finance, marketing, or management areas of a for-profit corporation qualifies as business research. A broader definition of business, however, includes not-for-profit organizations, such as the American Heart Association, the San Diego Zoo, and the Boston Pops Orchestra. Each of these organizations exists to satisfy social needs, and each requires business skills to produce and distribute the services that people want. Business research may be conducted by organizations that are not business organizations. (The federal government, for example, performs many functions that are similar, if not identical, to those of business organizations. Federal managers may use research techniques for evaluative purposes in much the same way as managers at DuPont or Ford.) This book uses the term *business research* because all research techniques are applicable to business settings.

Business research covers a wide range of phenomena. For managers the purpose of research is to fulfill the need for knowledge of the organization, the market, the economy, or another area of uncertainty. A financial manager may ask, "Will the environment for long-term financing be better 2 years from now?" A personnel manager may ask, "What kind of training is necessary for production employees?" or "What is the reason for the company's high employee turnover?" A marketing manager may ask, "How can I monitor my retail sales and retail trade activities?" Each of these questions requires information about how the environment, employees, customers, or the economy will respond to executives' decisions. Research may be one of the principal tools for answering these practical questions.

The development and implementation of plans and strategies require information, and every day managers translate their experiences with business phenomena into tactics and strategies. Managers often rely on their own intuition and experience in making decisions because of time pressure or because a problem is minor. However, the primary task of management is effective decision making. "Flying by the seat of the pants" decision making, without systematic inquiry, is like betting on a long shot at the racetrack because the horse's name is appealing. Occasionally there are successes, but in the long run, intuition without research can lead to disappointment. Business research helps decision makers shift from intuitive information gathering to systematic and objective investigation.

A business researcher conducting research within an organization may be referred to as a "marketing researcher," an "organizational researcher," a "director of financial and economic research," or one of many other titles. Although business researchers are specialized, the term *business research* encompasses all of these functional specialties. While researchers in different functional areas may investigate different phenomena, they are comparable to one another because they use similar research methods.

Now that we have illustrated the nature and importance of business research, it is appropriate to provide a formal definition and consider its implications.

BUSINESS RESEARCH DEFINED

business research
The systematic and objective process of gathering, recording, and analyzing data for aid in making business decisions.

The task of business research is to generate accurate information for use in decision making. As we saw above, the emphasis of business research is on shifting decision makers from intuitive information gathering to systematic and objective investigation. **Business research** is defined as the systematic and objective process of gathering, recording, and analyzing data for aid in making business decisions.

This definition suggests, first, that research information is neither intuitive nor haphazardly gathered. Literally, research *(re-search)* means to "search again." It connotes patient study and scientific investigation wherein the researcher takes another, more careful look at data to discover all that can be known about the subject of study.

Second, if the information generated or data collected and analyzed are to be accurate, the business researcher must be objective. The need for objectivity was cleverly stated by the 19th-century American humorist Artemus Ward, who said, "It ain't the things we don't know that gets us in trouble. It's the things we know that ain't so." Thus, the role of the researcher is to be detached and impersonal rather than engaging in a biased attempt to prove preconceived ideas. If bias enters the research process, the value of the data is considerably reduced.

A developer who owned a large area of land on which he wished to build a high-prestige shopping center wanted a research report to demonstrate to prospective retailers that there was a large market potential for such a center. Because he conducted his survey *exclusively* in an elite neighborhood, not surprisingly his findings showed that a large percentage of respondents wanted a "high-prestige" shopping center. Results of this kind are misleading, of course, and should be disregarded. If the user of such findings discovers how they were obtained, the developer loses credibility. If the user is ignorant of the bias in the design and unaware that the researchers were not impartial, his decision may have consequences more adverse than if he had made it strictly on intuition. The importance of objectivity cannot be overemphasized. Without objectivity, research is valueless.

Third, the above definition of business research points out that its objective is to facilitate the managerial decision-making process for all aspects of a business: finance, marketing, personnel, and so on. The definition is not restricted to one aspect of business. An essential tool for management in its problem-solving and decision-making activities, business research generates and provides the necessary qualitative or quantitative information upon which

Some 700 million Sacagawea golden dollars were circulated in the first year they were issued—seven times the initial projection of 100 million coins.[10] The last dollar coin, the Susan B. Anthony, took 14 years to reach the 500 million mark. Extensive business research helped the U.S. Mint, a not-for-profit government agency, design, market, and gain popular support for the Sacagawea dollar.

to base decisions. By reducing the uncertainty of decisions, research reduces the risk of making wrong decisions. However, research should be an *aid* to managerial judgment, not a substitute for it. There is more to management than research. Applying research remains a managerial art.

BASIC RESEARCH AND APPLIED RESEARCH

basic (pure) research
Research that is intended to expand the boundaries of knowledge itself or to verify the acceptability of a given theory.

One reason for conducting research is to develop and evaluate concepts and theories, and **basic**—or **pure—research** attempts to expand the limits of knowledge. It does not directly involve the solution to a particular, pragmatic problem. It has been said that "there is nothing so practical as a good theory." Although this statement is true in the long run, *basic* research findings generally cannot be immediately implemented. Basic research is conducted to verify the acceptability of a given theory or to discover more about a certain concept.

For example, consider this basic research conducted at a university. Academic researchers investigated whether an individual's perception that he or she was doing well on a task would have any influence on future performance. Two nearly identical groups of adults were given the same set of ten puzzles to solve. After the subjects had given their solutions to the researchers, they were told "how well" they did on the test. All members of the first group were told that they had done well: 70 percent correct (regardless of the actual percent correct). The members of the other group were told that they had done poorly (30 percent correct). Then both groups were given another set of ten puzzles. Those subjects who had been told they had done well on the first set of puzzles performed better with the second set of puzzles than did those who had been told they had been relatively unsuccessful with the first puzzle solving. The results of this basic research expand scientific knowledge about theories of general performance behavior. This study was conducted because the researchers thought the theory being tested was far-reaching and applicable to a broad range of situations and circumstances.

applied research
Research undertaken to answer questions about specific problems or to make decisions about a particular course of action or policy decision.

Applied research is conducted when a decision must be made about a specific real-life problem. Applied research encompasses those studies undertaken to answer questions about specific problems or to make decisions about a particular course of action or policy. For example, an organization contemplating a paperless office and a networking system for the company's personal computers may conduct research to learn the amount of time its employees spend at personal computers in an average week.

scientific method
Techniques or procedures used to analyze empirical evidence in an attempt to confirm or disprove prior conceptions.

The procedures and techniques utilized by basic and applied researchers do not differ substantially. Both employ the **scientific method** to answer the questions at hand. Broadly characterized, the scientific method refers to techniques and procedures that help the researcher to know and understand business phenomena. The scientific method requires systematic analysis and logical interpretation of empirical evidence (facts from observation or experimentation) to confirm or disprove prior conceptions. In basic research, first testing these prior conceptions or hypotheses and then making inferences and conclusions about the phenomena lead to the establishment of general laws about the phenomena.

Use of the scientific method in applied research assures objectivity in gathering facts and testing creative ideas for alternative business strategies. The essence of research, whether basic or applied, lies in the scientific method, and much of this book deals with *scientific methodology.* The difference in the techniques of basic and applied research is largely a matter of degree rather than substance.

MANAGERIAL VALUE OF BUSINESS RESEARCH

We have argued that research facilitates effective management. At many companies research drives every aspect of major decision making. For example, at Ford Motor Company, research is so fundamental that management makes hardly any significant decision without the benefit of some kind of business research.

The prime managerial value of business research is that it reduces uncertainty by providing information that improves the decision-making process. The decision-making process associated with the development and implementation of a strategy involves four interrelated stages:

1. Identifying problems or opportunities
2. Diagnosing and assessing problems or opportunities
3. Selecting and implementing a course of action
4. Evaluating the course of action

Business research, by supplying managers with pertinent information, may play an important role by reducing managerial uncertainty in each of these stages.

Identifying Problems or Opportunities

TO THE POINT

The secret of success is to know something nobody else knows.

ARISTOTLE ONASSIS

Before any strategy can be developed, an organization must determine where it wants to go and how it will get there. Business research can help managers plan strategies by determining the nature of situations or by identifying the existence of problems or opportunities present in the organization.

Business research may be used as a scanning activity to provide information about what is occurring within an organization or in its environment. The mere description of some social or economic activity may familiarize managers with organizational and environmental occurrences and help them understand a situation. Consider two examples:

- The description of the dividend history of stocks in an industry may point to an attractive investment opportunity. Information supplied by business research may also indicate problems.
- Employee interviews undertaken to characterize the dimensions of an airline reservation clerk's job may reveal that reservation clerks emphasize competence in issuing tickets over courtesy and friendliness in customer contact.

Once business research indicates a problem or opportunity, managers may feel that the alternatives are clear enough to make a decision based on experience or intuition, or they may decide that more business research is needed to generate additional information for a better understanding of the situation.

Diagnosing and Assessing Problems or Opportunities

After an organization recognizes a problem or identifies a potential opportunity, an important aspect of business research is the provision of diagnostic information that clarifies the situation. Managers need to gain insight about the underlying factors causing the situation. If there is a problem, they need to specify what happened and why. If an opportunity exists, they may need to explore, clarify, and refine the nature of the opportunity. If multiple opportunities exist, research may be conducted to set priorities. Quantitative or qual-

A cruise line industry study shows that although 43.6 million Americans have considered taking a cruise, 88 percent of Americans have not been on a ship.[11] Further, business research suggests that consumers perceive cruising to be sedentary, regimented, and boring. Most people have the attitude that a shipboard vacation involves sitting around the pool, playing shuffleboard, and putting on pounds. Royal Caribbean Cruise Lines' assessment of these findings led to service changes and new ads showing that its ships are for the adventurous and active. Their large ships have rock climbing walls, jet skis, basketball courts, and more. In television commercials a guest may be shown snorkeling in turquoise waters among tropical fish that glimmer like jewels or riding in a helicopter over majestic seas of ice.

itative investigations may help managers better understand what alternative courses of action are practical.

Selecting and Implementing a Course of Action

After the alternative courses of action have been clearly identified, business research is often conducted to obtain specific information that will aid in evaluating the alternatives and in selecting the best course of action. For example, suppose a fax machine manufacturer must decide to build a factory either in Japan or in South Korea. In such a case, business research can be designed to supply the relevant information necessary to determine which course of action is best for the organization.

Opportunities may be evaluated through the use of various performance criteria. For example, estimates of market potential allow managers to evaluate the revenue that will be generated by each of the possible opportunities. A good forecast supplied by business researchers is among the most useful pieces of planning information a manager can have. Of course, complete accuracy in forecasting the future is not possible, because change is constantly occurring in the business environment. Nevertheless, objective information generated by business research to forecast environmental occurrences may be the foundation for selecting a particular course of action.

Even the best plan is likely to fail if it is not properly implemented. Business research may be conducted with the people who will be affected by a pending decision to indicate the specific tactics required to implement that course of action.

Evaluating the Course of Action

After a course of action has been implemented, business research may serve as a tool to inform managers whether planned activities were properly executed and whether they accomplished what they were expected to accomplish. In other words, managers may use evaluation research to provide feedback for evaluation and control of strategies and tactics.

evaluation research
The formal, objective measurement and appraisal of the extent to which a given activity, project, or program has achieved its objectives.

Evaluation research is the formal, objective measurement and appraisal of the extent to which a given activity, project, or program has achieved its objectives. In addition to measuring the extent to which completed programs achieved their objectives or whether continuing programs are presently performing as projected, evaluation research may provide information about the major factors influencing the observed performance levels.

In addition to business organizations, nonprofit organizations, such as agencies of the federal government, frequently conduct evaluation research. Every year thousands of federal evaluation studies are undertaken to systematically assess the effects of public programs. For example, the General Accounting Office has been responsible for measuring outcomes of the Employment Opportunity Act, the Job Corps program, and Occupational and Safety and Health Administration (OSHA) programs.

performance-monitoring research
Research that regularly provides feedback for evaluation and control of business activity.

Performance-monitoring research is a specific type of evaluation research that regularly, perhaps routinely, provides feedback for the evaluation and control of recurring business activity. For example, most firms continuously monitor wholesale and retail activity to ensure early detection of sales declines and other anomalies. In the grocery and retail drug industries, sales research may use the universal product code (UPC) for packages, together with computerized cash registers and electronic scanners at checkout counters, to provide valuable market-share information to store and brand managers interested in the retail sales volume of specific products.

total quality management (TQM)
A business philosophy that focuses on integrating customer-driven quality throughout the organization.

Performance-monitoring research is an integral aspect of total quality management programs. **Total quality management (TQM)** is a business philosophy that embodies the belief that the management process must focus on integrating customer-driven quality throughout the organization. Total quality management stresses continuous improvement of product quality and service. Managers improve durability and enhance features as the product ages. They strive to improve delivery and other services to keep their companies competitive.

United Airlines' Omnibus in-flight survey provides a good example of performance-monitoring research for quality management. United routinely selects sample flights and administers a questionnaire about in-flight service, food, and other aspects of air travel. The Omnibus survey is conducted quarterly to determine who is flying and for what reasons. It enables United to track demographic changes and to monitor customer ratings of its services on a continuing basis, allowing the airline to gather vast amounts of information at low cost. The information relating to customer reaction to services can be compared over time. For example, suppose United decided to change its menu for in-flight meals. The results of the Omnibus survey might indicate that, shortly after the menu changed, the customers' rating of the airline's food declined. Such information about product quality would be extremely valuable, as it would allow management to quickly spot trends among passengers in other aspects of air travel, such as airport lounges, gate-line waits, or

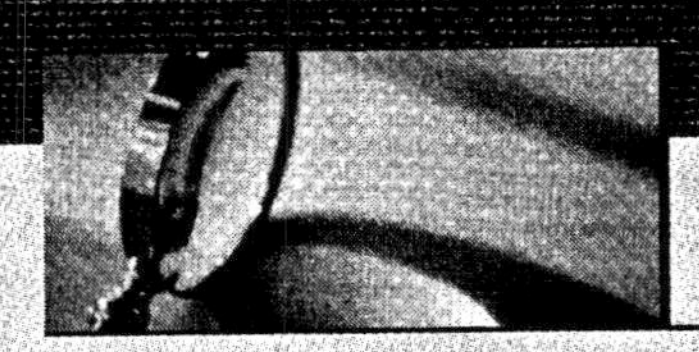

RESEARCH INSIGHT

TQM: NO SWEAT AT JEEP

Chrysler Corporation, Jeep's parent company, asked about 380 paint line workers who wash, wipe, and prepare Jeep Cherokees and Comanches for painting to stop using antiperspirants as part of the company's total quality management effort.[12] Business research on production quality indicated that falling flakes from antiperspirants leave costly blemishes on the sport utility vehicles. Chrysler's investigation showed that antiperspirants worn by workers flaked and fell onto the new paint. Antiperspirants contain chemicals, such as zinc zirconium, that can damage paint. The paint flows away from a fallen flake of these chemicals, causing a depression about the size of a baby's fingertip. George Nancarrow, a regional service manager for the paint maker BASF Corp., said the problem extends to all automakers. He heads a team that investigates cratering in auto finishes. "Craters have a thousand mothers," Nancarrow said. "It can be caused if somebody comes in with too much hand cream on and touches the vehicle, or somebody goes at lunchtime and buys a bag of microwave popcorn and eats it and wipes his hands on the coverall and leans on the car."

Chrysler looked into the matter after its quality control system reported that every vehicle coming off the line had up to 50 imperfections on the roof and hood. Such damage can be enough for an inspector to send a car back for thousands of dollars in repairs.

Because of these findings, managers are trying to persuade workers to switch to deodorants, which control odor but do not stop sweating. Jeep workers are not banned from wearing antiperspirants, but they are being educated about the problem. An awareness program that employees helped develop includes a training session that shows some of the common causes of paint flaws. "You do what you got to do," said one paint line worker. "We want to turn out the best Jeeps. If antiperspirants are causing problems, you got to give them up."

cabin cleanliness. Then managers could rapidly take action to remedy such problems.

When analysis of performance indicates that all is not going as planned, business research may be required to explain why something went wrong. Detailed information about specific mistakes or failures is frequently sought. If a general problem area is identified, breaking down industry sales volume and a firm's sales volume into different geographic areas may provide an explanation of specific problems, and exploring these problems in greater depth may indicate which managerial judgments were erroneous.

Implementing a total quality management program requires considerable measurement. It involves routinely asking customers to rate a company against its competitors, measuring employee attitudes, and monitoring company performance against benchmark standards. It uses a lot of business research. Thus, outside business research with external customers and internal business research with employees in the organization are both important components of a total quality management program.

In Chapter 9, a major section on implementing total quality management discusses planning and researching quality in detail. However, throughout this book, we will explain how business research may contribute to the achievement of customer-driven quality.

WHEN IS BUSINESS RESEARCH NEEDED?

A manager faced with two or more possible courses of action faces the initial decision of whether or not research should be conducted. The determination of the need for research centers on (1) time constraints, (2) the availability of data, (3) the nature of the decision that must be made, and (4) the value of the business research information in relation to its costs.

Time Constraints

Conducting research systematically takes time. In many instances management concludes that, because a decision must be made immediately, there will be no time for research. As a consequence, decisions are sometimes made without adequate information or thorough understanding of the situation. Although such rapid decision making is not ideal, sometimes the urgency of a situation precludes the use of research.

Availability of Data

Often managers already possess enough information to make sound decisions with no business research. When they lack adequate information, however, research must be considered. Managers must ask themselves if the research will provide the information needed to answer the basic questions about a decision. Furthermore, if a potential source of data exists, managers will want to know how much it will cost to obtain the data.

If the data cannot be obtained, research cannot be conducted. For example, many African nations have never conducted a population census. Organizations engaged in international business often find that data about business activity or population characteristics that are readily available in the United States are nonexistent or sparse in developing countries. For example, imagine the problems facing marketing researchers who wish to investigate market potential in places like Uzbekistan, Yugoslavian Macedonia, and Rwanda.

Nature of the Decision

The value of business research will depend on the nature of the managerial decision to be made. A routine tactical decision that does not require a substantial investment may not seem to warrant a substantial expenditure for research. For example, a computer company must update its operator's instruction manual when it makes minor product modifications. The research cost of determining the proper wording to use in updating the manual is likely to be too high for such a minor decision.

The nature of the decision is not totally independent of the next issue to be considered: the benefits versus the costs of the research. In general, however, the more strategically or tactically important the business decision, the more likely it is that research will be conducted.

Benefits versus Costs

Some of the managerial benefits of business research have already been discussed. Of course, conducting research activities to obtain these benefits requires an expenditure; thus, there are both costs and benefits in conducting business research. In any decision-making situation, managers must identify alternative courses of action, then weigh the value of each alternative against its cost. It is useful to think of business research as an investment alternative.

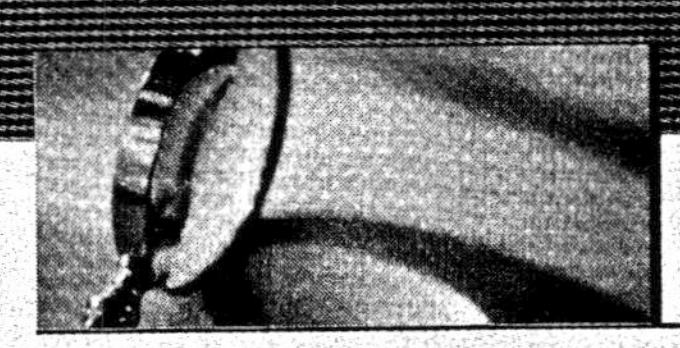

Research Insight

Rolling Rock

For many years Rolling Rock beer was a regional brand in western Pennsylvania.[13] Its signature package was a longneck green bottle with white painted label featuring icons such as a horsehead, a steeplechase fence, and the number "33," which concludes a legend about the beer being brought to you "from the glass-lined tanks of Old Latrobe." The brand, now marketed by Labatt USA, expanded nationally during the 1980s by focusing on core consumers who purchased specialty beers for on-premise consumption and were willing to pay prices higher than those of national brands such as Budweiser.

As years went by packaging options expanded to include bottles with mystique-less paper labels for take-home consumption, often packaged in 12-packs. In the mid-1990s, in response to a competitive explosion from microbrews, Rolling Rock offered a number of line extensions, such as Rock Bock and amber Rock Ice. They failed. Sales stagnated. In New York and other crucial markets price reductions to the level of Budweiser and Miller became inhibiting aspects of the marketing program. Marketing executives held the view that the longneck painted bottle was the heart of the brand. However, earlier efforts to develop a cheaper imitation of the painted-label look had not achieved success.

Rolling Rock executives decided to conduct a massive business research project, recruiting consumers at shopping malls and other venues to view "live" shelf sets of beer, not just specialty beer but beer at every price range from sub-premiums and up. Consumers given money to spend in the form of chips were exposed to "old-bundle" packages (the old graphics, and the paper-label stubbies) and "new-bundle" packages (two new graphics approaches, including the one ultimately selected, and painted-label longnecks), at a variety of price points, and asked to allocate their next ten purchases. Some were even invited to take the "new-bundle" packages home with them for followup research.

As the execs had hoped, the results did not leave any room for interpretation: not only did the new packages meet with consumers' strong approval, but consumers consistently indicated that they would be willing to pay more for the brand in those packages. In fact, not only were they *willing* to pay more, they *expected* to pay more, particularly those already in the Rock franchise. In three regions, the Northeast, Southeast, and West, purchase intent among users increased dramatically both at prices 20 cents higher per sixpack and at prices 40 cents higher. The increase in purchase intent was milder in the Midwest, but Rock there already commanded a higher price than Bud and other premium beers. The sole exception to that trend was in the brand's core markets in Pennsylvania and Ohio, where Rock has never entirely escaped its shot-and-a-beer origins, and even there, purchase intent declined by only 2 percent at each of the higher prices.

When deciding whether to make a decision without research or to postpone the decision in order to conduct research, managers should ask: (1) Will the payoff or rate of return be worth the investment? (2) Will the information gained by business research improve the quality of the decision to an extent sufficient to warrant the expenditure? and (3) Is the proposed research expenditure the best use of the available funds?

For example, *TV Cable Week* was not test-marketed before its launch. While the magazine had articles and stories about television personalities and events, its main feature was a channel-by-channel program listing showing the exact programs that a particular subscriber could receive. To produce a "custom" magazine for each individual cable television system in the country

EXHIBIT 1.1 DETERMINING WHEN BUSINESS RESEARCH SHOULD BE CONDUCTED

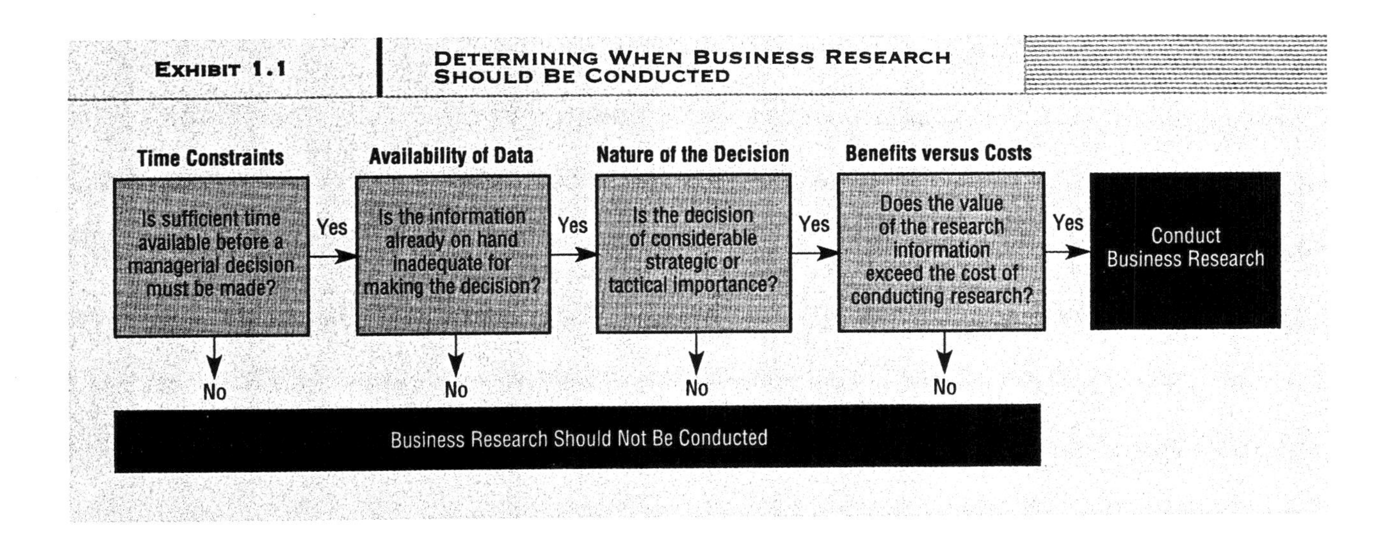

required developing a costly computer system. Because the development of the computer system required a substantial expenditure, one that could not be scaled down for research, the conducting of research was judged to be an unwise investment. The value of the research information was not positive, because the cost of the information exceeded its benefits. Unfortunately, pricing and distribution problems became so compelling after the magazine was launched that it was a business failure. Nevertheless, the publication's managers, without the luxury of hindsight, made a reasonable decision not to conduct research. They analyzed the cost of the information (i.e., the cost of business research) relative to the potential benefits. Exhibit 1.1 outlines the criteria for determining when to conduct business research.

MAJOR TOPICS FOR RESEARCH IN BUSINESS

Research is expected to improve the quality of business decisions, but what kinds of business decisions benefit most from research efforts? Exhibit 1.2 lists several major topics for research in business.

Exhibit 1.2 is arranged, to a large extent, according to the traditional business functions. However, many business efforts, such as new product development, are not neatly classified as financial projects, marketing projects, or information system projects. They are cross-functional efforts.

Cross-Functional Teams

As more companies awake to the challenge of the global information age and the need to act quickly, old forms of organizational structures are fading fast. Today, in progressive organizations, everyone from accountants to engineers engages in a unified effort to consider all issues related to the development, production, or marketing of new products.

cross-functional teams
Teams of people from various departments within a company, who work together to accomplish a common goal.

Cross-functional teams are composed of individuals from various organizational departments such as engineering, production, finance, and marketing who share a common purpose. Current management thinking suggests that cross-functional teams help organizations focus on a core business process, such as customer service or new product development. Working in teams

EXHIBIT 1.2 | **MAJOR TOPICS FOR RESEARCH IN BUSINESS**

General Business Conditions and Corporate Research

Short-range forecasting (up to 1 year)
Long-range forecasting (over 1 year)
Business and industry trends
Global environments
Inflation and pricing
Plant and warehouse location
Acquisitions

Financial and Accounting Research

Forecasts of financial interest-rate trends
Stock, bond, and commodity value predictions
Capital formation alternatives
Mergers and acquisitions
Risk–return trade-offs
Impact of taxes
Portfolio analysis
Research on financial institutions
Expected rate of return
Capital asset pricing models
Credit risk
Cost analysis

Management and Organizational Behavior Research

Total quality management
Morale and job satisfaction
Leadership style
Employee productivity
Organizational effectiveness
Structural issues
Absenteeism and turnover
Organizational climate
Organizational communication
Time and motion
Physical environment
Labor union trends

Sales and Marketing Research

Market potentials
Market share
Market segmentation
Market characteristics
Sales analysis
Establishment of sales quotas, territories
Distribution channels
New product concepts
Test markets
Advertising research
Buyer behavior
Customer satisfaction
Web site visitation rates

Information Systems Research

Knowledge and information needs assessment
Computer information system use and evaluation
Technical support satisfaction
Database analysis
Data mining
Enterprise resource planning systems
Customer relationship management systems

Corporate Responsibility Research

Ecological impact
Legal constraints on advertising and promotion
Sex, age, and racial discrimination/worker equity
Social values and ethics

reduces the tendency for employees to focus single-mindedly on an isolated functional activity. The use of cross-functional teams to help employees to improve product quality and increase customer value is a major trend in business today.

At trend-setting organizations, many business research directors are members of cross-functional teams. New product development, for example, may be done by a cross-functional team of engineers, finance executives, production personnel, marketing managers, and business researchers who take an integrated approach to solve problems or exploit opportunities. In the old days, business researchers may not have been involved in developing new products until long after many key decisions about product specifications and manufacturing had been made. Now, business researchers' input is part of an integrated team effort. Researchers act both as business consultants and as providers of technical services. Researchers working in teams are more likely to understand the broad purpose of their research and less likely to focus exclusively on research methodology.

Cross-functional teams are having a dramatic impact on how business research is viewed within the organization.

BUSINESS RESEARCH IN THE 21ST CENTURY

Business research has been strongly influenced by two major trends in business: increased globalization and the rapid growth of the Internet and other information technologies. These trends will continue, and likely accelerate, as the 21st century progresses. This section outlines their significance for business research.

Global Business Research

Business research has become increasingly global and will become more so in the 21st century. Some companies have extensive international business research operations. Upjohn conducts business research in 160 different countries. A. C. Nielsen International, with its television ratings, is the world's largest business research company. Two-thirds of its business comes from outside the United States.[14]

Companies that conduct business in foreign countries must understand the nature of those particular markets and judge whether they require customized strategies. For example, although the 15 nations of the European Union share a single formal market, business research shows that Europeans do not share identical tastes for many consumer products. Business researchers have found no such thing as a typical European consumer; language, religion, climate, and centuries of tradition divide the nations of the European Union. Scantel Research, a British firm that advises companies on color preferences, found inexplicable differences in Europeans' preferences concerning medicines. The French prefer to pop purple pills, but the English and Dutch favor white ones. Consumers in all three countries dislike bright red capsules, which are big sellers in the United States. This example illustrates that companies that do business in Europe must judge whether they need to adapt to local customs and buying habits.[15]

Although the nature of business research can differ around the globe, the need for business research is universal. Throughout this book, we will discuss the practical problems involved in conducting business research in Europe, Asia, Latin America, the Middle East, and elsewhere.

Growth of the Internet

The Internet is transforming society. Time is collapsing. Distance is no longer an obstacle. Crossing oceans requires only a mouse click. People are connected 24 hours a day, 7 days a week. "Instantaneous" has a new meaning.[16]

The Internet is a worldwide network of computers that allows users access to information and documents from distant sources. Many people believe that the Internet is the most important communications medium since television. It has certainly changed the way millions of people think about getting and distributing information. And, of course, obtaining and communicating information is the essence of business research. Consider that a researcher seeking facts and figures about a business issue may find more extensive information

The world economy has become global, and corporations market products in many countries. People think of their home culture as the normal way of life, but consumers in other cultures may have different values, beliefs, and behaviors. Business research helps marketers understand cultural differences. Colgate-Palmolive is a progressive company that conducts business research around the world. Colgate-Palmolive used business research when it introduced a new and improved toothpaste in Colombia.

on the Internet more quickly than by visiting a library. Another researcher who is questioning people from around the globe may do so almost instantaneously with an Internet survey and get responses 24 hours a day, 7 days a week. Visitors to an organization's Web site may find that online questions are personalized, because the site incorporates information technology that remembers the particular "click-stream" of the Web pages they visited. These few examples illustrate how the Internet and other information technologies are dramatically changing the face of business research.

In the 21st century, business research on the Internet is moving out of the introductory stage of its product life cycle into the growth stage. The rest of the book reflects this change. Throughout the book, we will discuss the latest information technologies and their application to business research. Business research via the Internet has come of age.

SUMMARY

Business research is a management tool that companies use to reduce uncertainty. Business research, managers' source of information about organizational and environmental conditions, covers topics ranging from long-range planning to the most ephemeral tactical decisions.

Business research is the systematic and objective process of gathering, recording, and analyzing data for decision making. The research must be systematic, not haphazard. It must be objective to avoid the distorting effects of personal bias. The objective of applied business research is to facilitate managerial decision making. Basic or pure research is used to increase knowledge about theories and concepts.

Managers can use business research in all stages of the decision-making process: to define problems, to identify opportunities, to diagnose causal factors, and to clarify alternatives. Research is also used to evaluate current programs and courses of action, to explain what went wrong with managerial efforts in the past, and to forecast future conditions.

Total quality management (TQM) is a business philosophy that embodies the belief that the management process must focus on integrating the idea of customer-driven quality throughout the organization. Total quality management stresses continuous improvement of product quality and service delivery. Business research plays a major role in total quality management programs.

A manager determines whether business research should be conducted by considering (1) time constraints, (2) the availability of data, (3) the nature of the decision to be made, and (4) the benefits of the research information in relation to its costs.

Applied research is directed at a broad variety of topics, such as general business conditions and corporate research; financial and accounting research; management and organizational behavior research; sales and marketing research; information system research; and corporate responsibility research.

The Internet and other information technologies are dramatically changing the face of business research. Business research has become increasingly global. Multinational companies must understand the particular nature of foreign markets and determine whether they require customized business strategies.

Key Terms

business research
basic (pure) research
applied research
scientific method
evaluation research
performance-monitoring research
total quality management (TQM)
cross-functional team

Questions for Review and Critical Thinking

1. What are some examples of business research in your particular field of interest?
2. In your own words, define *business research* and list its tasks.
3. How might a not-for-profit organization use business research?
4. What is the difference between applied and basic research?
5. Classify each of the following examples as basic or applied research.
   (a) A researcher investigates whether different sites in a manager's brain (e.g., right versus left hemisphere) are active during different kinds of managerial decision making.
   (b) A researcher investigates consumers' attitudes toward a prototype of an innovative home cleaning kit for use on clothes that require dry cleaning.
   (c) A researcher investigates five personality traits to see if they can explain the purchasing behavior of automobile buyers.
   (d) A new technology that nullifies the need to refrigerate fish has been invented. Heat processing and the use of flexible pouches for storage help retain the freshness of fish for 3 years. A researcher investigates how this new technology will affect the market for fish in India.
   (e) A researcher working for a candy company has children evaluate concepts and prototypes for new candies. The researchers ask children to taste the products and rate them. Sometimes, the candy company develops unique items that taste good and researchers ask children to name the product.
   (f) A researcher investigates whether introducing a "subbrand" at new-car dealerships, identified by an AutoNation USA logo below the dealership name, is an effective basic strategy that can be applied to all its dealerships.
6. Discuss how business research can be used in each stage of the decision-making process.

7. In your own words, describe the scientific method and state why it is an essential part of business research.
8. Describe a situation in which business research *is not* needed and one in which business research *is* needed. What factors differentiate the two situations?
9. In your own words, what is the role of business research in a total quality management program?
10. What is a cross-functional team? What types of projects might use business research directed by a cross-functional team?
11. Suppose you have been hired as a consultant by an American fast-food restaurant chain that plans to expand into Europe. What role would business research play, if any, in providing advice to your client?

Exploring the Internet: What Is Ahead?

Exploring the Internet is a feature that will give you an opportunity to use the Internet to gain additional insights about business research. The Internet is discussed in depth in Chapter 2, and Internet exercises are included in each of the remaining chapters.

The home page for this textbook is at

http://zikmund.swcollege.com

or you may go directly to the business research supplemental materials at

http://www.swcollege.com/management/strategy_suite/strategy_suite.html

The author's home page is at

http://www2.bus.okstate.edu/mktg/zikmund/index.htm

Case Suggestions

Case 1: The Atlanta Braves
Video Case 1: Polaroid I-Zone
Video Case 2: WBRU
Video Case 3: Ben & Jerry's
Video Case 4: Fossil—A Watch for Every Wrist

2

THEORY BUILDING

What you will learn in this chapter

- To understand the goals of theory.
- To define the meaning of *theory.*
- To understand the terms *concept, proposition, variable,* and *hypothesis.*
- To understand that because concepts abstract reality, it is possible to discuss concepts at various levels of abstraction.
- To understand the scientific method.
- To discuss how theories are generated.

The purpose of science concerns the expansion of knowledge and the discovery of truth. Theory building is the means by which basic researchers hope to achieve this purpose. ■

WHAT ARE THE GOALS OF THEORY?

A scientist investigating business phenomena wants to know what produces inflation. Another person wants to know if organizational structure influences leadership style. Both want to be able to predict behavior, to be able to say that if we do such and such, then so and so will happen.[1]

Prediction and understanding are the two purposes of theory.[2] Accomplishing the first goal allows the theorist to predict the behavior or characteristics of one phenomenon from the knowledge of another phenomenon's characteristics. A business researcher may theorize that older investors tend to be more interested in investment income than younger investors. This theory, once verified, should allow researchers to predict the importance of expected dividend yield on the basis of investors' ages. The ability to anticipate future conditions in the environment or in an organization may be extremely valuable, yet prediction alone may not satisfy the scientific researcher's goals. Successfully forecasting an election outcome does not satisfy one's curiosity about the reason *why* a candidate won the election. A researcher also wants to gain understanding. In most situations, of course, prediction and understanding go hand in hand. To predict phenomena, we must have an explanation of why variables behave as they do. Theories provide these explanations.

TO THE POINT

Theories are nets cast to catch what we call "the world": to rationalize, to explain, and to master it. We endeavour to make the mesh ever finer and finer.

—KARL R. POPPER, THE LOGIC OF SCIENTIFIC DISCOVERY

THE MEANING OF THEORY

> Like all abstractions, the word "theory" has been used in many different ways, in many different contexts, at times so broadly as to include almost all descriptive statements about a class of phenomena, and at other times so narrowly as to exclude everything but a series of terms and their relationships that satisfies certain logical requirements.[3]

For our purposes, a **theory** is a coherent set of general propositions, used as principles of explanation of the apparent relationships of certain observed phenomena. A key element in our definition is the term *proposition*. Before we can see what a proposition is, however, we must discuss the nature of *theoretical concepts*.

theory
A coherent set of general propositions used to explain the apparent relationships among certain observed phenomena. Theories allow generalizations beyond individual facts or situations.

CONCEPTS

Theory development is essentially a process of describing phenomena at increasingly higher levels of abstraction. Things that we observe can be described as concepts. A **concept** (or construct) is a generalized idea about a class of objects, attributes, occurrences, or processes that has been given a name. If you, as an organizational theorist, were to describe phenomena such as supervisory behavior, you would categorize empirical events or real things into concepts. Concepts are building blocks, and in organizational theory, "leadership," "productivity," and "morale" are concepts. In the theory of finance, "gross national product," "asset," and "inflation" are frequently used concepts.

concept
A generalized idea about a class of objects; an abstraction of reality that is the basic unit for theory development.

Concepts abstract reality. That is, concepts are expressed in words that refer to various events or objects. For example, the concept "asset" is an abstract term that may, in the concrete world of reality, refer to a specific punch press machine. Concepts, however, may vary in degree of abstraction. The abstraction

Exhibit 3.1 A Ladder of Abstraction for Concepts

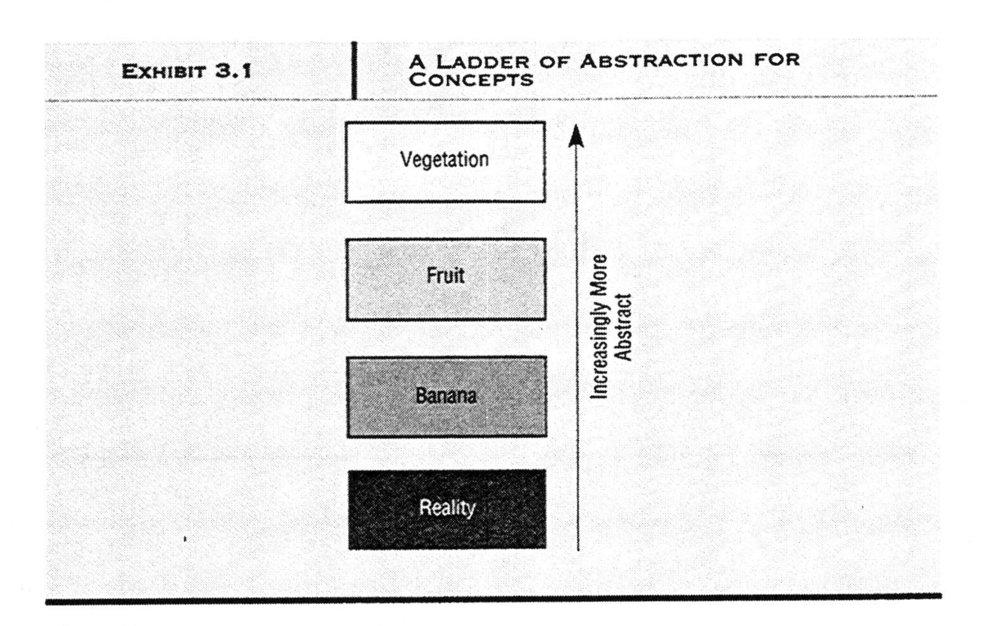

ladder in Exhibit 3.1 indicates that it is possible to discuss concepts at various levels of abstraction. Moving up the **ladder of abstraction,** the basic concept becomes more abstract, wider in scope, and less amenable to measurement. The basic or scientific business researcher operates at two levels: on the **abstract level** of concepts (and propositions) and on the empirical level of variables (and hypotheses). At the **empirical level,** we "experience" reality—that is, we observe or manipulate objects or events (see Exhibit 3.2).[4]

ladder of abstraction
Organization of concepts in sequence from the most concrete and individual to the most general.

abstract level
In theory development, the level of knowledge expressing a concept that exists only as an idea or a quality apart from an object.

empirical level
Level of knowledge that is verifiable by experience or observation.

If the organizational researcher says "Older workers prefer different rewards than younger workers," two concepts—age of worker and reward preference—are the subjects of this abstract statement. If the researcher wishes to test this hypothesis, John, age 19, Chuck, age 45, and Mary, age 62—along with other workers—may be questioned about their preferences for salary, retirement plans, intrinsic job satisfaction, and the like. Recording their ages and observing their stated preferences are activities that occur at the empirical level.

Researchers are concerned with the observable world, or what we shall loosely term "reality." Theorists translate their conceptualization of reality into

Exhibit 3.2 Concepts Are Abstractions of Reality

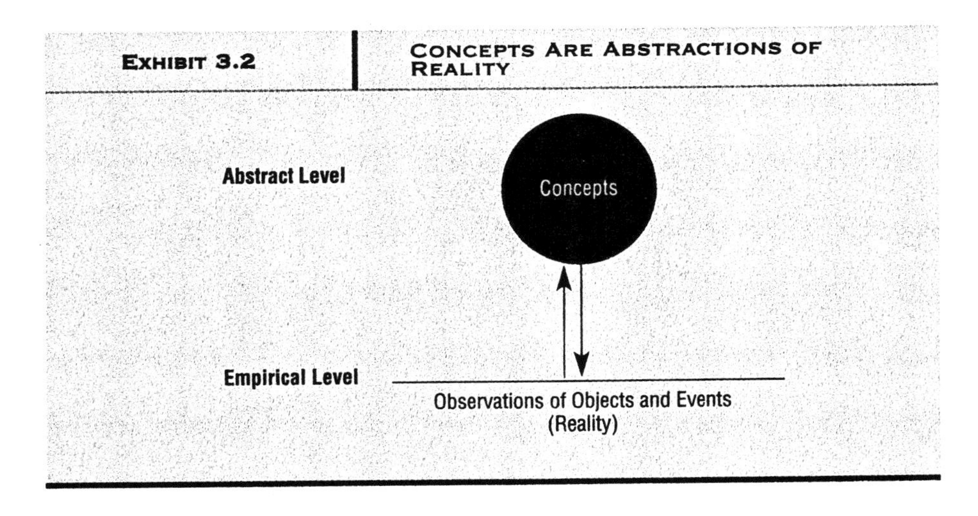

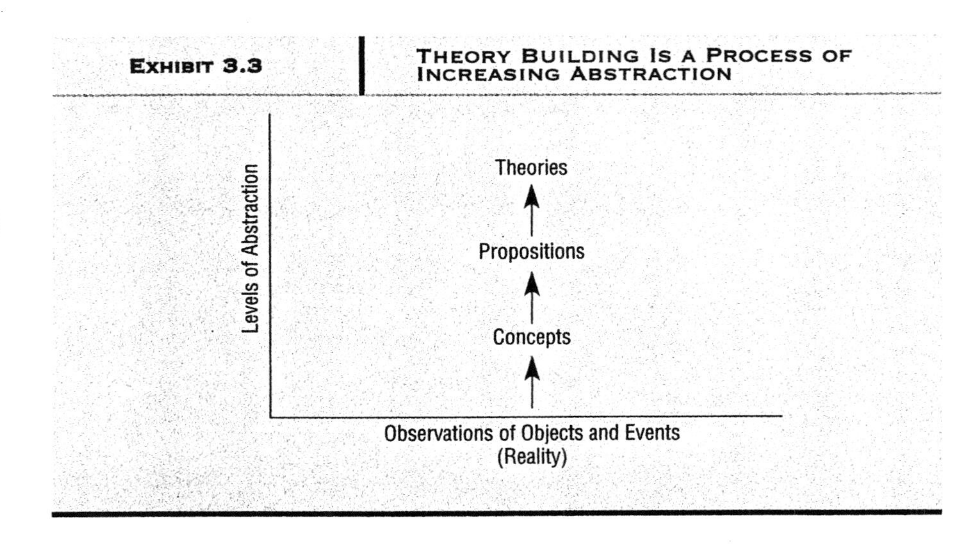

Reality is merely an illusion, albeit a very persistent one.

ALBERT EINSTEIN

abstract ideas. Thus, theory deals with abstraction. Things are not the essence of theory; ideas are.[5] Concepts in isolation are not theories. Only when we explain how concepts relate to other concepts do we begin to construct theories.

NATURE OF PROPOSITIONS

proposition
A statement concerned with the relationships among concepts; an assertion of a universal connection between events that have certain properties.

Concepts are the basic units of theory development. However, theories require an understanding of the relationship among concepts. Thus, once reality is abstracted into concepts, the scientist is interested in the relationship among various concepts. **Propositions** are statements concerned with the relationships among concepts. A proposition explains the *logical* linkage among certain concepts by asserting a universal connection between concepts. A proposition states that every concept about an event or thing either has a certain property or stands in a certain relationship to other concepts about the event or thing.[6]

Consider the following behavioral science proposition that permeates many business theories: If reinforcements follow each other at evenly distributed intervals, and everything else is held constant, the resulting habit will increase in strength as a positive growth function of the number of trials.[7] This proposition identifies theoretical relationships between the concepts "reinforcements" and "habit." It identifies the direction and magnitude of these relationships.

We have indicated that a theory is an abstraction from observed reality. Concepts are at one level of abstraction (see Exhibit 3.3). Investigating propositions requires that we increase our level of abstract thinking. When we think about theories, we are at the highest level of abstraction because we are investigating the relationship between propositions. Theories are networks of propositions.

THE SCIENTIFIC METHOD

scientific method
Techniques or procedures used to analyze empirical evidence in an attempt to confirm or disprove prior conceptions.

The **scientific method** is a set of prescribed procedures for establishing and connecting theoretical statements about events, for analyzing empirical evidence, and for predicting events yet unknown. There is no consensus concerning exact procedures for the scientific method, but most discussions of the scientific method include references to "empirical testability." *Empirical* means verifiable

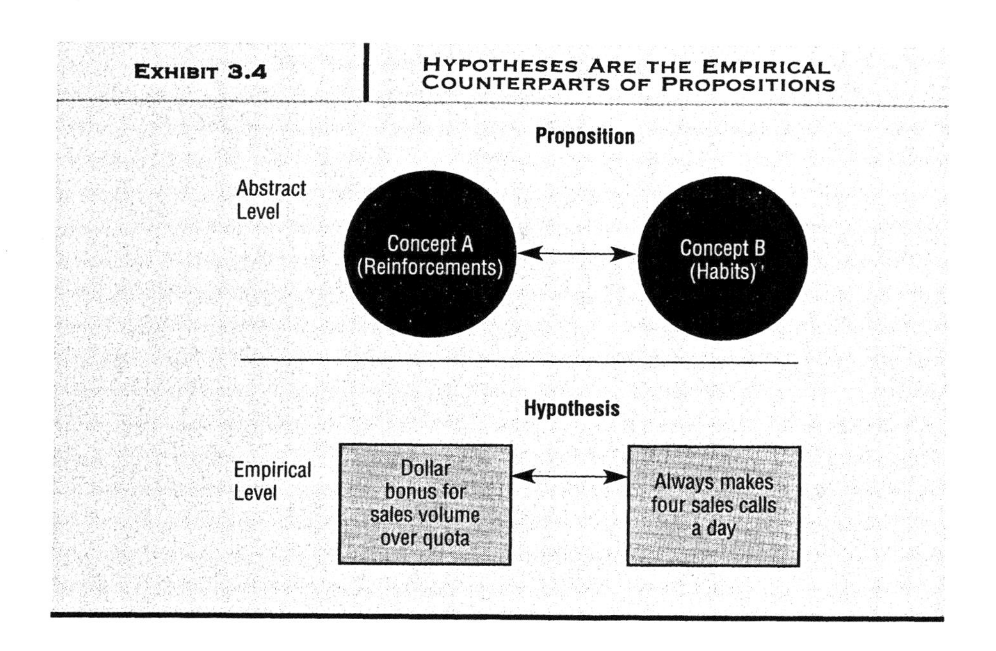

by observation, experimentation, or experience. The process of empirical verification cannot be divorced from the process of theory development.

hypothesis
An unproven proposition or supposition that tentatively explains certain facts or phenomena; a proposition that is empirically testable.

variable
Anything that may assume different numerical values.

A **hypothesis** is a proposition that is empirically testable. It is an empirical statement concerned with the relationship among variables. The abstract proposition "Reinforcements will increase habit strength" may be tested empirically with a hypothesis. Exhibit 3.4 shows that the hypothesis "Bonus pay given for sales volume consistently above quota will be associated with the number of sales calls a day" is an empirical counterpart of the proposition. Bonus pay and sales calls are **variables,** reflecting the concepts of reinforcement and habits. Because variables are at the empirical level, variables may be measured. Thus, the scientific method has two basic levels:

> ... the empirical and the abstract, conceptual. The empirical aspect is primarily concerned with the facts of the science as revealed by observation and experiments. The abstract or theoretical aspect, on the other hand, consists in a serious attempt to understand the facts of the science, and to integrate them into a coherent, i.e., a logical, system. From these observations and integrations are derived, directly or indirectly, the basic laws of the science.[8]

AN EXAMPLE OF A THEORY

Exhibit 3.5 is a simplified portrayal of a theory to explain voluntary job turnover—that is, the movement of employees to other organizations. Two concepts—(1) the *perceived desirability of movement* to another organization and (2) the *perceived ease of movement* from the present job—are expected to be the primary determinants of *intention to quit.* This is a proposition. Further, the concept *intention to quit* is expected to be a necessary condition for the actual *voluntary job turnover behavior* to occur. This is a second proposition that links concepts together in this theory. In the more elaborate theory, *job performance* is another concept considered to be the primary determinant influencing

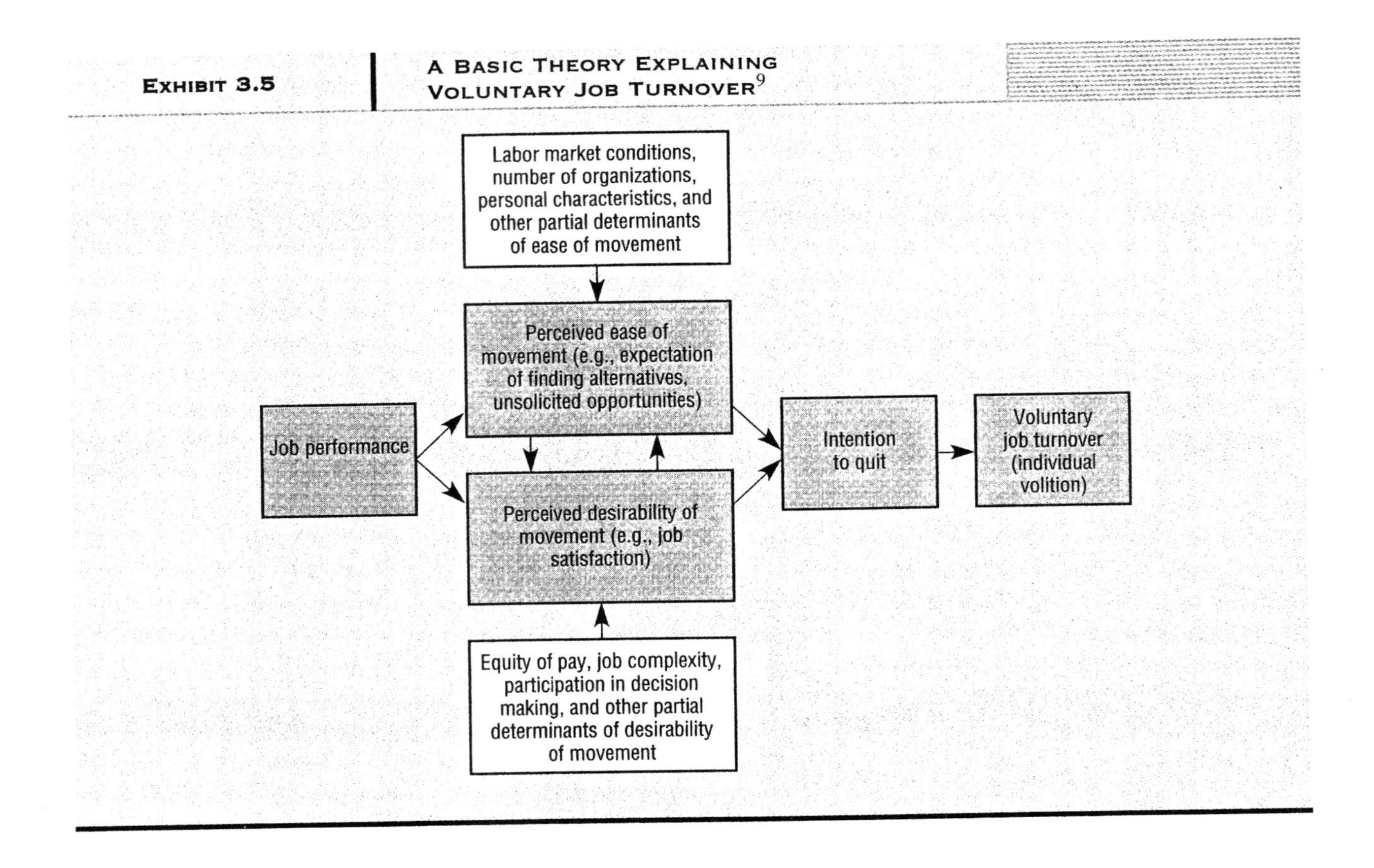

EXHIBIT 3.5 A BASIC THEORY EXPLAINING VOLUNTARY JOB TURNOVER[9]

both *perceived ease of movement* and *perceived desirability of movement.* Moreover, perceived ease of movement is related to other concepts such as *labor market conditions, number of organizations visible* to the individual, and *personal characteristics.* Perceived desirability of movement is influenced by concepts such as *equity of pay, job complexity,* and *participation in decision making.*

A complete explanation of this theory is not possible; however, this example should help you understand the terminology used by theory builders.

VERIFYING THEORY

If facts conflict with a theory, either the theory must be changed or the facts.

BENEDICT SPINOZA

In most scientific situations there are alternative theories to explain certain phenomena. To determine which is the better theory, researchers gather empirical data or make observations to verify the theories.

Maslow's hierarchical theory of motivation offers one explanation of human behavior. For example, Maslow theorizes that individuals will attempt to satisfy physiological needs before self-esteem needs. An alternative view of motivation is provided by Freudian (psychoanalytic) theory, which suggests that unconscious, emotional impulses are the basic influences on behavior. One task of science is to determine if a given theoretical proposition is false or if there are inconsistencies between competing theories. Just as records are made to be broken, theories are made to be tested.

> It must be possible to demonstrate that a given proposition or theory is false. This may at first glance appear strange. Why "false" rather than "true"?

RESEARCH INSIGHT

THEORY AND SONG

This song (attributed to George Schultz, a former U.S. Secretary of State) is sung to the lively tune *Silver Dollar*.[10]

A fact without a theory
Is like a ship without a sail,
Is like a boat without a rudder,
Is like a kite without a tail.
A fact without a figure
Is a tragic final act,
But one thing worse
In this universe
Is a theory without a fact.

> Technically, there may be other untested theories which could account for the results we obtained in our study of a proposition. At the very least, there may be a competing explanation which could be the "real" explanation for a given set of research findings. Thus, we can never be certain that our proposition or theory is the correct one. The scientist can only say, "I have a theory which I have objectively tested with data and the data are consistent with my theory." If the possibility of proving an idea false or wrong is not inherent in our test of an idea, then we cannot put much faith in the evidence that suggests it to be true. No other evidence was allowed to manifest itself.[11]

Business research gathers facts to verify theories. However, the researcher who wishes to identify inconsistency within a particular theory must understand the difference between facts and theories:

> Facts and theories are different things, not rungs in a hierarchy of increasing certainty. Facts are the world's data. Theories are structures of ideas that explain and interpret facts. Facts do not go away when scientists debate rival theories to explain them. Einstein's theory of gravitation replaced Newton's, but apples did not suspend themselves in midair pending the outcome.[12]

HOW ARE THEORIES GENERATED?

Many students ask, "Where do theories come from?" Although this is not an easy question to answer in a short chapter on theory in business research, we shall nevertheless explore this topic briefly.

In this chapter, theory has been explained at the abstract, conceptual level and at the empirical level. Theory generation may occur at either level.

deductive reasoning
The logical process of deriving a conclusion about a specific instance based on a known general premise or something known to be true.

At the abstract, conceptual level, a theory may be developed with deductive reasoning by going from a general statement to a specific assertion. **Deductive reasoning** is the logical process of deriving a conclusion about a specific instance based on a known general premise or something known to be

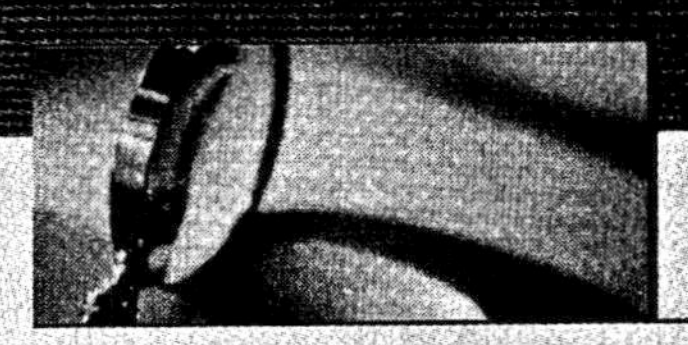

RESEARCH INSIGHT

BALLISTIC THEORY

Ballistic theory is a theory because it deals with measurable factors, because it states their relationships in detail, and because any one factor can be fairly completely determined by a knowledge of all the others.[13] Given all of the factors except the initial speed of the projectile, an engineer can determine what that speed was. Asked to change the point of impact, he can suggest several ways in which this can be accomplished—all of which will work.

It is common knowledge that the behavioral sciences are not as advanced as the physical sciences. What this means, in effect, is that no one has yet defined all of the factors in human behavior or determined the influence that each has on events. In fact, no one has really done a very good job of determining what an event is, that is, how to measure it or what to consider relevant about it.

Again, an example may help explain the dilemma. It is irrelevant to ballistic theory that John Gingrich is standing beside the 155 mm rifle when it is fired. It may not be irrelevant to consumer behavior theory that he is standing beside the person who selects a necktie. It is not relevant to ballistic theory that the gunner's father once carried an M-1. It may be relevant to consumer behavior theory that the automobile purchaser's grandfather once owned a Ford.

true. For example, we know that *all managers are human beings.* If we also know that *Steve Hazelwood is a manager,* then we can deduce that *Steve Hazelwood is a human being.*

inductive reasoning
The logical process of establishing a general proposition on the basis of observation of particular facts.

At the empirical level, a theory may be developed with inductive reasoning. **Inductive reasoning** is the logical process of establishing a general proposition on the basis of observation of particular facts. All managers that have ever been seen are human beings; therefore, all managers are human beings.

Suppose a stockbroker with 15 years' experience trading on the New York Stock Exchange repeatedly notices that the price of gold and the price of gold stocks rise whenever there is a hijacking, terrorist bombing, or military skirmish. In other words, similar patterns occur whenever a certain type of event occurs. The stockbroker may induce from these empirical observations the more general situation that the price of gold is related to political stability. Thus, the stockbroker states a proposition based on his or her experience or specific observations.

Over the course of time, theory construction is often the result of a combination of deductive and inductive reasoning. Our experiences lead us to draw conclusions that we then try to verify empirically by using the scientific method.

OVERVIEW OF THE SCIENTIFIC METHOD

It is useful to look at the analytic process of scientific theory building as a series of stages. Seven operations may be viewed as the steps involved in the application of the scientific method:

1. Assessment of relevant existing knowledge of a phenomenon
2. Formulation of concepts and propositions

3. Statement of hypotheses
4. Design of research to test the hypotheses
5. Acquisition of meaningful empirical data
6. Analysis and evaluation of data
7. Proposal of an explanation of the phenomenon and statement of new problems raised by the research[14]

An excellent overview of the scientific method is presented in Robert Pirsig's book *Zen and the Art of Motorcycle Maintenance:*

> Actually I've never seen a cycle-maintenance problem complex enough really to require full-scale formal scientific method. Repair problems are not that hard. When I think of formal scientific method an image sometimes comes to mind of an enormous juggernaut, a huge bulldozer—slow, tedious, lumbering, laborious, but invincible. It takes twice as long, five times as long, maybe a dozen times as long as informal mechanic's techniques, but you know in the end you're going to get it. There's no fault isolation problem in motorcycle maintenance that can stand up to it. When you've hit a really tough one, tried everything, racked your brain and nothing works, and you know that this time Nature has really decided to be difficult, you say, "Okay, Nature, that's the end of the nice guy," and you crank up the formal scientific method.
>
> For this you keep a lab notebook. Everything gets written down, formally, so that you know at all times where you are, where you've been, where you're going and where you want to get. In scientific work and electronics technology this is necessary because otherwise the problems get so complex you get lost in them and confused and forget what you know and what you don't know and have to give up. In cycle maintenance things are not that involved, but when confusion starts it's a good idea to hold it down by making everything formal and exact. Sometimes just the act of writing down the problems straightens out your head as to what they really are.
>
> The logical statements entered into the notebook are broken down into six categories: (1) statement of the problem, (2) hypotheses as to the cause of the problem, (3) experiments designed to test each hypothesis, (4) predicted results of the experiments, (5) observed results of the experiments and (6) conclusions from the results of the experiments. This is not different from the formal arrangement of many college and high-school lab notebooks but the purpose here is no longer just busywork. The purpose now is precise guidance of thoughts that will fail if they are not accurate.
>
> The real purpose of scientific method is to make sure Nature hasn't misled you into thinking you know something you don't actually know. There's not a mechanic or scientist or technician alive who hasn't suffered from that one so much that he's not instinctively on guard. That's the main reason why so much scientific and mechanical information sounds so dull and so cautious. If you get careless or go romanticizing scientific information, giving it a flourish here and there, Nature will soon make a complete fool out of you. It does it often enough anyway even when you don't give it opportunities. One must be extremely careful and rigidly logical when dealing with Nature: one logical slip and an entire scientific edifice comes tumbling down. One false deduction about the machine and you can get hung up indefinitely.
>
> In Part One of formal scientific method, which is the statement of the problem, the main skill is in stating absolutely no more than you are positive you know. It is much better to enter a statement "Solve Problem: Why doesn't

cycle work?" which sounds dumb but is correct, than it is to enter a statement "Solve Problem: What is wrong with the electrical system?" when you don't absolutely know the trouble is in the electrical system. What you should state is "Solve Problem: What is wrong with cycle?" and then state as the first entry of Part Two: "Hypothesis Number One: The trouble is in the electrical system." You think of as many hypotheses as you can, then you design experiments to test them to see which are true and which are false.

This careful approach to the beginning questions keeps you from taking a major wrong turn which might cause you weeks of extra work or can even hang you up completely. Scientific questions often have a surface appearance of dumbness for this reason. They are asked in order to prevent dumb mistakes later on.

Part Three, that part of formal scientific method called experimentation, is sometimes thought of by romantics as all of science itself because that's the only part with much visual surface. They see lots of test tubes and bizarre equipment and people running around making discoveries. They do not see the experiment as part of a larger intellectual process and so they often confuse experiments with demonstrations, which look the same. A man conducting a gee-whiz science show with fifty thousand dollars' worth of Frankenstein equipment is not doing anything scientific if he knows beforehand what the results of his efforts are going to be. A motorcycle mechanic, on the other hand, who honks the horn to see if the battery works is informally conducting a true scientific experiment. He is testing a hypothesis by putting the question to nature. The TV scientist who mutters sadly, "The experiment is a failure; we have failed to achieve what we had hoped for," is suffering mainly from a bad scriptwriter. An experiment is never a failure solely because it fails to achieve predicted results. An experiment is a failure only when it also fails adequately to test the hypothesis in question, when the data it produces don't prove anything one way or another.

TO THE POINT

A motorcycle mechanic . . . who honks the horn to see if the battery works is informally conducting a true scientific experiment. He is testing a hypothesis by putting the question to nature.

ROBERT M. PIRSIG

Skill at this point consists of using experiments that test only the hypothesis in question, nothing less, nothing more. If the horn honks, and the mechanic concludes that the whole electrical system is working, he is in deep trouble. He has reached an illogical conclusion. The honking horn only tells him that the battery and horn are working. To design an experiment properly he has to think very rigidly in terms of what directly causes what. This you know from the hierarchy. The horn doesn't make the cycle go. Neither does the battery, except in a very indirect way. The point at which the electrical system directly causes the engine to fire is at the spark plugs, and if you don't test here, at the output of the electrical system, you will never really know whether the failure is electrical or not.

To test properly the mechanic removes the plug and lays it against the engine so that the base around the plug is electrically grounded, kicks the starter lever and watches the spark-plug gap for a blue spark. If there isn't any he can conclude one of two things: (a) there is an electrical failure or (b) his experiment is sloppy. If he is experienced he will try it a few more times, checking connections, trying every way he can think of to get that plug to fire. Then, if he can't get it to fire, he finally concludes that (a) is correct, there's an electrical failure, and the experiment is over. He has proved that his hypothesis is correct.

In the final category, conclusions, skill comes in stating no more than the experiment has proved. It hasn't proved that when he fixes the electrical system the motorcycle will start. There may be other things wrong. But he does know that the motorcycle isn't going to run until the electrical system is working and he sets up the next formal question: "Solve problem: What is wrong with the electrical system?"

He then sets up hypotheses for these and tests them. By asking the right questions and choosing the right tests and drawing the right conclusions the mechanic works his way down the echelons of the motorcycle hierarchy until he has found the exact specific cause or causes of the engine failure, and then he changes them so that they no longer cause the failure.

An untrained observer will see only physical labor and often get the idea that physical labor is mainly what the mechanic does. Actually the physical labor is the smallest and easiest part of what the mechanic does. By far the greatest part of his work is careful observation and precise thinking. That is why mechanics sometimes seem so taciturn and withdrawn when performing tests. They don't like it when you talk to them because they are concentrating on mental images, hierarchies, and not really looking at you or the physical motorcycle at all. They are using the experiment as part of a program to expand their hierarchy of knowledge of the faulty motorcycle and compare it to the correct hierarchy in their mind. They are looking at underlying form.[15]

PRACTICAL VALUE OF THEORIES

As the above excerpt makes evident, theories allow us to generalize beyond individual facts or isolated situations. Theories provide a framework that can guide managerial strategy by providing insights into general rules of behavior. When different incidents may be theoretically comparable in some way, the scientific knowledge gained from theory development may have practical value. A good theory allows us to generalize beyond individual facts so that general patterns may be predicted and understood. For this reason it is often said there is nothing so practical as a good theory.

SUMMARY

Prediction and understanding are the two purposes of theory. A theory is a coherent set of general propositions used as principles of explanation of the apparent relationships of certain observed phenomena. Concepts and propositions are the elements of theory at the abstract level. At the empirical level, theory is concerned with variables and testable hypotheses, the empirical counterparts of concepts and propositions. The scientific method is a series of stages utilized to develop and refine theory.

Key Terms

theory
concept
ladder of abstraction
abstract level
empirical level
proposition
scientific method
hypothesis
variable
deductive reasoning
inductive reasoning

Questions for Review and Critical Thinking

1. What are some theories offered to explain aspects of your field of business?
2. How do propositions and hypotheses differ?
3. How do concepts differ from variables?
4. Comment on this statement: "There is nothing so practical as a good theory."
5. The 17th-century Dutch philosopher Benedict Spinoza said, "If the facts conflict with a theory, either the theory must be changed or the facts." What is the practical meaning of this statement?
6. Find another definition of *theory*. How is the definition you found similar to this book's definition? How is it different?

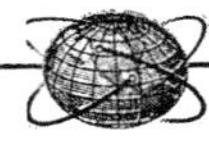

Exploring the Internet

1. The *American Heritage Dictionary of the English Language* can be found at http://www.bartleby.com/am/. What is the definition of *theory* given at this site? How does it compare to the definition given in this chapter?
2. Go to http://www.utm.edu/research/iep/ to find the Internet Encyclopedia of Philosophy. Look up the term *logical positivism*. Is empirical verification important in this field of philosophy?
3. The *Logic of Scientific Discovery* is an important theoretical work. Visit The Karl Popper Web site at http://www.eeng.dcu.ie/~tkpw/ to learn about its author and his work.

Case Suggestion

Case 27: Old School versus New School Sports Fans

3

THE RESEARCH PROCESS: An Overview

What you will learn in this chapter

- To classify business research as exploratory research, descriptive research, or causal research.
- To list the stages in the business research process.
- To identify and briefly discuss the various decision alternatives available to the researcher during each stage of the research process.
- To explain the difference between a research project and a research program.

Two contrasting models dominate the way managers think about the design of the work process.[1] On the one hand, a task may require the input of several highly interdependent people. One example of a design to accomplish such a task is a team responsible for creating a new advertising campaign. The team might include copywriters, graphic artists, and project managers, all of whose contributions are necessary for completing the task, and all of whom are held collectively accountable for the quality of the new promotion strategy. Alternatively, work can be structured to be performed by highly independent individuals. The reward system in that case must be designed to reinforce individual excellence. An example is a sales team in which each member is given responsibility for sales in one specific territory and is paid a commission based solely on his or her individual sales performance.

A third model has received relatively little attention: a "hybrid" design that combines elements of interdependent and independent work. One example of such a design is a group of researchers in a development laboratory, each of whom pursues independent research projects and, in addition, collaborates on some larger shared enterprise. Members of such hybrid groups sometimes operate entirely independently and sometimes work as a team.

Suppose a manager wanted to determine how important interdependence is for accomplishing a particular task. Suppose the manager was also interested in knowing how to assess and reward both independent performance and interdependent teamwork performance. Should a survey of employees be taken? Should employees be observed on the job? Should an experiment be designed to evaluate the distinct forms of interdependence? Should a survey of managers be part of the research strategy?

This chapter discusses how managers make decisions about planning research strategies and tactics. ■

DECISION MAKING

Formally defined, *decision making* is the process of resolving a problem or choosing among alternative opportunities. The keys to decision making are recognizing the nature of the problem/opportunity, identifying how much information is available, and determining what information is needed. Every business problem or decision-making situation can be classified on a continuum ranging from complete certainty to absolute ambiguity. To facilitate discussion, the scale in Exhibit 4.1 shows three categories: certainty, uncertainty, and ambiguity.[2]

Certainty

Complete certainty means that the decision maker has all the information that he or she needs. The decision maker knows the exact nature of the business problem or opportunity. For example, an airline may need to know the demographic characteristics of its pilots. The firm knows exactly what information it needs and where to find it. If a manager is completely certain about both the problem/opportunity and future outcomes, then research may not be needed at all. However, perfect certainty, especially about the future, is rare.

Uncertainty

Uncertainty means that managers grasp the general nature of the objectives they wish to achieve, but the information about alternatives is incomplete. Predictions about the forces that will shape future events are educated guesses. Under conditions of uncertainty, effective managers recognize potential value in spending additional time gathering information to clarify the nature of the decision.

Ambiguity

Ambiguity means that the nature of the problem to be solved is unclear. The objectives are vague and the alternatives are difficult to define. This is by far the most difficult decision situation.

Business managers face a variety of decision-making situations. Under conditions of complete certainty, when future outcomes are predictable, business research may be a waste of time. However, under conditions of uncertainty or ambiguity, business research becomes more attractive to decision makers. The more ambiguous a situation is, the more likely it is that additional time and money must be spent on business research.

EXHIBIT 4.1 DECISIONS ARE NOT ALL THE SAME: A CONTINUUM OF DECISION MAKING

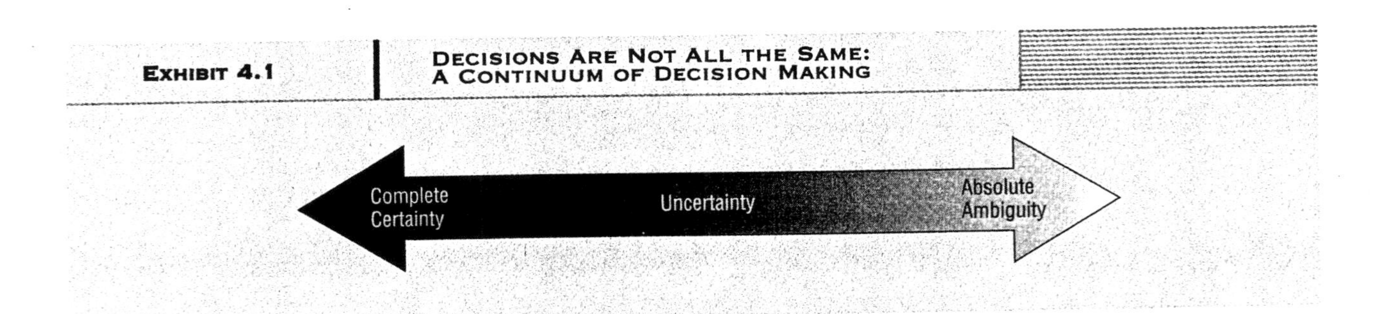

TYPES OF BUSINESS RESEARCH

Business research produces information to reduce uncertainty. It helps focus decision making. In a number of situations business researchers know exactly what their business problems are and design studies to test specific hypotheses. For example, a soft drink company introducing a new iced coffee might want to know whether a gold or a silver label would make the packaging more effective. This problem is fully defined and an experiment may be designed to answer the business question with little preliminary investigation. In other, more ambiguous circumstances management may be totally unaware of a business problem. For example, a plant manager may notice when employee turnover increases dramatically but be totally ignorant of the reason for the increase. Some exploratory research may be necessary to gain insights into the nature of such a problem.

Because of the variety of research activity, it will be helpful to categorize the types of business research. Business research can be classified on the basis of either technique or function. Experiments, surveys, and observational studies are just a few common research *techniques.* Classifying business research on the basis of purpose or *function* allows us to understand how the nature of the problem influences the choice of research method. The nature of the problem will determine whether the research is (1) exploratory, (2) descriptive, or (3) causal.

Exploratory Studies

exploratory research
Initial research conducted to clarify and define the nature of a problem.

Exploratory research is conducted to clarify ambiguous problems. Management may have discovered general problems, but research is needed to gain better understanding of the dimensions of the problems. Exploratory studies provide

Descriptive research often is used to reveal the nature of shopping or other consumer behavior. Bride *magazine's descriptive research revealed that the average bride tries on 12 wedding gowns; one in five considers more than 21 dresses before choosing the right one; and 20 percent cry when they find it.*[3]

information to use in analyzing a situation, but uncovering conclusive evidence to determine a particular course of action is *not* the purpose of exploratory research. Usually, exploratory research is conducted with the expectation that *subsequent* research will be required to provide conclusive evidence. It is a serious mistake to rush into detailed surveys before less expensive and more readily available sources of information have been exhausted.

In an organization considering a program to help employees with child-care needs, for example, exploratory research with a small number of employees who have children might determine that many of them have spouses who also work and that these employees have positive reactions to the possibility of an on-site child-care program. In such a case exploratory research helps to crystallize a problem and identify information needs for future research.

Descriptive Research

descriptive research
Research designed to describe characteristics of a population or a phenomenon.

The major purpose of **descriptive research**, as the term implies, is to describe characteristics of a population or phenomenon. Descriptive research seeks to determine the answers to *who, what, when, where,* and *how* questions. Every month the Bureau of Labor Statistics (BLS) conducts descriptive research in the form of the *Current Population Survey.* Official statistics on unemployment and other characteristics of the labor force are derived from this survey.

Descriptive research often helps segment and target markets. For example, business researchers conducted descriptive surveys to identify the characteristics of consumers who purchase organic food products. Such consumers tend to live in larger cities, those with populations over 500,000. More than half live on the coasts, with the majority residing on the West Coast. The most frequent buyers of organic foods are affluent men and women ages 45–54 (36 percent) and 18–34 (35 percent).[4] Interestingly, consumers who buy organic foods are not very brand-oriented—81 percent of them cannot name a single organic brand.

Consider another example of descriptive research. A university career placement service may want to determine if its facilities and services are adequate. A descriptive study might be initiated to determine how many interviews each student wants to schedule, whether students are able to schedule appointments with certain desirable organizations, and if there are any problems with physical facilities. It should be clear that simply describing a situation may provide important information and that in many situations descriptive information is all that is needed to solve business problems—even though such research may not answer the *why* question.

Accuracy is of paramount importance in descriptive research. Although errors cannot be completely eliminated, good researchers strive for descriptive precision. Suppose the purpose of a study is to describe the market potential of portable digital music players for MP3 formats. If the study does not present a precise measurement of sales volume, it will mislead the managers who are making production scheduling, budgeting, and other decisions based on that study.

Unlike exploratory research, descriptive studies are based on some previous understanding of the nature of the research problem. For example, state societies of certified public accountants (CPAs) conduct annual practice management surveys that ask questions such as "Do you charge clients for travel time at regular rates?" "Do you have a program of continuing education on a regular basis for professional employees?" "Do you pay incentive bonuses to professional staff?" Although the researcher may have a general understanding

RESEARCH INSIGHT

POETRY AND RESEARCH: AN ODD COUPLE?

I keep six honest serving men,
(they taught me all I knew).
Their names are What, and Why, and When,
and How, and Where, and Who.

—Rudyard Kipling, *Just So Stories*

Kipling's words can be helpful to the business researcher. Those who ask the *what, why, when, how, where,* and *who* questions will be started on the right road to solving their business research problems.

of the business practices of CPAs, conclusive evidence in the form of answers to questions of fact must be collected. Frequently, descriptive research will attempt to determine the extent of differences in the needs, perceptions, attitudes, and characteristics of subgroups.

The purpose of many organizational behavior studies, for example, is to describe the reasons employees give for their explanations of the nature of things. In other words, a **diagnostic analysis** is performed when employees in the various subgroups are asked questions such as "Why do you feel that way?" Although the reasons employees feel a certain way are described, the findings of descriptive studies such as this, sometimes called *diagnostics,* do not provide evidence of a causal nature.

diagnostic analysis
Analysis used to clarify research findings, such as explanations respondents give for a behavior or attitude.

Causal Research

causal research
Research conducted to identify cause-and-effect relationships among variables when the research problem has already been narrowly defined.

The main goal of **causal research** is to identify cause-and-effect relationships among variables. (Exploratory and descriptive research normally precede cause-and-effect relationship studies.) In causal studies it is typical to have an expectation of the relationship to be explained, such as a prediction about the influence of price, packaging, advertising, and the like on sales. Thus, researchers must be knowledgeable about the research subject. Ideally, a manager would like to establish that one factor (say, a new package) is the means for producing another event (an increase in sales).

Causal research attempts to establish that when we do one thing, another thing will follow. The word *cause* is frequently used in everyday conversation, but from a scientific research perspective, a causal relationship is impossible to prove. Nevertheless, researchers seek certain types of evidence to help them understand and predict relationships.

A typical causal study has management change one variable (e.g., training) and then observe the effect on another variable (e.g., productivity). In this situation there is evidence for establishing causality because it appears that the cause precedes the effect. In other words, having an appropriate causal order of events, or temporal sequence, is one criterion that must be met to establish a causal relationship. If an organizational behavior theorist wishes to show that attitude change *causes* behavior change, one criterion that must be established is that attitude change *precedes* behavior change.

Further, there is some evidence of concomitant variation in that, in our example, increased training and increased productivity appear to be associated.

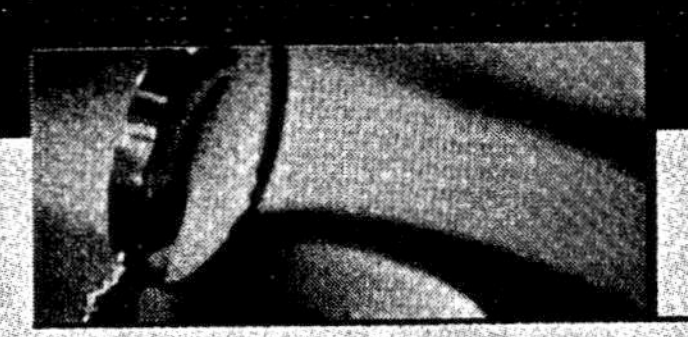

Research Insight

Lay's New Global Package Design

PepsiCo Foods International, marketer of Lay's potato chips, the number one potato chip in the United States, unified its market-leading potato chip brands, such as Walkers Crisps in the United Kingdom, Papas Sabritas in Mexico, and Matutano chips in Spain, with the Lay's name and a new global package design highlighted by a bold red and yellow color scheme and centered on a new icon called the "Banner Sun."[5]

This global initiative followed the most comprehensive business research program in food products history. More than 100,000 consumers were interviewed in over 30 countries to describe, understand, and develop the worldwide potato chip market. From its global research program, PepsiCo learned that potato chips are "the cola of snacks." The descriptive research showed that in country after country, potato chips are consumers' favorite snack, ranked ahead of chocolate bars, ice cream and candy, and all other salty snacks. The company's new worldwide marketing approach enables Lay's to communicate and enhance the concept of potato chips as a timeless, simple pleasure to consumers around the world.

Concomitant variation is the occurrence of two phenomena or events that vary together. When the criterion of concomitant variation is not met—that is, when there is no association between variables—reason suggests that no causal relationship exists. If two events vary together, one *may* be the cause. However, concomitant variation by itself is not sufficient evidence for causality, because the two events may have a common cause—that is, both may be influenced by a third variable.

For instance, one morning at Atlantic City's beach a large number of ice cream cones are sold, and that afternoon there are a large number of drownings. Most of us would not conclude that eating ice cream cones causes drownings. More likely, the large number of people at the beach probably influenced both ice cream cone sales and drownings. It may be that the "effect" was produced in other ways. Just because there is concomitant variation and a proper time sequence between the occurrence of Event A and Event B, causation is not certain. There may be plausible alternative explanations for an observed relationship.[6] A plurality of causes is possible.

Consider a presidential candidate who reduces advertising expenditures near the end of the primary campaign and wins many more delegates in the remaining primaries. To infer causality—that reducing advertising increases the number of delegates—might be inappropriate, because the *presumed* cause of the increase may not be the real cause. It is likely that, near the end of a race, marginal candidates withdraw. Thus, the real cause may be unrelated to advertising.

In these examples, the third variable that is the source of the spurious association is a very salient factor readily identified as the more likely influence on change. However, within the complex environment in which managers operate, it is difficult to identify alternative or complex causal factors.

In summary, research with the purpose of inferring causality should do the following:

1. Establish the appropriate causal order or sequence of events

2. Measure the concomitant variation between the presumed cause and the presumed effect
3. Recognize the presence or absence of alternative plausible explanations or causal factors[7]

Even when these three criteria for causation are present, the researcher can never be certain that the causal explanation is adequate.

Most basic scientific studies in business (e.g., the development of organizational behavior theory) ultimately seek to identify cause-and-effect relationships. When one thinks of science, one often associates it with experiments. Thus, to predict a relationship between, say, price and perceived quality of a product, causal studies often create statistical experimental controls to establish "contrast groups." A number of business experiments are conducted by both theory developers and pragmatic business people. (More will be said about experiments and causal research in Chapter 12.)

INFLUENCE OF UNCERTAINTY OF TYPE OF RESEARCH

The uncertainty of the research problem is related to the type of research project. Exhibit 4.2 illustrates that exploratory research is conducted during the early stages of decision making when the decision situation is ambiguous and management is very uncertain about the nature of the problem. When management is aware of the problem but not completely knowledgeable about the situation, descriptive research is usually conducted. Causal studies can only be conducted when a problem is sharply defined.

EXHIBIT 4.2 RELATIONSHIP OF UNCERTAINTY TO TYPE OF BUSINESS RESEARCH

	Exploratory Research (Ambiguous Problem)	Descriptive Research (Aware of Partially Defined Problem)	Causal Research (Clearly Defined Problem)
Examples of Business Problems	"Absenteeism is increasing and we don't know why." "Would people be interested in our new product idea?" "What task conditions influence the leadership process in our organization?"	"What kind of people favor trade protectionism?" "Did last year's product recall have an impact on our company's stock price?" "Has the average merger rate for savings and loans increased in the past decade?"	"Which of two training programs is more effective?" "Can I predict the value of energy stocks if I know the current dividends and growth rates of dividends?" "Will buyers purchase more of our product in a new package?"

Note: The degree of uncertainty about the research problem determines the research methodology.

STAGES IN THE RESEARCH PROCESS

As previously noted, business research can take many forms, but systematic inquiry is a common thread. Systematic inquiry requires careful planning of an orderly investigation. Business research, like other forms of scientific inquiry, is a sequence of highly interrelated activities. The stages in the research process overlap continuously, and it is somewhat of an oversimplification to state that every research project has exactly the same ordered sequence of activities. Nevertheless, business research often follows a general pattern. The stages are (1) defining the problem, (2) planning a research design, (3) planning a sample, (4) collecting data, (5) analyzing the data, and (6) formulating the conclusions and preparing the report. These six stages are portrayed in Exhibit 4.3 as a cyclical, or circular-flow process, because conclusions from research studies usually generate new ideas and problems that need to be further investigated.

In practice, the stages overlap chronologically and are functionally interrelated. Sometimes the later stages are completed before the earlier ones. The terms *forward* and *backward linkage* reflect the interrelatedness of the various stages.[8] The term **forward linkage** implies that the earlier stages of research will influence the design of the later stages. Thus, the objectives of the research outlined in the problem definition will have an impact on the selection of the sample and the way in which the data will be collected. The decision concerning who will be sampled will affect the wording of questionnaire items. For example, if the research concentrates on respondents who have low educational levels, the wording of the questionnaire will be simpler than it would be if the respondents were college graduates. The notion of **backward linkage** implies that the later steps have an influence on the earlier stages in the research process. If it is known that the data will be analyzed by computer, then computer coding requirements are included in the questionnaire design.

forward linkage
A term implying that the early stages of the research process will influence the design of the later stages.

backward linkage
A term implying that the late stages of the research process will have an influence on the early stages.

EXHIBIT 4.3 PHASES OF THE RESEARCH PROCESS

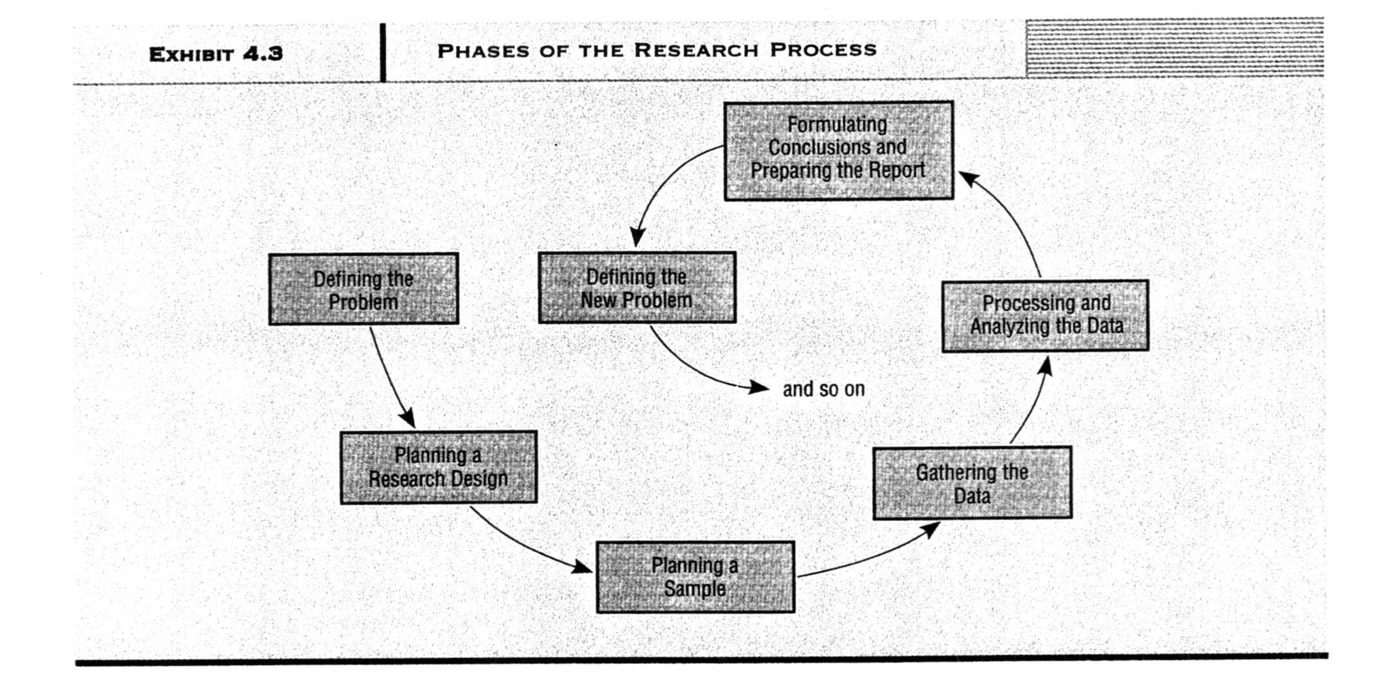

Perhaps the most important example of backward linkage is the knowledge that the executives who will read the research report need certain information. The professional researcher anticipates executives' needs for information in the planning process and considers these needs during the analysis and tabulation stages.

Decision Alternatives in the Research Process

A number of alternatives are available to the researcher during each of the six stages of the research process. The research process can be compared with a guide or a map.[9] On a map some paths are better charted than others. Some are difficult to travel, and some are more interesting and scenic than others. Rewarding experiences may be gained during the journey. It is important to remember there is no single right path or best path for all journeys. The road one takes depends on where one wants to go and the resources (money, time, labor, and so on) one has available for the trip. The map analogy is useful for the business researcher because at each stage of the research process there are several paths to follow. In some instances the quickest path will be the appropriate means of research because of pressing time constraints. In other circumstances, when money and human resources are plentiful, the path the research takes may be quite different. Exploration of the various paths of business research decisions is our primary purpose.

Each of the six stages in the research process is briefly described below. (Each stage is discussed in greater depth in later chapters.) Exhibit 4.4 shows the decisions that researchers must make in each stage of the research process. This discussion of the research process begins with problem discovery and definition, because most research projects, albeit at an earlier moment in time, are initiated because of some uncertainty about some aspect of the firm or its environment.

Discovering and Defining the Problem

In Exhibit 4.4 the research process begins with problem discovery, and identifying the problem is the first step toward its solution. The word *problem,* in general usage, suggests that something has gone wrong. Unfortunately, the word *problem* does not connote a business opportunity, such as the chance to expand operations into a foreign country, nor does it connote the need for evaluation of an existing program, such as a professional development program for employees. Actually, the research task may be to clarify a problem, to evaluate a program, or to define an opportunity, and we will discuss *problem discovery and definition* in this broader context. It should be noted that the initial stage is problem *discovery,* rather than *definition.* (The researcher may not have a clear-cut statement of the problem at the outset of the research process.) Often, only symptoms are apparent to begin with. Profits may be declining, but management may not know the exact nature of the problem. Thus, the problem statement is often made only in general terms. What is to be investigated is not yet specifically identified.

A Problem Well Defined

The adage "a problem well defined is a problem half solved" is worth remembering. This adage emphasizes that an orderly definition of the research problem gives a sense of direction to the investigation. Careful attention to

EXHIBIT 4.4 FLOWCHART OF THE RESEARCH PROCESS

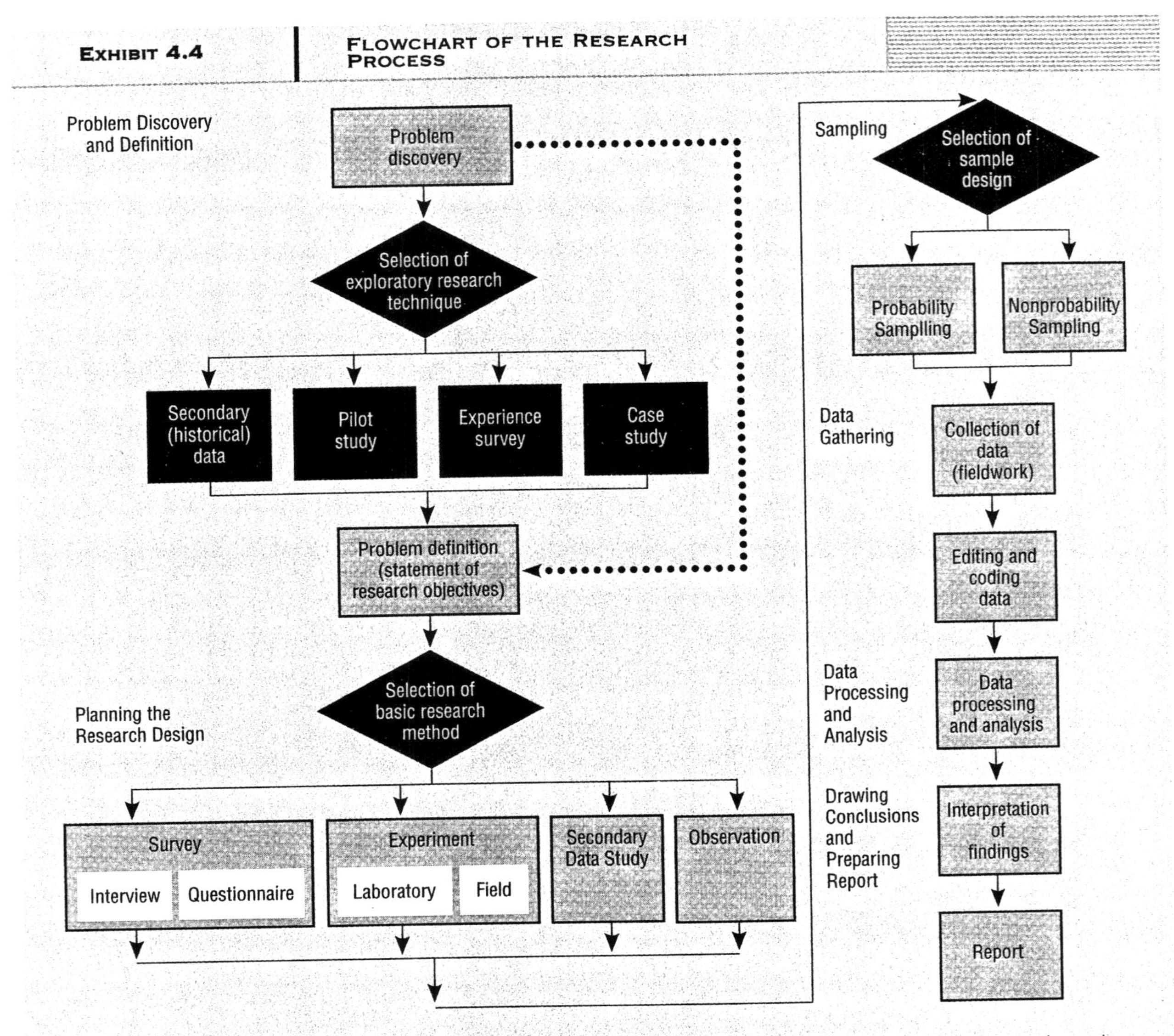

Note: Diamond-shaped boxes indicate a stage of the research design process where a choice of one or more techniques must be made. A dotted line indicates an alternative path when exploratory research is not used.

problem definition
The indication of a specific business decision area that will be clarified by answering some research questions.

problem definition allows a researcher to set the proper research objectives. If the purpose of the research is clear, the chances of collecting the necessary and relevant information—and not collecting surplus information—will be much greater.

It was Albert Einstein who noted that "the formulation of a problem is often more essential than its solution."[10] This is good advice for managers. Too often managers concentrate on finding the right answer rather than asking the right question. Many do not realize that defining a problem may be more difficult than solving it. In business research, if the data are collected before the nature of the business problem is carefully thought out, the data probably will not help solve the problem.

To be efficient, business research must have clear objectives and definite designs. Unfortunately, in many cases little or no planning goes into the formulation of a research problem. Consider the case of the Ha-Pah-Shu-Tse (a Pawnee Indian word for red corn) brand of Indian fried bread mix. The owner of the company, Mr. Ha-Pah-Shu-Tse, thought his product, one of the few American Indian food products available in the United States, wasn't selling because it wasn't highly advertised. He wanted a management consulting group to conduct some research concerning advertising themes. However, the management consultants pointed out to the Ha-Pah-Shu-Tse family that the brand (family) name on the bread mix might be a foremost source of concern. They suggested that investigating the brand image and consumer behavior should be the starting point, rather than focusing on advertising copy research. Family management agreed. (It should be emphasized that we are now using "problem" to refer to the managerial problem, which may be a lack of knowledge about consumers or advertising effectiveness and the lack of needed information.)

Frequently business researchers will not be involved until management discovers that information is needed about a particular aspect of the decision at hand. Even at this point the exact nature of the problem may not be well defined. Once a problem area has been discovered, the researcher can begin the process of precisely defining it.

Although the problem definition stage of the research process is probably the most important stage, it is frequently a neglected area of research. Too often managers forget that the best place to begin a research project is at the end. Knowing what is to be accomplished determines the research process. An error or omission in problem definition is likely to be a costly mistake that cannot be corrected in later stages of the process. (Chapter 6 discusses problem definition in greater detail.)

Exploratory Research

Many research projects with clearly defined problems, such as an annual survey of industry compensation, do not require exploratory research. In many situations, however, the definition of the problem would be inadequate if exploratory research were not conducted.

Exploratory research is usually conducted during the initial stage of the research process. The preliminary activities undertaken to refine the problem into a researchable one need not be formal or precise. The purpose of the exploratory research process is to progressively narrow the scope of the research topic and to transform discovered problems into defined ones, incorporating specific research objectives. By analyzing any existing studies on the subject, by talking with knowledgeable individuals, and by informally investigating the situation, the researchers can progressively sharpen the concepts. After such exploration the researchers should know exactly what data to collect during the formal project and how the project will be conducted. Exhibit 4.4 indicates that managers and researchers must decide whether to use one or more exploratory research techniques. As Exhibit 4.4 indicates, this stage of research is optional.

There are four basic categories of techniques for obtaining insights and gaining a clearer idea of a problem: secondary data analysis, pilot studies, case studies, and experience surveys. These are discussed in detail in Chapter 7. The next two sections briefly discuss secondary data analysis and a very popular type of pilot study, the focus group interview.

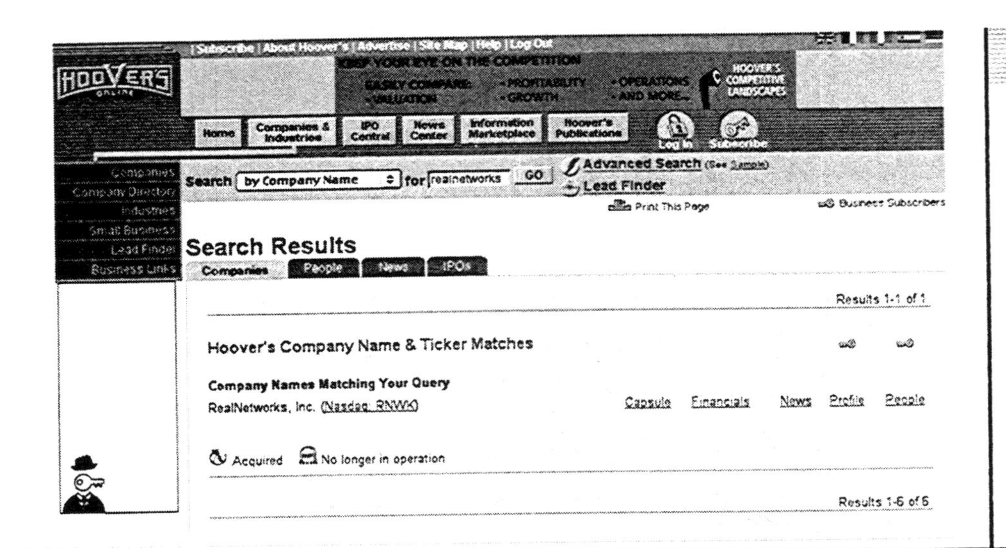

Business researchers find Hoover's Online to be an excellent secondary data source for financial information. Information about IPOs and Securities and Exchange Commission (SEC) data about thousands of companies allow researchers to make comparisons between companies over time and across industries.

secondary data
Data that have been previously collected for some project other than the one at hand.

primary data
Data gathered and assembled specifically for the research project at hand.

Secondary Data **Secondary data**, or historical data, are data previously collected and assembled for some project other than the one at hand. **Primary data** are data gathered and assembled specifically for the project at hand. Secondary data can often be found inside the company, in the library, and on the Internet, or they can be purchased from firms that specialize in providing information, such as economic forecasts, that is useful to organizations. The researcher who assembles data from the *Census of Population* or the *Survey of Current Business* is using secondary sources.

A review of the literature—a survey of published articles and books discussing theories and past empirical studies about a topic—is almost universal in academic research projects. It is also common in many applied research studies. Students who have written term papers should be familiar with the process of checking card catalogs, indexes to published literature, and other library resources to establish a bibliography of past research. Suppose, for example, a bank is interested in determining the best site for additional ATM machines. A logical first step would be to investigate the factors that bankers in other parts of the country consider important. By reading articles in banking journals, the bank management might quickly discover that the best locations are inside supermarkets located in residential areas where people are young, highly educated, and earning higher-than-average incomes. These data might lead the bank to investigate census information to determine where in the city such people live. Reviewing and building on the work already compiled by others are economical starting points for most research.

Secondary data can almost always be gathered faster and more inexpensively than primary data. However, secondary data may be outdated or may not exactly meet the needs of the researcher because they were collected for another purpose. Nevertheless, secondary sources often prove to be of great value in exploratory research. Investigating such sources has saved many a researcher from "reinventing the wheel" in primary data collection.

pilot study
Any small-scale exploratory research technique that uses sampling but does not apply rigorous standards.

Pilot Studies **Pilot studies** collect data from the ultimate subjects of the research project to serve as a guide for the larger study.[12] When the term *pilot study* is used in the context of exploratory research, it refers to a study whose

Jelly Belly brand sells 50 varieties of jelly beans. The company uses applied business research to increase the number of flavors it offers every year. Some of the flavors under development have been suggested by visitors to Jelly Belly's Web site. In return for filling out an interactive questionnaire, visitors get samples sent to them. One question asks for customers' input on new flavors. Jelly Belly gets a great response to this, and marketers take all the suggestions seriously. Researchers categorize them by similar flavors. Some of the ideas are put back on the Web so that people can vote for their favorites. The company has received some really off-the-wall suggestions. Among the strangest are flavors such as Dill Pickle, Tacos, Persimmon Pudding, Blackened Plantain, and Cream of Wheat.[11]

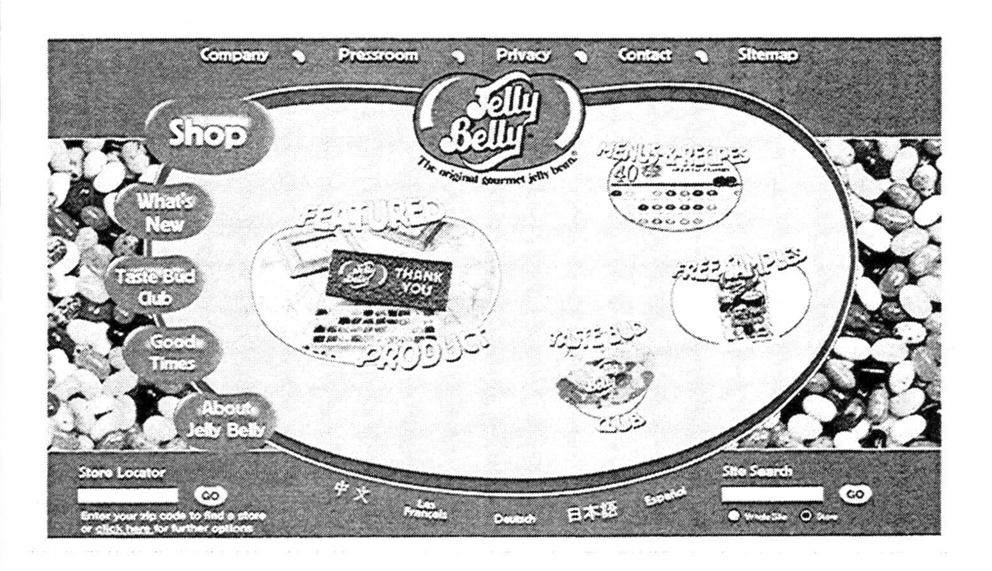

data collection methods are informal and whose findings may lack precision because rigorous standards are relaxed. For instance, a downtown association concerned with revitalization of the city's central business district (CBD) conducted a very flexible survey with questions that were open-ended. The interviewers were given considerable latitude to identify the opinions of local executives (the ultimate subjects) about future requirements in the downtown area. The results of this survey were used to suggest possible topics for formal investigation.

The *focus group interview* is a more elaborate exploratory pilot study. Increasingly popular in recent years, the focus group gathers six to ten people for a group dynamics session. This loosely structured discussion assumes that individuals are more willing to share their ideas when they are able to hear the ideas of others. Qualitative information obtained in these studies serves as a basis for subsequent quantitative study.

For example, the Philadelphia Museum used focus groups to investigate how well its exhibits and shows catered to the public. A local resident who had never visited the museum mentioned that he was not aware of any important artwork there. Another participant in the same focus group voiced the opinion that the museum would be filled with "pictures I would not understand. . . . I've seen art where it looked like kids splashed paint." These findings (confirmed by other research) influenced the museum to reinstate an image of van Gogh's *Sunflowers* on the cover of its brochures.[13]

Four basic types of exploratory research have been identified, but there is no standard design for such research. Since the purposes of exploratory research are to gain insights and to discover new ideas, researchers may use considerable creativity and flexibility. It is common to collect data using several exploratory techniques. Exhausting these sources is generally worth the effort because the expense is relatively low. Further, insights into how and how not to conduct research may be gained from activities during the problem definition stage. If the conclusions made during this stage suggest business opportunities, the researcher is in a position to begin planning a formal, quantitative research project.

Statement of Research Objectives

After identifying and clarifying the problem, with or without exploratory research, researchers should make a formal statement of the problem and the research objectives. A decision must initially be made as to precisely what should be researched, so as to delineate the type of information that should be collected and provide a framework for the scope of the study, or the **research project.**

research project
A specific research investigation; a study that completes or is planned to follow the stages in the research process.

The answers to questions such as "To what extent did the new compensation program achieve its objectives?" are typical research objectives. In this sense the statement of the problem is a research question.

The best expression of a research objective is a well-formed, testable research hypothesis; a *hypothesis* is a statement that can be refuted or supported by empirical data. For example, an exploratory study might lead to the hypothesis that male-dominated unions discriminate against women who want to enter the trades. In basic research, theory is the guide that helps generate hypotheses. Once the hypothesis has been developed, researchers are ready to select a research design.

Planning the Research Design

After the researcher has formulated the research problem, the research design must be developed. A **research design** is a master plan specifying the methods and procedures for collecting and analyzing the needed information. It is a framework or blueprint that plans the action for the research project. The objectives of the study determined during the early stages of the research are included in the design to ensure that the information collected is appropriate for solving the problem. The research investigator must also specify the sources of information, the research method or technique (survey or experiment, for example), the sampling methodology, and the schedule and cost of the research.

research design
A master plan specifying the methods and procedures for collecting and analyzing the needed information.

Selecting the Appropriate Research Design

Again, the researcher must make a decision. Exhibit 4.4 indicates there are four basic research methods for descriptive and causal research: surveys, experiments, secondary data studies, and observation. The objectives of the research methods, the available data sources, the urgency of the decision, and the cost of obtaining the data will determine which method is chosen. The managerial aspects of selecting the research method will be considered later.

You cannot put the same shoe on every foot.

PUBILIUS SYRUS (c. 42 BC)

The Partnership for a Drug Free America is a nonprofit organization that conducts applied business research. Its research indicated that the Partnership should target younger children. As a result, it created a public service announcement called "Big Ol' Bug" to appeal to children ages 6 to 8. The rock music lyrics include the line "I'd rather be a big ol' bug than ever try a stupid drug." The research also led to another public service announcement called "Brain Damaged" to appeal to preteens. Talking in the first person, a funny, likeable brain explains that drugs make a brain slow, confused, and barely able to think.

Surveys The most common method of generating primary data is through surveys. Most people have seen the results of political surveys by Gallup or HarrisInteractive, and some have been respondents (members of a sample that supply answers) to business research questionnaires. A *survey* is a research technique in which information is gathered from a sample of people using a questionnaire. The task of writing a list of questions and designing the exact format of the printed or written questionnaire is an essential aspect of the development of a survey research design.

Research investigators may choose to contact respondents in person, by telephone, by mail, or on the Internet. An advertiser who spends over $2,000,000 for 30 seconds of commercial time during the Super Bowl may telephone people to quickly gather information concerning their response to the advertising. Your congressional representative may mail you a questionnaire to learn how he or she should vote on issues. A mail survey is an inexpensive method of data collection for a member of Congress or any person. A forklift truck manufacturer trying to determine why sales in the wholesale grocery industry are low might choose an Internet questionnaire because the appropriate executives are hard to reach by telephone. In contrast, a computer manufacturer wishing to conduct an organizational survey of employees might need a versatile survey method whereby an interviewer can ask a variety of personal questions in a flexible format. Although personal interviews are expensive, they are valuable because investigators can utilize visual aids and supplement the interview with observations. Each of these survey methods has advantages and disadvantages. The researcher's task is to choose the most appropriate one for collecting the information needed.

Experiments Business experiments hold the greatest potential for establishing cause-and-effect relationships. The use of experimentation allows investigation of changes in one variable, such as productivity, while manipulating one or two other variables, perhaps social rewards or monetary rewards, under controlled conditions. Ideally, experimental control provides a basis for isolating causal factors, because outside (or exogenous) influences do not come into play.

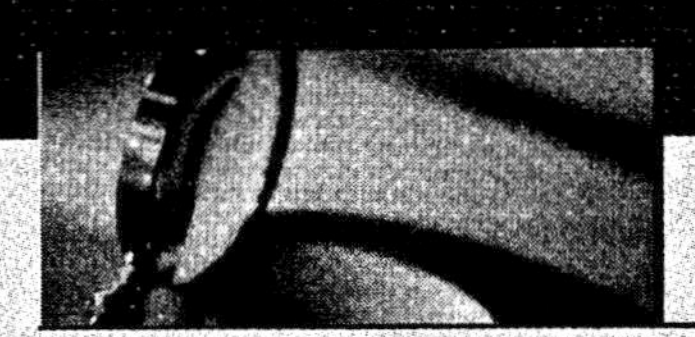

RESEARCH INSIGHT

BUSINESS RESEARCH SOLVES A PROBLEM

Febreze Fabric Refresher, which can be used on clothing or upholstery, uses a proprietary cleaning formula that penetrates fabrics to eliminate odors, not just cover them up with perfumes.[14] Procter & Gamble began test market experiments for Febreze Fabric Refresher in May 1996 in Phoenix, Boise, and Salt Lake City.

The initial strategy was to position Febreze as a niche product for smokers to use on dry-clean-only clothes. A television commercial showed a woman seated in the smoking section of a restaurant who is frustrated because her blazer smells like cigarette smoke, even though it has just come back from the dry cleaner. The friend she is talking to explains how Febreze neutralizes cigarette odors to bring fabric back to fresh. The research showed that after 6 months this advertising was not broadly relevant or emotional and the focus on cigarette smoke did nothing for the brand.

The researchers focused efforts on what went wrong. The company's researchers began to realize that because they were dealing with a totally new product category, the advertising found it difficult to articulate consumers' need for the innovation. Consumers did not grasp that they had a problem and could not clarify how the product could be improved because they didn't know of any alternative. Consumer studies sometimes took the product team in the wrong direction. Consumers insisted they did not want a product with perfume, but market tests in retail stores showed that the more perfume that was added, the more Febreze sold.

The product was repositioned after research indicated that those who bought Febreze were using it on upholstery and carpeting in addition to clothing. A second ad aimed at pet owners showed a dog sitting on a couch to illustrate how animals can leave odors on upholstery. A woman says that "in a perfect world, my dog Sophie wouldn't get on the furniture—but she does and it smells. I want to get rid of the odor, not Sophie." Consumers found this advertising insensitive and insulting, because it strongly suggested that "your dog smells." Although the ad communicated that Febreze also worked on clothes, it did not do a good job communicating the product's varied uses.

Subsequent survey research indicated the need for consumer education and revealed more about consumers' personal feelings about odors. Researchers learned that odors are an extremely delicate and emotional issue. The company concluded that they had to be careful to communicate with people in a positive manner. This meant putting out a message that said "we can make your clothes smell more pleasant" rather than "you stink," or "this is what your dog is preventing you from doing" instead of "your dog smells."

The finding about the value of consumer education led to an increased use of demonstrations in stores and at community events that included a teaching element explaining how the smell trapped in the fibers was cleaned away. The advertising message was reframed to reduce the negativity. The final test market version showed a mom with five kids. When her firefighter son gets home, "thinking the smoke alarm is going to go off," she sprays Febreze on the couch where he's tossed his fire jacket. Another scene shows her daughter playing in a marching band, and the mom is thinking "it's hot out there and they sweat." The mom solves the problem by spraying Febreze on the band uniform. The message is communicated by illustrating the problems of one family and a mom who understands that Febreze cleans life's smells out of fabrics.

The test market experiments and consumer research lasted 2 years. The marketing effort revamped package size, strength formulations for clothes and household fabrics, and retail prices. The long and expensive process to develop "new product category" innovation paid off: Febreze, with $250 million in retail sales the following year, was an unqualified success. Business research played a major role in its success.

Direct marketers often conduct experiments to determine how to increase response to pamphlets, catalogs, or special offerings. Experiments have shown that the wording of headline copy and prices can greatly influence the success of direct marketing.

Test marketing is a frequent form of business experimentation. The example of Chelsea, Anheuser-Busch's "not-so-soft soft drink," illustrates the usefulness of experiments. Anheuser-Busch first introduced Chelsea as a socially acceptable alternative to beer for adults who didn't want to get intoxicated. Because of the natural flavorings used, Chelsea contained a slight amount of alcohol (less than 0.5 percent)—well within the FDA guidelines for classification as a soft drink. During an experiment to test market the "not-so-soft soft drink" and the "not-so-sweet" concept, a Virginia nurses' association and some religious groups strongly criticized the company and the new product. These critics suggested that Anheuser-Busch had introduced a product that might encourage children to become beer drinkers. They contended that Chelsea was packaged like beer and looked, foamed, and poured like beer. The criticism led the brewery to suspend production, advertising, and promotion of the drink. It later reintroduced the product as a soft drink, with only "a trace of alcohol" and with not-so-sweet and stylish attributes, as a "natural alternative" to other soft drinks. This experiment pointed out to Anheuser-Busch that an extraneous variable—alcohol level—caused an inadvertent miscommunication: Consumers confused the original Chelsea with beer.

An experiment controls conditions so that one or more variables can be manipulated in order to test a hypothesis. In the Chelsea situation there was a trial of a proposed course of action and observation of the effect on sales. This case illustrates that extraneous variables are difficult to control and can influence results. It also portrays a field experiment that led to a deliberate modification of marketing strategy.

Other experiments—laboratory experiments—are deliberate modifications of an environment created for the research itself. Laboratory experiments are often used in basic research to test theories. Consider a laboratory experiment designed as a test of equity theory. Student subjects, hired and paid to code research questionnaires, were separated into two groups. One group was led to believe that it was less qualified than the other workers because it lacked previous experience in coding questionnaires. The group was also told that even though it was less qualified, its pay would be the same as the pay for experienced workers. Thus, the students believed themselves to be overpaid. The other group did not receive any messages about the others' experience and thus was led to believe that the pay was equitable. Both groups coded the questionnaires for 2 hours. The "equitably" paid group was less productive than the group that believed it was overpaid.[15]

Secondary Data Studies Like exploratory research, descriptive and causal studies use previously collected data. (Although the terms *secondary data* and *historical data* are interchangeable, we will use *secondary data*.) An example of a secondary data study is the development of a mathematical model to predict sales on the basis of past sales or on the basis of a correlation with related variables. Manufacturers of digital cameras may find that sales to households are highly correlated with discretionary personal income. To predict future market potential, data concerning projections of disposable personal income may be acquired from the government or from a university. This information can be mathematically manipulated to forecast sales. Formal secondary data studies have benefits and limitations similar to those of exploratory studies that use secondary data. The analysis of secondary data studies, however, generally requires greater quantitative sophistication than does exploratory research.

Observation Techniques In many situations the objective of a research project is merely to record what can be observed—for example, the number of automobiles that pass the proposed site for a gas station. This can be mechanically recorded or observed by any person. The amount of time it takes an employee to perform a task may be observed in a time-and-motion study. Research personnel, known as "mystery shoppers," may act as customers to observe the actions of sales personnel or may do comparison shopping to learn the prices charged at competing outlets.

The main advantage of the observation technique is that it records behavior without relying on reports from respondents. Observational data are often collected unobtrusively and passively without a respondent's direct participation. For instance, the A. C. Nielsen Company's "people meter" is a machine attached to television sets to record the programs being watched by various members of the household. This eliminates the possible bias due to respondents' stating that they watched the president's State of the Union address rather than the situation comedy that was on another channel.

Observation is more complex than mere "nose counting," and the task is more difficult to administer than the inexperienced researcher would imagine. Several things of interest simply cannot be observed. Attitudes, opinions, motivations, and other intangible states of mind cannot be recorded by using the observation method.

Evaluating Research Designs

Researchers argue that there is no one best research design for all situations. There are no hard-and-fast rules for good business research. This does not mean that the researcher, when faced with a problem, is also faced with chaos and confusion. It means that the researcher has many alternative methods for solving the problem. An eminent behavioral researcher has stated this concept quite eloquently:

> There is never a single, standard, correct method of carrying out a piece of research. Do not wait to start your research until you find out the proper approach, because there are many ways to tackle a problem—some good, some bad, but probably several good ways. There is no single perfect design. A research method for a given problem is not like the solution to a problem in algebra. It is more like a recipe for beef Stroganoff; there is no one best recipe.[16]

Knowing how to select the most appropriate research design develops with experience. Inexperienced researchers often jump to the conclusion that the survey method is the best design, because they are most familiar with this method. When Chicago's Museum of Science and Industry wanted to determine the relative popularity of its exhibits, it could have conducted a survey. Instead, a creative researcher, familiar with other research designs, suggested a far less expensive alternative—an unobtrusive observation technique. The researcher suggested that the museum merely keep track of how often the floor tiles in front of the various exhibits had to be replaced—which would indicate where the heaviest traffic occurred. When this was done, it was found that the chick-hatching exhibit was most popular.[17] This method provided the same results as a survey, but at a much lower cost.

Once an appropriate design has been determined, the researcher moves on to the next stage—planning the sample to be used.

Sampling

Although the sampling plan is outlined in the research design, the actual sampling is a separate stage of the research process. However, for convenience, the sample planning and sample generation processes are treated together in this section.

If you take your first bite of a steak and conclude it needs salt, you have just conducted a sample. Sampling involves any procedure that uses a small number of items or a portion of a population to make a conclusion regarding the whole population. In other words, a sample is a subset from a larger population. If certain statistical procedures are followed, it is unnecessary to select every item in a population because the results of a good sample should have the same characteristics as the population as a whole. Of course, when errors are made, samples do not give reliable estimates of the population. A famous example of error due to sample selection is the 1936 *Literary Digest* fiasco. The magazine conducted a survey and predicted that Republican Alf Landon would win over Democrat Franklin D. Roosevelt by a landslide in that year's presidential election. This prediction was wrong—and the error was due to sample selection. The postmortems showed that *Literary Digest* had sampled readers of its magazine and telephone subscribers. In 1936 these people were not a representative cross section of voters, because in those days people who could afford magazine subscriptions and phone service were generally well-to-do—and a disproportionate number of them were Republicans.

This famous example teaches that the first sampling question that must be asked is "Who is to be sampled?" Answering this primary question requires the identification of a target population. Defining the population and determining the sampling units may not be obvious. For example, for answers to image questions, a savings and loan company may survey people who already have accounts. The selected sampling units will not represent potential customers

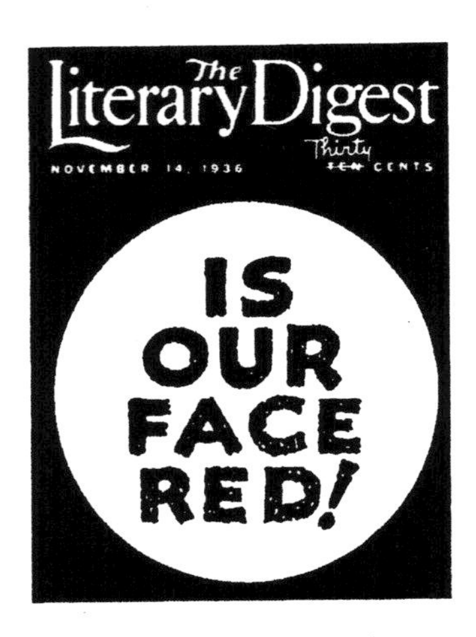

Surveys should be representative. In 1936, telephone subscribers and subscribers to Literary Digest *were disproportionately Republicans who did not support Roosevelt.*

who do not have accounts with the savings and loan. Specifying the target population is a crucial aspect of the sampling plan.

The next sampling issue concerns sample size. How big should the sample be? Although management may wish to examine every potential buyer of a product, every employee, or every stock traded on an exchange, it is unnecessary (as well as unrealistic) to do so. Typically, large samples are more precise than small samples, but if proper probability sampling is implemented, a small proportion of the total population will give a reliable measure of the whole. (A later discussion will explain how large a sample must be to be truly representative of a universe or population.)

The final sampling decision requires the researcher to choose how the sampling units are to be selected. Students who have taken their first statistics course generally are familiar with simple random sampling, whereby every unit in the population has an equal and known chance of being selected. However, this is only one type of sampling. For example, a cluster sampling procedure may be selected because it may reduce costs and make the data-gathering procedures more efficient. If members of the population are found in close geographic clusters, a sampling procedure that selects area clusters rather than individual units in the population will reduce costs. In other words, rather than selecting 1,000 individuals throughout the United States, it may be more economical to select 25 counties and then sample within those counties. This substantially reduces travel, hiring, and training costs. In determining the appropriate sample plan, the researcher will have to select the most appropriate sampling procedure to meet established study objectives.

There are two basic sampling techniques: probability sampling and nonprobability sampling. A *probability sample* is defined as a sample in which every member of the population has a known, nonzero probability of selection. If sample units are selected on the basis of personal judgment (e.g., a test plant is selected because it appears to be typical), the sample method is a *nonprobability sample.* In actuality, the sampling decision is not a simple choice between two methods. Simple random samples, stratified samples, quota samples, cluster samples, and judgmental samples are some of the many types of samples that may be drawn. (Chapter 16 gives full discussion of these techniques.)

Collecting Data

Once the research design (including the sampling plan) has been formalized, the process of gathering information from respondents may begin. Obviously, because there are many research techniques, there are many methods of data collection. When the survey method is utilized, some form of direct participation by the respondent is necessary during the process. The respondent may participate by filling out a questionnaire or by interacting with an interviewer. If an unobtrusive method of data collection is utilized, the subjects do not actively participate. For instance, a simple count of motorists driving past a proposed franchising location is one kind of data collection. However the data are collected, it is important to minimize errors in the data collection process. For example, it is important that the data collection be consistent in all geographic areas. If an interviewer phrases questions incorrectly or records a respondent's statements inaccurately (not verbatim), this will cause major data collection errors.

Often there are two phases to the process of collecting data: pretesting and the main study. A *pretesting phase,* using a small subsample, may determine whether the data collection plan for the main study is an appropriate procedure. Thus, a small-scale pretest study provides an advance opportunity for the investigator to check the data collection form to minimize errors due to improper design, such as poorly worded or organized questions. There is also the chance to discover confusing interviewing instructions, learn if the questionnaire is too long or too short, and uncover other such field errors. Tabulation of data from the pretests provides the researcher with a format for the knowledge that may be gained from the actual study. If the tabulation of the data and statistical tests do not answer the researcher's questions, the investigator may need to redesign the study.

Processing and Analyzing Data

Editing and Coding

Once the fieldwork has been completed, the data must be converted into a format that will answer the decision maker's questions. Data processing generally begins with the editing and coding of the data. Editing involves checking the data collection forms for omissions, legibility, and consistency in classification. The editing process corrects problems such as interviewer errors (e.g., an answer recorded on the wrong portion of a questionnaire) before the data are transferred to a computer or readied for tabulation.

Before data can be tabulated, meaningful categories and character symbols must be established for groups of responses. The rules for interpreting, categorizing, and recording the data are called *codes.*[18] This coding process facilitates computer or hand tabulation. Of course, if computer analysis is to be utilized, the data are entered into the computer and verified. Computer-assisted (online) interviewing is an example of the impact of technological change on the research process. Telephone interviewers are seated at computer terminals, where survey questions are printed out on the screen. The interviewer asks the questions and then types in the respondents' answers. Thus, answers are collected and processed into the computer at the same time, eliminating intermediate steps where errors could creep in.

Analysis

Analysis is the application of reasoning to understand and interpret the data that have been collected. In simple descriptive research, analysis may involve determining consistent patterns and summarizing the appropriate details revealed in the investigation. The appropriate analytical technique for data analysis will be determined by management's information requirements, the characteristics of the research design, and the nature of the data collected. Statistical analysis may range from portraying a simple frequency distribution to very complex multivariate analysis, such as multiple regression. Later chapters will discuss three general categories of statistical analysis: univariate analysis, bivariate analysis, and multivariate analysis.

Drawing Conclusions and Preparing a Report

As mentioned earlier, most business research is applied research. Hence, the purpose of the research is to make a business decision. An important but often overlooked aspect of the researcher's job is to look at the analysis of the collected information and ask "What does this mean to management?" The final stage in the research process is to interpret the information and draw conclusions relevant to managerial decisions. Making recommendations is often a part of this process.

The research report should communicate the research findings effectively. All too often the report is a complicated statement of the study's technical aspects and sophisticated research methods. Often, management is not interested in detailed reporting of the research design and statistical findings but wants only a summary of the findings. It cannot be overemphasized that if the findings remain unread on the manager's desk, the research study is useless. Research is only as good as the applications made of it. Business researchers must communicate their findings to a managerial audience. The manager's information needs should determine how much detail is provided in the written report. The written report serves another purpose: It is a historical document, a record that may be referred to later if the research is to be repeated or if further research is to be based on what has come before.

Now that we have outlined the research process, note that the order of topics in this book follows the flowchart of the research process presented in Exhibit 4.4. You should keep this flowchart in mind as you read future chapters.

RESEARCH PROJECT VERSUS RESEARCH PROGRAM

Discussion of the business research process began with the assumption that the research investigator wished to gather information to achieve a specific objective. We have emphasized the researcher's need to select specific techniques for solving one-dimensional problems, such as identifying the characteristics of productive employees, selecting the best packaging design, or forecasting bond values.

However, if you think about a firm's strategic activity in a given period of time, perhaps a year, you'll realize that business research is not a one-shot approach. Research is a continuous process. A company may conduct an exploratory research study and then conduct a survey. It is very likely that a specific research project will be conducted for each aspect of a program. If a new product is being developed, the different types of research might include market potential studies, to identify the size and characteristics of the market; product usage testing, which records consumers' reactions to using prototype products; and brand-name and packaging research, to determine the product's symbolic connotations. Ultimately, the new product may go into a test market.

research program
Planning activity that identifies an ongoing series of research projects designed to supply an organization's continuing information needs.

Because research is a continuous process, management should view research at a strategic planning level. A **research program** refers to a firm's overall strategy for utilizing business research. This program is a planning activity that places each research project into the company's strategic plan.

SUMMARY

Decision making is the process of resolving a problem or choosing from alternative opportunities. Decision makers must recognize the nature of the problem/opportunity, identify how much information is available, and recognize what information is needed. Every business decision can be classified on a continuum ranging from complete certainty to absolute ambiguity.

There are three major types of business research projects. Which one is to be used is decided by the clarity with which the research problem is defined. Exploratory research is chosen when management knows only the general problem. It is not conducted to provide conclusive evidence but to clarify problems. Descriptive research is conducted when there is some understanding of the nature of the problem; such research is used to provide a more specific description of the problem. Causal research identifies cause-and-effect relationships when the research problem has been narrowly defined.

The research process proceeds in a series of six interrelated phases. The first is problem definition, which may include exploratory research. Once the problem is defined, the researcher selects a research design, including an appropriate method. The major designs are surveys, experiments, secondary data studies, and observation. Creative selection of the research design can minimize the cost of obtaining reliable results. After the design has been selected, a sampling plan is chosen, using a probability sample, a nonprobability sample, or a combination of the two.

The design is put into action in the data collection phase. This phase may involve a small pretest before the main study is undertaken. In the analysis stage the data are edited and coded, then processed, usually by computer. The results are interpreted in light of the decisions that management must make. Finally, the analysis is presented to decision makers in a written or oral report. This last step is crucial, because an excellent project will not lead to proper action if the results are poorly communicated.

Quite often research projects are conducted as parts of an overall research program. Such programs can involve successive projects that incorporate earlier findings into later research designs.

A major problem facing students of business research is that it is difficult to consider each stage in the research process separately. However, without concentrated emphasis on each stage of the total process, it is difficult to understand the individual stages. Thus, learning business research is like walking a tightrope between too broad an outlook and too narrow a focus.

Key Terms

exploratory research
descriptive research
diagnostic analysis
causal research
forward linkage
backward linkage
problem definition
secondary data
primary data
pilot study
research project
research design
research program

Questions for Review and Critical Thinking

1. For each situation, decide whether the research should be exploratory, descriptive, or causal:
   (a) Establishing the functional relationship between advertising and sales
   (b) Investigating reactions to the idea of a new method of defense budgeting
   (c) Identifying target-market demographics for a shopping center
   (d) Estimating prices for IBM stock 2 years in the future
   (e) Learning how many organizations are actively involved in just-in-time production
   (f) Learning the extent of job satisfaction in a company
2. Describe a research situation that allows the inference of causality.
3. A researcher is interested in knowing the answer to a *why* question, but does not know what sort of answer will be satisfying. Is this exploratory, descriptive, or causal research? Explain.
4. Do the stages in the research process follow the scientific method?
5. Why is the problem definition stage probably the most important stage in the research process?
6. The U.S. Department of the Treasury is considering technological research into creation of a plasticlike substance on which currency notes can be printed. Being printed on this substance would increase the circulation life of low-value currency notes and enhance their utility in vending equipment. What type of research should be conducted?
7. What research design seems appropriate for each of the following studies?
   (a) The manufacturer and marketer of flight simulators and other pilot-training equipment wish to forecast sales volume for the next 5 years.
   (b) A local chapter of the American Lung Association wishes to identify the demographic characteristics of individuals who donate more than $500 per year.
   (c) A manager notices the number of grievances is increasing and wishes to investigate this trend.
   (d) A financial analyst wishes to investigate whether load or no-load mutual funds have higher yields.
   (e) A corporation wishes to evaluate the quality of its college-graduate recruitment program.
   (f) An academic researcher wishes to investigate if the United States is losing its competitive edge in world trade.
   (g) A food company researcher is interested in knowing what types of food are carried in brown-bag lunches to learn if the company can capitalize on this phenomenon.
8. Why is a knowledge of forward and backward linkages in the research process important?
9. Give an example of a program research project in your field of interest.
10. In your field of interest, which research design (surveys, observation, experiments, or secondary data studies) is the most popular?

Exploring the Internet

1. Use a Web browser to go to the Gallup Organization's home page at http://www.gallup.com. The Gallup home page changes regularly. However, it should provide an opportunity to read the results of a political poll. After reading the results of one of Gallup's polls, click on How Polls Are Conducted. List the various stages of the research process and how they were followed in Gallup's project.
2. Use a Web browser to access Lycos (http://www.lycos.com). What keyword topics can be investigated? How might the information you find help you design a research project?

Case Suggestions

Case 3: Tulsa's Central Business District (A)
Video Case 6: Fisher-Price Rescue Heroes
Video Case 12: Burke, Inc.
Video Case 13: Walker Information Group

4

PROBLEM DEFINITION AND THE RESEARCH PROPOSAL

What you will learn in this chapter

- To discuss the nature of decision makers' objectives and the role they play in defining the research problem.
- To understand that proper problem definition is essential for effective business research.
- To explain the iceberg principle.
- To understand that identifying key variables is important.
- To discuss how formulation of research questions and hypotheses adds clarity to the problem definition.
- To discuss the influence of the statement of the business problem on the specific research objectives.
- To state research problems in terms of clear and precise research objectives.
- To explain the purpose of the research proposal.
- To outline a research proposal.

Once upon a time a Sea Horse gathered up his seven pieces of eight and cantered out to find his fortune.[1] Before he had traveled very far he met an Eel, who said, "Psst. Hey, bud. Where ya goin'?"

"I'm going out to find my fortune," replied the Sea Horse, proudly.

"You're in luck," said the Eel. "For four pieces of eight you can have this speedy flipper, and then you'll be able to get there a lot faster."

"Gee, that's swell," said the Sea Horse, and paid the money and put on the flipper and slithered off at twice the speed. Soon he came upon a Sponge, who said, "Psst. Hey, bud. Where ya goin'?"

"I'm going out to find my fortune," replied the Sea Horse.

"You're in luck," said the Sponge. "For a small fee I will let you have this jet-propelled scooter so that you will be able to travel a lot faster."

So the Sea Horse bought the scooter with his remaining money and went zooming through the sea five times as fast. Soon he came upon a Shark, who said, "Psst. Hey, bud. Where ya goin'?"

"I'm going out to find my fortune," replied the Sea Horse.

"You're in luck. If you'll take this short cut," said the Shark, pointing to his open mouth, "you'll save yourself a lot of time."

"Gee, thanks," said the Sea Horse, and zoomed off into the interior of the Shark, there to be devoured.

The moral of this fable is that if you're not sure where you're going, you're liable to end up someplace else—and not even know it. ■

Before choosing a research design, managers and researchers need a sense of direction for the investigation. The adage "If you do not know where you are going, any road will take you there" suggests some good advice to managers and researchers: It is extremely important to define the business problem carefully because the definition determines the purpose of the research and, ultimately, the research design.

This chapter explains how to define a business problem and how to prepare a research proposal.

THE NATURE OF THE BUSINESS PROBLEM

Chapter 4 indicated that a decision maker's degree of uncertainty influences decisions about the type of research that will be conducted. This chapter elaborates on the conditions under which decision making occurs and the process managers use to clearly define business problems and opportunities.

Remember that managers may be completely certain about situations they face. For example, a retail store may have been recording and analyzing scanner data for years and know exactly what information its optical scanners need to record every day. Well-tested research techniques are regularly used to investigate routine problems that have already been defined.

At the other extreme, a manager or researcher may face a decision-making situation that is absolutely ambiguous. The nature of the problem to be solved is unclear. The objectives are vague, and the alternatives are difficult to define. This is by far the most difficult decision situation.

Most decision-making situations fall somewhere between these two extremes. Managers often grasp the general nature of the objectives they wish to achieve, but some uncertainty remains about the nature of the problem. They often need more information about important details. Their information is incomplete. They need to clear up ambiguity or uncertainty before making a formal statement of the business problem.

IMPORTANCE OF PROPER PROBLEM DEFINITION

The formal quantitative research process should not begin until the problem has been clearly defined. However, properly and completely defining a business problem is easier said than done. When a problem or opportunity is discovered, managers may have only vague insights about a complex situation. For example, suppose morale is declining at a West Coast television studio, and management does not know the reason. If quantitative research is conducted before learning exactly what issues are important, false conclusions may be drawn from the investigation. The right answer to the wrong question may be absolutely worthless. A decision made on the basis of a solution to the wrong problem may actually be harmful.

Consider what happened in the 1980s when Coca-Cola made the decision to change its formula and introduce "new" Coke. The company's managers decided to investigate consumers' reactions to the taste of reformulated Coke and nothing more. (The company carried out a series of taste tests in shopping malls. No take-home taste tests were conducted.) The results of the taste test led to the introduction of "new" Coke and the withdrawal of regular Coke from the market. As soon as consumers learned the company's original formula was no longer available, there were emotional protests from Coca-Cola loyalists. The consumer protests were so passionate and determined that the original formula was quickly brought back as Coca-Cola Classic. Coke's business research was too narrow in scope, and the problem was not adequately defined. Coca-Cola tested one thing and one thing only. In retrospect we know there was a larger problem. The business research failed to identify consumers' emotional attachment and loyalty to the brand as a problem for investigation. There is a lesson to be learned from the Coca-Cola mistake: Do not ignore investigating the emotional aspects of human behavior.

problem definition
The crucial first stage in the research process—determining the problem to be solved and the objectives of the research.

Just because a problem has been discovered or an opportunity has been recognized does not mean that the problem has been defined. A **problem definition** indicates a specific managerial decision area to be clarified or problem to be solved. It specifies research questions to be answered and the objectives of the research.

THE PROCESS OF PROBLEM DEFINITION

Defining a research problem involves several interrelated steps. As shown in Exhibit 6.1, they are:

1. Ascertain the decision maker's objectives
2. Understand the background of the problem
3. Isolate and identify the problem rather than its symptoms
4. Determine the unit of analysis
5. Determine the relevant variables
6. State the research questions (hypotheses) and research objectives

Ascertain the Decision Maker's Objectives

As a staff person, the research investigator must attempt to satisfy the objectives of the line manager who requests the project. Management theorists suggest that the decision maker should express his or her goals to the researcher in measurable terms. However, expecting a decision maker to follow this recommendation is, unfortunately, somewhat optimistic:

> Despite a popular misconception to the contrary, objectives are seldom clearly articulated and given to the researcher. The decision maker seldom formulates his objectives accurately. He is likely to state his objectives in the form of platitudes which have no operational significance. Consequently, objectives usually have to be extracted by the researcher. In so doing, the researcher may well be performing his most useful service to the decision maker.[2]

EXHIBIT 6.1 | THE PROCESS OF PROBLEM DEFINITION

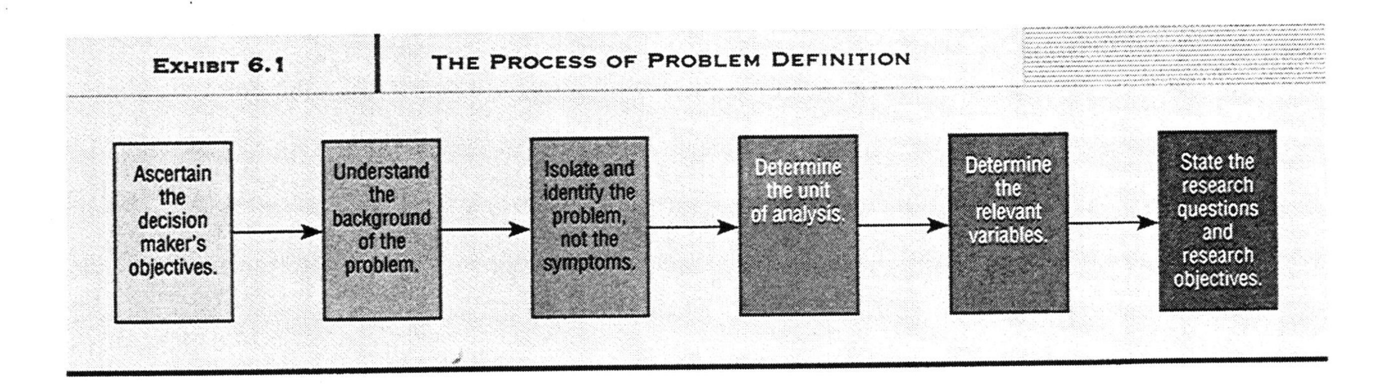

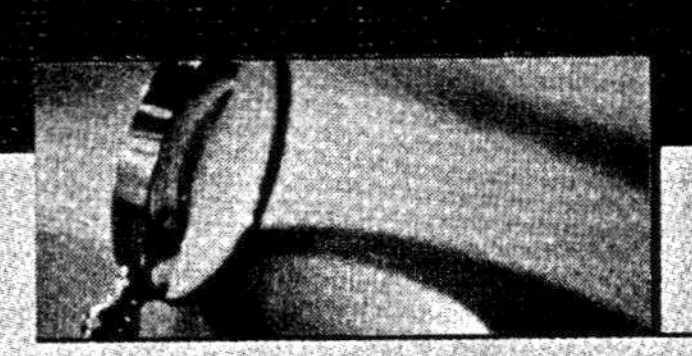

RESEARCH INSIGHT

THEY MAY WANT TO STRANGLE YOU!

Hugh Dubberly, a manager with the Times-Mirror Company, advocates a step-by-step process to help clearly define the problem to be solved.[3]

"How do we define the problem? Begin by assembling all the relevant players in a room. Ask each player to describe the unmet need, or in other words, to suggest the cause of the problem. Write down each suggestion. Nothing you will do on the project will be more important. With each suggestion, ask in turn for its cause. And then the cause of the cause. And then the cause of the cause of the cause. Keep at it like a 2-year-old. By the time everyone in the room wants to strangle you, you will very likely have found the root cause of the problem.

After you've developed the problem statement, you need to be sure to gain consensus on it from all the relevant parties. Failure to get 'buy-in' from all the right people at this stage creates the potential for trouble later in the process. Someone who hasn't agreed on the definition up front is likely to want to change it later."

Researchers who must conduct investigations when a line manager wants the information "yesterday" do not usually get a great deal of assistance when they ask, "What are your objectives for this study?" Nevertheless, both parties should attempt to have a clear understanding of the purpose for undertaking the research.

One effective technique for uncovering elusive research objectives is to present the manager with each possible solution to a problem and ask whether he or she would follow that course of action. If the decision maker says "no," further questioning to determine why the course of action is inappropriate usually will help formulate objectives.

Often exploratory research can illuminate the nature of the opportunity or problem and help managers clarify their objectives and decisions.

Iceberg Principle

iceberg principle
The idea that the dangerous part of many business problems is neither visible to nor understood by business managers.

Why do so many business research projects begin without clear objectives or adequate problem definitions? Managers are logical people, and it seems logical that definition of the problem is the starting point for any enterprise. Frequently researchers and managers cannot discover the actual problem because they lack sufficiently detailed information; the **iceberg principle** serves as a useful analogy. A sailor on the open sea notices only a small part of an iceberg. Only 10 percent of it is above the surface of the water, and 90 percent is submerged. The dangerous part of many business problems, like the submerged portion of the iceberg, is neither visible to nor understood by managers. If the submerged portions of the problem are omitted from the problem definition (and subsequently from the research design), the decisions based on the research may be less than optimal. The example of the new Coke is a case in point. Omission of important information or a faulty assumption about the situation can be extremely costly.

Understand the Background of the Problem

Although no textbook outline exists for identifying a business problem, the iceberg principle illustrates that understanding the background of a problem is vital. Often experienced managers know a great deal about a situation and can provide researchers with considerable background information about previous events and why those events occurred. In situations in which the decision maker's objectives are clear, the problem may be diagnosed exclusively by exercising managerial judgment. In other situations, when information about what has happened previously is inadequate or when managers have trouble identifying the problem, a situation analysis is the logical first step in defining the problem. A **situation analysis** involves a preliminary investigation or informal gathering of background information to familiarize researchers or managers with the decision area. Gaining an awareness of organizational or environmental conditions and an appreciation of the situation often requires exploratory research. The many exploratory research techniques that have been developed to help formulate clear definitions of problems will be covered in Chapter 7.

situation analysis
A preliminary investigation or informal gathering of background information to familiarize researchers or managers with the decision area.

Isolate and Identify the Problem, Not the Symptoms

Anticipating all of the dimensions of a problem is impossible for any researcher or executive. For instance, a firm may have a problem with its advertising effectiveness. The possible causes of this problem may be low brand awareness, the wrong brand image, use of the wrong media, or perhaps too small a budget. Management's job is to isolate and identify the most likely causes. Certain occurrences that appear to be "the problem" may be only symptoms of a deeper problem. Exhibit 6.2 illustrates how symptoms may be mistaken for the true problem.

Other problems may be identified only after gathering background information and after conducting exploratory research. How does one ensure that the fundamental problem, rather than symptoms associated with the problem, has been identified? There is no easy or simple answer to this question. Executive judgment and creativity must be exercised. The archeological puzzle in Exhibit 6.3 (page 98) shows that good researchers must be creative in developing problem definitions by investigating situations in new ways.

The real voyage of discovery consists not in seeking new landscapes, but in having new eyes.
MARCEL PROUST

Determine the Unit of Analysis

Defining the problem requires that the researcher determine the unit of analysis for study. The researcher must specify whether the level of investigation will focus on the collection of data about the entire organization, departments, work groups, individuals, or objects. In studies of home buying, for example, the husband–wife dyad rather than the individual typically is the unit of analysis, because the purchase decision is made jointly by husband and wife. In studies of organizational behavior, cross-functional teams rather than individual employees may be selected as the unit of analysis.

Researchers who think carefully and creatively about situations often discover that a problem may be investigated at more than one level of analysis. Determining the unit of analysis, although relatively straightforward in most projects, should not be overlooked during the problem-definition stage of the research. It is a crucial aspect of problem definition.

EXHIBIT 6.2 | **SYMPTOMS CAN BE CONFUSING**

Organization	Symptoms	Problem Definition Based on Symptoms	True Problem
Twenty-year-old neighborhood swimming association in a mid-size town	Membership has been declining for years; new water park with wave pool and water slides moved into town a few years ago.	Neighborhood residents prefer the more expensive water park and have a negative image of the swimming pool.	Demographic changes: Children in the neighborhood have grown up, and older residents no longer swim at all.
Cellular phone manufacturer	Women employees complain that salaries are too low.	Salaries need to be compared to industry averages.	Benefits program is not suited to women's needs (e.g., maternity leave).
Brewery	Consumers prefer taste of competitor's product.	Taste of brewery's product needs to be reformulated.	Old-fashioned package is influencing taste perception.
Television station	Few employees change retirement plan after money market annuity option becomes available.	Attributes of money market annuity program need to be changed.	Except for those close to retirement, most employees are not highly involved in detailed pension-investment decisions; knowledge about plan is minimal.

Determine the Relevant Variables

variable
Anything that may assume different numerical or categorical values.

Another aspect of problem definition is identification of the key variables. The term *variable* is an important one in research. A **variable** is defined as anything that varies or changes in value. Because a variable represents a quality that can exhibit differences in value, usually in magnitude or strength, it may be said that a variable generally is anything that may assume different numerical or categorical values.

Key variables should be identified in the problem definition stage. Attitude toward Internet brokerage firms may be a variable, for example, as people's attitudes may vary from positive to negative. The attitude toward each of the many characteristics of brokerage firms, such as availability of investment advisory services, real-time quotes, toll-free calls, and the like, would be a variable.

categorical variable
Any variable that has a limited number of distinct values.

continuous variable
Any variable that has an infinite number of possible values.

In statistical analysis a variable is identified by a symbol, such as X. Categories or numerical values may then be associated with this symbol. The variable "sex" may be categorized as male or female; sex is therefore a **categorical**—or classificatory—**variable** because it has a limited number of distinct values. On the other hand, sales volume may encompass an infinite range of numbers; it is therefore a **continuous variable**—one with an infinite number of possible values.

To address the specific problem, managers and researchers should be careful to identify all of the relevant variables that must be studied. Variables that are superfluous (i.e., not directly relevant to the problem) should not be included.

EXHIBIT 6.3 | **LOOK AGAIN**[4]

What language is written on this stone found by archaeologists?

Answer (turn book upside down):

The language is English: TO/TIE/MULES/TO. A great deal of time and effort is spent looking at familiar problems. Managers often do not look at these problems in a new light, however. Too often they see what they want to see or what they expect. They give stereotyped answers to problems. A good researcher creatively develops a hypothesis by looking at problems in a new way.

dependent variable
A criterion or a variable that is to be predicted or explained.

independent variable
A variable that is expected to influence the dependent variable. Its value may be changed or altered independently of any other variable.

In causal research the terms *dependent variable* and *independent variable* are frequently encountered. A **dependent variable** is a criterion or a variable that is to be predicted or explained. An **independent variable** is a variable that is expected to influence the dependent variable. For example, average hourly rate of pay may be a dependent variable that is influenced or can be predicted by an independent variable such as number of years of experience.

These terms are discussed in greater detail in the chapters on experimentation and data analysis.

State the Research Questions and Research Objectives

Both managers and researchers expect problem definition efforts to result in statements of research questions and research objectives. At the end of the problem definition stage of the research process, researchers should prepare a written statement that clarifies any ambiguity about what they hope the research will accomplish.

How Can the Problem Statement Be Clarified?

Formulating a series of research questions and hypotheses can add clarity to the statement of the business problem. For example, a company made the following statement to define a training problem: "The problem is to determine the best ways our company can train existing and potential users of networked personal computers." This problem statement led to the following research questions: "How familiar are employees with the various software applications for personal computers? What attitudes do employees have toward these software packages? How important are the various factors for evaluating the use of a personal computer? How effective are training efforts in increasing knowledge and use of the new applications?"

The inclusion of research questions in the statement of a business problem makes it easier to understand what is perplexing managers and indicates the issues to be resolved. A research question is the researcher's translation of the business problem into a specific need for inquiry. For example, a research question such as "Is advertising copy X better than advertising copy Y?" is vague and too general. Advertising effectiveness can be variously measured—by sales, recall of sales message, brand awareness, intentions to buy, and so on. A more specific research question such as "Which advertisement has a higher day-after recall score?" helps the researcher design a study that will produce pertinent information. The answer to the research question should be a criterion that can be utilized as a standard for selecting alternatives. This stage of the research is obviously related to problem definition. The goal of defining the problem is to state the research questions clearly and to have well-formulated hypotheses.

hypothesis
An unproven proposition or supposition that tentatively explains certain facts or phenomena; a proposition that is empirically testable.

A **hypothesis** is an unproven proposition or possible solution to a problem. Hypothetical statements assert probable answers to research questions. A hypothesis is also a statement about the nature of the world, and in its simplest form it is a guess. A manager may hypothesize that salespersons who show the highest job satisfaction will be the most productive. An organizational researcher may believe that if workers' attitudes toward an organizational climate are changed in a positive direction, there will be an increase in organizational effectiveness among these workers.

Problem statements and hypotheses are similar. Both state relationships, but problem statements are often phrased as questions, whereas hypotheses are declarative. Sometimes they are almost identical in substance. An important difference, however, is that hypotheses are usually more specific than problem statements; they usually more closely reflect the actual research operations and testing.[5] Hypotheses are statements that can be empirically tested.

Formal statements of hypotheses have considerable practical value in planning and designing research. They force researchers to be clear about what they expect to find through the study, and further, the formal statement raises crucial questions about the data that will be required in the analysis stage.[6] When evaluating a hypothesis, researchers should make sure the information collected will be useful in decision making. Notice how the following hypotheses express expected relationships between variables:

> There is a positive relationship between Internet shopping and the presence of younger children in the home.
>
> Voluntary turnover (quitting) will be higher among employees who perceive themselves to be inequitably paid than among employees who perceive themselves to be equitably paid.
>
> Among nonexporters, the degree of perceived importance of overcoming barriers to exporting is related positively to general interest in exporting (export intentions).
>
> Common stocks bought at high dividend yields will afford lower average returns than securities bought at lower dividend yields.
>
> Managers with liberal arts educations will process less accounting data than will those with masters degrees in business administration.
>
> Opinion leaders are more affected by mass media communication sources than are nonleaders.

research objective
The purpose of the research, expressed in measurable terms; the definition of what the research should accomplish.

Decision-Oriented Research Objectives

The **research objective** is the researcher's version of the business problem. Once the research questions and/or hypotheses have been stated, the research project objectives are derived from the problem definition. These objectives

Exhibit 6.4 | **Business Problem Translated into Research Objectives**

Problem/Questions	Research Questions	Research Objectives
Should the organization offer outplacement services?	Are managers aware of outplacement services?	To determine managers' awareness using aided recall
	How concerned are managers about outplacement services?	To measure managers' satisfaction with existing personnel policies
Which of the services should be offered? Severance pay? New employment assistance? Personal counseling? Job contacts?	How do managers evaluate the need for . . . Severance pay? New employment assistance? Personal counseling? Job contacts?	To obtain ratings and rankings of the various outplacement services
Should the services be provided by in-house personnel or outside consultants?	What are the benefits of each outplacement service?	To identify perceived benefits and perceived disadvantages of each outplacement service
	Would managers prefer in-house personnel or outside consultants?	To measure managers' perceptions of the benefits and disadvantages of in-house versus outside consultants
		To measure managers' preferences for these alternatives if discharge occurred
	How much would each alternative cost?	To identify costs associated with each alternative
Do employees with 10 or more years of service have different awareness levels, etc., than employees with fewer than 10 years of service?	Do the answers to the above questions differ by employees' years of service?	To compare, using cross-tabulations, levels of awareness, evaluations, etc., of managers with 10 or more years of service with those of managers with fewer than 10 years of service

Note: For simplification, hypotheses are omitted from the table.

explain the purpose of the research in measurable terms and define standards of what the research should accomplish. In addition to stating the reasons for initiating the research project, the objectives help to ensure that the project will be manageable in size. Exhibit 6.4 illustrates how the business problem of a large organization is translated into research objectives. The organization wants to research the question of whether it should offer outplacement services (e.g., severance pay) to discharged executives.

In some instances the business problem and the research objectives are the same. The objectives must, however, specify the information needed to make a decision. Identifying the information needed may require managers or researchers to be as specific as listing the exact wording of the question in a survey or explaining exactly what behavior might be observed or recorded in an experiment. Statements about the required precision of the information or the source of the information may be required to clearly communicate exactly what information is needed. Many career decisions, for example, are made by both husband and wife. If this is the case, the husband–wife decision-making unit is the unit of analysis. The objective of obtaining *X* information about research questions from this unit should be specifically stated.

It is useful to express the research objective as a managerial action standard. If the criterion to be measured (e.g., absenteeism, sales, or attitude changes) turns out to be higher than some predetermined level, then management will do *A;* if it is not, then management will do *B.* This type of objective leaves no uncertainty about the decision to be made once the research is finished.

The number of research objectives should be limited to a manageable quantity. The fewer the study objectives, the easier it is to ensure that each will be addressed fully.

Exhibit 6.5 shows that the statement of the business problem influences the research objectives. The specific objectives, in turn, are the basis for the research design.

In our earlier example of an organization's research concerning outplacement services, the broad research objective—to determine managers' perceived need for outplacement services in the organization—was translated into specific objectives, namely, to determine ranked preferences for severance pay, new employment assistance, and the like; to compare the needs of employees with more than 10 years of service with those having fewer than 10 years of service; and so on. Therefore, specific objectives influence the research design because they indicate the type of information needed. Once the research is conducted, the results may show an unanticipated aspect of the problem and may suggest that additional research is necessary to satisfy the

EXHIBIT 6.5 | **THE STATEMENT OF THE BUSINESS PROBLEM INFLUENCES THE RESEARCH OBJECTIVES AND DESIGN**

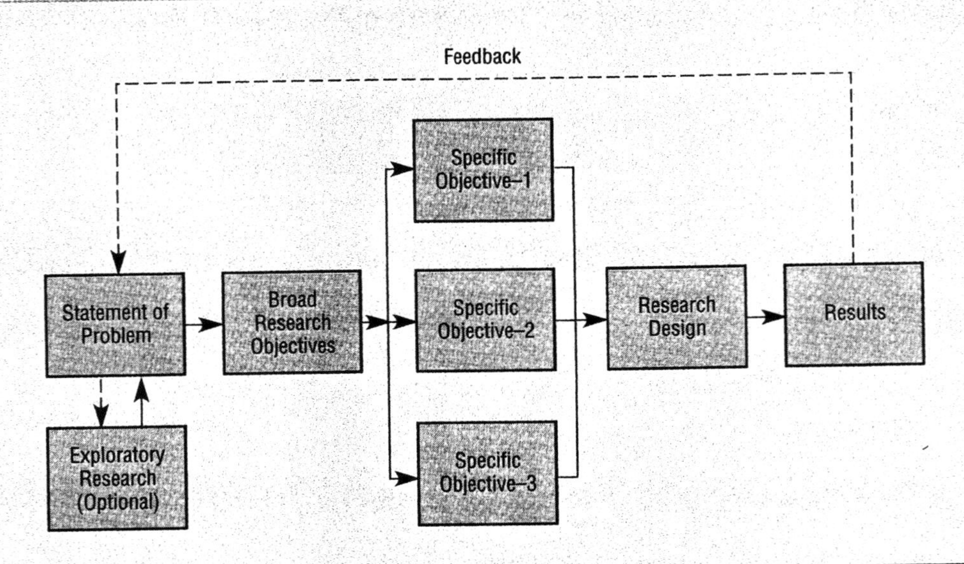

main objective. Exhibit 6.5 also shows that exploratory research may help in the overall definition of the management problem. In routine situations or when managers are quite familiar with background information, however, it is quite likely the problem definition will be based exclusively on the decision maker's objectives.

How Much Time Should Be Spent Defining the Problem?

Budget constraints usually influence the amount of effort that will be spent defining the problem. Most business situations are complex, and numerous variables may have some influence. It is impractical to search for every conceivable cause and minor influence. The importance of the recognized problem will dictate what is a reasonable amount of time and money to spend to determine which explanations or solutions are most likely.

Managers—those responsible for decision making—generally want the problem definition process to proceed quickly, whereas researchers usually take long periods of time to carefully define problems and thereby frequently frustrate managers. Nevertheless, the time spent to identify the correct problem to be researched is time well spent.

THE RESEARCH PROPOSAL

research proposal
A written statement of the research design that includes a statement explaining the purpose of the study and a detailed, systematic outline of a particular research methodology.

The **research proposal** is a written statement of the research design. It always includes an explanation of the purpose of the study (the research objectives) or a definition of the problem. It systematically outlines the particular research methodology and details the procedures that will be utilized at each stage of the research process. Normally a schedule of costs and deadlines is included in the research proposal. Exhibit 6.6 illustrates a short research proposal for an Internal Revenue Service study to explore public attitudes toward a variety of tax-related issues.

Preparation of a research proposal forces the researcher to think critically about each stage of the research process. Vague plans, abstract ideas, and sweeping generalizations about problems or procedures must become concrete and precise statements about specific events. What information will be obtained and what research procedures will be implemented have to be clearly specified so that others may understand their exact implications. All ambiguities about why and how the research will be conducted must be clarified before the proposal is complete.

Because the proposal is a clearly outlined plan submitted to management for acceptance or rejection, it initially performs a communication function; it serves as a mechanism that allows managers to evaluate the details of the proposed research design and determine if alterations are necessary. The proposal helps managers decide if the proper information will be obtained and if the proposed research will accomplish what is desired. If the business problem has not been adequately translated into a set of specific research objectives and a research design, the client's assessment of the proposal will help ensure that the researchers revise it to meet the client's information needs.

The proposal needs to communicate exactly what information will be obtained, where it will be obtained, and how it will be obtained. For this reason, proposals must be explicit about sample selection, measurement, fieldwork, and so on. For instance, most survey proposals include a copy of the proposed questionnaire (or at least some sample questions) to ensure that

EXHIBIT 6.6 | **AN ABBREVIATED VERSION OF A RESEARCH PROPOSAL FOR THE IRS**[7]

Purpose of the Research

The general purpose of this study is to determine the taxpaying public's perceptions of the role of the IRS in administering the tax laws. In defining the limits of this study, the IRS identified study areas to be addressed. A careful review of those question areas led to the development of the following specific research objectives:

1. To identify the extent to which taxpayers cheat on their returns, their reasons for doing so, and approaches that can be taken to deter this behavior
2. To determine taxpayers' experience and satisfaction with various IRS services
3. To determine what services taxpayers need
4. To develop an accurate profile of taxpayers' behavior relative to the preparation of their income tax returns
5. To assess taxpayers' knowledge and opinions about various tax laws and procedures

Research Design

The survey research method will be the basic research design. Each respondent will be interviewed in his or her home. The personal interviews are generally expected to last between 35 and 45 minutes, although the length of the interview will vary depending on the previous tax-related experiences of the respondent. For example, if a respondent has never been audited, questions on audit experience will not be addressed. Or, if a respondent has never contacted the IRS for assistance, certain questions concerning reactions to IRS services will be skipped.

Some sample questions that will be asked are

Did you or your spouse prepare your federal tax return for (year)?

- Self
- Spouse
- Someone else

Did the federal income tax package you received in the mail contain all the forms necessary for you to fill out your return?

- Yes
- No
- Didn't receive one in the mail
- Don't know

If you were calling the IRS for assistance and someone were not able to help you immediately, would you rather get a busy signal or be asked to wait on hold?

- Busy signal
- Wait on hold
- Neither
- Don't know

During the interview a self-administered written questionnaire will be given to the taxpayer. The questionnaire will ask certain sensitive questions; for example, Have you ever claimed a dependent on your tax return that you weren't really entitled to?

- Yes
- No

Sample Design

A survey of approximately 5,000 individuals located in 50 counties throughout the country will provide the database for this study. The sample will be selected on a probability basis from all households in the continental United States.

Eligible respondents will be adults over the age of 18. Within each household an effort will be made to interview the individual who is most familiar with completing the federal tax forms. When there is more than one taxpayer in the household, a random process will be used to select the taxpayer to be interviewed.

Data Gathering

The fieldworkers of a field research organization will conduct the interviews.

Data Processing and Analysis

Standard editing and coding procedures will be utilized. Simple tabulation and cross-tabulations will be utilized to analyze the data.

Report Preparation

A written report will be prepared, and an oral presentation of the findings will be made by the research analyst at the convenience of the IRS.

Budget and Time Schedule

[Any complete research proposal should include (1) a schedule of how long it will take to conduct each stage of the research and (2) a statement of itemized costs.]

managers and researchers agree on the information to be obtained and how questions should be worded.

The format for the IRS research proposal in Exhibit 6.6 follows the six stages in the research process outlined in Exhibit 4.4. At each stage, one or more questions must be answered before the researcher can select one of the various alternatives. For example, before a proposal can be completed, the researcher has to ask "What is to be measured?" Simply answering "market share" may not be enough—market share may be measured by auditing retailers' or wholesalers' sales, by using trade association data, or by asking consumers what brands they buy. The question of what is to be measured is just one of the important questions that must be answered before setting the research process in motion. This issue will be addressed in greater detail in Chapter 13. For now, Exhibit 6.7 presents an overview of some of the basic questions that managers and researchers typically have to answer when planning a research design.

Review the IRS research proposal in Exhibit 6.6 to see how some of the questions in Exhibit 6.7 were answered in a specific situation. The remainder of this book will have to be read before these issues can be fully understood, however.

In business, one often hears the adage "Don't say it, write it." This is wise advice for the researcher who is proposing a research project to management. Misstatements and faulty communication may occur if the parties rely only on each individual's memory of what occurred at a planning meeting. Writing a proposal for a research design, specifying exactly what will be done, creates a record to which everyone can refer and eliminates many problems that might arise after the research has been conducted. With a written proposal, management and researchers alike are less likely to discover after the fact (after the research) that information related to a particular variable was omitted or that the sample size was too small for a particular subgroup. Further, as a statement of agreement between executives and researchers, the formal proposal will reduce the tendency for someone reading the results to say, "Shouldn't we have had a larger sample?" or "Why didn't you do it this way?" As a record of the researcher's obligation, the proposal also provides a standard for determining if the actual research was conducted as originally planned.

When a consultant or an outside research supplier will be conducting the research, the written proposal serves as that person's or company's bid to offer a specific service. Typically, a sponsoring client solicits several competitive proposals, and these written offers help management judge the relative quality of alternative research suppliers.

One final comment needs to be made about the nature of research proposals: Proposals do not all follow the same format. The researcher must adapt his or her proposal to the audience to whom it will be submitted.[8] An extremely brief proposal submitted by an organization's internal research department to its own executives bears little resemblance to a complex proposal submitted by a university professor to an agency of the federal government to test a basic theory about international financial markets.

ANTICIPATING OUTCOMES

The description of the data processing and analysis stage in Exhibit 6.6 is extremely brief because this topic will not be discussed until Chapter 19. However, at this point some advice about data analysis is in order.

EXHIBIT 6.7 | **BASIC QUESTIONS TYPICALLY ASKED WHEN PLANNING A RESEARCH DESIGN**

Decision to Make	Basic Questions
Problem definition	What is the purpose of the study? How much is already known? Is additional background information necessary? What is to be measured? How? Can the data be made available? Should research be conducted? Can a hypothesis be formulated?
Selection of basic research design	What types of questions need to be answered? Are descriptive or causal findings required? What is the source of the data? Can objective answers be obtained by asking people? How quickly is the information needed? How should survey questions be worded? How should experimental manipulations be made?
Selection of sample	Who or what is the source of the data? Can the target population be identified? Is a sample necessary? How accurate must the sample be? Is a probability sample necessary? Is a national sample necessary? How large a sample is necessary? How will the sample be selected?
Data gathering	Who will gather the data? How long will data gathering take? How much supervision is needed? What procedures will data collectors need to follow?
Data analysis and evaluation	Will standardized editing and coding procedures be utilized? How will the data be categorized? Will computer or hand tabulation be utilized? What questions need to be answered? How many variables are to be investigated simultaneously? What are the criteria for evaluation of performance?
Type of report	Who will read the report? Are managerial recommendations requested? How many presentations are required? What will be the format of the written report?
Overall evaluation	How much will the study cost? Is the time frame acceptable? Do we need outside help? Will this research design attain the stated research objectives? When should the research begin?

One aspect of problem definition often lacking in research proposals is anticipating the outcome, that is, the statistical findings, of the study. The use of a dummy table in the research proposal often helps the manager gain a better understanding of what the actual outcome of the research will be. **Dummy tables** are representations of the actual tables that will be in the findings section of the final report. They are called *dummy tables* because the researcher fills in, or "dummies up," the tables with likely, but fictitious, data. In other words, the researcher anticipates what the final research report will contain (table by table) before the project begins.

dummy table
Representation of an actual table that will be in the findings section of the final report; used to provide a better understanding of what the actual outcome of the research will be.

A research analyst can present dummy tables to the decision maker and ask, "Given findings like these, will you be able to make a decision to solve your managerial problem?" If the decision maker says yes, then the proposal may be accepted. However, if the decision maker cannot glean enough information from these dummy tables to make a decision about what the company would do with the hypothetical outcome suggested by the tables, then the decision maker must rethink what outcomes and data analyses are necessary to solve the problem. In other words, the business problem is clarified by deciding on action standards or performance criteria and by recognizing what type of research findings are necessary to make a specific decision.

SUMMARY

The first step in any business research project is to define the problem or opportunity. Decision makers must express their objectives to researchers to avoid getting the right answer to the wrong question. Defining the problem is often complicated in that portions of the problem may be hidden from view. The research must help management isolate and identify the problem to ensure that the real problem, rather than a symptom, is investigated.

A variable is anything that changes in value. Variables may be categorical or continuous. One aspect of problem definition is the identification of the key dependent and independent variables.

Research questions and hypotheses are translations of the business problem into business research terms. A hypothesis is an unproven proposition or a possible solution to the problem. Hypotheses state relationships between variables that can be tested empirically. Research objectives specify information needs. For the research project to be successful, the research problem must be stated in terms of clear and precise research objectives.

The research proposal is a written statement of the research design that will be followed in addressing a specific problem. The research proposal allows managers to evaluate the details of the proposed research and determine if alterations are needed. Most research proposals include the following sections: purpose of the research, research design, sample design, data gathering and/or fieldwork techniques, data processing and analysis, budget, and time schedule.

Key Terms

problem definition
iceberg principle
situation analysis
variable
categorical variable
continuous variable
dependent variable
independent variable
hypothesis
research objective
research proposal
dummy table

Questions for Review and Critical Thinking

1. In its broadest context, what is the task of problem definition?
2. In the nine-dot square below, connect all nine dots using no more than four straight lines and without lifting the pencil from the paper. What analogy can you make between the solution of this problem and the definition of a business problem?

• • •
• • •
• • •

3. What is the iceberg principle?
4. State a problem in your field of interest, and list some variables that might be investigated to solve this problem.
5. Go to the library, find business journals, and record and evaluate some hypotheses that have been investigated in recent years. Identify the key independent and dependent variables.
6. Evaluate the statement of the business problem in each of the following situations:
   (a) *A farm implement manufacturer:* Our objective is to learn the most effective form of capitalization so that we can maximize profits.
   (b) *An employees' credit union:* Our problem is to determine the reasons why employees join the credit union, to determine members' awareness of credit union services, and to measure attitudes and beliefs about how effectively the credit union is operated.
   (c) *The producer of a television show:* We have a problem: The program's ratings are low. We need to learn how to improve our ratings.
   (d) *A soft-drink manufacturer:* The problem is that we do not know if our bottlers are more satisfied with us than our competitors' bottlers are with them.
   (e) *A women's magazine:* Our problem is to document the demographic changes that have occurred in recent decades in the lives of women and to put these changes in historic perspective; to examine several generations of American women through most of this century, tracking their roles as students, workers, wives, and mothers and noting the changes in timing, sequence, and duration of these roles; to examine at what age and for how long a woman enters each of the various stages of her life: school, work, marriage, childbearing, divorce. This documentation will be accomplished by analyzing demographic data over several generations.
   (f) *A manufacturer of fishing boats:* The problem is to determine sales trends over the past 5 years by product category and to determine the seasonality of quarterly unit boat sales by region of the country.
   (g) *The inventor of a tension headache remedy (a cooling pad that is place on the forehead for up to 4 hours):* The purpose of this research is (1) to identify the market potential for the product, (2) to identify what desirable features the product should possess, and (3) to determine possible advertising strategies/channel strategies for the product.
7. What purposes does a research proposal serve?
8. What role should managers play in the development of the research proposal?
9. Comment on the following statements:
   (a) "The best business researchers are prepared to rethink and rewrite their proposals."
   (b) "The client's signature is an essential element of the research proposal."
10. You have been hired by a group of hotel owners, restaurant owners, and other people engaged in businesses that benefit from tourism on South Padre Island, Texas. They wish to learn how they can attract a larger number of college students to their town during spring break. Define the business research problem. (You may substitute a beach town in Florida or California, if you prefer.)
11. The military wishes to understand its image from the public's point of view. Define the business problem.
12. You have solicited research proposals from several firms. The lowest bidder has the best questionnaire and proposal. However, you particularly like one feature from the proposal submitted by a firm that will not receive the job. How should you handle this situation?

Exploring the Internet

1. How could the Internet help in defining a business problem that needs to be researched?
2. Could e-mail be used to solicit research proposals from business research suppliers? What would be the advantages and disadvantages of using this method of solicitation?

Case Suggestions

Case 3: Tulsa's Central Business District (A)
Case 5: Middlemist Precision Tool Company
Case 6: EZ Pass

5

QUESTIONNAIRE DESIGN

What you will learn in this chapter

- To recognize that questionnaire design is not a simple task and that proper wording of relevant questions can contribute immensely to improving the accuracy of surveys.
- To recognize that the type of information needed to answer a manager's questions will substantially influence the structure and content of questionnaires.
- To recognize that decisions about the data collection method (mail, Internet, telephone, or personal interview) will influence question format and questionnaire layout.
- To recognize the difference between open-ended response questions and fixed-alternative questions.
- To understand the guidelines that help to prevent the most common mistakes in questionnaire design.
- To discuss how decisions about the sequence of questions may improve questionnaires.
- To understand how to plan and design a questionnaire layout.
- To understand the importance of pretesting and revising questionnaires.

Results of an early Gallup Poll illustrate that the answer to a question is frequently a function of the question's wording.[1] "People were asked if they owned any stock. A surprisingly high degree of stock ownership turned up in interviews in the Southwest, where respondents were naturally thinking of livestock. The question had to be reworded to make reference to 'securities listed on any stock exchange.' "

Many experts in survey research believe that improving the wording of questions can contribute far more to accuracy than can improvements in sampling. Experiments have shown that the range of error due to vague questions or use of imprecise words may be as high as 20 or 30 percent. Consider the following example, which illustrates the critical importance of selecting the word with the right meaning. The following questions differ only in the use of the words *should, could,* and *might:*

- Do you think anything *should* be done to make it easier for people to pay doctor or hospital bills?
- Do you think anything *could* be done to make it easier for people to pay doctor or hospital bills?
- Do you think anything *might* be done to make it easier for people to pay doctor or hospital bills?[2]

The results from the matched samples: 82 percent replied something *should* be done, 77 percent replied something *could* be done, and 63 percent replied something *might* be done. Thus, a 19 percent difference occurred between the two extremes, *should* and *might.* Ironically, this is the same percentage point error as in the *Literary Digest* Poll, which is a frequently cited example of error associated with sampling. ■

This chapter outlines a procedure for questionnaire design and illustrates that a little bit of research knowledge can be a dangerous thing.

A SURVEY IS ONLY AS GOOD AS THE QUESTIONS IT ASKS

Each stage of the business research process is important because of its interdependence with other stages of the process. However, a survey is only as good as the questions it asks. The importance of wording questions is easily overlooked, but questionnaire design is one of the most critical stages in the survey research process.

"A good questionnaire appears as easy to compose as does a good poem. The end product should look as if effortlessly written by an inspired child—but it is usually the result of long, painstaking work."[3] Business people who are inexperienced in business research frequently believe that constructing a questionnaire is a simple task. Amateur researchers find it easy to prepare a short questionnaire in a matter of hours. Unfortunately, newcomers who naively believe that common sense and good grammar are all that are needed to construct a questionnaire generally learn that their hasty efforts are inadequate.

While common sense and good grammar are important in question writing, more is required in the art of questionnaire design. To assume that people will understand the questions is a common error. People simply may not know what is being asked. They may be unaware of the product or topic of interest, they may confuse the subject with something else, or the question may not mean the same thing to everyone interviewed. Respondents may refuse to answer personal questions. Further, properly wording the questionnaire is crucial, as some problems may be minimized or avoided altogether if a skilled researcher composes the questions.

TO THE POINT

How often misused words generate misleading thoughts.

HERBERT SPENCER

QUESTIONNAIRE DESIGN: AN OVERVIEW OF THE MAJOR DECISIONS

Relevance and *accuracy* are the two basic criteria a questionnaire must meet if it is to achieve the researcher's purposes.[4] To achieve these ends, a researcher who systematically plans a questionnaire's design will be required to make several decisions—typically, but not necessarily, in the order listed below:

1. What should be asked?
2. How should each question be phrased?
3. In what sequence should the questions be arranged?
4. What questionnaire layout will best serve the research objectives?
5. How should the questionnaire be pretested? Does the questionnaire need to be revised?

WHAT SHOULD BE ASKED?

During the early stages of the research process, certain decisions will have been made that will influence the questionnaire design. The preceding chapters stressed the need to have a good problem definition and clear objectives for the study. The problem definition will indicate which type of information must be collected to answer the manager's questions; different types of questions may be better at obtaining certain types of information than others. Further, the communication medium used for data collection—telephone interview, personal interview, or self-administered survey—will have been determined. This decision is another forward linkage that influences the structure and content of the questionnaire. The specific questions to be asked will be a function of the previous decisions. Later stages of the research process also have an important impact on questionnaire wording. For example, determination of the questions that should be asked will be influenced by the requirements for data analysis. As the questionnaire is being designed, the researcher should be thinking about the types of statistical analysis that will be conducted.

Questionnaire Relevancy

A questionnaire is *relevant* if no unnecessary information is collected and if the information that is needed to solve the business problem is obtained.

Asking the wrong or an irrelevant question is a pitfall to be avoided. If the task is to pinpoint compensation problems, for example, questions asking for general information about morale may be inappropriate. To ensure information relevancy, the researcher must be specific about data needs, and there should be a rationale for each item of information.

After conducting surveys, many disappointed researchers have discovered that some important questions were omitted. Thus, when planning the questionnaire design, it is essential to think about possible omissions. Is information being collected on the relevant demographic and psychographic variables? Are there any questions that might clarify the answers to other questions? Will the results of the study provide the solution to the manager's problem?

Questionnaire Accuracy

Once the researcher has decided what should be asked, the criterion of accuracy becomes the primary concern.

Accuracy means that the information is reliable and valid. While experienced researchers generally believe that one should use simple, understandable, unbiased, unambiguous, nonirritating words, no step-by-step procedure to ensure accuracy in question writing can be generalized across projects. Obtaining accurate answers from respondents is strongly influenced by the researcher's ability to design a questionnaire that facilitates recall and that will motivate the respondent to cooperate.

Respondents tend to be most cooperative when the subject of the research is interesting. Also, if questions are not lengthy, difficult to answer, or ego-threatening, there is a higher probability of obtaining unbiased answers. Question wording and sequence substantially influence accuracy. These topics are treated in subsequent sections of this chapter.

PHRASING QUESTIONS

There are many ways to phrase questions, and many standard question formats have been developed in previous research studies. This section presents a classification of question types and provides some helpful guidelines to researchers who must write questions.

Open-Ended Response versus Fixed-Alternative Questions

open-ended response question
A question that poses some problem and asks the respondent to answer in his or her own words.

Questions may be categorized as either of two basic types, according to the amount of freedom respondents are given in answering them. **Open-ended response questions** pose some problem or topic and ask the respondent to answer in his or her own words. For example:

What things do you like most about your job?
What names of local banks can you think of offhand?
What comes to mind when you look at this advertisement?
Do you think that there are some ways in which life in the United States is getting worse? How is that?

fixed-alternative question
A question in which the respondent is given specific limited-alternative responses and asked to choose the one closest to his or her own viewpoint.

If the question is asked in a personal interview, the interviewer may probe for more information by asking such questions as: Anything else? or Could you tell me more about your thinking on that? Open-ended response questions are free-answer questions. They may be contrasted to the **fixed-alternative question**, sometimes called a "closed question," in which the respondent is given specific, limited-alternative responses and asked to choose the one closest to his or her own viewpoint. For example:

Did you work overtime or at more than one job last week?
Yes ____ No ____

Compared to ten years ago, would you say that the quality of most products made in Japan is higher, about the same, or not as good?
Higher ____ About the same ____ Not as good ____

How much of your shopping for clothes and household items do you do in warehouse club stores? Would you say:
All of it ____
Most of it ____
About half of it ____
About one-quarter of it ____
Less than one-quarter of it ____

In management, is there a useful distinction between what is legal and what is ethical?
Yes ____ No ____

In Aesop's fable "The Ant and the Grasshopper," the ant spent his time working and planning for the future, while the grasshopper lived for the moment and enjoyed himself. Which are you more like?
1. The ant
2. The grasshopper

Open-ended response questions are most beneficial when the researcher is conducting exploratory research, especially if the range of responses is not known. Open-ended questions can be used to learn what words and phrases people spontaneously give to the free-response questions. Respondents are free to answer with whatever is uppermost in their thinking. By gaining free and uninhibited responses, a researcher may find some unanticipated reaction toward the topic. As the responses have the "flavor" of the conversational language that people use in talking about products or jobs, responses to these questions may be a source for effective communication.

Open-ended response questions are especially valuable at the beginning of an interview. They are good first questions because they allow respondents to warm up to the questioning process.

The cost of open-ended response questions is substantially greater than that of fixed-alternative questions, because the job of coding, editing, and analyzing the data is quite extensive. As each respondent's answer is somewhat unique, there is some difficulty in categorizing and summarizing the answers. The process requires an editor to go over a sample of questions to classify the responses into some sort of scheme; then all the answers are reviewed and coded according to the classification scheme.

Another potential disadvantage of the open-ended response question is that interviewer bias may influence the responses. While most instructions state that the interviewer is to record answers verbatim, rarely can even the best interviewer get every word spoken by the respondent. There is a tendency for interviewers to take short cuts in recording answers—but changing even a few of the respondents' words may substantially influence the results. Thus, the final answer often is a combination of the respondent's and the interviewer's ideas rather than the respondent's ideas alone.

Articulate individuals tend to give longer answers to open-ended response questions. These articulate respondents often are better educated and in higher income groups, and thus may not be representative of the entire population, and yet they may give a large share of the responses.

In contrast to open-ended questions, fixed-alternative questions require less interviewer skill, take less time, and are easier for the respondent to answer. This occurs because closed questions require classification of the answer into standardized groupings prior to data collection. Standardizing alternative responses to a question provides comparability of answers, which facilitates coding, tabulating, and, ultimately, interpreting the data.

Earlier in the chapter a variety of fixed-alternative questions were presented. We will now identify and categorize the various types of fixed-alternative questions.

simple-dichotomy question
A fixed-alternative question that requires the respondent to choose one of two alternatives.

The **simple-dichotomy,** or **dichotomous-alternative, question** requires the respondent to choose one of two alternatives. The answer can be a simple "yes" or "no" or a choice between "this" and "that." For example:

Did you make any long-distance calls last week?
☐ Yes ☐ No

determinant-choice question
A type of fixed-alternative question that requires a respondent to choose one (and only one) response from among several possible alternatives.

Several types of questions provide the respondent with *multiple-choice alternatives.* The **determinant-choice question** requires the respondent to choose one—and only one—response from among several possible alternatives. For example:

Please give us some information about your flight. In which section of the aircraft did you sit?
☐ First class ☐ Business class ☐ Coach class

frequency-determination question
A type of fixed-alternative question that asks for an answer about general frequency of occurrence.

The **frequency-determination question** is a determinant-choice question that asks for an answer about general frequency of occurrence. For example:

How frequently do you watch the MTV television channel?
Every day . . . . ☐
5–6 times a week . . . . ☐
2–4 times a week . . . . ☐
Once a week. . . . . ☐
Less than once a week . . . . ☐
Never . . . . ☐

attitude rating scale
Measures used to rate attitudes, such as the Likert scale, semantic differential, and Stapel scale.

Attitude rating scales, such as the Likert scale, semantic differential, and Stapel scale, are also fixed-alternative questions. These were discussed in Chapter 14.

checklist question
A type of fixed-alternative question that allows the respondent to provide multiple answers to a single question.

The **checklist question** allows the respondent to provide multiple answers to a single question. The respondent indicates past experience, preference, and the like merely by checking off an item. In many cases the choices are adjectives that describe a particular object. A typical checklist follows:

Please check which of the following sources of information about investments you regularly use, if any.
- ☐ **Personal advice of your broker(s)**
- ☐ **Brokerage newsletters**
- ☐ **Brokerage research reports**
- ☐ **Investment advisory service(s)**
- ☐ **Conversations with other investors**
- ☐ **Reports on the Internet**
- ☐ **None of these**
- ☐ **Other (please specify)** ______________________

A major problem in developing dichotomous or multiple-choice alternatives is framing the response alternatives. There should be no overlap among categories. Alternatives should be *mutually exclusive;* that is, only one dimension of the issue should be related to that alternative. The following listing of income groups illustrates a common error:

Under $20,000 ____
$20,000–$35,000 ____
$35,000–$60,000 ____
$60,000–$80,000 ____
Over $80,000 ____

How many people with incomes of $35,000 will be in the second group and how many will be in the third group? There is no way to determine the answer. Grouping alternatives without forethought about analysis may cause loss of accuracy.

It should also be noted that few people relish being in the lowest category. Including a category lower than the answers you expect often helps to negate the potential bias caused by respondents' tendency to avoid an extreme category.

When a researcher is unaware of the potential responses to a question, fixed-alternative questions obviously cannot be used. If the researcher assumes what the responses will be, but is in fact wrong, he or she will have no way of knowing the extent to which the assumption was incorrect.

Unanticipated alternatives emerge when respondents think the closed answers do not adequately reflect their feelings. Comments are made to the interviewer or additional answers are written on the questionnaire, indicating that the exploratory research did not yield a complete array of responses. After the fact, not much can be done to correct a closed question that does not provide enough alternatives; therefore, the time spent conducting exploratory research with open-ended response questions is well worth the effort. The researcher should strive to ensure that there are sufficient response choices to include almost all possible answers.

Respondents may check off obvious alternatives, such as price or durability, if they do not see the choice they would prefer. Also, a fixed-alternative question may tempt respondents to check an answer that is untrue but perhaps more prestigious or socially acceptable than the true answer. Rather than stating they do not know why they chose a given product, they may select an alternative among those presented. As a matter of convenience, they may select a given alternative rather than think of the most correct alternative.

Most questionnaires include a mixture of open-ended and closed questions. Each form has unique benefits; in addition, a change of pace can eliminate respondent boredom and fatigue.

Phrasing Questions for Self-Administered, Telephone, and Personal Interview Surveys

The means of data collection (personal interview, telephone, mail, or Internet questionnaire) will influence the question format and question phrasing. In general, questions for mail and telephone surveys must be less complex than those utilized in personal interviews. Questionnaires for telephone and personal interviews should be written in a conversational style. Exhibit 15.1 illustrates how a question may be revised for a different medium.

Consider the following question from a personal interview:

There has been a lot of discussion about the potential health threat to nonsmokers from tobacco smoke in public buildings, restaurants, and business offices. How serious a health threat to you personally is the inhaling of this secondhand smoke, often called passive smoking: Is it a very serious health threat, somewhat serious, not too serious, or not serious at all?

1. **Very serious**
2. **Somewhat serious**
3. **Not too serious**
4. **Not serious at all**
5. **(Don't know)**

EXHIBIT 15.1 | **REDUCING QUESTION COMPLEXITY BY PROVIDING FEWER RESPONSES**[5]

Mail Form:

How satisfied are you with your community?

1. Very satisfied
2. Quite satisfied
3. Somewhat satisfied
4. Slightly satisfied
5. Neither satisfied nor dissatisfied
6. Slightly dissatisfied
7. Somewhat dissatisfied
8. Quite dissatisfied
9. Very dissatisfied

Revised for Telephone:

How satisfied are you with your community? Would you say you are very satisfied, somewhat satisfied, neither satisfied nor dissatisfied, somewhat dissatisfied, or very dissatisfied?

Very satisfied 1
Somewhat satisfied 2
Neither satisfied nor dissatisfied . . . 3
Somewhat dissatisfied 4
Very dissatisfied 5

You probably noticed that the last portion of the question was a listing of the four alternatives that serve as answers. This listing at the end is often used in interviews to remind the respondent of alternatives, because the choices are not presented visually. The fifth alternative (Don't know) is in parentheses because, although the interviewer knows it is an acceptable answer, it is not read because the researcher prefers to "force" the respondent to choose from among the four listed alternatives.

The data collection technique also influences the layout of the questionnaire. Layout will be discussed in a later section of this chapter.

THE ART OF ASKING QUESTIONS

In developing a questionnaire, there are no hard-and-fast rules. Fortunately, however, some guidelines that help to prevent the most common mistakes have been developed from research experience.

Avoid Complexity: Use Simple, Conversational Language

Words used in questionnaires should be readily understandable to all respondents. The researcher usually has the difficult task of adopting the conversational language of people from the lower educational levels without talking down to better-educated respondents. Remember, not all people have the vocabulary of a college student. A substantial number of Americans never go beyond high school.

> **TO THE POINT**
>
> *I don't know the rules of grammar. . . . If you're trying to persuade people to do something, or buy something, it seems to me you should use their language, the language they use every day, the language in which they think. We try to write in the vernacular.*
>
> DAVID OGILVY

Respondents can probably tell an interviewer whether they are married, single, divorced, separated, or widowed, but providing their "marital status" may present a problem. Also, the technical jargon of corporate executives should be avoided when surveying retailers, factory employees, or industrial users. "Marginal analysis," "decision support systems," and other words from the language of the corporate staff will not have the same meaning to—or be understood by—a store owner-operator in a retail survey. The vocabulary in the following question (from an attitude survey on social problems) is probably confusing for many respondents:

When effluents from a paper mill can be drunk and exhaust from factory smokestacks can be breathed, then humankind will have done a good job in saving the environment. . . . Don't you agree that what we want is zero toxicity: no effluents?

This lengthy question is also a leading question.

Avoid Leading and Loaded Questions

Leading and loaded questions are a major source of bias in question wording. **Leading questions** suggest or imply certain answers. In a study of the dry-cleaning industry, this question was asked:

> **leading question**
> A question that suggests or implies certain answers.

Many people are using dry cleaning less because of improved wash-and-wear clothes. How do you feel wash-and-wear clothes have affected your use of dry-cleaning facilities in the past 4 years?

____ Use less ____ No change ____ Use more

The potential "bandwagon effect" implied in this question threatens the study's validity.

loaded question
A question that suggests a socially desirable answer or is emotionally charged.

Loaded questions suggest a socially desirable answer or are emotionally charged. Consider the following:

In light of today's farm crisis, it would be in the public's best interest to have the federal government require labeling of imported meat.
___ Strongly Agree ___ Agree ___ Uncertain ___ Disagree ___ Strongly Disagree

Answers might be different if the loaded portion of the statement, "farm crisis," had another wording suggesting a problem of less magnitude than a crisis.

A television station produced the following 10-second spot asking for viewer feedback:

We are happy when you like programs on Channel 7. We are sad when you dislike programs on Channel 7. Write us and let us know what you think of our programming.

Most people do not wish to make others sad. This question is likely to elicit only positive comments.

Some answers to certain questions are more socially desirable than others. For example, a truthful answer to the following classification question might be painful:

Where did you rank academically in your high school graduating class?
Top quarter 2nd quarter 3rd quarter 4th quarter

When taking personality tests, respondents frequently are able to determine which answers are most socially acceptable, even though those answers do not portray their true feelings. For example, which are the socially desirable answers to the following questions on a self-confidence scale?

I feel capable of handling myself in most social situations.
____ Agree ____ Disagree
I seldom fear my actions will cause others to have a low opinion of me.
____ Agree ____ Disagree

Invoking the status quo is a form of loading that results in bias because the majority of respondents tend to be resistant to change.[6]

An experiment conducted in the early days of polling illustrates the unpopularity of change.[7] Comparable samples of respondents were simultaneously asked two questions about the presidential succession. One sample was asked: **"Would you favor or oppose *adding* a law to the Constitution preventing a president from succeeding himself more than once?"** The other sample was asked: **"Would you favor or oppose *changing* the Constitution in order to prevent a president from succeeding himself more than once?"** To the first question, 50 percent of the respondents answered in the negative; to the second question, 65 percent answered in the negative. Thus the public would rather *add to* than *change* the Constitution.

Partial mention of alternatives is another form of loading.

Building more nuclear power plants, like Three Mile Island, should not be allowed.

How do you generally spend your free time, watching television or what?[8]
Are you familiar with any companies that currently recycle aluminum, such as Coors?

Asking respondents "how often" they use a product or perform a task leads them to generalize about their behavior, because there usually is some variance in their behavior. One is likely to portray one's *ideal* behavior rather than one's average behavior. For instance, all of us should brush our teeth after every meal, but if a person is busy, a brushing or two may be skipped. An introductory statement, or preamble, to a question that reassures the respondent that his embarrassing behavior is not abnormal may yield truthful responses: **"Some people have the time to brush three times daily; others do not. Would you please tell me how often you brushed your teeth yesterday?"**

The question below asked a sample of college professors to record both actual and ideal amounts of time they spend on professional activities. This approach reduces the tendency to idealize the actual amount of time spent in professional activities.

Please indicate (A) your estimate of the actual percentage of time you spend on professional activities during the academic year, and (B) what you consider to be the ideal division of your time as a university professor.

Percentage of Time		
A—Actual	B—Ideal	
		Formal instruction (including preparation, presentation, grading, etc.)
		Informal instruction, advisement, student counseling
		Scholarly research and writing
		Academic administration
		Part-time professional employment outside the university (e.g., private practice, consulting)
		Professional activities outside the university (e.g., speaking, conferences, professional association duties)
100%	100%	

counterbiasing statement
An introductory statement or preface to a question that reduces a respondent's reluctance to answer potentially embarrassing questions.

split-ballot technique
A technique used to control for response bias. Two alternative phrasings of the same questions are utilized for respective halves of the sample to yield a more accurate total response than would be possible if only a single phrasing were utilized.

If a question embarrasses the respondent, it may elicit no answer or a biased response. This is particularly true with regard to personal and classification data such as income and education. The problem may be mitigated by introducing the section of the questionnaire with a **counterbiasing statement** such as: "To help classify your answers, we'd like to ask you a few questions. Again, your answers will be kept in strict confidence."

A question may be leading because it is phrased to reflect either the negative or positive aspects of the issue. To control for this bias, the wording of attitudinal questions may be reversed for 50 percent of the sample. This **split-ballot technique** is utilized with the expectation that two alternative phrasings of the same question will yield a more accurate total response than would be possible with only a single phrasing. A study of small-car-buying behavior, for example, gave one-half of the sample of imported-car purchasers a questionnaire in which they were asked to agree or disagree with the statement **"Small U.S. cars are cheaper to maintain than small imported cars."** The other half of the imported-car owners received a questionnaire in which the statement read **"Small imported cars are cheaper to maintain than small U.S. cars."**

Avoid Ambiguity: Be as Specific as Possible

Items on questionnaires are often ambiguous because they are too general. Consider indefinite words such as *often, occasionally, usually, regularly, frequently, many, good, fair,* and *poor.* Each of these words has many meanings. For one person, *frequent* reading of *Fortune* magazine may be reading six or seven issues a year; for another it may be two issues a year. The word *fair* has a great variety of meanings; the same is true for many indefinite words.

Questions such as the following should be interpreted with care:

How often do you feel that you can consider all of the alternatives before making a decision to follow a specific course of action?
____ Always ____ Fairly often ____ Occasionally ____ Seldom ____ Never

In addition to utilizing words like *occasionally,* this question asks respondents to generalize about their decision-making behavior. The question is not specific. What does *consider* mean? The respondents may have a tendency to provide stereotyped "good" management responses rather than to describe their actual behavior. People's memories are not perfect. We tend to remember the good and forget the bad.

Another example of an ambiguous question is **"Do you usually work alone?"** It would be less ambiguous if the question were restated to something like

> **Which of the following best describes your working behavior?**
> **I never work alone.**
> **I work alone less than half the time.**
> **I work alone most of the time.**

Similarly, although the following question may be important to the researcher, its wording could confuse respondents: **"How difficult is it for you to get the necessary information about divisional or company objectives or goals for decision making?"** The term *necessary information* is highly subjective. It could be interpreted to mean the *minimum* necessary information or the *optimal* necessary information.

Which of the following is ambiguous?

> **If something happens that puts your immediate supervisor "on the spot," what is he most likely to do?**
> **Should managers be held personally responsible for the wrongdoings of corporations?**

As the reader can tell, question ambiguity is a pervasive problem. It is not easily eliminated.

Some scholars have suggested that the rate of diffusion of an innovation is related to the perception of the innovation's attributes, such as divisibility, which

RESEARCH INSIGHT

"I DON'T UNDERSTAND THE QUESTION"[9]

1. The company should continue its excellent fringe benefit programs.
   a. Yes
   b. No

COMMENT: The fringe benefit programs may not be excellent at all. By answering "yes," the respondent is implying that things are just fine as they are. By answering "no," he implies that the company should discontinue the fringe benefits. Don't place the respondent in that sort of a bind.

BETTER: How satisfied are you with the company's fringe benefit programs?
   a. Very satisfied
   b. Somewhat satisfied
   c. Neither satisfied nor dissatisfied
   d. Somewhat dissatisfied
   e. Very dissatisfied

2. Do you understand and like the company's new hiring policy?
   a. Yes
   b. No

COMMENT: There are really two questions here:
(1) Do you understand the company's new hiring policy?
(2) Do you like it?
The answers to the original question are ambiguous.

BETTER: Do you like the company's new hiring policy?
   a. I don't know what the company policy is.
   b. I don't like it.
   c. I neither like nor dislike it.
   d. I like it.

3. Your supervisor is handling the frequent and serious problems with work quality better now than six months ago.
   a. Strongly disagree
   b. Disagree
   c. Neither agree nor disagree
   d. Agree
   e. Strongly agree

COMMENT: The statement automatically puts respondents in a box, since it assumes that there are frequent, serious problems with their work groups' work quality.

BETTER: Compared with six months ago, how well does your supervisor handle difficult work-related problems?
   a. Much better
   b. Somewhat better
   c. About the same
   d. Somewhat worse
   e. Much worse

4. What makes your job a good one?
   a. The good pay
   b. The opportunity for advancement
   c. A good supervisor
   d. Interesting work

COMMENT: This question assumes that the employee's job is a good one, while the employee may not feel that it is particularly good. There is no provision for selecting one or more than one of the choices. If you really want to find out what the employee likes best about his job, you may want to ask an open-ended question, or you may need to ask a series of questions about different aspects of the job.

BETTER: What do you like best about your job?
   a. The pay
   b. The opportunities for advancement
   c. The working conditions
   d. The people you work with
   e. Your supervisor
   f. The work
   g. The fringe benefits program

refers to the extent to which an innovation may be tried or tested on a limited scale.[10] An empirical attempt to test this theory by using semantic differentials was a disaster. Pretesting found the bipolar adjectives *divisible–not divisible* were impossible for respondents to understand because they did not have the theory in mind as a frame of reference. A revision of the scale used these bipolar adjectives:

Testable (sample use possible) ____ : ____ : ____ : ____ : ____ : ____ : ____ **Not Testable (sample use not possible)**

But the question remained ambiguous because the meaning still was not clear.

A brewing industry study on point-of-purchase displays asked:

What degree of durability do you prefer in your point-of-purchase advertising?
____ Permanent (lasting more than 6 months)
____ Semipermanent (lasting from 1 to 6 months)
____ Temporary (lasting less than 1 month)

Here the researchers clarified the terms *permanent, semipermanent,* and *temporary* by defining them for the respondent. However, the question remains somewhat ambiguous. Beer companies often use a variety of point-of-purchase devices to serve different purposes. Which purpose was the researcher asking about? Furthermore, analysis was difficult because respondents were merely asked to indicate a preference rather than a degree of preference. Thus, the meaning of questions may not be clear because the frame of reference is inadequate for interpreting the context of the question.[11] A student research group asked this question:

What one of these media do you rely on most?
Television ____ Radio ____ Internet ____ Newspapers ____

This question is ambiguous because it does not ask about the content of the media. "Rely on most" for *what*—news, sports, entertainment?

Avoid Double-Barreled Items

double-barreled question
A question that may induce bias because it covers two issues at once.

A question covering several issues at once is referred to as **double-barreled** and should always be avoided. It's easy to make the mistake of asking two questions rather than one. For example, **"Please indicate if you agree or disagree with the following statement: 'I have called in sick or left work to golf.'"** Which reason is it: calling in sick or leaving work (perhaps with permission) to play golf?

When multiple questions are asked in one question, the results may be exceedingly difficult to interpret. For example, consider the following question from a magazine survey entitled "How Do You Feel about Being a Woman?"

Between you and your husband, who does the housework (cleaning, cooking, dishwashing, laundry) over and above that done by any hired help?
I do all of it
I do almost all of it
I do over half of it
We split the work fifty-fifty
My husband does over half of it

The answers to this question do not tell us if the wife cooks and the husband dries the dishes.

Another survey, by a university library, asked:

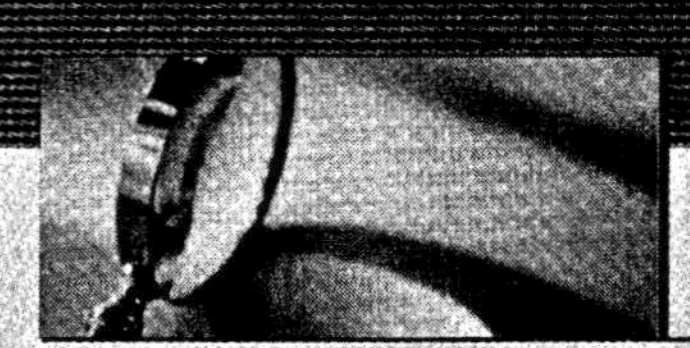

RESEARCH INSIGHT

ONE OR TWO QUESTIONS?

This study was a part of an ongoing series of "research-on-research" investigations.[12] Its purpose was to establish an accurate means of measuring rate of purchase. Like other such studies, it involved demographically matched samples of households, with each sample receiving a different treatment. Self-administered questionnaires were mailed to female heads of households, and purchase data were obtained for the following products: all-purpose white glue, aspirin, replacement automobile tires, and record albums.

Two different ways of asking the purchase incidence questions were investigated. Alternative A was sent to a sample of 1,000 homes; Alternative B was sent to another sample of 1,000 homes. The samples were closely matched in terms of age, income, geography, and city size. To the right is a sample pair of questions.

The table below lists the percentages of respondents who reported purchasing items in the past 3 months, as revealed by the two forms of the question.

ALTERNATIVE A

Below are listed several products. Please "X" each product you or anyone in your household *bought* in the PAST THREE MONTHS.

ALTERNATIVE B

Below are listed several products. Please "X" each product you or anyone in your household *ever bought.* For each product ever bought, "X" the box that best describes when the product was *purchased most recently:*

- ☐ **Within the past 3 months**
- ☐ **4–6 months ago**
- ☐ **7–12 months ago**
- ☐ **Over 12 months ago**

	PURCHASED WITHIN PAST 3 MONTHS		
	A 1-Step Question (%)	B 2-Step Question (%)	Percentage Point Difference
White glue	46	32	+14
Aspirin	68	57	+11
Replacement auto tires	32	24	+8

Are you satisfied with the present system of handling "closed-reserve" and "open-reserve" readings? (Are enough copies available? Are the required materials ordered promptly? Are the borrowing regulations adequate for students' use of materials?)
____ Yes ____ No

Here a respondent may feel torn between a "Yes" to one part of the question and a "No" to another part. The answer to this question does not tell the researchers which problem or combination of problems concerns the library user.

Consider this very appropriate comment about double-barreled questions:

> Generally speaking, it is hard enough to get answers to one idea at a time without complicating the problem by asking what amounts to two questions at once. If two ideas are to be explored, they deserve at least two questions. Since question marks are not rationed, there is little excuse for the needless confusion that results in the double-barreled question.[13]

Avoid Making Assumptions

Consider the following question:

Should Macy's continue its excellent gift-wrapping program?
☐ **Yes** ☐ **No**

This question contains the implicit assumption that people believe the gift-wrapping program is excellent. By answering yes, the respondent implies that the program is, in fact, excellent and that things are just fine as they are. By answering no, he or she implies that the store should discontinue the gift wrapping. The researcher should not place the respondent in that sort of bind by including an implicit assumption in the question.

Another mistake that question writers sometimes make is assuming that the respondent has previously thought about an issue. For example, the following question appeared in a survey concerning Jack-in-the-Box restaurants: **"Do you think Jack-in-the-Box restaurants should consider changing their name?"** It is very unlikely that the respondent has thought about this question before being asked to answer it. Most respondents will answer the question even though they had no prior opinion concerning the name change of Jack-in-the-Box. Research that induces people to express attitudes on subjects they do not ordinarily think about is meaningless.

Avoid Burdensome Questions That May Tax the Respondent's Memory

A simple fact of human life is that people forget. Researchers writing questions about past behavior or events should recognize that certain questions may make serious demands on the respondent's memory. Writing questions about prior events requires a conscientious attempt to minimize the problem associated with forgetting.

In many situations, respondents cannot recall the answer to a question. For example, a telephone survey conducted during the 24-hour period following the airing of the Super Bowl might establish whether the respondent watched the Super Bowl and then ask: **"Do you recall any commercials on that program?"** If the answer is positive, the interviewer might ask: **"What brands were advertised?"** These two questions measure *unaided recall,* because they give the respondent no clue as to the brand of interest.

If the researcher suspects that the respondent forgot the answer to a question, he or she may rewrite the question in an *aided-recall* format—that is, in a format that provides a clue to help jog the respondent's memory. For instance, the question about the advertised beer in an aided-recall format might be: **"Do you recall whether there was a brand of beer advertised on that program?"** or **"I am going to read you a list of beer brand names. Can you pick out the name of the beer that was advertised on the program?"**

While aided recall is not as strong a test of attention or memory as unaided recall, this type of question is less taxing to the respondent's memory.

Telescoping and squishing are two additional consequences of respondents' forgetting the exact details of their behavior. *Telescoping* occurs when respondents believe that past events happened more recently than they actually did. The opposite effect, *squishing,* occurs when respondents think that recent events took place longer ago than they really did. A solution to this problem may be to refer to a specific event that is memorable—for example, **"How often have you gone to a sporting event since the Super Bowl?"**[14] Because forgetting tends to increase over time, the question may concern a recent period: **"How often did you watch Home Box Office on cable television *last week?*"** (During the editing stage, the results can be transposed to the appropriate time period.)

In situations in which "I don't know" or "I can't recall" is a meaningful answer, simply including a "don't know" response category may solve the question writer's problem.

WHAT IS THE BEST QUESTION SEQUENCE?

The order of questions, or the question sequence, may serve several functions for the researcher. If the opening questions are interesting, simple to comprehend, and easy to answer, respondents' cooperation and involvement can be maintained throughout the questionnaire. Asking easy-to-answer questions teaches respondents their role and builds confidence; they know this is a researcher and not another salesperson posing as an interviewer. If respondents' curiosity is not aroused at the outset, they can become disinterested and terminate the interview. A mail research expert reports that a mail survey among department store buyers drew an extremely poor return.[15] However, when some introductory questions related to the advisability of congressional action on pending legislation of great importance to these buyers were placed first on the questionnaire, a substantial improvement in response rate occurred. Respondents completed all the questions, not only those in the opening section.

In their attempts to "warm up" respondents toward the questionnaire, student researchers frequently ask demographic or classification questions at the beginning of the questionnaire. This is generally not advisable, because asking for personal information, such as income level or education, may embarrass or threaten respondents. It is generally better to ask embarrassing questions at the middle or end of the questionnaire, after rapport has been established between respondent and interviewer.

order bias
Bias caused by the influence of earlier questions in a questionnaire or by an answer's position in a set of answers.

Order bias can result from a particular answer's position in a set of answers or from the sequencing of questions. In political elections in which candidates lack high visibility, such as elections for county commissioners and judges, the first name listed on the ballot often receives the highest percentage of votes. For this reason many election boards print several ballots so that each candidate's name appears in every possible position (order) on the ballot.

Order bias can also distort survey results. For example, suppose a questionnaire's purpose is to measure levels of awareness of several charitable organizations. If Big Brothers and Big Sisters is always mentioned first, the Red Cross second, and the American Cancer Society third, Big Brothers and Big Sisters may receive an artificially high awareness rating because respondents are prone to yea-saying (by indicating awareness of the first item in the list).

Sequencing specific questions before asking about broader issues is a common cause of order bias. For example, bias may arise if questions about a specific clothing store are asked prior to those concerning the general criteria for selecting a clothing store. Suppose a respondent who indicates in the first portion of a questionnaire that she shops at a store where parking needs to be improved. Later in the questionnaire, to avoid appearing inconsistent, she may state that parking is less important a factor than she really believes it is. Specific questions may thus influence the more general ones. Therefore, it is advisable to ask general questions before specific questions to obtain the freest of open-ended responses. This procedure, known as the **funnel technique**, allows the researcher to understand the respondent's frame of reference before asking more specific questions about the level of the respondent's information and the intensity of his or her opinions.

funnel technique
Asking general questions before specific questions in order to obtain unbiased responses.

Consider how later answers might be biased by previous questions in this questionnaire on environmental pollution:

Circle the number that best expresses your feelings about the severity of each environmental problem:

Problem	Not a Problem				Very Severe Problem
Air pollution from automobile exhausts	1	2	3	4	5
Air pollution from open burning	1	2	3	4	5
Air pollution from industrial smoke	1	2	3	4	5
Air pollution from foul odors	1	2	3	4	5
Noise pollution from airplanes	1	2	3	4	5
Noise pollution from cars, trucks, motorcycles	1	2	3	4	5
Noise pollution from industry	1	2	3	4	5

Not surprisingly, researchers found that responses to the air pollution questions were highly correlated, almost identical.

Further, when one is using attitude scales, there may be an *anchoring effect*. The first concept measured tends to become a comparison point from which subsequent evaluations are made.[16] Randomization of items on a questionnaire susceptible to the anchoring effect helps minimize order bias.

A related problem is bias caused by the order of the alternatives on closed questions. To avoid this problem, the order of these choices should be rotated if producing alternative forms of the questionnaire is possible. However, business researchers rarely print alternative questionnaires to eliminate problems resulting from order bias. A more common practice is to pencil in Xs or check marks on printed questionnaires to indicate where the interviewer should start a series of repetitive questions. For example, the capitalized phrase and sentence in the following question provide instructions to the interviewer to "rotate" brands, starting with the one checked.

I would like to determine how likely you would be to buy certain brands of candy in the future. Let's start with (X'ED BRAND). (RECORD BELOW UNDER APPROPRIATE BRAND. REPEAT QUESTIONS FOR ALL REMAINING BRANDS.)

START HERE:	( ) Mounds	(x) Almond Joy	( ) York Peppermint Patties
Definitely would buy	–1	–1	–1
Probably would buy	–2	–2	–2
Might or might not buy	–3	–3	–3
Probably would not buy	–4	–4	–4
Definitely would not buy	–5	–5	–5

One advantage of Internet surveys is the ability to reduce order bias by having the computer randomly order questions and/or response alternatives. With complete randomization, question order is random and respondents see response alternatives in random positions. Asking a question that doesn't apply to the respondent or that the respondent is not qualified to answer may be irritating or may cause a biased response because the respondent wishes to please the interviewer or to avoid embarrassment. Including a **filter question** minimizes the chance of asking questions that are inapplicable. Asking **"Where do you generally have check-cashing problems in Springfield?"** may elicit a response even though the respondent has not had any check-cashing problems and may simply wish to please the interviewer with an answer. A filter question such as

filter question
A question in a questionnaire that screens out respondents not qualified to answer a second question.

Do you ever have a problem cashing a check in Springfield?
____ Yes ____ No

would screen out the people who are not qualified to answer. Exhibit 15.2 gives an example of a flowchart plan for a questionnaire that uses filter questions.

Another form of filter question, the **pivot question,** can be used to obtain income information and other data that respondents may be reluctant to provide. For example, a respondent is asked

pivot question
A filter question used to determine which version of a second question will be asked.

"Is your total family income over $50,000?" IF UNDER, ASK, "Is it over or under $25,000?" IF OVER, ASK, "Is it over or under $75,000?"
1. Under $25,000
2. $25,001–$50,000
3. $50,001–$75,000
4. Over $75,000

Structuring the order of questions so that they are logical will help to ensure the respondent's cooperation and eliminate confusion or indecision. The researcher maintains legitimacy by making sure that the respondent can comprehend the relationship between a given question (or section of the questionnaire) and the overall purpose of the study. Further, a logical order may aid the individual's memory. Transitional comments explaining the logic of the questionnaire may help guarantee that the respondent continues. Here are some examples:

We have been talking so far about general shopping habits in this city. Now I'd like you to compare two types of department stores—regular department stores and discount department stores.

So that I can combine your answers with those of other farmers who are similar to you, I need some personal information

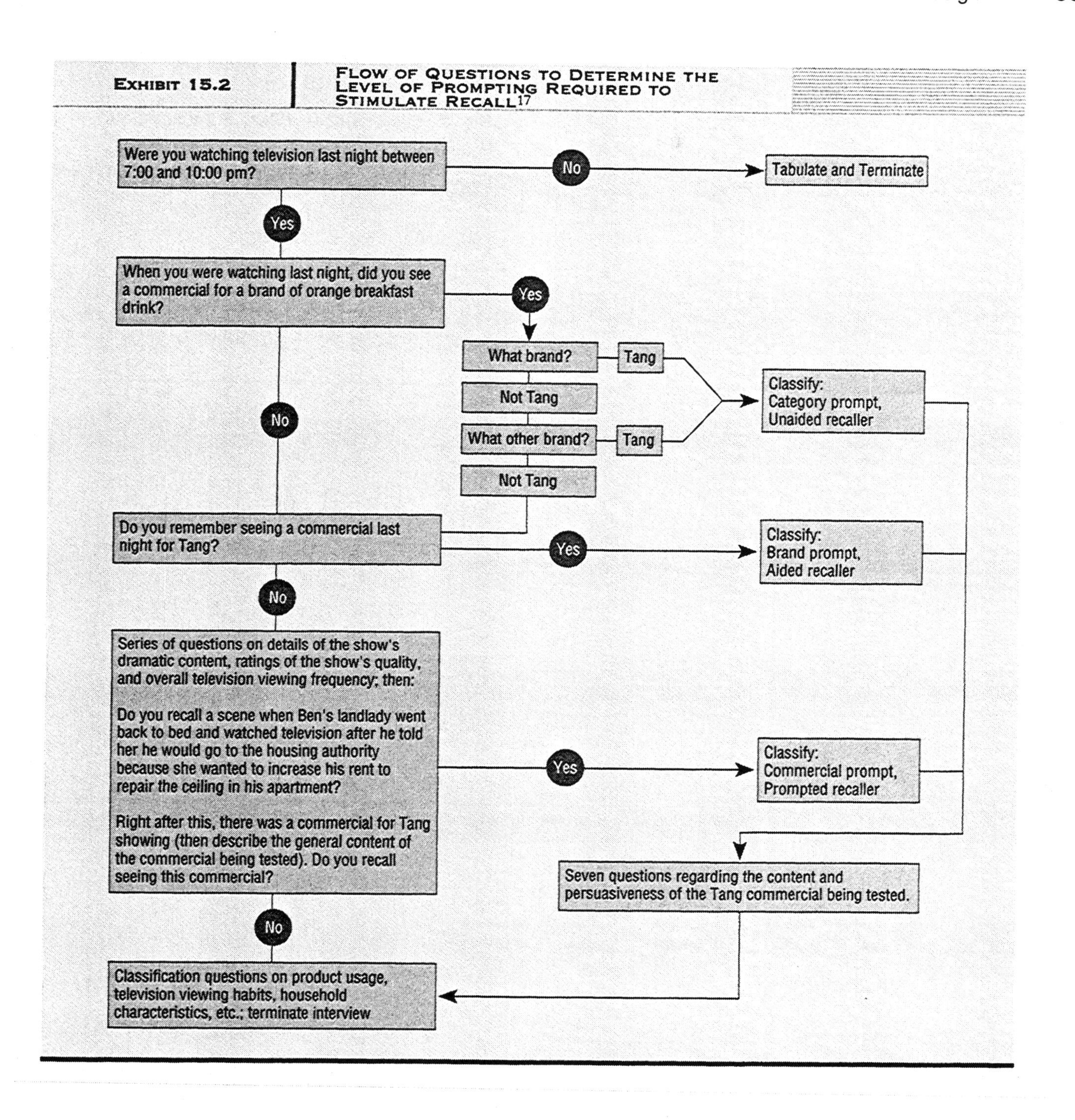

about you. Your answers to these questions—as well as all of the others you've answered—are confidential, and you will never be identified to anyone without your permission.

Thanks for your help so far. If you'll answer the remaining questions, it will help me analyze all your answers.

WHAT IS THE BEST LAYOUT?

Good layout and physical attractiveness are crucial in mail, Internet, and other self-administered questionnaires. For different reasons it is also important to have a good layout in questionnaires designed for personal and telephone interviews.

Layout of Traditional Questionnaires

Exhibit 15.3 shows a page from a telephone questionnaire. The layout is neat and attractive, and the instructions for the interviewer (all boldface capital letters) are easy to follow. The responses "It Depends," "Refused," and "Don't Know" are enclosed in a box to indicate that these answers are acceptable but

EXHIBIT 15.3 LAYOUT OF A PAGE FROM A TELEPHONE QUESTIONNAIRE

5. Now I'm going to read you some types of professions. For each one, please tell me whether you think the work that profession does, on balance, has a very positive impact on society, a somewhat positive impact, a somewhat negative impact, a very negative impact, or not much impact either way on society. First . . . **(START AT X'ED ITEM. CONTINUE DOWN AND UP THE LIST UNTIL ALL ITEMS HAVE BEEN READ AND RATED.)**

Start Here:	Very Positive Impact	Somewhat Positive Impact	Somewhat Negative Impact	Very Negative Impact	Not Much Impact	(DO NOT READ) It Depends	Refused	Don't Know
[ ] Members of Congress	1	2	3	4	5	0	X	Y (24)
[ ] Business executives	1	2	3	4	5	0	X	Y (25)
[ ] Physicians	1	2	3	4	5	0	X	Y (26)
[ ] Political pollsters—that is, people who conduct surveys for public officials or political candidates	1	2	3	4	5	0	X	Y (27)
[ ] Researchers in the media—that is, people in the media such as television, newspapers, magazines and radio, who conduct surveys about issues later reported in the media	1	2	3	4	5	0	X	Y (28)

EXHIBIT 15.3 LAYOUT OF A PAGE FROM A TELEPHONE QUESTIONNAIRE (CONTINUED)

Start Here:	Very Positive Impact	Somewhat Positive Impact	Somewhat Negative Impact	Very Negative Impact	Not Much Impact	(DO NOT READ) It Depends	(DO NOT READ) Refused	(DO NOT READ) Don't Know
[ ] Telemarketers—that is, people who sell products or services over the phone	1	2	3	4	5	0	X	Y (29)
[ ] Used car salesmen	1	2	3	4	5	0	X	Y (30)
[ ] Market researchers—that is, people who work for commercial research firms who conduct surveys to see what the public thinks about certain kinds of consumer products or services	1	2	3	4	5	0	X	Y (31)
[ ] Biomedical researchers	1	2	3	4	5	0	X	Y (32)
[ ] Public-opinion researchers—that is, people who work for commercial research firms who conduct surveys to see what the public thinks about important social issues	1	2	3	4	5	0	X	Y (33)
[ ] College and university professors	1	2	3	4	5	0	X	Y (34)
[ ] Attorneys	1	2	3	4	5	0	X	Y (35)
[ ] Members of the clergy	1	2	3	4	5	0	X	Y (36)
[ ] Journalists	1	2	3	4	5	0	X	Y (37)

responses from the 5-point scale are preferred. (To see the entire questionnaire, go to the Web site of the Council of American Survey Research Organizations at http://www.casro.org/ and check out their poll about polls.)

Often rate of return can be increased by using money that might have been spent on an incentive to improve the attractiveness and quality of the questionnaire. Mail questionnaires should never be overcrowded. Margins should be of decent size, white space should be used to separate blocks of print, and any unavoidable columns of multiple boxes should be kept to a minimum. Questionnaires should be designed to appear as brief and small as possible. Sometimes it is advisable to use a booklet form of questionnaire, rather than a large number of pages stapled together. In situations where it is necessary to conserve space on the questionnaire or to facilitate entering the data into a computer or tabulating the data, a multiple-grid layout may be used. In this type of layout, a question is followed by corresponding response alternatives arranged in a grid or matrix format. For example:

Airlines often offer special-fare promotions. On a business trip, would you take a connecting flight instead of a nonstop flight if the connecting fare were lower?

	Yes	**No**	**Not Sure**
One hour longer?	☐	☐	☐
Two hours longer?	☐	☐	☐
Three hours longer?	☐	☐	☐

Experienced researchers have found that it pays to phrase the title of the questionnaire carefully. In self-administered and mail questionnaires a carefully constructed title may by itself capture the respondent's interest, underline the importance of the research ("Nationwide Study of Blood Donors"), emphasize the interesting nature of the study ("Study of Internet Usage"), appeal to the respondent's ego ("Survey among Top Executives"), or emphasize the confidential nature of the study ("A Confidential Survey among . . ."). The researcher should take steps to ensure that the wording of the title will not bias the respondent in the same way that a leading question might.

When an interviewer is to administer the questionnaire, the analyst can design the questionnaire to make the job of following interconnected questions much easier by utilizing instructions, directional arrows, special question formats, and other tricks of the trade. Exhibit 15.4 and Exhibit 15.5 (pages 352–353) illustrate portions of telephone and personal interview questionnaires. Note how the layout and easy-to-follow instructions for interviewers in Exhibit 15.4 (e.g., questions 1, 2, and 3) help the interviewer follow the question sequence. The series of questions in Exhibit 15.4 makes use of "skip" questions. Either instructions to skip or an arrow drawn to the next question are provided to help the respondent (or the interviewer) know which question comes next.

Note that Questions 3 and 6 in Exhibit 15.5 instruct the interviewer to hand the respondent a card that bears a list of alternatives. Cards may help respondents to grasp the intended meaning of the question and to help them remember all the brand names or list of items they are being asked about. Also, Questions 2, 3, and 6 instruct the interviewer to start the bank ratings with the bank that has been checked in red pencil on the printed questionnaire. The name of the red-checked bank is not the same on every questionnaire. By rotating the order of the check marks, the researchers attempt to reduce order

EXHIBIT 15.4 | **TELEPHONE QUESTIONNAIRE WITH SKIP QUESTIONS**

1. Did you take the car you had checked to the Standard Auto Repair Center for repairs?
   - 1 Yes **(Skip to Q. 3)** – 2 No

2. **(If no, ask:)** Did you have the repair work done?
   - 1 Yes ↓
     1. Where was the repair work done? ______
     2. Why didn't you have the repair work done at the Standard Auto Repair Center? ______
   - 2 No ↓
     1. Why didn't you have the car repaired? ______

3. **(If yes to Q. 1, ask:)** How satisfied were you with the repair work? Were you . . .
   - 1 Very satisfied
   - 2 Somewhat satisfied
   - 3 Somewhat dissatisfied
   - 4 Very dissatisfied

   (If somewhat or very dissatisfied:) In what way were you dissatisfied? ______

4. **(Ask everyone:)** Do you ever buy gas at the 95th Street Standard Center?
   - 1 Yes – 2 No **(Skip to Q. 6)**

5. **(If yes, ask:)** How often do you buy gas there?
   - 1 Always
   - 2 Almost always
   - 3 Most of the time
   - 4 Part of the time
   - 5 Hardly ever

6. Have you ever had your car washed there? – 1 Yes – 2 No

7. Have you ever had an oil change or lubrication done there? – 1 Yes – 2 No

bias caused by respondents' tendency to react more favorably to the first set of questions. To facilitate coding, question responses should be precoded when possible, as in Exhibit 15.4.

Layout is especially important when questionnaires are long or require the respondent to fill in a large amount of information. The use of headings or subtitles to identify groups of questions can help the respondent grasp the scope or nature of the questions to be asked. The respondent can follow the logic of the questionnaire at a glance, because the headings indicate groups of similar questions.

Layout of Internet Questionnaires

Layout is also an important issue for questionnaires appearing on the Internet. A questionnaire on a Web site should be easy to use, flow logically, and have a graphic look and overall feel that motivate the respondent to cooperate from

EXHIBIT 15.5 | **PERSONAL INTERVIEW QUESTIONNAIRE**[18]

"Hello, my name is ______________. I'm a Public Opinion Interviewer with Research Services, Inc. We're making an opinion survey about banks and banking, and I'd like to ask you . . ."

1. What are the names of local banks you can think of offhand? (INTERVIEWER: List names in order mentioned.)
   a. ______________________________
   b. ______________________________
   c. ______________________________
   d. ______________________________
   e. ______________________________
   f. ______________________________
   g. ______________________________

2. Thinking now about the experiences you have had with the different banks here in Boulder, have you ever talked to or done business with . . . (INTERVIEWER: Insert name of bank checked in red below.)
   a. Are you personally acquainted with any of the employees or officers at ______________?
   b. (If YES) Who is that?
   c. How long has it been since you have been inside ______________?
   (INTERVIEWER: Now go back and repeat 2–2c for all other banks listed.)

	(2) Talked		(2a and 2b) Know Employee or Officer		(2c) Been in Bank in:				
	Yes	**No**	**No**	**Name**	**Last Year**	**1–5**	**5-Plus**	**No**	**DK**
Boulder National Bank	1	2	1	______	1	2	3	4	5
First National Bank	1	2	1	______	1	2	3	4	5
Arapahoe National Bank	1	2	1	______	1	2	3	4	5
Security Bank	1	2	1	______	1	2	3	4	5
United Bank of Boulder	1	2	1	______	1	2	3	4	5
National State Bank	1	2	1	______	1	2	3	4	5

3. (HAND BANK RATING CARD.) On this card there are a number of contrasting phrases or statements—for example, "Large" and "Small." We'd like to know how you rate (NAME OF BANK CHECKED IN RED BELOW) in terms of these statements or phrases. Just for example, let's use the terms "fast service" and "slow service." If you were to rate a bank #1 on this scale, it would mean you find its service "very fast." On the other hand, a #7 rating would indicate you feel its service is "very slow," whereas a #4 rating means you don't think of it as being either "very fast" or "very slow." Are you ready to go ahead? Good! Tell me then how you would rate (NAME OF BANK CHECKED IN RED) in terms of each of the phrases or statements on that card.
   How about (READ NEXT BANK NAME)? (INTERVIEWER: Continue on until respondent has evaluated all six banks.)

	Arapahoe National	**First National**	**Boulder National**	**Security Bank**	**United Bank**	**National State**
a. Service	______	______	______	______	______	______
b. Size	______	______	______	______	______	______
c. Business vs. family	______	______	______	______	______	______
d. Friendliness	______	______	______	______	______	______
e. Big/small business	______	______	______	______	______	______
f. Rate of growth	______	______	______	______	______	______
g. Modernness	______	______	______	______	______	______
h. Leadership	______	______	______	______	______	______
i. Loan ease	______	______	______	______	______	______
j. Location	______	______	______	______	______	______
k. Hours	______	______	______	______	______	______
l. Ownership	______	______	______	______	______	______
m. Community involvement	______	______	______	______	______	______

EXHIBIT 15.5 | **PERSONAL INTERVIEW QUESTIONNAIRE (CONTINUED)**

4. Suppose a friend of yours who has just moved to Boulder asked you to recommend a bank. Which local bank would you recommend? Why would you recommend that particular bank?

Arapahoe National	1
First National	2
Boulder National	3
Security Bank	4
United Bank of Boulder	5
National State Bank	6
Other (specify) ________	
DK/Wouldn't	8

5. Which of the local banks do you think of as: (INTERVIEWER: Read red-checked item first, then read each of the other five.)
   the newcomer's bank? ________
   the student's bank? ________
   the personal banker bank? ________
   the bank where most C.U. faculty and staff bank? ________
   the bank most interested in this community? ________
   the most progressive bank? ________

6. Which of these financial institutions, if any (HAND CARD #2), are you or any member of your immediate family who lives here in this home doing business with now?

   (IF NONE, skip to #19.)

Bank	1
Credit union	2
Finance company	3
Savings and loan	4
Industrial bank	5
None of these	6
DK/not sure	8

7. If a friend of yours asked you to recommend a place where he could get a loan with which to buy a home, which financial institution would you probably recommend? (INTERVIEWER: Probe for specific name.) Why would you recommend (INSTITUTION NAMED)?

Would recommend: ________	
Wouldn't	0
DK/not sure	8

start to finish. Many of the guidelines for layout of paper questionnaires apply to Internet questionnaires. There are, however, some important differences.

With *graphical user interface (GUI)* software, the researcher can exercise control over the background, colors, fonts, and other visual features displayed on the computer screen so as to create an attractive and easy-to-use interface between the computer user and the Internet survey. GUI software allows the researcher to design questionnaires in which respondents click on the appropriate answer rather than having to type answers or codes.

Researchers often use Web publishing software, such as WebSurveyor, FrontPage, or Netscape Composer, to format a questionnaire so that they will know how it should appear online. However, several features of a respondent's computer may influence the appearance of an Internet questionnaire. For example, discrepancies between the designer's and the respondent's computer settings for screen configuration (e.g., 640 x 480 pixels versus 800 x 600 pixels) may result in questions not being fully visible on the respondent's screen, misaligned text, or other visual problems.[19] The possibility that the questionnaire the researcher/designer constructs on his or her computer may look different from the questionnaire that appears on the respondent's computer should always be considered when designing Internet surveys. One sophisticated remedy is to use the first few questions on an Internet survey to ask about operating system, browser software, and other computer configuration issues so that the questionnaire that is delivered is as compatible as possible with the respondent's. A simpler solution is to limit the horizontal width of the questions to 70 characters or less, to decrease the likelihood of wrap-around text.

Layout Issues

Even if the questionnaire designer's computer and the respondents' computers are compatible, there are several layout issues a Web questionnaire designer should consider. The first decision is whether the questionnaire will appear page by page, with individual questions on separate screens (Web pages), or on a scrolling basis, with the entire questionnaire appearing on a single Web page that the respondent scrolls from top to bottom. The *paging layout* (going from screen to screen) greatly facilitates skip patterns. Based on a respondent's answers to filter questions, the computer can automatically insert relevant questions on subsequent pages. If the entire questionnaire appears on one page (the *scrolling layout*) the display should advance smoothly, as if it were a piece of paper being moved up or down. The scrolling layout gives the respondent the ability to read any portion of the questionnaire at any time, but the absence of page boundaries can cause problems. For example, suppose a Likert scale consists of 15 statements in a grid-format layout, with the response categories **Strongly Agree, Agree, Disagree,** and **Strongly Disagree** at the beginning of the questionnaire. Once the respondent has scrolled down beyond the first few statements, he or she may not be able to see both the statements at the end of the list and the response categories at the top of the grid simultaneously. Thus, avoiding the problems associated with splitting questions and response categories may be difficult with scrolling questionnaires.

When a scrolling questionnaire is long, category or section headings are helpful to respondents. It is also a good idea to provide links to the top and bottom parts of each section, so that users can navigate through the questionnaire without having to scroll through the entire document.[20]

push button
On an Internet questionnaire, a small outlined area, such as a rectangle or an arrow, that the respondent clicks on to select an option or perform a function, such as Submit.

Whether an Internet survey is in page-by-page or scrolling format, **push buttons** with labels should clearly describe the actions to be taken. For example, if the respondent is to go to the next page, a large arrow labeled "NEXT" might appear in color at the bottom of the screen.

Decisions must be made about the use of color, graphics, animation, sound, and other special features that the Internet makes possible. One thing to remember is that, although sophisticated graphics are not a problem for people with very powerful computers, many respondents' computers are not powerful enough to deliver complex graphics at a satisfactory speed, if at all. A textured background, colored headings, and small graphics can make a questionnaire more interesting and appealing, but they may present problems for respondents with older computers and/or low-bandwidth Internet connections.

status bar
In an Internet questionnaire, a visual indicator that tells the respondent what portion of the survey he or she has completed.

With a paper questionnaire, the respondent knows how many questions he or she must answer. Because many Internet surveys offer no visual clues about the number of questions to be asked, it is important to provide a **status bar** or some other visual indicator of questionnaire length. For example, including a partially filled rectangular box as a visual symbol and a statement such as "The status bar at top right indicates approximately what portion of the survey you have completed" increases the likelihood that the respondent will finish the entire sequence of questions.

An Internet questionnaire uses windows known as dialog boxes to display questions and record answers. Exhibit 15.6 portrays four common ways of dis-

EXHIBIT 15.6 ALTERNATIVE WAYS OF DISPLAYING INTERNET QUESTIONS

Radio button

Last month, did you purchase products or services over the Internet?

O **Yes**

O **No**

How familiar are you with Microsoft's X-box video game player?

Know Extremely Well	Know Fairly Well	Know a Little	Know Just Name	Never Heard of
O	O	O	O	O

Drop-down box, closed position

In which country or region do you currently reside?

Click Here

Drop-down box, open position

In which country or region do you currently reside?

Click Here

Click Here

United States
Asia/Pacific (excluding Hawaii)
Africa
Australia or New Zealand
Canada
Europe
Latin America, South America, or Mexico
Middle East
Other

Check box

From which location(s) do you access the Internet? Select all that apply.

- ☐ Home
- ☐ Work
- ☐ Other Location

Please indicate which of the following Web sites you have ever visited or used. (CHOOSE ALL THAT APPLY.)

- ☐ E*Trade's Web site
- ☐ Waterhouse's Web site
- ☐ Merrill Lynch's Web site
- ☐ Fidelity's Web site
- ☐ Schwab's Web site
- ☐ Powerstreet
- ☐ Yahoo! Finance
- ☐ Quicken.com
- ☐ Lycos Investing
- ☐ AOL's Personal Finance
- ☐ None of the above

Open-ended, one-line box

What company do you think is the most visible sponsor of sports?

Open-ended, scrolling text box

What can we do to improve our textbook?

radio button
In an Internet questionnaire, a circular icon, resembling a button, that activates one response choice and deactivates others when a respondent clicks on it.

drop-down box
In an Internet questionnaire, a space-saving device that reveals responses when they are needed but otherwise hides them from view.

check box
In an Internet questionnaire, a small graphic box, next to an answer, that a respondent clicks on to choose that answer; typically, a check mark or an X appears in the box when the respondent clicks on it.

open-ended box
In an Internet questionnaire, a box where respondents can type in their own answers to open-ended questions.

pop-up boxes
In an Internet questionnaire, boxes that appear at selected points and contain information or instructions for respondents.

playing questions on a computer screen. Many Internet questionnaires require the respondent to activate his or her answer by clicking on a **radio button** for a response. Radio buttons work like push buttons on automobile radios: Clicking on an alternative response deactivates the first choice and replaces it with the new response. A **drop-down box,** such as the one shown in Exhibit 15.6, is a space-saving device that allows the researcher to provide a list of responses that are hidden from view until they are needed. A general statement, such as "Please select" or "Click here" is shown initially. Clicking on the downward-facing arrow makes the full range of choices appear. If the first choice in a list, such as "Strongly Agree," is shown while the other responses are kept hidden, the chance that response bias will occur is increased. Drop-down boxes may present a problem for individuals with minimal computer skills, as they may not know how to reveal responses hidden behind a drop-down menu or how to move from one option to another in a moving-bar menu. However, because a drop-down box only shows permissible alternatives, this question format prevents respondents from entering unacceptable answers.

Checklist questions may be followed by **check boxes,** several, none, or all of which may be checked by the respondent. **Open-ended boxes** are boxes in which respondents type their answers to open-ended questions. Open-ended boxes may be designed as *one-line text boxes* or *scrolling text boxes,* depending on the breadth of the expected answer. Of course, open-ended questions require that respondents have both the skill and the willingness to keyboard lengthy answers on the computer. Some open-ended boxes are designed so that respondents can enter numbers for frequency response, ranking, or rating questions. For example:

> **Below you will see a series of statements that might or might not describe how you feel about your career. Please rate each statement using a scale from 1 to 4, where 4 means "Totally Agree," 3 means "Somewhat Agree," 2 means "Somewhat Disagree," and 1 means "Totally Disagree."**
>
> ***Please enter your numeric answer in the box provided next to each statement.* Would you say that . . . ?**
>
> **A lack of business knowledge relevant to my field/career could hurt my career advancement.** [ ]
>
> **My career life is an important part of how I define myself.** [ ]

Pop-up boxes are message boxes that can be used to highlight important information. For example, pop-up boxes may be use to provide a privacy statement, such as the following:

> **IBM would like your help in making our Web site easier to use and more effective.**
>
> **Choose to complete the survey now or not at all.**
>
> [Complete] [No Thank You] [Privacy Statement]

Clicking on Privacy Statement opens the following pop-up box:

Survey Privacy Statement

This overall Privacy Statement verifies that IBM is a member of the TRUSTe program and is in compliance with TRUSTe principles. This survey is strictly for market research purposes. The information you provide will be used only to improve the overall content, navigation, and useability of www.ibm.com.

In some cases, respondents can learn more about how to use a particular scale or get a definition of a term by clicking on a link that generates a pop-up box. One of the most common reasons for using pop-up boxes is *error trapping,* a topic discussed in the next section.

Chapter 14 described graphic rating scales, which present respondents with a graphic continuum. On the Internet, researchers can take advantage of scroll bars or other GUI software features to make these scales easy to use. For example, the graphic continuum may be drawn as a measuring rod with a plus sign on one end and a minus sign on the other. The respondent then moves a small rectangle back and forth between the two ends of the scale to scroll to any point on the continuum. Scoring, as discussed in Chapter 14, is in terms of some measure of the length (millimeters) from one end of the graphic continuum to the point marked by the respondent.

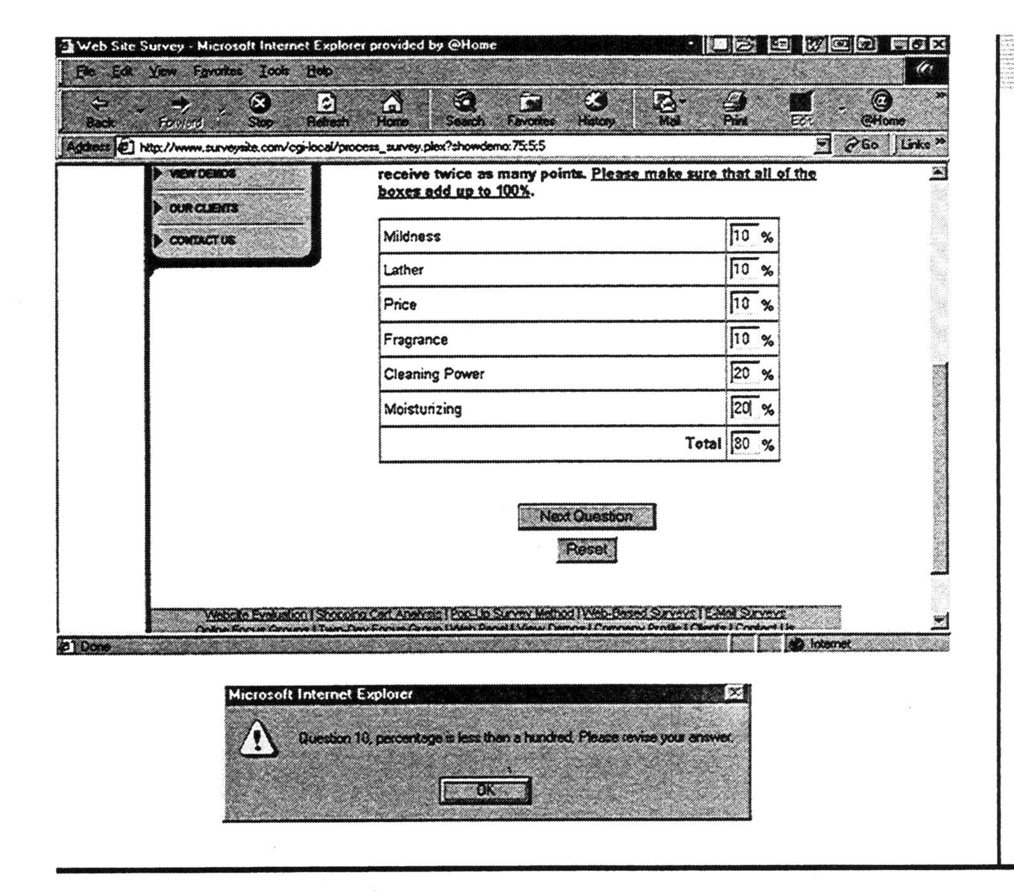

The respondent's answers to this constant-sum scale incorrectly total 80 percent—not the required 100 percent. When mistakes occur, error trapping software may cause a pop-up box to appear, with a message instructing the respondent to adjust his or her answer. With forced answering respondents cannot skip over questions as they do in mail surveys.

Finally, it is a good idea to include a customized thank-you page at the end of an Internet questionnaire, so that a brief thank-you note pops onto their screens when respondents click on the Submit push button.[21]

Software That Makes Questionnaires Interactive

Computer code can be written to make Internet questionnaires interactive and less prone to errors. The writing of software programs is beyond the scope of this discussion. However, several of the interactive functions that software makes possible should be mentioned here.

As discussed in Chapter 10, Internet software allows the branching off of questioning into two or more different lines, depending on a particular respondent's answer, and the skipping or filtering questions. Questionnaire-writing software with Boolean skip and branching logic is readily available. Most of these programs have *hidden skip logic* so that respondents never see any evidence of skips. It is best if the questions the respondent sees flow in numerical sequence.[22] However, some programs number all potential questions in numerical order, and the respondent sees only the numbers on the questions he or she answers. Thus, a respondent may answer questions 1 through 11 and next see a question numbered 15 because of the skip logic.

variable piping software
Software that allows variables to be inserted into an Internet questionnaire as a respondent is completing it.

Software can systematically or randomly manipulate the questions a respondent sees. **Variable piping software** allows variables, such as answers from previous questions, to be inserted into unfolding questions. Other software can randomly rotate the order of questions, blocks of questions, and response alternatives from respondent to respondent.

error trapping
Using software to control the flow of an Internet questionnaire—for example, to prevent respondents from backing up or failing to answer a question.

forced answering software
Software that prevents respondents from continuing with an Internet questionnaire if they fail to answer a question.

Researchers can use software to control the flow of a questionnaire. Respondents can be blocked from backing up, or they can be allowed to stop in mid-questionnaire and come back later to finish. A questionnaire can be designed so that if the respondent fails to answer a question or answers it with an incorrect type of response, an immediate error message appears. This is called **error trapping.** With **forced answering software,** respondents cannot skip over questions as they do in mail surveys. The program will not let them continue if they fail to answer a question.[23] The software may insert a boldface error message on the question screen or insert a pop-up box instructing the respondent how to continue. For example, if a respondent does not answer a question and tries to proceed to another screen, a pop-up box might present the following message:

> **You cannot leave a question blank. On questions without a "Not sure" or "Decline to answer" option, please choose the response that best represents your opinions or experiences.**

The respondent must close the pop-up box and answer the question in order to proceed to the next screen.

interactive help desk
In an Internet questionnaire, a live, real-time support feature that solves problems or answers questions respondents may encounter in completing the questionnaire.

Some designers include **interactive help desks** for their Web questionnaires, so that respondents can solve problems they encounter in completing a questionnaire. A respondent might e-mail questions to the survey help desk or get live, interactive, real-time support via an online help desk.

Some respondents will leave the questionnaire Web site, prematurely terminating the survey. In many cases sending an e-mail message to these respondents at a later date, encouraging them to revisit the Web site, will persuade them to complete the questionnaire. Through the use of software and cookies researchers can ensure that the respondent who revisits the Web site will be able to pick up at the point where he or she left off.

Once an Internet questionnaire has been designed, it is important to pretest it to ensure that it works with Internet Explorer, Netscape, AOL, WebTV, and other browsers. Some general-purpose programming languages, such as Java, do not always work with all browsers. Because different browsers have different peculiarities, a survey that works perfectly well with one may not function at all with another.[24]

HOW MUCH PRETESTING AND REVISING ARE NECESSARY?

Many novelists write, rewrite, and revise certain chapters, paragraphs, and even sentences of their books. The research analyst lives in a similar world. Rarely does one write only a first draft of a questionnaire. Usually, the questionnaire is tried out on a group that is selected on a convenience basis and that is similar in makeup to the one that ultimately will be sampled. Researchers should select a group that is not too divergent from the actual respondents (e.g., business students as surrogates for businesspeople), but it is not necessary to get a statistical sample for pretesting. The pretesting process allows the researchers to determine if the respondents have any difficulty understanding the questionnaire and whether there are any ambiguous or biased questions. This process is exceedingly beneficial. Making a mistake with 25 or 50 subjects can avert the disaster of administering an invalid questionnaire to several hundred individuals.

preliminary tabulation
Tabulation of the results of a pretest.

Tabulating the results of a pretest helps determine whether the questionnaire will meet the objectives of the research. A **preliminary tabulation** often illustrates that although respondents can easily comprehend and answer a given question, it is an inappropriate question because it does not solve the business problem.

Consider the following example from a survey among distributors of powder-actuated tools concerning the percentage of sales to given industries.

Please estimate what percentage of your fastener and load sales go to the following industries:
____ % heating, plumbing, and air-conditioning
____ % carpentry
____ % electrical
____ % maintenance
____ % other (please specify)
____

The researchers were fortunate to learn in pretesting that asking the question in this manner made it virtually impossible to obtain the information actually desired. Most respondents' answers did not total 100 percent. The question had to be revised. Usually a questionnaire goes through several revisions.

Getting respondents to add everything correctly is a problem. Notice how the questions from the survey on secretarial support in Exhibit 15.7 are designed to mitigate this problem. Pretesting difficult questions like this is essential.

What administrative procedures should be implemented to maximize the value of a pretest? Administering a questionnaire exactly as planned in the actual study often is not possible. For example, mailing out a questionnaire might require several weeks. Pretesting a questionnaire in this manner might provide

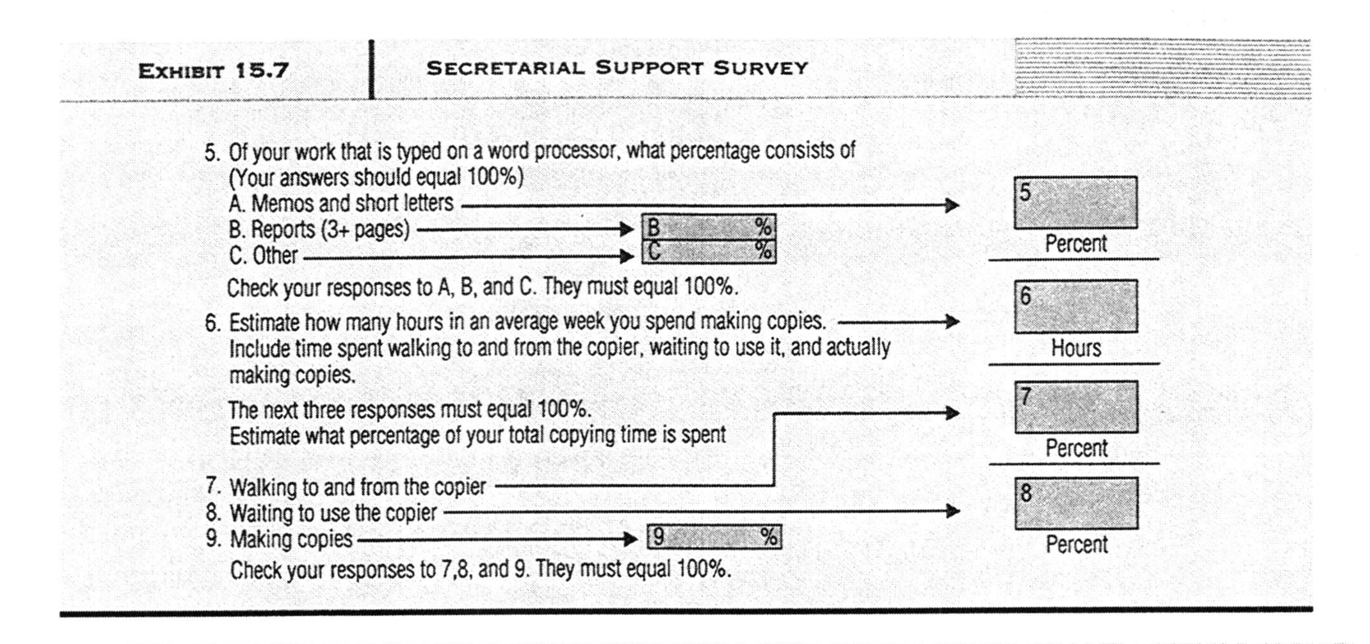
EXHIBIT 15.7 SECRETARIAL SUPPORT SURVEY

5. Of your work that is typed on a word processor, what percentage consists of (Your answers should equal 100%)
A. Memos and short letters → [5] Percent
B. Reports (3+ pages) → [B %]
C. Other → [C %]
Check your responses to A, B, and C. They must equal 100%.
6. Estimate how many hours in an average week you spend making copies. → [6] Hours
Include time spent walking to and from the copier, waiting to use it, and actually making copies.
The next three responses must equal 100%.
Estimate what percentage of your total copying time is spent
7. Walking to and from the copier → [7] Percent
8. Waiting to use the copier → [8] Percent
9. Making copies → [9 %]
Check your responses to 7,8, and 9. They must equal 100%.

important information on response rate, but it may not point out why questions were skipped or why respondents found certain questions ambiguous or confusing. The ability of a personal interviewer to record requests for additional explanation and to register comments indicating respondents' difficulty with question sequence or other factors is the primary reason why interviewers are often used for pretest work. Self-administered questionnaires are not reworded to be personal interviews, but interviewers are instructed to observe the person filling out the questionnaire and to ask for the respondent's comments after he or she completes the questionnaire. When pretesting personal or telephone interviews, interviewers may test alternative wordings and question sequences to determine which format is best suited to the respondents.

No matter how the pretest is conducted, the researcher should remember that its purpose is to alert researchers to potential problems that may be caused by the questionnaire. Thus, pretests are typically conducted to answer questions about the questionnaire such as the following:

- Can the questionnaire format be followed by the interviewers?
- Does the questionnaire flow naturally and conversationally?
- Can respondents answer the questions easily?
- Which alternative forms of questions work best?[25]

Pretesting also provides the means to test the sampling procedure. Pretests may determine if interviewers follow the sampling instructions properly and if the procedure is efficient. They also provide estimates of the response rate for mail surveys and the completion rate for telephone surveys.

DESIGNING QUESTIONNAIRES FOR GLOBAL RESEARCH

Now that business research is being conducted around the globe, researchers must take cultural factors into account when designing questionnaires. The most widespread problem involves the translation of a questionnaire into other languages. A questionnaire developed in one country may not easily cross a border because equivalent language concepts do not exist or because of differences in idiom and vernacular. For example, the concepts uncle and aunt are not the same in the United States as in India. In India, the terms *uncle* and *aunt* are different for the maternal and paternal sides of the family.[26] Although Spanish is spoken in both Mexico and Venezuela, one researcher found out that a translation of the English term *retail outlet* worked in Mexico, but not in Venezuela. Venezuelans interpreted the translation to be an electrical outlet, an outlet of a river into an ocean, or the passageway into a patio.

back translation
Taking a questionnaire that has previously been translated into another language and then having a second, independent translator translate it back into the original language.

International business researchers often have questionnaires back translated. **Back translation** is the process of taking a questionnaire that has previously been translated from one language to another and having it translated back into the original language by a second, independent translator. The back translator is often a person whose native tongue is the language that will be used on the questionnaire. Thus, inconsistencies between the English version and the translation can be identified and modified, if necessary. For example, a soft drink company translated its slogan, "Baby, it's cold inside," into Cantonese for research in Hong Kong. The slogan was retranslated as "Small Mosquito, on the inside, it is very cold." (In Hong Kong *small mosquito* is a colloquial expression for a small child.) Clearly, the intended meaning of the advertising message was lost in the translated questionnaire.[27] In another international marketing research project, "out of sight, out of mind" was back translated as "invisible things are insane."[28]

As indicated in Chapter 9, literacy influences the choice between self-administered questionnaires and interviews. This makes knowledge of literacy rates in foreign countries vital, especially for research in countries that are just developing modern economies.

SUMMARY

Good questionnaire design is a key to obtaining good survey results. The specific questions asked will be a function of the type of information needed to answer the manager's questions and of the communication medium for data collection. Relevance and accuracy are the basic criteria for judging questionnaire results. A questionnaire is *relevant* if no unnecessary information is collected and the information necessary for solving the business problem is obtained. *Accuracy* means that the information is reliable and valid.

Knowing how each question should be phrased requires familiarity with the different types of questions. Open-ended response questions present some problem or question and ask the respondent to answer in his or her own words. Fixed-alternative questions require less interviewer skill, take less time, and are easier to answer. In fixed-alternative questions the respondent is given specific limited alternative responses and asked to choose the one closest to his or her own viewpoint. Standardized responses are easier to code, tabulate, and interpret. Care must be taken to formulate the responses so they do not overlap. Respondents whose answers don't fit any of the fixed alternatives may be forced to select alternatives they really don't mean.

Open-ended questions are especially useful in exploratory research or at the beginning of a questionnaire. They make a questionnaire more expensive to analyze because of the uniqueness of the answers. Interviewer bias can also influence the responses to open-ended questions.

Some guidelines to questionnaire construction have emerged from research experience. The language should be simple to allow for variations in educational levels. Researchers should avoid leading or loaded questions, which suggest answers to the respondents, as well as questions that induce them to give socially desirable answers. Respondents have a bias against questions suggesting changes in the status quo. Their reluctance to answer personal questions can be reduced by explaining the need for the questions and by assuring respondents of the confidentiality of their replies. Researchers should be careful to avoid ambiguity in questions. Another common problem is the double-barreled question, which asks two questions at once. Researchers should avoid burdensome questions that may tax the respondent's memory.

Question sequence can be very important to the success of a survey. The opening questions should be designed to interest respondents and keep them involved. Personal questions should be postponed to the middle or end of the questionnaire. General questions should precede specific ones. In a series of attitude scales, the first response may be used as an anchor for comparison to the other responses. The order of alternatives on closed questions can affect the results. Filter questions are useful to avoid unnecessary questions that don't apply to a particular respondent. Such questions may be put into a flowchart for personal or telephone interviewing.

The layout of a mail or other self-administered questionnaire can affect the response rate. An attractive questionnaire encourages a response; a carefully phrased title can also encourage responses. Internet questionnaires present unique design issues. Decisions must be made about the use of color, graphics, animation, sound, and other special layout effects that the Internet makes possible. Pretesting helps reveal errors while they can still be easily corrected.

International business researchers must take cultural factors into account when designing questionnaires. The most widespread problem involves translation into another language. International questionnaires are often back translated.

Key Terms

open-ended response question
fixed-alternative question
leading question
loaded question
counterbiasing statement
split-ballot technique
double-barreled question
order bias
funnel technique
filter question
pivot question
push button
status bar
radio button
drop-down box
check box
open-ended box
pop-up box
variable piping software
error trapping
forced answering software
interactive help desk
preliminary tabulation
back translation

Questions for Review and Critical Thinking

1. Evaluate and comment on the following questions from several different questionnaires:

   (a) A university computer center survey on SPSS usage:

   How often do you use SPSS? Please check one.
   ____ Infrequently (once a semester)
   ____ Occasionally (once a month)
   ____ Frequently (once a week)
   ____ All the time (daily)

   (b) A survey of U.S. congressmen:

   Do you understand and like the current tax laws that allow people who file their federal income tax returns to deduct from their personal income the amount they pay in state and local taxes?
   ____ Yes
   ____ No

(c) A survey on a new, small electric car:

Assuming 90 percent of your driving is in town, would you buy this type of car?
____ Yes
____ No

If this type of electric car had the same initial cost as a current "Big 3" full-sized, fully equipped car but operated at one-half the cost over a 5-year period, would you buy one?
____ Yes
____ No

(d) A student survey:

Since the beginning of this semester approximately what percentage of the time did you get to campus using each of the forms of transportation available to you per week?
Walk ____ Bicycle ____
Public transportation ____
Motor vehicle ____

(e) A survey of employers:

Should the company continue its generous medical insurance program?
____ Yes
____ No

(f) A personnel manager's survey of employees:

In your opinion, are women discriminated against, treated equitably, or given preference in promotion practices?

Discriminated Against	Treated Equitably	Treated Preferentially
☐	☐	☐

(g) A survey of voters:

To make up for past discrimination, do you favor or oppose programs that make special efforts to help minorities get ahead?
☐ Favor
☐ Oppose

(h) A government survey of gasoline retailers:

Suppose the full-service selling price for regular gasoline is 92.8 cents per gallon on the first day of the month. Suppose on the 10th of the month the price is raised to 94.9 cents per gallon; and on the 25th of the month it is reduced to 91.9 cents per gallon. In order to provide the required data, you should list the accumulator reading on the full-service regular gasoline pump when the station opens on the first day, the 10th day, and the 25th day of the month, and when the station closes on the last day of the month.

(i) An antigun-control group's survey:

Do you believe that private citizens have the right to own firearms to defend themselves, their families, and their property from violent criminal attack?
____ Yes
____ No

(j) A survey of the general public:

In the next year, after accounting for inflation, do you think your real personal income will go up or down?

1. Up
2. Stay the same
3. Down
4. (Don't know)

(k) A survey of the general public:

Some people say that companies should be required by law to label all chemicals and substances that the government states are potentially harmful. The label would tell what the chemical or substance is, what dangers it might pose, and what safety procedures should be used in handling the substance. Other people say that such laws would be too strict. They say the law should require labels on only those chemicals and substances that the companies themselves decide are potentially harmful. Such a law, they say, would be less costly for the companies and would permit them to exclude those chemicals and substances they consider to be trade secrets. Which of these views is closest to your own?

1. Require labels on all chemicals and substances that the government states are potentially harmful.
2. (Don't know)
3. Require labels on only those chemicals and substances that companies decide are potentially harmful.

(l) A survey of voters:

Since agriculture is vital to our state's economy, how do you feel about the administration's farm policies?
Strongly favor
Somewhat favor
Somewhat oppose
Strongly oppose
Unsure

2. The following question was asked in an Internet survey:

We are going to ask you to classify the type of fan you consider yourself to be for different sports and sports programs.
Diehard Fan: Watch games, follow up on scores and sports news multiple times a day
Avid Fan: Watch games, follow up on scores and sports news once a day
Casual Fan: Watch games, follow-up on scores and sports news occasionally
Championship Fan: Watch games, follow up on scores and sports news only during championships or playoffs
Non-Fan: Never watch games or follow up on scores
Anti-Fan: Dislike, oppose, or object to a certain sport

Does this question do a good job of avoiding ambiguity?

3. How might the wording of a question asking about income influence the answers of respondents?
4. Design an open-ended response question to measure reactions to a Xerox magazine ad.
5. What is the difference between a leading question and a loaded question?
6. Design a complete questionnaire to evaluate job satisfaction.
7. Design a complete (but short) questionnaire to measure student evaluations of a college course.
8. Develop a checklist of things to consider in questionnaire construction.
9. The Apple Assistance Center offers a hotline to solve problems for users of Macintosh computers and other Apple products. Design a short (postcard-size) questionnaire to evaluate consumer satisfaction/service quality for the Apple Assistance Center.
10. A client tells a researcher that she wants a questionnaire to evaluate the importance of 30 product characteristics and to determine how her firm's brand and 10 competing brands rate on these characteristics. The researcher believes that this questionnaire will induce respondent fatigue because it is far too long. Should the researcher do exactly what the client says or risk losing the business by suggesting a different approach?
11. A lobbying organization designs a short questionnaire about its political position. It also includes a membership solicitation with the questionnaire. Is this approach ethical?

Exploring the Internet

1. Visit the Strategos Institute at http://www.strategos.com/survey/. Evaluate the questions on the questionnaire.
2. Visit Google at http://www.google.com and conduct a search using the key phrase "Questionnaire Design." How many Web sites contain this phrase?

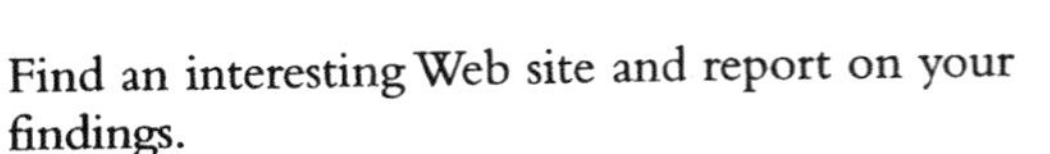

Find an interesting Web site and report on your findings.

3. A language translator (English to Spanish, French to English, etc.) can be found at http://babelfish.altavista.com/translate.dyn.

WebSurveyor Activities

Video Games

Run the WebSurveyor Desktop software, and click "From a template" under the heading "Create a new survey" from the Getting Started Wizard. (If the Getting Started Wizard does not appear, click Tools and then Options from the main menu, make sure "Display the Getting Started Wizard for new surveys" is checked, and then click OK. Next click File and then New from the main menu, and then click "From a template" under the heading "Create a new survey.") Use the Survey Builder Wizard and click on the "Marketing Competitive Intelligence" category. Then select the Product Recall Survey template. Identify a product category that interests you (perhaps video games) and identify three or four brands in the product category (perhaps Nintendo Gamecube, Sony PlayStation, and Microsoft Xbox). Create a questionnaire using the standard template. What questions need to be added or deleted to make this questionnaire fit your research objectives?

Starry Nights

The Starry Nights questionnaire was developed using the WebSurveyor's Survey Builder Wizard. The category "Marketing Customer Needs" was chosen and then "Customer Satisfaction—Consumer Service." Some questions were modified. Using the WebSurveyor Desktop software, select File and then Open from the main menu, and then select the file named "StarryNights.ws3." The Question List will appear. Click on "Preview" under Survey Editing to view the questionnaire as a Web page. Do other changes need to be made?

Human Resource Questionnaire

A manager used WebSurveyor's question library to create a questionnaire with 20 attitude scales. Using the WebSurveyor Desktop software, open the survey named "HumanResources.ws3." The Question List will appear. Click on "Preview" under Survey Editing to view the questionnaire as a Web page. Evaluate the questionnaire and, if necessary, create a revised questionnaire.

Designing Your Own Questionnaire

- Using the WebSurveyor Desktop software, design a short but complete questionnaire to measure consumer satisfaction with an airline.
- Using the WebSurveyor Desktop software, design a questionnaire for your local Big Brothers and Big Sisters organization to investigate awareness of and willingness to volunteer time to this organization.

Case Suggestions

Case 20: Canterbury Travels
Case 21: United States Postal Service
Case 22: Schönbrunn Palace in Vienna

6

Sampling and Sampling Distributions

Learning Objectives

The two main objectives for Chapter 7 are to give you an appreciation for the proper application of sampling techniques and an understanding of the sampling distributions of two statistics, thereby enabling you to:

1. Determine when to use sampling instead of a census.
2. Distinguish between random and nonrandom sampling.
3. Decide when and how to use various sampling techniques.
4. Be aware of the different types of error that can occur in a study.
5. Understand the impact of the central limit theorem on statistical analysis.
6. Use the sampling distributions of $\overline{X}$ and $\hat{p}$.

This chapter explores the process of sampling and the sampling distributions of some statistics. How do we obtain the data used in statistical analysis? Why do researchers often take a sample rather than conduct a census? What are the differences between random and nonrandom sampling? This chapter addresses these and other questions about sampling.

Also presented are the distributions of two statistics: the sample mean and the sample proportion. It has been determined that statistics such as these are approximately normally distributed under certain conditions. Knowledge of this is important in the study of statistics and is basic to much of statistical analysis.

7.1 Sampling

Sampling is widely used in business as a means of gathering useful information about a population. Data are gathered from samples and conclusions are drawn about the population as a part of the inferential statistics process. For example, suppose a researcher wants to ascertain the viewpoints of maquiladora workers along the U.S.-Mexico border. To do this, a random sample of workers could be taken from a wide selection of companies in several industries in many of the key border cities. A carefully constructed questionnaire that is culturally sensitive to Mexicans could be administered to the selected workers to determine work attitudes, expectations, and cultural differences between workers and companies. The researchers could compile and analyze the data gleaned from the responses. Summaries and observations could be made about worker outlook and culture in the maquiladora program. Management and decision makers could then attempt to use the results of the study to improve worker performance and motivation. Often, a sample provides a reasonable means for gathering such useful decision-making information that might be otherwise unattainable and unaffordable.

Reasons for Sampling

There are several good reasons for taking a sample instead of conducting a census.

1. The sample can save money.
2. The sample can save time.
3. For given resources, the sample can broaden the scope of the study.
4. Because the research process is sometimes destructive, the sample can save product.
5. If accessing the population is impossible, the sample is the only option.

A sample can be cheaper to obtain than a census for a given magnitude of questions. For example, if an 8-minute telephone interview is being undertaken, conducting the interviews with a sample of 100 customers rather than with a population of 100,000 customers obviously is less expensive. In addition to the cost savings, the significantly smaller number of interviews usually requires less total time. Thus, if there is an urgency about obtaining the results, sampling can provide them more quickly. With the volatility of some markets and the constant barrage of new competition and new ideas, sampling has a strong advantage over a census in terms of research turnaround time.

If the resources allocated to a research project are fixed, more detailed information can be gathered by taking a sample than by conducting a census. With resources concentrated on fewer individuals or items, the study can be broadened in scope to allow for more specialized questions. One organization budgeted \$100,000 for a study and opted to take a census instead of a sample by using a mail survey. The researchers mass-mailed thousands of copies of a computer card that looked like a major league all-star ballot. The card contained 20 questions to which the respondent could answer yes or no by punching out a perforated hole. The information retrieved amounted to the percentages of respondents who answered yes and no on the 20 questions. For the same amount of money, the company could have taken a random sample from the population, held interactive one-on-one sessions with highly trained interviewers, and gathered detailed information about the process being studied. By using the money on a sample, the researchers could have spent significantly more time with each respondent and thus increased the potential for gathering useful information.

Some research processes are destructive to the product or item being studied. For example, if light bulbs are being tested to determine how long they burn or if candy bars are being taste tested to determine whether the taste is acceptable, the product is destroyed. If a census were conducted for this type of research, there would be no product to sell. Hence, taking a sample is the only realistic option for testing such products.

Sometimes a population is virtually impossible to access for research. For example, some people refuse to answer sensitive questions, and some telephone numbers are unlisted. Some items of interest (like a 1957 Chevrolet) are so scattered that locating all of them would be extremely difficult. When the population is inaccessible for these or other reasons, sampling is the only option.

Reasons for Taking a Census

Sometimes taking a census makes more sense than using a sample. One reason to take a census is to eliminate the possibility that by chance a randomly selected sample might not be representative of the population. Even when all the proper sampling techniques are implemented, a sample that is nonrepresentative of the population can be selected by chance. For example, if the population of interest is all truck owners in the state of Colorado, a random sample of owners could yield mostly ranchers, when in fact many of the truck owners in Colorado are urban dwellers.

A second reason to take a census is that the client (person authorizing and/or underwriting the study) does not have an appreciation for random sampling and feels more comfortable with conducting a census. Both of these reasons for taking a census are based on the assumption that enough time and money are available to conduct such a census.

Frame

Every research study has a target population that consists of the individuals, institutions, or entities that are the object of investigation. The sample is taken from a population *list, map, directory, or other source that is being used to represent the population.* This list, map, or directory is called the **frame,** which can be school lists, trade association lists, or even lists sold by list brokers. Ideally, there is a one-to-one correspondence between the frame units and the population units. In reality, the frame and the target population are often different. For example, suppose the target population is all families living in Detroit. A feasible frame would be the residential pages of the Detroit telephone books. How would the frame differ from the target population? Some families have no telephone. Other families have unlisted numbers. Still other families might have moved and/or changed numbers since the directory was printed. Some families even have multiple listings under different names.

Frame
A list, map, directory, or some other source that is being used to represent the population in the process of sampling.

Frames that have *overregistration* contain all the target population units plus some additional units. Frames that have *underregistration* contain fewer units than does the target population. Sampling is done from the frame, not the target population. In theory, the target population and the frame are the same. In reality, a researcher's goal is to minimize the differences between the frame and the target population.

Random versus Nonrandom Sampling

The two main types of sampling are random and nonrandom. In **random sampling** *every unit of the population has the same probability of being selected into the sample.* Random sampling implies that chance enters into the process of selection. For example, most

Random sampling
Sampling in which every unit of the population has the same probability of being selected for the sample.

Americans would like to believe that winners of nationwide magazine sweepstakes are selected by some random draw of numbers. Late in the 1960s when the military draft lottery was being used, most people eligible for the draft trusted that a given birthdate was selected by chance as the first date to use to draft people. In both of these situations, members of the population believed that selections were made by chance.

Nonrandom sampling Sampling in which not every unit of the population has the same probability of being selected into the sample.

In **nonrandom sampling** *not every unit of the population has the same probability of being selected into the sample.* Members of nonrandom samples are not selected by chance. For example, they might be selected because they are at the right place at the right time or because they know the people conducting the research.

Sometimes random sampling is called *probability sampling,* and nonrandom sampling is called *nonprobability sampling.* Because every unit of the population is not equally likely to be selected, assigning a probability of occurrence in nonrandom sampling is impossible. The statistical methods presented and discussed in this text are based on the assumption that the data come from random samples. *Nonrandom sampling methods are not appropriate techniques for gathering data to be analyzed by most of the statistical methods presented in this text.* However, several nonrandom sampling techniques are described in this section, primarily to alert you to their characteristics and limitations.

Random Sampling Techniques

The four basic random sampling techniques are simple random sampling, stratified random sampling, systematic random sampling, and cluster (or area) random sampling. Each technique has advantages and disadvantages. Some techniques are simpler to use, some are less costly, and others have the potential for reducing sampling error.

Simple random sampling The most elementary of the random sampling techniques; involves numbering each item in the population and using a list or roster of random numbers to select items for the sample.

SIMPLE RANDOM SAMPLING The most elementary random sampling technique is **simple random sampling.** Simple random sampling can be viewed as the basis for the other three random sampling techniques. With simple random sampling, each unit of the frame is numbered from 1 to N (where N is the size of the population). Next, a table of random numbers or a random number generator is used to select n items into the sample. A *random number generator* is usually a computer program that allows computer to calculator output to yield random numbers. Table 7.1 contains a brief table of random numbers. Table A.1 in Appendix A contains a full table of random numbers. These numbers are random in all directions. The spaces in the table are there only for ease of reading the values. For each number, any of the 10 digits (0–9) is equally likely, so getting the same digit twice or more in a row is possible.

As an example, from the population frame of companies listed in Table 7.2, we will use simple random sampling to select a sample of six companies. First, we number every member of the population. We select as many digits for each unit sampled as there are in the largest number in the population. For example, if a population has 2000 members, we select four-digit numbers. Because the population in Table 7.2 contains 30 members, only two digits need be selected for each number. The population is numbered from 01 to 30, as shown in Table 7.3.

TABLE 7.1
A Brief Table of Random Numbers

91567	42595	27958	30134	04024	86385	29880	99730
46503	18584	18845	49618	02304	51038	20655	58727
34914	63976	88720	82765	34476	17032	87589	40836
57491	16703	23167	49323	45021	33132	12544	41035
30405	83946	23792	14422	15059	45799	22716	19792
09983	74353	68668	30429	70735	25499	16631	35006
85900	07119	97336	71048	08178	77233	13916	47564

The object is to sample six companies, so six different two-digit numbers must be selected from the table of random numbers. Because this population contains only 30 companies, all numbers greater than 30 (31–99) must be ignored. If, for example, the number 67 is selected, the process is continued until a value between 1 and 30 is obtained. If the same number occurs more than once, we proceed to another number. For ease of understanding, we start with the first pair of digits in Table 7.1 and proceed across the first row until $n = 6$ different values between 01 and 30 are selected. If additional numbers are needed, we proceed across the second row, and so on. Often a researcher will start at some randomly selected location in the table and proceed in a predetermined direction to select numbers.

In the first row of digits in Table 7.1, the first number is 91. This number is out of range so it is cast out. The next two digits are 56. Next is 74, followed by 25, which is the first usable number. From Table 7.3, we see that 25 is the number associated with Occidental Petroleum, so Occidental Petroleum is the first company selected into the sample. The next number is 95, unusable, followed by 27, which is usable. Twenty-seven is the number for Philadelphia Electric, so this company is selected. Continuing the process, we pass over the numbers 95 and 83. The next usable number is 01, which is the value for Alaska Airlines. Thirty-four is next, followed by 04 and 02, both of which are usable. These numbers are associated with Atlantic Richfield and Alcoa, respectively. Continuing along the first row, the next usable number is 29, which is associated with Sears. As this is the sixth selection, the sample is complete. The following companies constitute the final sample.

Alaska Airlines
Alcoa
Atlantic Richfield
Occidental Petroleum
Philadelphia Electric
Sears

TABLE 7.2
A Population Frame of 30 Companies

Alaska Airlines	DuPont	LTV
Alcoa	Exxon	Litton
Amoco	Farah	Mead
Atlantic Richfield	GTE	Mobil
Bank of America	General Electric	Occidental Petroleum
Bell of Pennsylvania	General Mills	JCPenney
Chevron	General Dynamics	Philadelphia Electric
Chrysler	Grumman	Ryder
Citicorp	IBM	Sears
Disney	Kmart	Time

TABLE 7.3
Numbered Population of 30 Companies

01	Alaska Airlines	11	DuPont	21	LTV
02	Alcoa	12	Exxon	22	Litton
03	Amoco	13	Farah	23	Mead
04	Atlantic Richfield	14	GTE	24	Mobil
05	Bank of America	15	General Electric	25	Occidental Petroleum
06	Bell of Pennsylvania	16	General Mills	26	JCPenney
07	Chevron	17	General Dynamics	27	Philadelphia Electric
08	Chrysler	18	Grumman	28	Ryder
09	Citicorp	19	IBM	29	Sears
10	Disney	20	Kmart	30	Time

Simple random sampling is easier to perform on small than on large populations. The process of numbering all the members of the population and selecting items is cumbersome for large populations.

Stratified random sampling
A type of random sampling in which the population is divided into various nonoverlapping strata and then items are randomly selected into the sample from each stratum.

STRATIFIED RANDOM SAMPLING A second type of random sampling is **stratified random sampling,** in which the population is divided into nonoverlapping subpopulations called *strata.* The researcher then extracts a simple random sample from each of the subpopulations. The main reason for using stratified random sampling is that it has the potential for reducing sampling error. Sampling error occurs when, by chance, the sample does not represent the population. With stratified random sampling, the potential to match the sample closely to the population is greater than it is with simple random sampling because portions of the total sample are taken from different population subgroups. However, stratified random sampling is generally more costly than simple random sampling because each unit of the population must be assigned to a stratum before the random selection process begins.

Strata selection is usually based on available information. Such information may have been gleaned from previous censuses or surveys. Stratification benefits increase as the strata differ more. Internally, a stratum should be relatively homogeneous; externally, strata should contrast with each other. Stratification is often done by using demographic variables, such as gender, socioeconomic class, geographic region, religion, and ethnicity. For example, if a U.S. presidential election poll is to be conducted by a market research firm, what important variables should be stratified? The gender of the respondent might make a difference because a gender gap in voter preference has been noted in past elections. That is, men and women have tended to vote differently in national elections. Geographic region also has been an important variable in national elections as voters are influenced by local cultural values that differ from region to region. Voters in the South voted almost exclusively for Democrats in the past, but recently they have tended to vote for Republican candidates in national elections. Voters in the Rocky Mountain states have supported Republican presidential candidates; in the industrial Northeast, voters have been more inclined toward Democratic candidates.

In FM radio markets, age of listener is an important determinant of the type of programing used by a station. Figure 7.1 contains a stratification by age with three strata, based on the assumption that age makes a difference in preference of programing. This stratification implies that listeners 20 to 30 years of age tend to prefer the same type of programing, which is different from that preferred by listeners 30 to 40 and 40 to 50 years of

Figure 7.1

Stratified random sampling of FM radio listeners

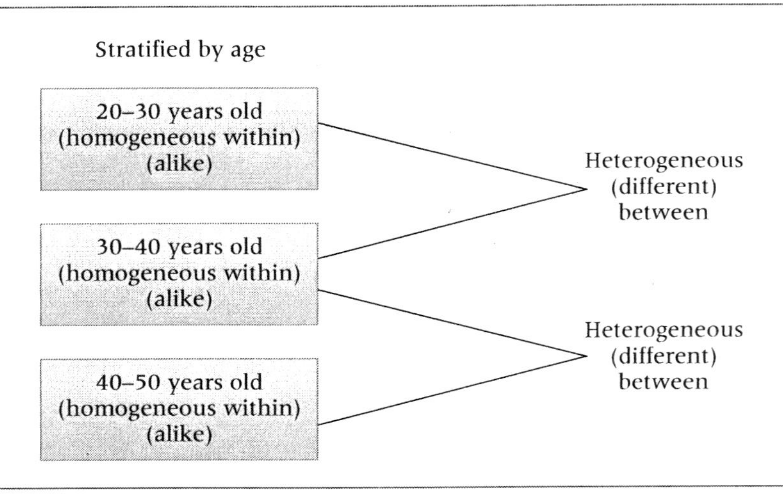

age. Within each age subgroup (stratum), *homogeneity* or alikeness is present; between each pair of subgroups a difference, or *heterogeneity,* is present.

Stratified random sampling can be either proportionate or disproportionate. **Proportionate stratified random sampling** occurs *when the percentage of the sample taken from each stratum is proportionate to the percentage that each stratum is within the whole population.* For example, suppose voters are being surveyed in Boston and the sample is being stratified by religion as Catholic, Protestant, Jewish, and others. If Boston's population is 90% Catholic and if a sample of 1000 voters is being taken, the sample would require inclusion of 900 Catholics to achieve proportionate stratification. Any other number of Catholics would be disproportionate stratification. The sample proportion of other religions would also have to follow population percentages. Or consider the city of El Paso, Texas, where the population is approximately 69% Hispanic. If a researcher is conducting a citywide poll in El Paso and if stratification is by ethnicity, a proportionate stratified random sample should contain 69% Hispanics. Hence, an ethnically proportionate stratified sample of 160 residents from El Paso's 600,000 residents should contain approximately 110 Hispanics. Whenever *the proportions of the strata in the sample are different than the proportions of the strata in the population,* **disproportionate stratified random sampling** occurs.

Proportionate stratified random sampling
A type of stratified random sampling in which the proportions of the items selected for the sample from the strata reflect the proportions of the strata in the population.

Disproportionate stratified random sampling
A type of stratified random sampling in which the proportions of items selected from the strata for the final sample do not reflect the proportions of the strata in the population.

SYSTEMATIC SAMPLING Systematic sampling is a third random sampling technique. Unlike stratified random sampling, systematic sampling is not done in an attempt to reduce sampling error. Rather, **systematic sampling** is used because of its convenience and relative ease of administration. With systematic sampling, *every* k*th item is selected to produce a sample of size* n *from a population of size* N. The value of k can be determined by the following formula. If k is not an integer value, the whole-number value should be used.

Systematic sampling
A random sampling technique in which every kth item or person is selected from the population.

DETERMINING THE VALUE OF k

$$k = \frac{N}{n}$$

where:
n = sample size
N = population size
k = size of interval for selection

As an example of systematic sampling, a management information systems researcher wanted to sample the manufacturers in Texas. He had enough financial support to sample 1000 companies (n). The *Directory of Texas Manufacturers* listed approximately 17,000 total manufacturers in Texas (N) in alphabetical order. The value of k was 17 (17,000/1000) and the researcher selected every 17th company in the directory for his sample.

Did the researcher begin with the first company listed or the 17th or one somewhere between? In selecting every kth value, a simple random number table should be used to select a value between 1 and k inclusive as a starting point. The second element for the sample is the starting point plus k. In the example, $k = 17$, so the researcher would have gone to a table of random numbers to determine a starting point between 1 and 17. Suppose he selected the number 5. He would have started with the 5th company, then selected the 22nd (5 + 17), and then the 39th, and so on.

Besides convenience, systematic sampling has other advantages. Because systematic sampling is evenly distributed across the frame, a knowledgeable person can easily determine whether a sampling plan has been followed in a study. However, a problem with systematic sampling can occur if there is periodicity in the data, and the sampling interval is in syncopation with it. For example, if a list of 150 college students is actually a merged

Figure 7.2

Some test market cities

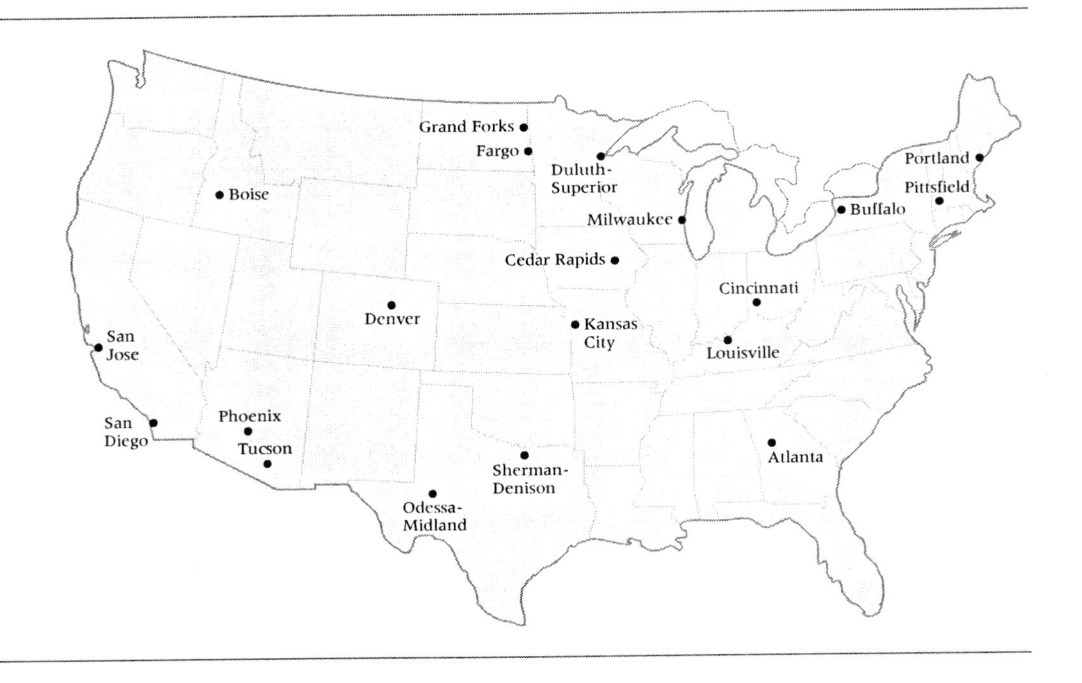

list of five classes with 30 students in each class and if each of the lists of the five classes has been ordered with the names of top students first and bottom students last, systematic sampling of every 30th student could cause selection of all top students, all bottom students, or all mediocre students. That is, there is a cyclical or periodic organization of the original list. Systematic sampling methodology is based on the assumption that the source of population elements is random.

Cluster (or area) sampling A type of random sampling in which the population is divided into nonoverlapping areas or clusters and elements are randomly sampled from the areas or clusters.

CLUSTER (OR AREA) SAMPLING Cluster (or area) sampling is a fourth type of random sampling. **Cluster (or area) sampling** involves dividing the population into nonoverlapping areas or clusters. However, in contrast to stratified random sampling where strata are homogeneous, cluster sampling identifies clusters that tend to be internally heterogeneous. In theory, each cluster contains a wide variety of elements, and the cluster is a miniature, or microcosm, of the population. Examples of clusters are towns, companies, homes, colleges, areas of a city, and geographic regions. Often clusters are naturally occurring groups of the population and are already identified, such as states or Standard Metropolitan Statistical Areas. Although area sampling usually refers to clusters that are areas of the population, such as geographic regions and cities, the terms *cluster sampling* and *area sampling* are used interchangeably in this text.

After choosing the clusters, the researcher randomly selects individual elements into the sample from the clusters. One example of business research that makes use of clustering is test marketing of new products. Often in test marketing, the United States is divided into clusters of test market cities, and individual consumers within the test market cities are surveyed.* Figure 7.2 shows some U.S. test market cities that are used as clusters to test products.

Two-stage sampling Cluster sampling done in two stages: A first round of samples is taken and then a second round is taken from within the first samples.

Sometimes the clusters are too large, and a second set of clusters is taken from each original cluster. This technique is called **two-stage sampling.** For example, a researcher could divide the United States into clusters of cities. She could then divide the cities into clusters of blocks and randomly select individual houses from the block clusters. The first stage is selecting the test cities and the second stage is selecting the blocks.

*Bristol Voss, "The Nation's Most Popular Test Markets," *Sales and Marketing Management*, March 1989, 141.

Cluster or area sampling has several advantages. Two of the foremost advantages are convenience and cost. Clusters are usually convenient to obtain, and the cost of sampling from the entire population is reduced because the scope of the study is reduced to the clusters. The cost per element is usually lower in cluster or area sampling than in stratified sampling because of lower element listing or locating costs. The time and cost of contacting elements of the population can be reduced, especially if travel is involved, because clustering reduces the distance to the sampled elements. In addition, administration of the sample survey can be simplified. Sometimes cluster or area sampling is the only feasible approach because the sampling frames of the individual elements of the population are unavailable and therefore other random sampling techniques cannot be used.

Cluster or area sampling also has several disadvantages. If the elements of a cluster are similar, cluster sampling may be statistically less efficient than simple random sampling. In an extreme case—when the elements of a cluster are the same—sampling from the cluster may be no better than sampling a single unit from the cluster. Moreover, the costs and problems of statistical analysis are greater with cluster or area sampling than with simple random sampling.

Nonrandom Sampling

Sampling techniques used to select elements from the population by any mechanism that does not involve a random selection process are called **nonrandom sampling techniques.** Because chance is not used to select items from the samples, these techniques are nonprobability techniques and are *not desirable for use in gathering data to be analyzed by the methods of inferential statistics presented in this text.* Sampling error cannot be determined objectively for these sampling techniques. Four nonrandom sampling techniques are presented here: convenience sampling, judgmental sampling, quota sampling, and snowball sampling.

Nonrandom sampling techniques
Sampling techniques used to select elements from the population by any mechanism that does not involve a random selection process.

CONVENIENCE SAMPLING In **convenience sampling,** *elements for the sample are selected for the convenience of the researcher.* The researcher typically chooses items that are readily available, nearby, and/or willing to participate. The sample tends to be less variable than the population because in many environments the extreme elements of the population are not readily available. The researcher will select more elements from the middle of the population. For example, a convenience sample of homes for door-to-door interviews might include houses where people are at home, houses with no dogs, houses near the street, first-floor apartments, and houses with friendly people. In contrast, a random sample would require the researcher to gather data only from houses and apartments that have been selected randomly, no matter how inconvenient or unfriendly the location. If a research firm is located in a mall, a convenience sample might be selected by interviewing only shoppers who pass the shop and look friendly.

Convenience sampling
A nonrandom sampling technique in which items for the sample are selected for the convenience of the researcher.

JUDGMENT SAMPLING **Judgment sampling** occurs when *elements selected for the sample are chosen by the judgment of the researcher.* Researchers often believe they can obtain a representative sample by using sound judgment, which will result in saving time and money. Sometimes ethical, professional researchers might believe they can select a more representative sample than the random process will provide. They might be right! However, some studies have shown that random sampling methods outperform judgment sampling in estimating the population mean even when the researcher who is administering the judgment sampling is trying to put together a very representative sample. When sampling is done by judgment, calculating the probability that an element is going to be selected into the sample is not possible. The sampling error cannot be determined objectively because probabilities are based on *nonrandom* selection.

Judgment sampling
A nonrandom sampling technique in which items selected for the sample are chosen by the judgment of the researcher.

Other problems are associated with judgment sampling. The researcher tends to make errors of judgment in one direction. These systematic errors lead to what are called *biases.* The researcher also is unlikely to include extreme elements. With judgment sampling, there is no objective method for determining whether one person's judgment is better than another's.

Quota sampling
A nonrandom sampling technique in which the population is stratified on some characteristic and then elements selected for the sample are chosen by nonrandom processes.

QUOTA SAMPLING A third nonrandom sampling technique is **quota sampling,** which appears to be similar to stratified random sampling. Certain population subclasses, such as age group, gender, or geographic region, are used as strata. However, instead of randomly sampling from each stratum, the researcher *uses a nonrandom sampling method to gather data from one stratum until the desired quota of samples is filled.* Quotas are described by quota controls, which set the sizes of the samples to be obtained from the subgroups. Generally, a quota is based on the proportions of the subclasses in the population. In this case, the quota concept is similar to that of proportional stratified sampling.

Quotas often are filled by using available, recent, or applicable elements. For example, instead of randomly interviewing people to obtain a quota of Italian Americans, the researcher would go to the Italian area of the city and interview there until enough responses are obtained to fill the quota. In quota sampling, an interviewer would begin by asking a few filter questions; if the respondent represents a subclass whose quota has been filled, the interviewer would terminate the interview.

Quota sampling can be useful if no frame is available for the population. For example, suppose a researcher wants to stratify the population into owners of different types of cars but fails to find any lists of Toyota van owners. Through quota sampling, the researcher would proceed by interviewing all car owners and casting out non-Toyota van owners until the quota of Toyota van owners is filled.

Quota sampling is less expensive than most random sampling techniques because it essentially is a technique of convenience. However, cost may have no meaning because the quality of nonrandom and random sampling techniques cannot be compared. Another advantage of quota sampling is the speed of data gathering. The researcher does not have to call back or send out a second questionnaire if there is no response; he just moves on to the next element. Also, preparatory work for quota sampling is minimal.

The main problem with quota sampling is that, when all is said and done, it still is only a *nonrandom* sampling technique. Some researchers have said that if the quota is filled by *randomly* selecting elements and discarding those that are not from a stratum, quota sampling is essentially a version of stratified random sampling. However, most quota sampling is carried out by the researcher going where the quota can be filled quickly. The object is to gain the benefits of stratification without the high field costs of stratification. Ultimately, it remains a nonprobability sampling method.

Snowball sampling
A nonrandom sampling technique in which survey subjects who fit a desired profile are selected based on referral from other survey respondents who also fit the desired profile.

SNOWBALL SAMPLING Another nonrandom sampling technique is **snowball sampling,** in which *survey subjects are selected based on referral from other survey respondents.* The researcher identifies a person who fits the profile of subjects wanted for the study. The researcher then asks this person for the names and locations of others who would also fit the profile of subjects wanted for the study. Through these referrals, survey subjects can be identified cheaply and efficiently, which is particularly useful when survey subjects are difficult to locate. This is the main advantage of snowball sampling; its main disadvantage is that it is nonrandom.

Sampling Error

Sampling error
Error that occurs when the sample is not representative of the population.

Sampling error occurs *when the sample is not representative of the population.* When random sampling techniques are used to select elements for the sample, sampling error occurs by chance. Many times the statistic computed on the sample is not an accurate estimate of the population parameter because the sample was not representative of the population. This result is caused by sampling error. With random samples, sampling error can be computed and analyzed.

Nonsampling Errors

All errors other than sampling errors are **nonsampling errors.** The many possible nonsampling errors include missing data, recording errors, input processing errors, and analysis errors. Other nonsampling errors have to do with the measurement instrument, such as errors of unclear definitions, defective questionnaires, and poorly conceived concepts. Improper definition of the frame is a nonsampling error. In many cases, finding a frame that perfectly fits the population is impossible. Insofar as it does not fit, a nonsampling error has been committed.

Nonsampling errors All errors other than sampling errors.

Response errors are also nonsampling errors. They occur when people do not know, will not say, or overstate. There is virtually no statistical way to measure or control for nonsampling errors. The statistical techniques presented in this text are based on the assumption that none of these nonsampling errors has been committed. The researcher must eliminate these errors through carefully planning and executing the research study.

Analysis Using Excel

It is possible to generate random numbers from six different types of distributions using Excel, including the binomial, the Poisson, the uniform, and the normal distributions. The process begins by selecting the **Random Number Generation** feature from the **Data Analysis** dialog box under **Tools.** The **Random Number Generation** dialog box is shown in Figure 7.3. Place the number of variables for which random numbers are to be

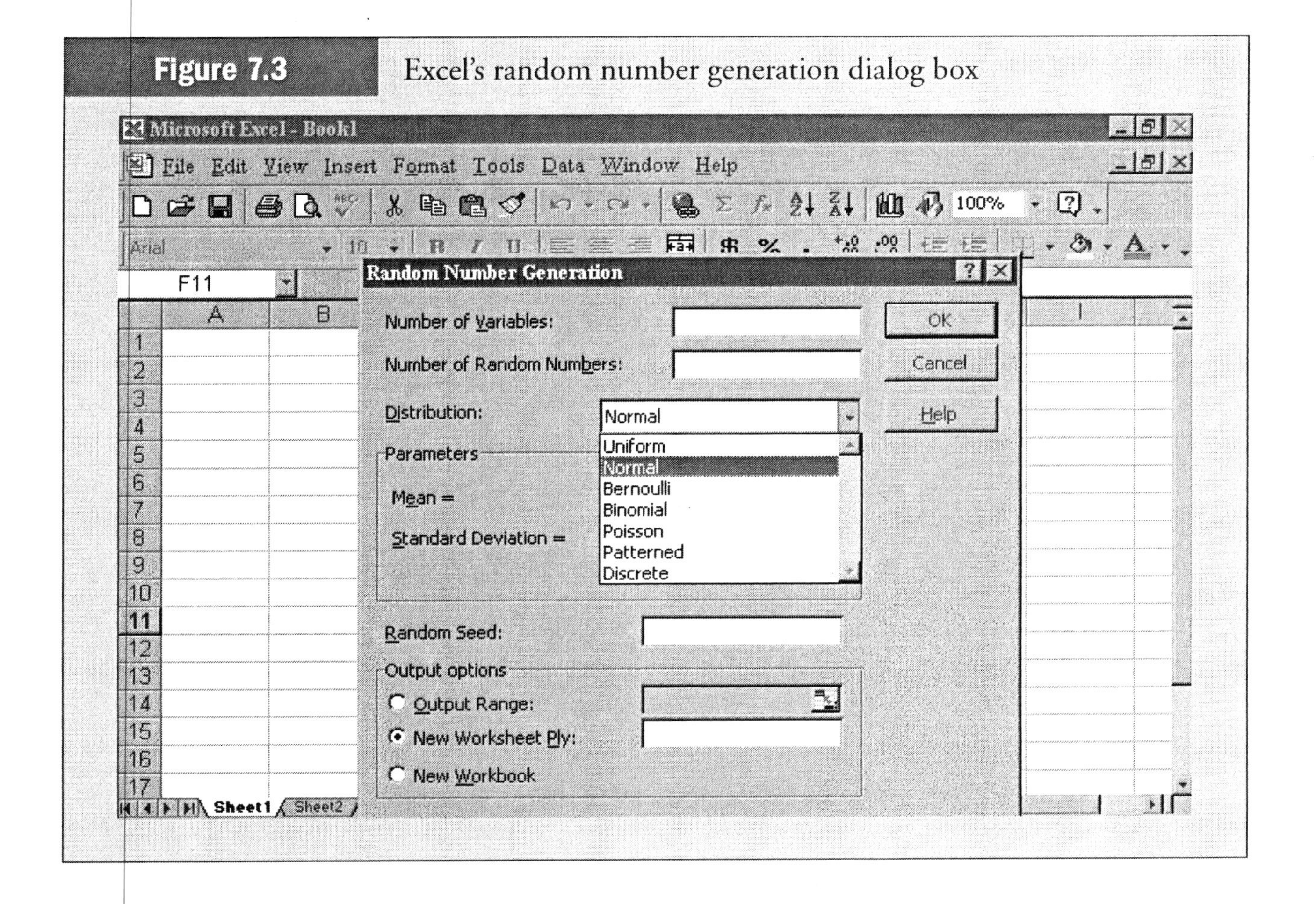

Figure 7.3 Excel's random number generation dialog box

generated in the first line of the dialog box. In the second line, insert the number of random numbers to be generated for each variable. The third line of the dialog box contains a pull-down menu with a list of the six types of distributions from which a distribution can be selected for generating the random numbers (this list also includes a non-random selection called patterned). You will be given different parameters to complete dependent upon which of the different distributions you select (e.g. for normal distribution, mean and standard deviation). You have the option of entering a seed number in the line denoted as ***Random* Seed** or leaving it blank (default option). Computerized random numbers are generated with a mathematical function. The starting value for the mathematical function is specified by the Random Seed. If the same seed number is used again, Excel will produce the same random numbers.

7.1
Problems

7.1 Develop a frame for the population of each of the following research projects.
a. Measuring the job satisfaction of all union employees in a company
b. Conducting a telephone survey in Utica, New York, to determine whether there is any interest in having a new hunting and fishing specialty store in the mall
c. Interviewing passengers of a major airline about its food service
d. Studying the quality control programs of boat manufacturers
e. Attempting to measure the corporate culture of cable television companies

7.2 Make a list of 20 people you know. Include men and women, various ages, various educational levels, and so on. Number the list and then use the random number list in Table 7.1 to select six people randomly from your list. How representative of the population is the sample? Find the proportion of men in your population and in your sample. How do the proportions compare? Find the proportion of 20-year-olds in your sample and the proportion in the population. How do they compare?

7.3 Use the random numbers in Table A.1 of Appendix A to select 10 of the companies from the 30 companies listed in Table 7.2. Compare the types of companies in your sample with the types in the population. How representative of the population is your sample?

7.4 For each of the following research projects, list three variables for stratification of the sample.
a. A nationwide study of motels and hotels is being conducted. An attempt will be made to determine the extent of the availability of online links for customers. A sample of motels and hotels will be taken.
b. A consumer panel is to be formed by sampling people in Michigan. Members of the panel will be interviewed periodically in an effort to understand current consumer attitudes and behaviors.
c. A large soft-drink company wants to study the characteristics of the U.S. bottlers of its products, but the company does not want to conduct a census.
d. The business research bureau of a large university is conducting a project in which the bureau will sample paper-manufacturing companies.

7.5 In each of the following cases, the variable represents one way that a sample can be stratified in a study. For each variable, list some strata into which the variable can be divided.
a. Age of respondent (person)
b. Size of company (sales volume)
c. Size of retail outlet (square feet)
d. Geographic location
e. Occupation of respondent (person)
f. Type of business (company)

7.6 A city's telephone book lists 100,000 people. If the telephone book is the frame for a study, how large would the sample size be if systematic sampling were done on every 200th person?

7.7 If every 11th item is systematically sampled to produce a sample size of 75 items, approximately how large is the population?

7.8 If a company employs 3500 people and if a random sample of 175 of these employees has been taken by systematic sampling, what is the value of k? The researcher would start the sample selection between what two values? Where could the researcher obtain a frame for this study?

7.9 For each of the following research projects, list at least one area or cluster that could be used in obtaining the sample.

a. A study of road conditions in the state of Missouri

b. A study of U.S. offshore oil wells

c. A study of the environmental effects of petrochemical plants west of the Mississippi River

7.10 Give an example of how judgment sampling could be used in a study to determine how district attorneys feel about attorneys advertising on television.

7.11 Give an example of how convenience sampling could be used in a study of *Fortune 500* executives to measure corporate attitude toward paternity leave for employees.

7.12 Give an example of how quota sampling could be used to conduct sampling by a company test marketing a new personal computer.

7.2 Sampling Distribution of $\overline{X}$

In the inferential statistics process, a random sample is selected from the population, a statistic is computed on the sample, and conclusions are reached about the population parameter from the statistic. In attempting to analyze the sample statistic, it is essential to know the distribution of the statistic. So far we have studied several distributions, including the binomial distribution, the Poisson distribution, the hypergeometric distribution, the uniform distribution, the normal distribution, and the exponential distribution.

In this section we explore the sample mean, $\overline{X}$, as the statistic. The sample mean is one of the more common statistics used in the inferential process. To compute and assign the probability of occurrence of a particular value of a sample mean, the researcher must know the distribution of the sample means. One way to examine the distribution possibilities is to take a population with a particular distribution, randomly select samples of a given size, compute the sample means, and attempt to determine how the means are distributed. Suppose a small finite population consists of only $N = 8$ numbers:

54, 55, 59, 63, 64, 68, 69, and 70.

Using an Excel-produced histogram, we can see the shape of the distribution of this population of data shown in Figure 7.4

Suppose we take all possible samples of size $n = 2$ from this population with replacement. The result is the following pairs of data.

(54,54)	(55,54)	(59,54)	(63,54)
(54,55)	(55,55)	(59,55)	(63,55)
(54,59)	(55,59)	(59,59)	(63,59)
(54,63)	(55,63)	(59,63)	(63,63)
(54,64)	(55,64)	(59,64)	(63,64)
(54,68)	(55,68)	(59,68)	(63,68)

continued

Figure 7.4

Histogram of eight numbers

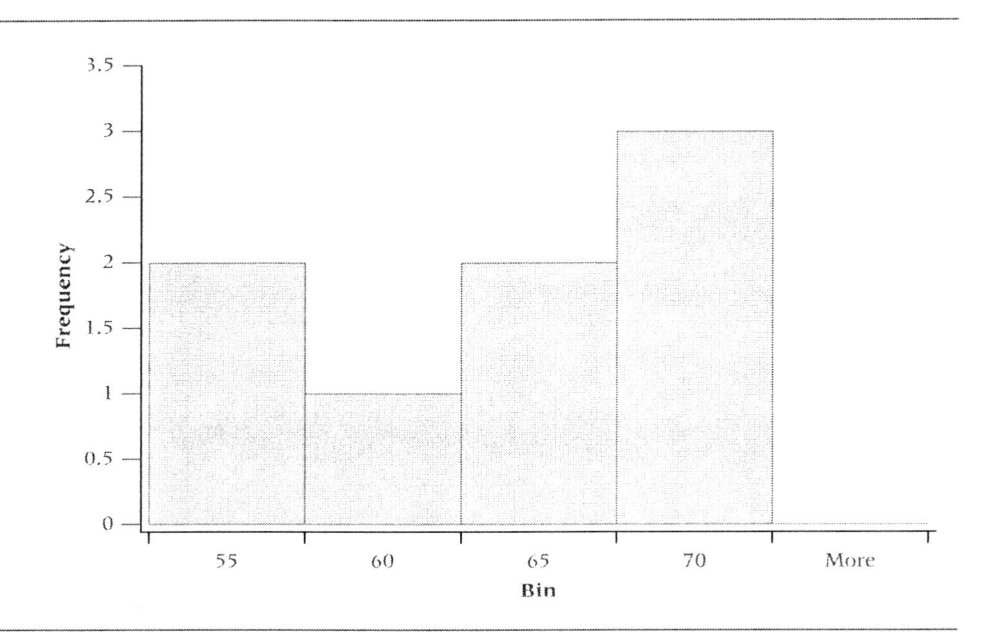

(54,69)	(55,69)	(59,69)	(63,69)
(54,70)	(55,70)	(59,70)	(63,70)
(64,54)	(68,54)	(69,54)	(70,54)
(64,55)	(68,55)	(69,55)	(70,55)
(64,59)	(68,59)	(69,59)	(70,59)
(64,63)	(68,63)	(69,63)	(70,63)
(64,64)	(68,64)	(69,64)	(70,64)
(64,68)	(68,68)	(69,68)	(70,68)
(64,69)	(68,69)	(69,69)	(70,69)
(64,70)	(68,70)	(69,70)	(70,70)

The means of each of these samples follow.

54	54.5	56.5	58.5	59	61	61.5	62
54.5	55	57	59	59.5	61.5	62	62.5
56.5	57	59	61	61.5	63.5	64	64.5
58.5	59	61	63	63.5	65.5	66	66.5
59	59.5	61.5	63.5	64	66	66.5	67
60	61.5	63.5	65.5	66	68	68.5	69
61.5	62	64	66	66.5	68.5	69	69.5
62	62.5	64.5	66.5	67	69	69.5	70

Again using an Excel histogram, we can see the shape of the distribution of these sample means in Figure 7.5. Notice that the shape of the histogram for sample means is quite unlike the shape of the histogram for the population. The sample means appear to "pile up" toward the middle of the distribution and "tail off" toward the extremes.

Figure 7.6 is an Excel histogram of the data from a Poisson distribution of values with a population mean of 1.25. Note that the histogram is skewed to the right. Suppose 90 samples of size $n = 30$ are taken randomly from a Poisson distribution with $\lambda = 1.25$ and the means are computed on each sample. The resulting distribution of sample means is

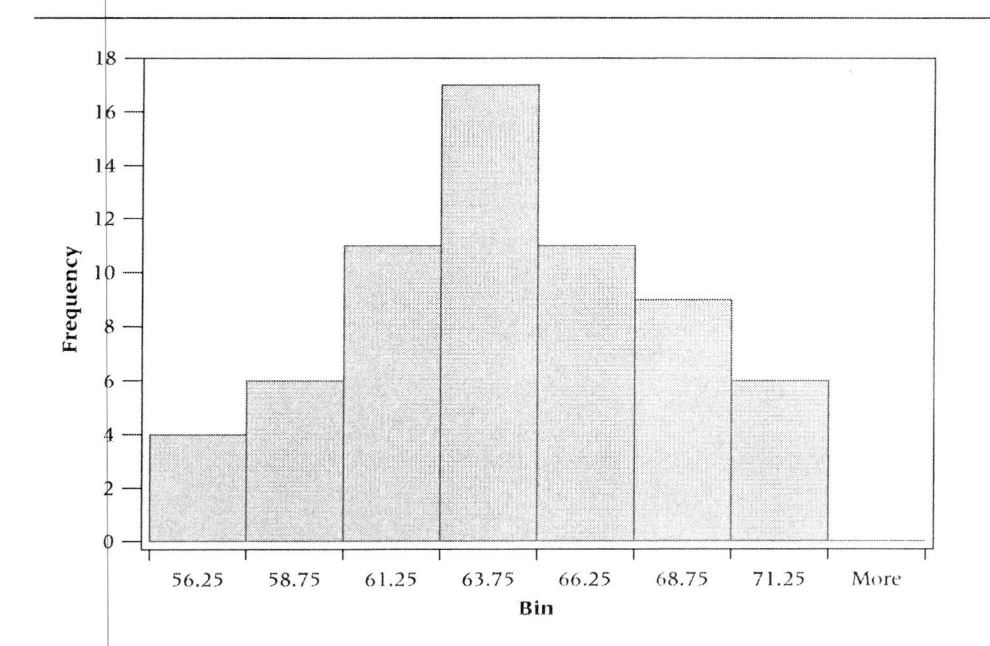

Figure 7.5

Histogram of sample means

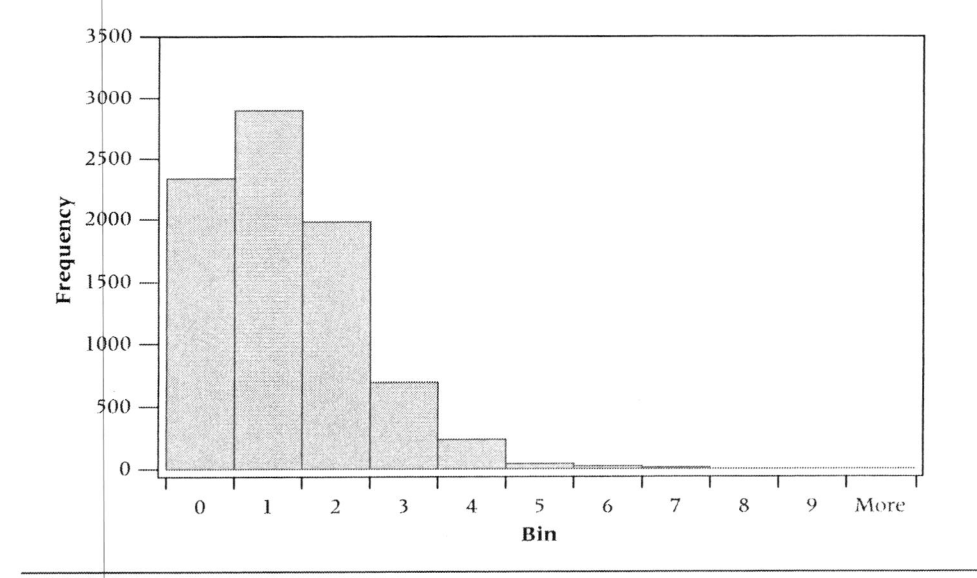

Figure 7.6

An Excel-produced histogram of a Poisson distributed population, $\lambda = 1.25$

displayed in Figure 7.7. Notice that although the samples were drawn from an exponential distribution, which is skewed to the right, the sample means form a distribution that approaches a symmetrical, nearly normal-curve-type distribution.

Suppose a population is uniformly distributed. If samples are selected randomly from a population with a uniform distribution, how are the sample means distributed? Figures 7.8a through e display the Excel histogram distributions of sample means from five different sample sizes. Each of these histograms represents the distribution of sample means from 90 samples generated randomly from a uniform distribution in which a was 10 and b was

Figure 7.7

An Excel histogram of 90 sample means from samples of size $n = 30$ from a Poisson distributed population

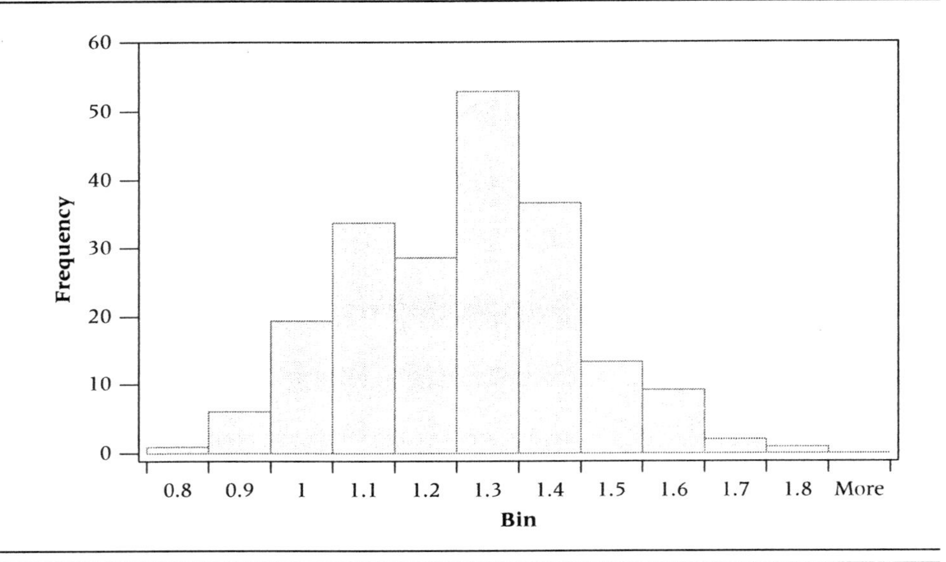

Figure 7.8a

Excel histogram outputs for sample means from 90 samples ranging in size from $n = 2$ to $n = 30$ from a uniformly distributed population with $a = 10$ and $b = 30$

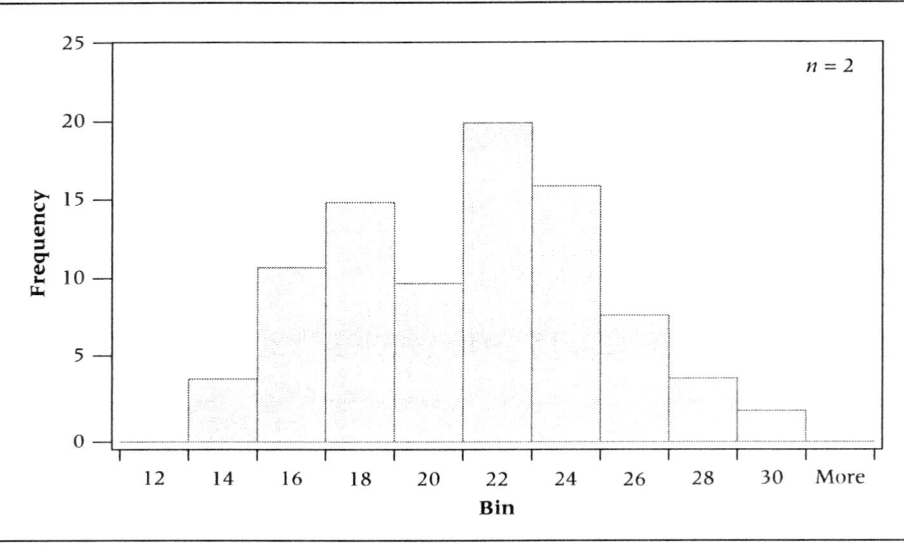

Figure 7.8b

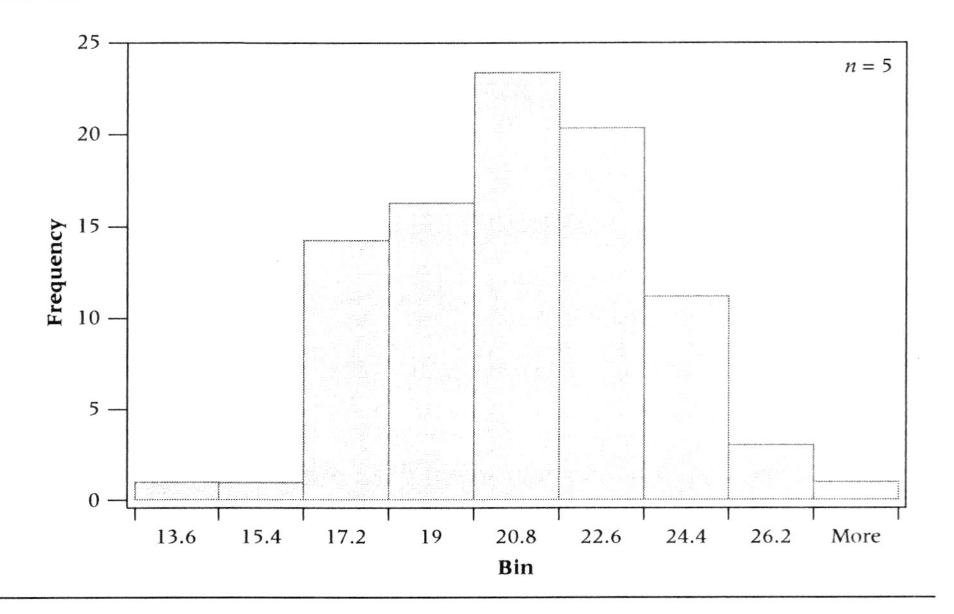

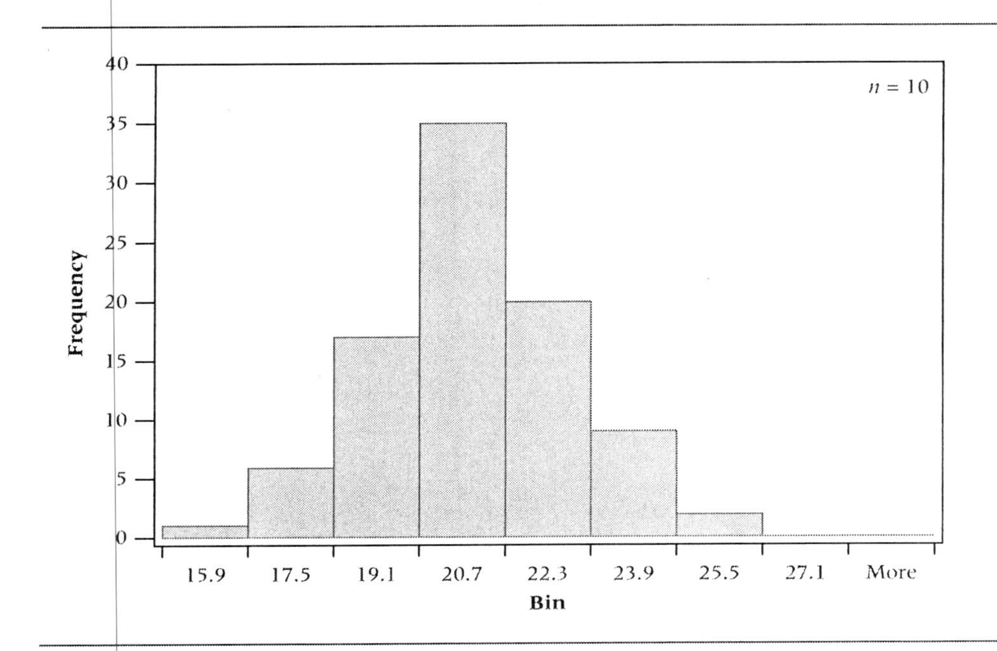

Figure 7.8c

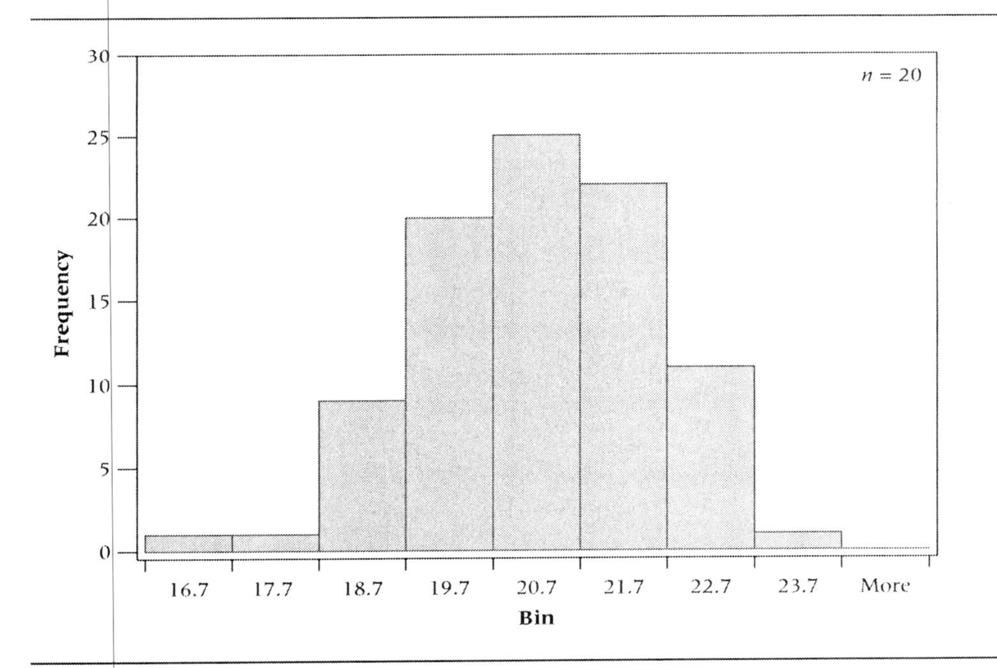

Figure 7.8d

30. Observe the shape of the distributions. Notice that even for small sample sizes, the distributions of sample means for samples taken from the uniformly distributed population begin to "pile up" in the middle. As sample sizes become much larger, the sample mean distributions begin to approach a normal distribution and the variation among the means decreases.

So far, we have examined three populations with different distributions. However, the sample means for samples taken from these populations appear to be approximately normally distributed, especially as the sample sizes become larger. What would happen to the distribution of sample means if we studied populations that have differently shaped distributions? The answer to that question is given in the **central limit theorem.**

Central limit theorem
A theorem that states that regardless of the shape of a population, the distributions of sample means and proportions are normal if sample sizes are large.

Figure 7.8e

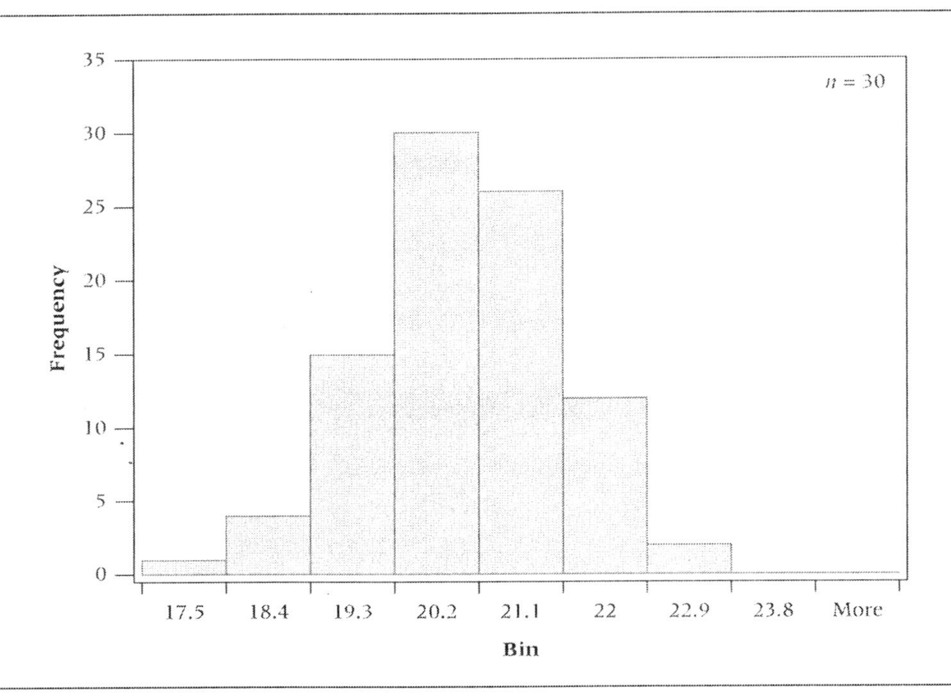

CENTRAL LIMIT THEOREM

If samples of size n are drawn randomly from a population that has a mean of μ and a standard deviation of σ, the sample means, $\bar{X}$, are approximately normally distributed for sufficiently large sample sizes ($n \geq 30$) regardless of the shape of the population distribution. If the population is normally distributed, the sample means are normally distributed for any size sample.

From mathematical expectation,* it can be shown that the mean of the sample means is the population mean,

$$\mu_{\bar{X}} = \mu,$$

and the standard deviation of the sample means is the standard deviation of the population divided by the square root of the sample size,

$$\sigma_{\bar{X}} = \frac{\sigma}{\sqrt{n}}.$$

The central limit theorem creates the potential for applying the normal distribution to many problems when sample size is sufficiently large. Sample means that have been computed for random samples drawn from normally distributed populations are normally distributed. However, the real advantage of the central limit theorem is that sample data drawn from populations not normally distributed or from populations of unknown shape also can be analyzed by using the normal distribution because the sample means are nor-

*The derivations are beyond the scope of this text and are not shown.

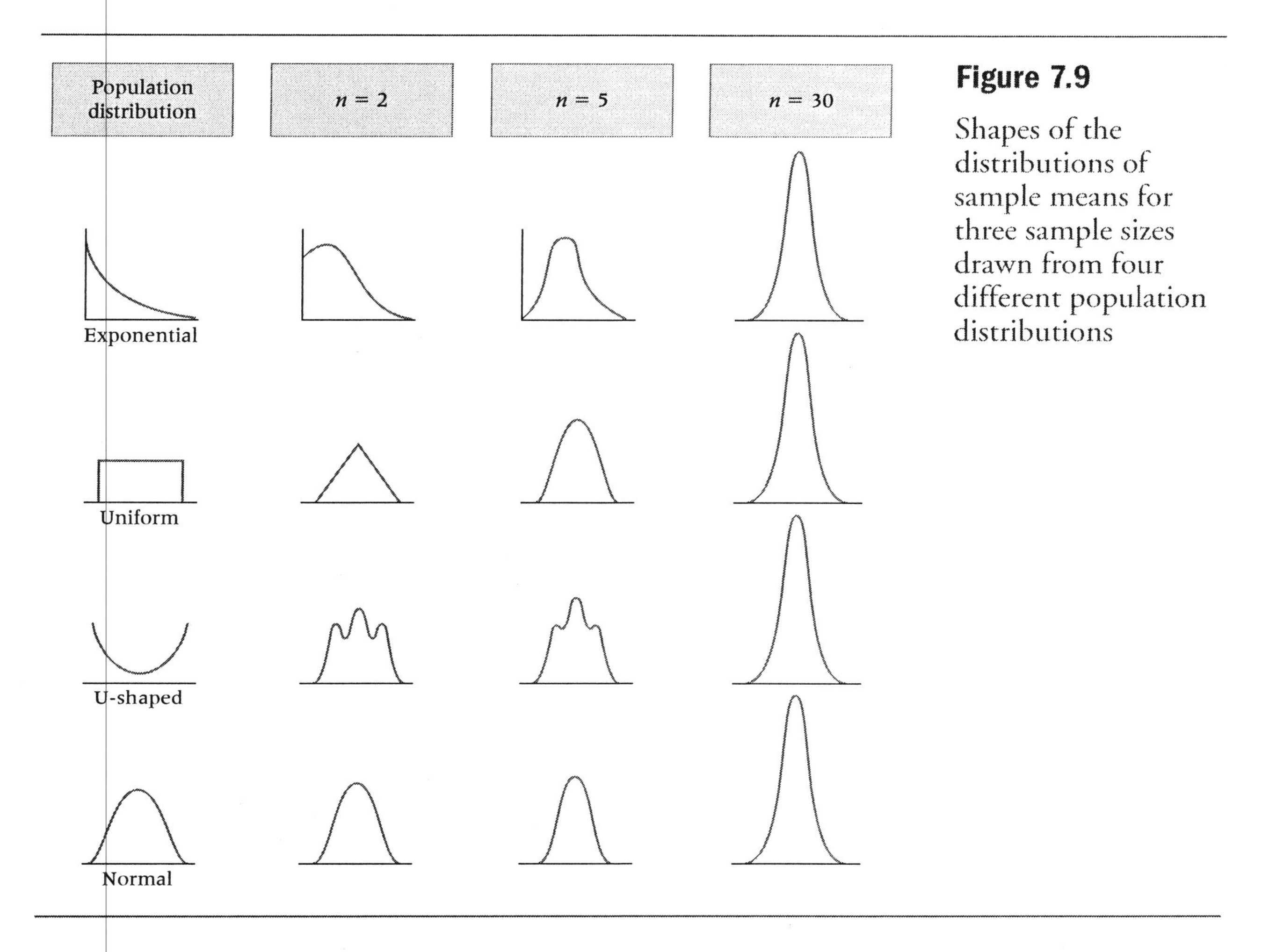

Figure 7.9

Shapes of the distributions of sample means for three sample sizes drawn from four different population distributions

mally distributed for sufficiently large sample sizes.* Column 1 of Figure 7.9 shows four different population distributions. Each succeeding column displays the shape of the distribution of the sample means for a particular sample size. Note in the bottom row for the normally distributed population that the sample means are normally distributed even for $n = 2$. Note also that with the other population distributions, the distribution of the sample means begins to approximate the normal curve as n becomes larger. For all four distributions, the distribution of sample means is approximately normal for $n = 30$.

How large must a sample be for the central limit theorem to apply? The sample size necessary varies according to the shape of the population. However, in this text (as in many others), a sample of *size 30 or larger* will suffice. Recall that if the population is normally distributed, the sample means are normally distributed for sample sizes as small as $n = 1$.

The shapes displayed in Figure 7.9 coincide with the results obtained empirically from the random sampling shown in Figures 7.6 and 7.7. As shown in Figure 7.9, and as indicated in Figure 7.7, as sample size increases, the distribution narrows, or becomes more leptokurtic. This makes sense because the standard deviation of the mean is $\sigma/\sqrt{n}$. This value will become smaller as the size of n increases.

*The actual form of the central limit theorem is a limit function of calculus. As the sample size increases to infinity, the distribution of sample means literally becomes normal in shape. The central limit theorem ensures that the sample mean is both unbiased and consistent, two important characteristics of estimators that are not discussed in this text.

TABLE 7.4
$\mu_{\bar{X}}$ and $\sigma_{\bar{X}}$ of 90 Random Samples for Five Different Sample Sizes

SAMPLE SIZE	MEAN OF SAMPLE MEANS	STANDARD DEVIATION OF SAMPLE MEANS	μ	$\sigma/\sqrt{n}$
$n = 2$	20.20	3.87	20	4.08
$n = 5$	20.00	2.63	20	2.58
$n = 10$	20.17	1.76	20	1.83
$n = 20$	20.20	1.29	20	1.29
$n = 30$	20.05	1.07	20	1.05

In Table 7.4, the means and standard deviations of the means are displayed for random samples of various sizes ($n = 2$ through $n = 30$) drawn from the uniform distribution of $a = 10$ and $b = 30$ shown in Figure 7.8. The population mean is 20, and the standard deviation of the population is 5.774. Note that the mean of the sample means for each sample size is approximately 20 and that the standard deviation of the sample means for each set of 90 samples is approximately equal to $\sigma/\sqrt{n}$. There is a small discrepancy between the standard deviation of the sample means and $\sigma/\sqrt{n}$, because not all possible samples of a given size were taken from the population (only 90). In theory, if all possible samples for a given sample size are taken, the mean of the sample means will equal the population mean and the standard deviation of the sample means will equal the population standard deviation divided by the square root of n.

The central limit theorem states that sample means are normally distributed regardless of the shape of the population for large samples and for any sample size with normally distributed populations. Thus sample means can be analyzed by using Z scores. Recall from Chapter 6 that

$$Z = \frac{X - \mu}{\sigma}.$$

If sample means are normally distributed, the Z score formula applied to sample means would be

$$Z = \frac{\bar{X} - \mu_{\bar{X}}}{\sigma_{\bar{X}}}.$$

Standard error of the mean
The standard deviation of the distribution of sample means.

This result follows the general pattern of Z scores: the difference between the statistic and its mean divided by the statistic's standard deviation. In this formula, the mean of the statistic of interest is $\mu_{\bar{X}}$ and *the standard deviation of the statistic of interest* is $\sigma_{\bar{X}}$, sometimes referred to as the **standard error of the mean.** To determine $\mu_{\bar{X}}$, the researcher would have to randomly draw out all possible samples of the given size from the population, compute the sample means, and average them. This task is virtually impossible to accomplish in any realistic period of time. Fortunately, $\mu_{\bar{X}}$ equals the population mean, μ, which is easier to access. Likewise, to determine directly the value of $\sigma_{\bar{X}}$, the researcher would have to take all possible samples of a given size from a population, compute the sample means, and determine the standard deviation of sample means. This task also is practically impossible. Fortunately, $\sigma_{\bar{X}}$ can be computed by using the population standard deviation divided by the square root of the sample size.

As sample size increases, the standard deviation of the sample means becomes smaller and smaller because the population standard deviation is being divided by larger and larger values of the square root of n. The ultimate benefit of the central limit theorem is a practical, useful version of the Z formula for sample means.

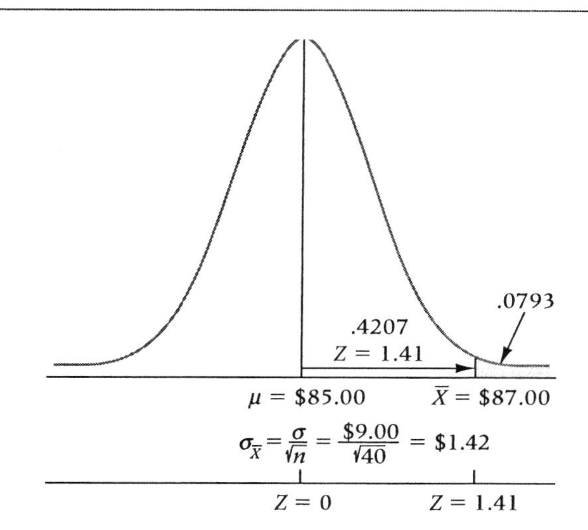

Figure 7.10

Graphical solution to the tire store example

$$Z = \frac{\overline{X} - \mu}{\frac{\sigma}{\sqrt{n}}}$$

Z FORMULA FOR SAMPLE MEANS

When the population is normally distributed and the sample size is 1, this formula for sample means becomes the original Z formula for individual values. The reason is that the mean of one value is that value, and when $n = 1$ the value of $\sigma/\sqrt{n} = \sigma$.

Suppose, for example, that the mean expenditure per customer at a tire store is $85.00, with a standard deviation of $9.00. If a random sample of 40 customers is taken, what is the probability that the sample average expenditure per customer for this sample will be $87.00 or more? Because the sample size is greater than 30, the central limit theorem can be used, and the sample means are normally distributed. With $\mu = \$85.00$, $\sigma = \$9.00$, and the Z formula for sample means, Z is computed as

$$Z = \frac{\overline{X} - \mu}{\frac{\sigma}{\sqrt{n}}} = \frac{\$87.00 - \$85.00}{\frac{\$9.00}{\sqrt{40}}} = \frac{\$2.00}{\$1.42} = 1.41.$$

For $Z = 1.41$ in the Z distribution (Table A.5), the probability is .4207. It is the probability of getting a mean between $87.00 and the population mean, $85.00. Solving for the tail of the distribution yields

$$.5000 - .4207 = .0793,$$

which is the probability of $\overline{X} \geq \$87.00$. That is, 7.93% of the time, a random sample of 40 customers from this population will yield a mean expenditure of $87.00 or more. Figure 7.10 shows the problem and its solution.

DEMONSTRATION PROBLEM 7.1

Suppose that during any hour in a large department store, the average number of shoppers is 448, with a standard deviation of 21 shoppers. What is the probability that a random sample of 49 different shopping hours will yield a sample mean between 441 and 446 shoppers?

SOLUTION

For this problem, $\mu = 448$, $\sigma = 21$, and $n = 49$. The problem is to determine $P(441 \le \bar{X} \le 446)$. The following diagram depicts the problem.

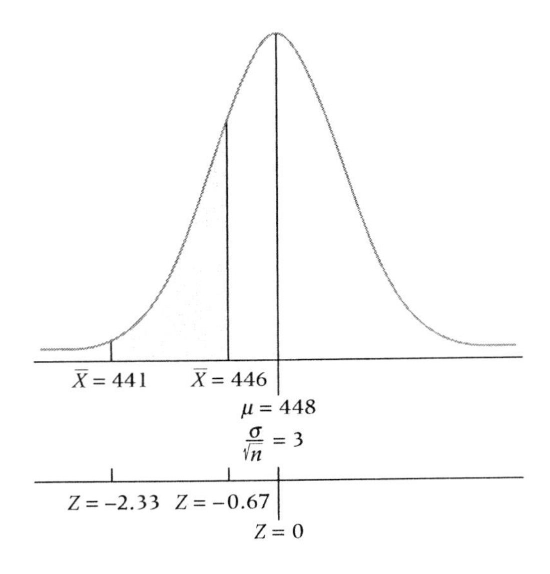

Solve this problem by calculating the Z scores and using Table A.5 to determine the probabilities.

$$Z = \frac{441 - 448}{\frac{21}{\sqrt{49}}} = \frac{-7}{3} = -2.33$$

and

$$Z = \frac{446 - 448}{\frac{21}{\sqrt{49}}} = \frac{-2}{3} = -0.67$$

Z VALUE	PROBABILITY
−2.33	.4901
−0.67	−.2486
	.2415

The probability of a value being between $Z = -2.33$ and -0.67 is .2415. That is, there is a 24.15% chance of randomly selecting 49 hourly periods for which the sample mean is between 441 and 446 shoppers.

POPULATION SIZE	SAMPLE SIZE	VALUE OF CORRECTION FACTOR
2000	30 (<5%N)	.993
2000	500	.866
500	30	.971
500	200	.775
200	30	.924
200	75	.793

TABLE 7.5
Finite Correction Factor for Some Sample Sizes

Sampling from a Finite Population

The example shown in this section and Demonstration Problem 7.1 was based on the assumption that the population was infinitely or extremely large. In cases of a finite population, *a statistical adjustment can be made to the Z formula for sample means.* The adjustment is called the **finite correction factor:** $\sqrt{(N-n)/(N-1)}$. It operates on the standard deviation of sample means, $\sigma_{\bar{X}}$. Following is the Z formula for sample means when samples are drawn from finite populations.

Finite correction factor
A statistical adjustment made to the Z formula for sample means; adjusts for the fact that a population is finite and the size is known.

$$Z = \frac{\bar{X} - \mu}{\dfrac{\sigma}{\sqrt{n}}\sqrt{\dfrac{N-n}{N-1}}}$$

Z FORMULA FOR SAMPLE MEANS WHEN THERE IS A FINITE POPULATION

If a random sample of size 35 were taken from a finite population of only 500, the sample mean would be less likely to deviate from the population mean than would be the case if a sample of size 35 were taken from an infinite population. For a sample of size 35 taken from a finite population of size 500, the finite correction factor is

$$\sqrt{\frac{500-35}{500-1}} = \sqrt{\frac{465}{499}} = .965.$$

Thus the standard deviation of the mean—sometimes referred to as the standard error of the mean—is adjusted downward by using .965. As the size of the finite population becomes larger in relation to sample size, the finite correction factor approaches 1. In theory, whenever researchers are working with a finite population, they can use the finite correction factor. A rough rule of thumb for many researchers is that, if the sample size is less than 5% of the finite population size, the finite correction factor does not significantly modify the solution. Table 7.5 contains some illustrative finite correction factors.

DEMONSTRATION PROBLEM 7.2

A production company's 350 hourly employees average 37.6 years of age, with a standard deviation of 8.3 years. If a random sample of 45 hourly employees is taken, what is the probability that the sample will have an average age of less than 40 years?

SOLUTION

The population mean is 37.6, with a population standard deviation of 8.3; that is, $\mu = 37.6$ and $\sigma = 8.3$. The sample size is 45, but it is being drawn from a finite population of 350;

that is, $n = 45$ and $N = 350$. The sample mean under consideration is 40, or $\overline{X} = 40$. The following diagram depicts the problem on a normal curve.

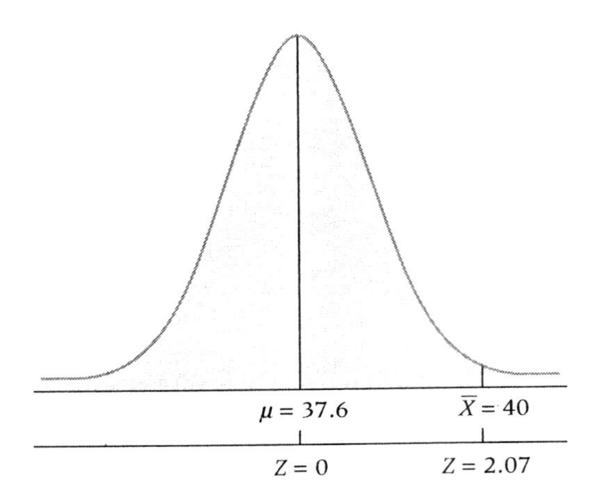

Using the Z formula with the finite correction factor gives

$$Z = \frac{40 - 37.6}{\frac{8.3}{\sqrt{45}}\sqrt{\frac{350 - 45}{350 - 1}}} = \frac{2.4}{1.157} = 2.07.$$

This Z value yields a probability (Table A.5) of .4808. Therefore, the probability of getting a sample average age of less than 40 years is .4808 + .5000 = .9808. Had the finite correction factor not been used, the Z value would have been 1.94, and the final answer would have been .9738.

7.2
Problems

7.13 A population has a mean of 50 and a standard deviation of 10. If a random sample of 64 is taken, what is the probability that the sample mean is each of the following?

a. Greater than 52
b. Less than 51
c. Less than 47
d. Between 48.5 and 52.4
e. Between 50.6 and 51.3

7.14 A population is normally distributed, with a mean of 23.45 and a standard deviation of 3.8. What is the probability of each of the following?

a. Taking a sample of size 10 and obtaining a sample mean of 22 or more
b. Taking a sample of size 4 and getting a sample mean of more than 26

7.15 Suppose a random sample of size 36 is being drawn from a population with a mean of 278. If 86% of the time the sample mean is less than 280, what is the population standard deviation?

7.16 A random sample of size 81 is being drawn from a population with a standard deviation of 12. If only 18% of the time a sample mean greater than 300 is obtained, what is the mean of the population?

7.17 Find the probability in each case.

a. $N = 1000$, $n = 60$, $\mu = 75$, and $\sigma = 6$; $P(\overline{X} < 76.5) = ?$
b. $N = 90$, $n = 36$, $\mu = 108$, and $\sigma = 3.46$; $P(107 < \overline{X} < 107.7) = ?$

c. $N = 250$, $n = 100$, $\mu = 35.6$, and $\sigma = 4.89$; $P(\bar{X} \geq 36) = ?$
d. $N = 5000$, $n = 60$, $\mu = 125$, and $\sigma = 13.4$; $P(\bar{X} \leq 125) = ?$

7.18 The *Statistical Abstract of the United States* published by the U.S. Bureau of the Census reports that the average annual consumption of fresh fruit per person is 99.9 pounds. The standard deviation of fresh fruit consumption is about 30 pounds. Suppose a researcher took a random sample of 38 people and had them keep a record of the fresh fruit they ate for 1 year.
a. What is the probability that the sample average would be less than 90 pounds?
b. What is the probability that the sample average would be between 98 and 105 pounds?
c. What is the probability that the sample average would be less than 112 pounds?
d. What is the probability that the sample average would be between 93 and 96 pounds?

7.19 Suppose a subdivision on the southwest side of Denver, Colorado, contains 1500 houses. The subdivision was built in 1983. A sample of 100 houses is selected randomly and evaluated by an appraiser. If the mean appraised value of a house in this subdivision for all houses is $147,000, with a standard deviation of $8500, what is the probability that the sample average is greater than $155,000?

7.20 Suppose the average checkout tab at a large supermarket is $65.12, with a standard deviation of $21.45. Twenty-three percent of the time when a random sample of 45 customer tabs is examined, the sample average should exceed what value?

7.21 According to Nielsen Media Research, the average number of hours of TV viewing per household per week in the United States is 50.4 hours. Suppose the standard deviation is 11.8 hours and a random sample of 42 U.S. households is taken.
a. What is the probability that the sample average is more than 52 hours?
b. What is the probability that the sample average is less than 47.5 hours?
c. What is the probability that the sample average is less than 40 hours? If the sample average actually is less than 40 hours, what could this mean in terms of the Nielsen Media Research figures?
d. Suppose the population standard deviation is unknown. If 71% of all sample means are greater than 49 hours and the population mean is still 50.4 hours, what is the value of the population standard deviation?

7.3 Sampling Distribution of $\hat{p}$

Sometimes in analyzing a sample, a researcher will choose to use the sample proportion, denoted $\hat{p}$, instead of the sample mean. If research produces *measurable* data such as weight, distance, time, and income, the sample mean is often the statistic of choice. However, if research results in *countable* items such as how many people in a sample choose Dr. Pepper as their soft drink or how many people in a sample have a flexible work schedule, the sample proportion is often the statistic of choice. Whereas the mean is computed by averaging a set of values, the **sample proportion** is *computed by dividing the frequency with which a given characteristic occurs in a sample by the number of items in the sample.*

SAMPLE PROPORTION

$$\hat{p} = \frac{X}{n}$$

where:
X = number of items in a sample that have the characteristic
n = number of items in the sample

Sample proportion The quotient of the frequency at which a given characteristic occurs in a sample and the number of items in the sample.

For example, in a sample of 100 factory workers, 30 workers might belong to a union. The value of $\hat{p}$ for this characteristic, union membership, is 30/100 = .30. Or, in a sample of 500 businesses in suburban malls, 10 might be shoe stores. The sample proportion of shoe stores is 10/500 = .02. The sample proportion is a widely used statistic and is usually computed on questions involving *yes* or *no* answers. For example, do you have at least a high school education? Are you predominantly right-handed? Are you female? Do you belong to the student accounting association?

Standard error of the proportion The standard deviation of the distribution of sample proportions.

How does a researcher use the sample proportion in analysis? The central limit theorem applies to sample proportions in that the normal distribution approximates the shape of the distribution of sample proportions if $n \cdot P > 5$ and $n \cdot Q > 5$ (P is the population proportion and $Q = 1 - P$). The mean of sample proportions for all samples of size n randomly drawn from a population is P (the population proportion) and *the standard deviation of sample proportions* is $\sqrt{(P \cdot Q)/n}$, sometimes referred to as the **standard error of the proportion.** Sample proportions also have a Z formula.

Z FORMULA FOR SAMPLE PROPORTIONS FOR $n \cdot P > 5$ AND $n \cdot Q > 5$

$$Z = \frac{\hat{p} - P}{\sqrt{\frac{P \cdot Q}{n}}}$$

where

$\hat{p}$ = sample proportion
n = sample size
P = population proportion
$Q = 1 - P$

Suppose 60% of the electrical contractors in a region use a particular brand of wire. What is the probability of taking a random sample of size 120 from these electrical contractors and finding that .50 or less use that brand of wire? For this problem,

$$P = .60, \quad \hat{p} = .50, \quad \text{and} \quad n = 120.$$

The Z formula yields

$$Z = \frac{.50 - .60}{\sqrt{\frac{(.60)(.40)}{120}}} = \frac{-.10}{.0447} = -2.24.$$

From Table A.5, the probability corresponding to $Z = -2.24$ is .4875. For $Z < -2.24$ (the tail of the distribution), the answer is .5000 – .4875 = .0125. Figure 7.11 shows the problem and solution graphically.

This answer indicates that a researcher would have difficulty (probability of .0125) finding that 50% or less of a sample of 120 contractors use a given brand of wire if indeed the population market share for that wire is .60. If this sample result actually occurs, either it is a rare chance result or perhaps the .60 proportion does not hold for this population.

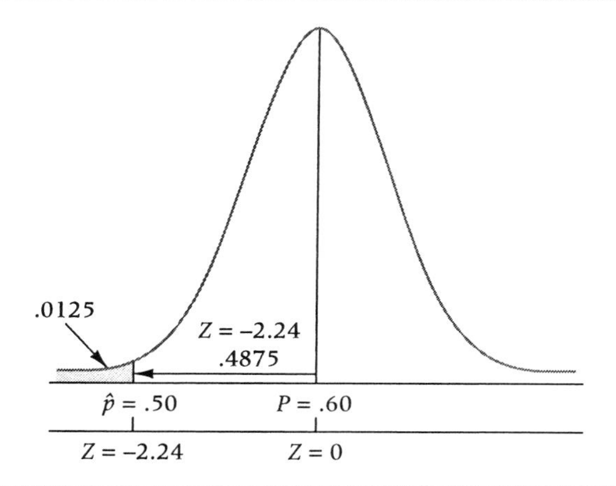

Figure 7.11

Graphical solution to the electrical contractor example

DEMONSTRATION PROBLEM 7.3

If 10% of a population of parts is defective, what is the probability of randomly selecting 80 parts and finding that 12 or more parts are defective?

SOLUTION

Here, $P = .10$, $\hat{p} = 12/80 = .15$, and $n = 80$. Using the Z formula gives

$$Z = \frac{.15 - .10}{\sqrt{\frac{(.10)(.90)}{80}}} = \frac{.05}{.0335} = 1.49.$$

Table A.5 gives a probability of .4319 for a Z value of 1.49, which is the area between the sample proportion, .15, and the population proportion, .10. The answer to the question is

$$P(\hat{p} \geq .15) = .5000 - .4319 = .0681.$$

Thus, about 6.81% of the time, 12 or more defective parts would appear in a random sample of 80 parts when the population proportion is .10. If this result actually occurred, the 10% proportion for population defects would be open to question. The diagram shows the problem graphically.

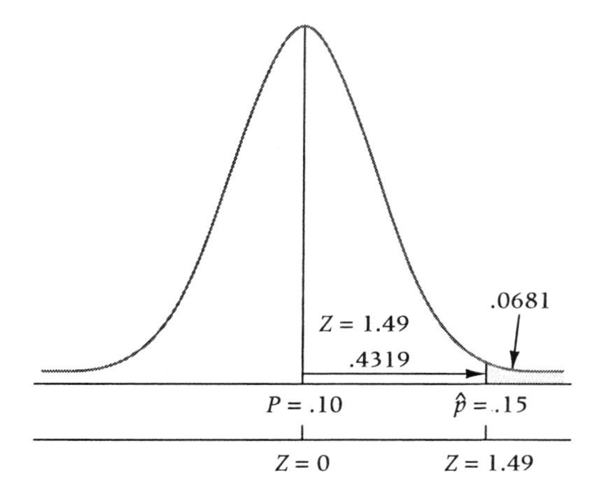

7.3
Problems

7.22 A given population proportion is .25. For the given value of n, what is the probability of getting each of the following sample proportions?

a. $n = 110$ and $\hat{p} \leq .21$
b. $n = 33$ and $\hat{p} > .24$
c. $n = 59$ and $.24 \leq \hat{p} < .27$
d. $n = 80$ and $\hat{p} > .30$
e. $n = 800$ and $\hat{p} > .30$

7.23 A population proportion is .58. Suppose a random sample of 660 items is sampled randomly from this population.

a. What is the probability that the sample proportion is greater than .60?
b. What is the probability that the sample proportion is between .55 and .65?
c. What is the probability that the sample proportion is greater than .57?
d. What is the probability that the sample proportion is between .53 and .56?
e. What is the probability that the sample proportion is less than .48?

7.24 Suppose a population proportion is .40 and 80% of the time when you draw a random sample from this population you get a sample proportion of .35 or more. How large a sample were you taking?

7.25 If a population proportion is .28 and if the sample size is 140, 30% of the time the sample proportion will be less than what value if you are taking random samples?

7.26 A *USA Today*/IntelliQuest survey of computer users revealed that 23% log onto the Internet and/or an online service user more than 20 times per month. Suppose a random sample of 600 computer users is taken. What is the probability that more than 150 computer users log onto the Internet and/or an online service user more than 20 times per month?

7.27 According to the Consumer Electronics Manufacturers Association, 39% of all U.S. households have a cellular phone. Suppose 200 U.S. households are randomly surveyed.

a. What is the probability that fewer than 70 households have a cellular phone?
b. What is the probability that more than 90 households have a cellular phone?
c. What is the probability that more than 65 households do not have a cellular phone?

7.28 The *Travel Weekly International Air Transport Association* survey asked business travelers about the purpose for their most recent business trip. Nineteen percent responded that it was for an internal company visit. Suppose 950 business travelers are randomly selected.

a. What is the probability that more than 25% of the business travelers say that the reason for their most recent business trip was an internal company visit?
b. What is the probability that between 15% and 20% of the business travelers say that the reason for their most recent business trip was an internal company visit?
c. What is the probability that between 133 and 171 of the business travelers say that the reason for their most recent business trip was an internal company visit?

Summary

For much business research, successfully conducting a census is virtually impossible and the sample is a feasible alternative. Other reasons for sampling include cost reduction, potential for broadening the scope of the study, and loss reduction when the testing process destroys the product.

To take a sample, a population has to be identified. Often the researcher has no exact roster or list of the population and so must find some way to identify the population as closely as possible. The final list or directory used to represent the population and from which the sample is drawn is called the frame.

The two main types of sampling are random and nonrandom. Random sampling occurs when each unit of the population has the same probability of being selected for the sample. Nonrandom sampling is any sampling that is not random. The four main types of random sampling discussed are simple random sampling, stratified sampling, systematic sampling, and cluster or area sampling.

In simple random sampling, every unit of the population is numbered. A table of random numbers or a random number generator is used to select n units from the population for the sample.

Stratified random sampling uses the researcher's prior knowledge of the population to stratify the population into subgroups. Each subgroup is internally homogeneous but different from the others. Stratified random sampling is an attempt to reduce sampling error and ensure that at least some of each of the subgroups appear in the sample. After the strata have been identified, units are sampled randomly from each stratum. If the proportions of units selected from each subgroup for the sample are the same as the proportions of the subgroups in the population, the process is called proportionate stratified sampling. If not, it is called disproportionate stratified sampling.

With systematic sampling, every kth item of the population is sampled until n units have been selected. Systematic sampling is used because of its convenience and ease of administration.

Cluster or area sampling involves subdividing the population into nonoverlapping clusters or areas. Each cluster or area is a microcosm of the population and is usually heterogeneous within. Individual units are then selected randomly from the clusters or areas to get the final sample. Cluster or area sampling is usually done to reduce costs. If a set of second clusters or areas is selected from the first set, the method is called two-stage sampling.

Four types of nonrandom sampling were discussed: convenience, judgment, quota, and snowball. In convenience sampling, the researcher selects units from the population to be in the sample for convenience. In judgment sampling, units are selected according to the judgment of the researcher. Quota sampling is similar to stratified sampling, with the researcher identifying subclasses or strata. However, the researcher selects units from each stratum by some nonrandom technique until a specified quota from each stratum is filled. With snowball sampling, the researcher obtains additional sample members by asking current sample members for referral information.

Sampling error occurs when the sample does not represent the population. With random sampling, sampling error occurs by chance. Nonsampling errors are all other research and analysis errors that occur in a study. They include recording errors, input errors, missing data, and incorrect definition of the frame.

According to the central limit theorem, if a population is normally distributed, the sample means for samples taken from that population also are normally distributed regardless of sample size. The central limit theorem also says that if the sample sizes are large ($n \geq 30$), the sample mean is approximately normally distributed regardless of the distribution shape of the population. This theorem is extremely useful because it enables researchers to analyze sample data by using the normal distribution for virtually any type of study in which means are an appropriate statistic, so long as the sample size is large enough. The central limit theorem states that sample proportions are normally distributed for large sample sizes.

Key Terms

central limit theorem
cluster (or area) sampling
convenience sampling
disproportionate stratified random sampling
finite correction factor
frame
judgment sampling
nonrandom sampling
nonrandom sampling techniques
nonsampling errors

proportionate stratified random sampling
quota sampling
random sampling
sample proportion
sampling error
simple random sampling
snowball sampling
standard error of the mean
standard error of the proportion
stratified random sampling
systematic sampling
two-stage sampling

SUPPLEMENTARY PROBLEMS

7.29 The mean of a population is 76 and the standard deviation is 14. The shape of the population is unknown. Determine the probability of each of the following occurring from this population.

a. A random sample of size 35 yielding a sample mean of 79 or more

b. A random sample of size 140 yielding a sample mean of between 74 and 77

c. A random sample of size 219 yielding a sample mean of less than 76.5

7.30 Forty-six percent of a population possess a particular characteristic. Random samples are taken from this population. Determine the probability of each of the following occurrences.

a. The sample size is 60 and the sample proportion is between .41 and .53

b. The sample size is 458 and the sample proportion is less than .40

c. The sample size is 1350 and the sample proportion is greater than .49

7.31 Suppose the age distribution in a city is as follows.

Under 18	22%
18–25	18%
26–50	36%
51–65	10%
Over 65	14%

A researcher is conducting proportionate stratified random sampling with a sample size of 250. Approximately how many people should he sample from each stratum?

7.32 Candidate Jones believes she will receive .55 of the total votes cast in her county. However, in an attempt to validate this figure, she has her pollster contact a random sample of 600 registered voters in the county. The poll results show that 298 of the voters say they are committed to voting for her. If she actually has .55 of the total vote, what is the probability of getting a sample proportion this small or smaller? Do you think she actually has 55% of the vote? Why or why not?

7.33 Determine a possible frame for conducting random sampling in each of the following studies.

a. The average amount of overtime per week for production workers in a plastics company in Pennsylvania

b. The average number of employees in all Alpha/Beta supermarkets in California

c. A survey of commercial lobster catchers in Maine

7.34 A particular automobile costs an average of \$17,755 in the Pacific Northwest. The standard deviation of prices is \$650. Suppose a random sample of 30 dealerships in Washington and Oregon is taken and their managers are asked what they charge for this automobile. What is the probability of getting a sample average cost of less than \$17,500? Assume that only 120 dealerships in the entire Pacific Northwest sell this automobile.

7.35 A company has 1250 employees, and you want to take a simple random sample of $n = 60$ employees. Explain how you would go about selecting this sample by using the table of random numbers. Are there numbers that you cannot use? Explain.

7.36 Suppose the average client charge per hour for out-of-court work by lawyers in the state of Iowa is \$125. Suppose further that a random telephone sample of 32 lawyers in Iowa is taken and that the sample average charge per hour for out-of-court work is \$110. If the population variance is \$525, what is the probability of getting a sample mean this large or larger? What is the probability of getting a sample mean larger than \$135 per hour? What is the probability of getting a sample mean of between \$120 and \$130 per hour?

7.37 A survey of 2645 consumers by DDB Needham Worldwide of Chicago for public relations agency Porter/Novelli showed that how a company handles a crisis when at fault is one of the top influences in consumer buying decisions, with 73% claiming it is an influence. Quality of product was the number-one influence, with 96% of consumers stating that quality has an influence on their buying decisions. How a company handles complaints was number two, with

85% of consumers reporting it as an influence in their buying decisions. Suppose a random sample of 1100 consumers is taken and each is asked which of these three factors influence their buying decisions.

a. What is the probability that more than 810 consumers claim that how a company handles a crisis when at fault is an influence in their buying decisions?

b. What is the probability that fewer than 1030 consumers claim that quality of product is an influence in their buying decisions?

c. What is the probability that between 82% and 84% of consumers claim that how a company handles complaints is an influence in their buying decisions?

7.38 Suppose you are sending out questionnaires to a randomly selected sample of 100 managers. The frame for this study is the membership list of the American Managers Association. The questionnaire contains demographic questions about the company and its top manager. In addition, it asks questions about the manager's leadership style. Research assistants are to score and enter the responses into the computer as soon as they are received. You are to conduct a statistical analysis of the data. Name and describe four nonsampling errors that could occur in this study.

7.39 A researcher is conducting a study of a *Fortune 500* company that has factories, distribution centers, and retail outlets across the country. How can she use cluster or area sampling to take a random sample of employees of this firm?

7.40 A directory of personal computer retail outlets in the United States contains 12,080 alphabetized entries. Explain how systematic sampling could be used to select a sample of 300 outlets.

7.41 In an effort to cut costs and improve profits, many U.S. companies have been turning to outsourcing. In fact, according to *Purchasing* magazine, 54% of companies surveyed outsourced some part of their manufacturing process in the past two to three years. Suppose 565 of these companies are contacted.

a. What is the probability that 339 or more companies have outsourced some part of their manufacturing process in the past two to three years?

b. What is the probability that 288 or more companies have outsourced some part of their manufacturing process in the past two to three years?

c. What is the probability that 50% or less of these companies have outsourced some part of their manufacturing process in the past two to three years?

7.42 The average cost of a one-bedroom apartment in a town is $550 per month. What is the probability of randomly selecting a sample of 50 one-bedroom apartments in this town and getting a sample mean of less than $530 if the population standard deviation is $100?

7.43 The Aluminum Association reports that the average American uses 56.8 pounds of aluminum in a year. A random sample of 51 households is monitored for 1 year to determine aluminum usage. If the population standard deviation of annual usage is 12.3 pounds, what is the probability that the sample mean will be each of the following?

a. More than 60 pounds

b. More than 58 pounds

c. Between 56 and 57 pounds

d. Less than 55 pounds

e. Less than 50 pounds

7.44 Use Table A.1 to select 20 three-digit random numbers. Did any of the numbers occur more than once? How can this happen? Make a histogram of the numbers. Do the numbers seem to be equally distributed, or are they bunched together?

7.45 Direct marketing companies are turning to the Internet for new opportunities. A recent study by Gruppo, Levey, & Co. showed that 73% of all direct marketers conduct transactions on the Internet. Suppose a random sample of 300 direct marketing companies is taken.

a. What is the probability that between 210 and 234 (inclusive) direct marketing companies are turning to the Internet for new opportunities?

b. What is the probability that 78% or more of direct marketing companies are turning to the Internet for new opportunities?

c. Suppose a random sample of 800 direct marketing companies is taken. Now what is the probability that 78% or more are turning to the Internet for new opportunities? How does this answer differ from the answer in part (b)? Why do the answers differ?

7.46 According to the U.S. Bureau of Labor Statistics, 20% of all people 16 years of age or older do volunteer work. Women volunteer slightly more than men, with 22% of women volunteering and 19% of men volunteering. What is the probability of randomly sampling 140 women 16 years of age or older and getting 35 or more who do volunteer work? What is the probability of getting 21 or fewer from this group? Suppose a sample of 300 men and women 16 years of age or older is selected randomly from the U.S. population. What is the probability that the sample proportion who do volunteer work is between 18% and 25%?

7.47 Suppose you work for a large firm that has 20,000 employees. The CEO calls you in and asks you to determine employee attitudes toward the company. She is willing to commit $100,000 to this project. What are the advantages of taking a sample versus conducting a census? What are the trade-offs?

7.48 In a particular area of the Northeast, an estimated 75% of the homes use heating oil as the principal heating fuel during the winter. A random telephone survey of 150 homes is taken in an attempt to determine whether this figure is correct. Suppose 120 of the 150 homes surveyed use heating oil as the principal heating fuel. What is the probability of getting a sample proportion this large or larger if the population estimate is true?

7.49 The U.S. Bureau of Labor Statistics released hourly wage figures for western countries in 1996 for workers in the manufacturing sector. The hourly wage was $28.34 in Switzerland, $20.84 in Japan, and $17.70 in the United States. Suppose 40 manufacturing workers are selected randomly from across Switzerland and asked what their hourly wage is. What is the probability that the sample average will be between $28 and $29? Suppose 35 manufacturing workers are selected randomly from across Japan. What is the probability that the sample average will exceed $22? Suppose 50 manufacturing workers are selected randomly from across the United States. What is the probability that the sample average will be less than $16.50? Assume that in all three countries, the standard deviation of hourly labor rates is $3.

7.50 Give a variable that could be used to stratify the population for each of the following studies. List at least four subcategories for each variable.

a. A political party wants to conduct a poll prior to an election for the office of U.S. senator in Minnesota.

b. A soft-drink company wants to take a sample of soft-drink purchases in an effort to estimate market share.

c. A retail outlet wants to interview customers over a 1-week period.

d. An eyeglasses manufacturer and retailer wants to determine the demand for prescription eyeglasses in its marketing region.

7.51 According to Runzheimer International, a typical business traveler spends an average of $281 per day in Chicago. This cost includes hotel, meals, car rental, and incidentals. A survey of 65 randomly selected business travelers who have been to Chicago on business recently is taken. For the population mean of $281 per day, what is the probability of getting a sample average of more than $273 per day if the population standard deviation is $47?

ANALYZING THE DATABASES

1. Let the manufacturing database be the frame for a population of manufacturers that are to be studied. This database has 140 different SIC codes. How would you proceed to take a simple random sample of size 6 from these industries? Explain how you would take a systematic sample of size 10 from this frame. Examine the variables in the database. Name two variables that could be used to stratify the population. Explain how these variables could be used in stratification and why they might be important strata.

2. Assume the manufacturing database is the population of interest. Compute the mean and standard deviation for cost of materials on this population. Take a random sample of 32 of the SIC code categories and compute the sample mean cost of materials on this sample. Using techniques presented in this chapter, determine the probability of getting a mean this large or larger from the population. Note that the population contains only 140 items. Work this problem with and without the finite correction factor. Compare the results and discuss the differences in answers.

3. Use the hospital database to calculate the mean and standard deviation of personnel. Assume that these figures are true for the population of hospitals in the United States. Suppose a random sample of 36 hospitals is taken from hospitals in the United States. What is the probability that the sample mean of personnel is less than 650? What is the probability that the sample mean of personnel is between 700 and 1100? What is the probability that the sample mean is between 900 and 950?

Determine the proportion of the hospital database that is under the control of nongovernment-not-for-profit organizations (category 2). Assume that this proportion represents the entire population of hospitals. If you randomly selected 500 hospitals from across the United States, what is the probability that 45% or more are under the control of nongovernment-not-for-profit organizations? If you randomly selected 100 hospitals, what is the probability that less than 40% are under the control of nongovernment-not-for-profit organizations?

CASE

SHELL ATTEMPTS TO RETURN TO PREMIER STATUS

The Shell Oil Company, which began around 1912, had been for decades a household name as a top-flight oil company in the United States. However, by the late 1970s much of its prestige as a premier company had disappeared. How could Shell regain its high status?

In the 1990s, Shell undertook an extensive research effort to find out what it needed to do to improve its image. As a first step, Shell hired Responsive Research, Inc. and the Opinion Research Corp. to conduct a series of focus-group and personal interviews among various segments of the population. Included in these were youths, minorities, residents in neighborhoods near Shell plants, legislators, academics, and present and past employees of Shell. The researchers learned that people believe that top companies are integral parts of the communities in which the companies are located rather than separate entities. These studies and others led to the development of materials that Shell used to explain their core values to the general public.

Next, PERT Survey Research ran a large quantitative study to determine which values were best received by the target audience. Social issues emerged as the theme with the most support. During the next few months, the advertising agency Ogilvy & Mather was hired by Shell to develop several campaigns with social themes. Two market research companies were hired to evaluate the receptiveness of the various campaigns. The result was the "Count on Shell" campaign, which featured safety messages with useful information about what to do in various dangerous situations.

A public "Count on Shell" campaign was launched in February 1998 and has met with considerable success: the ability to recall Shell advertising has jumped from 20% to 32% among opinion influencers; over a million copies of Shell's free safety brochures have been distributed; and activity on Shell's Internet "Count on Shell" site has been extremely strong. By promoting itself as a reliable company that cares, Shell seems to be regaining its premier status.

DISCUSSION

1. Suppose you were asked to develop a sampling plan to determine what a "premier company" is to the general public. What sampling plan would you use? What is the target population? What would you use for a frame? Which of the four types of random sampling discussed in this chapter would you use? Could you use a combination of two or more of the types (two-stage sampling)? If so, how?
2. It appears that at least one of the research companies hired by Shell used some stratification in their sampling. What are some of the variables on which they stratified? If you were truly interested in ascertaining opinions from a variety of segments of the population with regard to opinions on "premier" companies or about Shell, what strata might make sense? Name at least five and justify why you would include them.
3. Suppose that in 1979 only 12% of the general adult U.S. public believed that Shell was a "premier" company. Suppose further that you randomly selected 350 people from the general adult U.S. public this year and 25% said that Shell was a "premier"

company. If only 12% of the general adult U.S. public still believes that Shell is a "premier" company, how likely is it that the 25% figure is a chance result in sampling 350 people? *Hint:* Use the techniques in this chapter to determine the probability of the 25% figure occurring by chance.

4. PERT Survey Research conducted quantitative surveys in an effort to measure the effectiveness of various campaigns. Suppose they used a 1-to-5 scale where 1 denotes that the campaign is not effective at all, 5 denotes that the campaign is extremely effective, and 2, 3, and 4 fall in between on an interval scale. Suppose also that a particular campaign received an average of 1.8 on the scale with a standard deviation of .7 early in the tests. Later, after the campaign had been critiqued and improved, a survey of 35 people was taken and a sample mean of 2.0 was recorded. What is the probability of a mean this large or larger occurring if the actual population mean is still just 1.8? Based on this, do you think that a sample mean of 2.0 is probably just a chance fluctuation on the 1.8 population mean, or do you think that perhaps it is evidence that the population mean is now greater than 1.8? Support your conclusion. Suppose a sample mean of 2.5 is attained. What is the likelihood of a mean this large or larger occurring by chance when the population mean is 1.8? Suppose this actually happens after the campaign has been improved. What does this mean?

ADAPTED FROM: "Count on It," *American Demographics*, March 1999, 60.

7

BASIC DATA ANALYSIS: Descriptive Statistics

What you will learn in this chapter

- To understand that analysis consists of summarizing, rearranging, ordering, or manipulating data.
- To define *descriptive analysis.*
- To compute and explain the purposes of simple tabulations and cross-tabulations.
- To discuss how the calculation of percentages helps the researcher understand the nature of relationships.
- To discuss the relationship between two variables with cross-tabulation procedures.
- To elaborate and refine basic cross-tabulations.
- To define and explain *spurious relationships.*
- To understand quadrant analysis.
- To discuss data transformations.
- To calculate an index number.
- To explain some of the computer programs for analyzing descriptive data.
- To explain the purpose of interpretation.

More than half of office workers say that poor lighting in the workplace triggers tired or watery eyes (56 percent).[1] Another 30 percent say they suffer headaches from poor lighting. Moreover, 86 percent believe that making lighting improvements to the workplace would reduce eyestrain and headaches.

How significant are lighting problems in the office? The Steelcase Workplace Index, a semiannual survey that gauges workplace trends in the United States, indicates that eight out of every ten workers report they experience lighting glare. Approximately 38 percent of workers say the light level in their work area is either too dim (22 percent) or too bright (15 percent). And three out of four say they want more control over their lighting.

While lighting is a critical factor in worker health, comfort and productivity, most workers suffer in silence from eye strain. Some workers are taking matters into their own hands. At least three out of ten office workers say they have attempted to change the light levels in the workplace. If the place is too dark, people will either bring in their own lighting from home (15 percent) or obtain lighting from their employer or co-worker (13 percent). If the workplace is too bright, 15 percent of office workers have either removed or blocked the light.

Three out of four office workers indicate improved lighting could help them be more efficient and productive. And two out of every three office workers surveyed reported that improved lighting would help them be more creative.

These interesting findings illustrate the results of a typical descriptive analysis. This chapter explains how to perform descriptive analysis. ■

THE NATURE OF DESCRIPTIVE ANALYSIS

Business researchers edit and code data to provide input that results in tabulated information that will answer research questions. With this input, researchers logically and statistically describe project results. Within this context the term *analysis* is difficult to define because it refers to a variety of activities and processes. One form of analysis is summarizing large quantities of raw data so the results can be interpreted. Categorizing, or separating out the components or relevant parts of the whole data set, is also a form of analysis to make the data easily manageable. Rearranging, ordering, or manipulating data may provide descriptive information that answers questions posed in the problem definition. All forms of analysis attempt to portray consistent patterns in the data so the results may be studied and interpreted in a brief and meaningful way.

descriptive analysis
The transformation of raw data into a form that will make them easy to understand and interpret; rearranging, ordering, manipulating data to provide descriptive information.

Descriptive analysis refers to the transformation of raw data into a form that will make them easy to understand and interpret. Describing responses or observations is typically the first form of analysis. Calculating averages, frequency distributions, and percentage distributions are the most common ways of summarizing data.

As the analysis progresses beyond the descriptive stage, researchers generally apply the tools of inferential statistics. *Univariate analysis,* which is covered in Chapter 21, allows researchers to assess the statistical significance of various hypotheses about a single variable.

In Chapter 13 we saw that the type of measurement scale used determines the permissible arithmetic operations. Exhibit 20.1 outlines the most common descriptive statistics associated with each type of scale. It is important to remember that all descriptive statistics appropriate for a lower-order scale are also appropriate for higher-order scales.

Coca Cola's data analysis shows that the typical resident of Brooklyn, New York, drinks 105 Cokes annually.[2] On Staten Island, however, the average resident drinks a whopping 429 Cokes per year. Descriptive analysis transforms raw data into a form that is easy to understand and interpret.

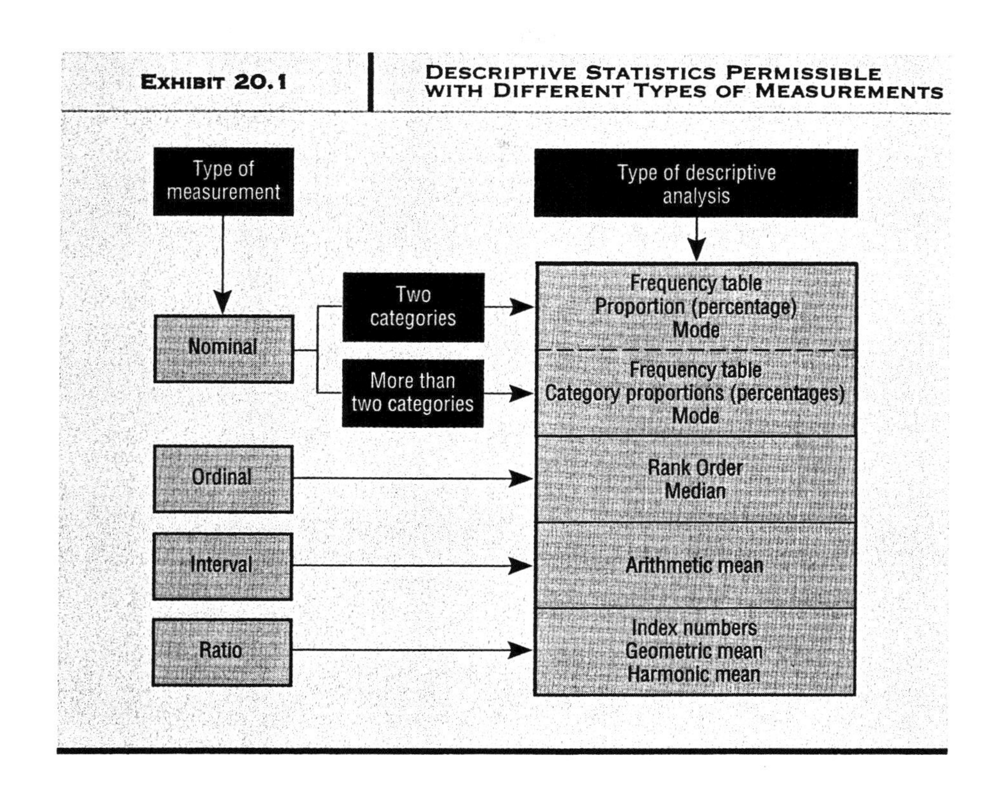

TABULATION

simple tabulation
Counting the number of different responses to a question and arranging them in a frequency distribution.

frequency table
A simple tabulation that indicates the frequency with which respondents give a particular answer.

Tabulation refers to the orderly arrangement of data in a table or other summary format. Counting the number of different responses to a question and putting them in a frequency distribution is a **simple**, or *marginal*, **tabulation.** Simple tabulation of the responses or observations on a question-by-question or item-by-item basis provides the most basic form of information for the researcher and in many cases the most useful information. It tells the researcher how frequently each response occurs. This starting point for analysis requires the counting of responses or observations for each of the categories or codes assigned to a variable. Table 20.1 illustrates a **frequency table.** When this tabulation process is done by hand, it is called *tallying.* Large sample sizes generally require computer tabulation of the data.

TABLE 20.1 FREQUENCY TABLE

DO YOU SHOP AT IGA?

Response	Frequency
Yes	330
No	120
Total	450

TABLE 20.2 AN ILLUSTRATION OF HOW PERCENTAGES AID IN THE INTERPRETATION OF FREQUENCY DISTRIBUTIONS AND CROSS-TABULATIONS[3]

A: United States Racial and Ethnic Composition (in thousands)

	2000	2010*	Change
Non-Hispanic White	197,061	202,390	5,329
Non-Hispanic Black	33,568	37,466	3,898
Non-Hispanic Asian/Pacific Islander	10,584	14,402	3,818
Non-Hispanic Other	2,054	2,320	266
Hispanic	31,366	41,139	9,773

B: United States Racial and Ethnic Composition (in thousands)

	2000	Percent of Population	2010*	Percent of Population	Change	Percent Change
Non-Hispanic White	197,061	71.8	202,390	68.0	5,329	+2.7
Non-Hispanic Black	33,568	12.2	37,466	12.6	3,898	+11.6
Non-Hispanic Asian/ Pacific Islander	10,584	3.9	14,402	4.8	3,818	+36.1
Non-Hispanic Other	2,054	0.7	2,320	0.8	266	+13.0
Hispanic	31,366	11.4	41,139	13.8	9,773	+31.2

*Projected

Percentages

Whether data are tabulated by computer or by hand, it is useful to have **percentages** and **cumulative percentages** as well as **frequency distributions.** For example, consider Table 20.2. Most people find part B easier to interpret than part A because the percentages are useful for comparing trends over the decades. When discussing percentages, researchers must speak or write with precise language. For example, the difference between 40 percent and 60 percent is not 20 percent, but 20 *percentage points;* this represents an increase of 50 percent.

percentage
A part of a whole expressed in hundredths.

cumulative percentage
A percentage (or percentage distribution) that has increased by successive additions.

frequency distribution
A set of data organized by summarizing the number of times a particular value of a variable occurs.

Measures of Central Tendency

According to Airport Interviewing and Research, Inc. the average number of trips taken annually by a business traveler was 15.[4] This is a measure of central tendency. Describing central tendencies of the distribution with the mean, median, or mode is another basic form of descriptive analysis. Of course, these measures are most useful when the purpose is to identify typical values of a variable or the most common characteristic of a group. If knowing the average or typical performance will satisfy the information need, the measures described in Chapter 17 should be considered.

CROSS-TABULATION

The mere tabulation of data may answer many research questions. In fact, many studies do not go beyond examining the simple tabulation of the question-by-question responses to a survey. On the other hand, although

TABLE 20.3 CROSS-TABULATION TABLE FROM A SURVEY ON ETHICS IN AMERICA

Activity	REPORTED BEHAVIOR (PERCENTAGE OF GENERAL PUBLIC WHO HAVE EVER DONE EACH ACTIVITY)					
	Under 50 Years Old	Over 50 Years Old	Men	Women	College Graduate	High School Graduate
Taken home work supplies	50	26	47	33	58	21
Called in sick to work when not ill	50	18	Not reported		36	21

Activity	REPORTED BEHAVIOR (PERCENTAGE WHO HAVE EVER DONE EACH ACTIVITY)	
	Business Executives	General Public
Taken home work supplies	74	40
Called in sick to work when not ill	14	31
Used company telephone for personal long-distance calls	78	15
Overstated deductions somewhat on tax forms	35	13
Driven while drunk	80	33
Saw a fellow employee steal something at work and did not report it	7	26

frequency counts, percentage distributions, and averages summarize a considerable amount of information, simple tabulation may not yield the full value of the research. Most data can be further organized in a variety of ways. For example, data from a survey that samples both men and women commonly are separated into groups or categories based on gender. Analyzing results by groups, categories, or classes is the technique of **cross-tabulation.**

cross-tabulation
Organizing data by groups, categories, or classes to facilitate comparisons; a joint frequency distribution of observations on two or more sets of variables.

The purpose of categorization and cross-tabulation is to allow the inspection of differences among groups and to make comparisons. This form of analysis also helps determine the form of relationship between two variables. Cross-tabulating the results of business research helps clarify the research findings as they pertain to industry, market, and organizational segments.

Table 20.3 presents a summary of several cross-tabulations from American citizens' responses to a questionnaire on ethical behavior in the United States. A researcher interested in the relative ethical perspectives of business executives and the general public can inspect this table and easily compare the two groups. The percentage table illustrates the added value of calculating percentages.

Examples of the usefulness of categorization and cross-tabulation can be found in most experiments. It is obvious that the data from the experimental and control groups should be separated or partitioned, because researchers wish to compare the effects of a treatment.

Contingency Table

contingency table
The results of a cross-tabulation of two variables, such as answers to two survey questions.

Part A of Table 20.4 shows how the cross-tabulation of answers to two survey questions (or two variables) results in a **contingency table,** or data matrix. The frequency counts for the question "Do you shop at IGA?" are presented as

TABLE 20.4 POSSIBLE CROSS-TABULATIONS OF ONE QUESTION

A. Cross-Tabulation of Question "Do You Shop at IGA?" by Sex of Respondent

	Yes	No	Total
Men	150	75	225
Women	180	45	225
Total	330	120	450

B. Percentage Cross-Tabulation of Question "Do You Shop at IGA?" by Sex of Respondent, Row Percentage

	Yes	No	Total (Base)
Men	66.7%	33.3%	100% (225)
Women	80.0%	20.0%	100% (225)

C. Percentage Cross-Tabulation of Question "Do You Shop at IGA?" by Sex of Respondent, Column Percentage

	Yes	No
Men	45.5%	62.5%
Women	54.5	37.5
Total	100.0	100.0
(Base)	(330)	(120)

column totals. The total number of men and women in the sample are presented as row totals. These row and column totals are often called *marginals,* because they appear in the table's margins. There are four *cells* within Part A, each representing a specific combination of the two variables. The cell representing women who said they do not shop at IGA has a frequency count of 45.

The contingency table in Part A is referred to as a 2 × 2 table because it has two rows and two columns. Any cross-tabulation table may be classified according to the number of rows by the number of columns (R by C). Thus, a 3 × 4 table is one with three rows and four columns.

Percentage Cross-Tabulations

base (base number)
The number of respondents or observations that indicate a total; used as a basis for computing percentages in each column or row in a cross-tabulation table.

When data from a survey are cross-tabulated, percentages help the researcher understand the nature of the relationship by allowing relative comparison. The total number of respondents or observations may be utilized as a **base** for computing the percentage in each cell. When the objective of the research is to identify a relationship between the answers to two questions (or two variables), it is common to choose one of the questions as the base for determining percentages. For example, look at the data in Parts A, B, and C of Table 20.4. Compare Part B with Part C. Selecting either the row percentages or the column percentages will emphasize a particular comparison or distribution. The nature of the problem the researcher wishes to investigate will determine which marginal total will be used as a base for computing percentages.

Fortunately, there is a conventional rule for determining the direction of percentages if the researcher has identified which variable is the independent variable and which is the dependent variable: The percentages should be computed *in the direction of the independent variable.* That is, the marginal total of the independent variable should be used as the base for computing the percentages. Although survey research does not identify cause-and-effect relationships, one might argue that it would be logical to assume that a variable such as one's gender might predict shopping behavior, in which case independent and dependent variables may be established for the purpose of presenting the most useful information.

Elaboration and Refinement

The *Oxford Universal Dictionary* defines *analysis* as "the resolution of anything complex into its simplest elements." This suggests that once the basic relationship between two variables has been examined, the researcher may wish to investigate this relationship under a variety of different conditions. Typically, a third variable is introduced into the analysis to elaborate and refine the researcher's understanding by specifying the conditions under which the relationship between the first two variables is strongest and weakest.[5] In other words, a more elaborate analysis asks: "Will interpretation of the relationship be modified if other variables are simultaneously considered?"

TO THE POINT

It is terrible to speak well and be wrong.

SOPHOCLES

elaboration analysis
An analysis of the basic cross-tabulation for each level of a variable not previously considered, perhaps subgroups of the sample.

Performing the basic cross-tabulation within various subgroups of the sample is a common form of **elaboration analysis.** The researcher breaks down the analysis for each level of another variable. For example, if the researcher has cross-tabulated shopping behavior by sex (see Table 20.4) and wishes to investigate another variable (perhaps marital status) that may modify the original relationship, a more elaborate analysis may be conducted. Table 20.5 breaks down the responses to the question "Do you shop at IGA?" by sex and marital status. The data show that marital status does not change the original cross-tabulation relationship among women, but it does change that relationship among men. The analysis suggests that our original conclusion about the relationship between sex and shopping behavior be retained for women; the data confirm the original interpretation. However, the refinements in analysis have pointed out a relationship among men that was not immediately discernible in the two-variable case. It may be concluded that marital status modifies the original relationship among men—that is, that there is an interaction

TABLE 20.5 CROSS-TABULATION OF MARITAL STATUS, SEX, AND RESPONSES TO THE QUESTION "DO YOU SHOP AT IGA?"

	MARRIED		SINGLE	
	Men	Women	Men	Women
"Do you shop at IGA?"				
Yes	55%	80%	86%	80%
No	45	20	14	20

moderator variable
A third variable that, when introduced into an analysis, alters or has a contingent effect on the relationship between an independent variable and a dependent variable.

spurious relationship
An apparent relationship between two variables that is not authentic, but appears authentic because an elaboration analysis with a third variable has not yet been conducted.

effect. In this situation marital status is a moderator variable. A **moderator variable** is a third variable that, when introduced into the analysis, alters or has a contingent effect on the relationship between an independent variable and a dependent variable.

In other situations the adding of a third variable to the analysis may lead us to reject the original conclusion about the relationship. When this occurs, the elaboration analysis will have indicated a **spurious relationship**—an apparent relationship between the original two variables that is not authentic. Our earlier example about high ice cream cone sales and drownings at the beach (Chapter 4) illustrated a spurious relationship. Additional discussion of this topic, dealing with measures of association, appears in Chapter 23.

Elaborating on the basic cross-tabulation is a form of *multivariate analysis,* because more than two variables are simultaneously analyzed to identify complex relationships. When a breakdown of the responses into three or more questions is required, there is usually a multivariate statistical technique for investigating the relationship. Such techniques are discussed in Chapter 24.

How Many Cross-Tabulations?

Surveys may ask dozens of questions. Computer-assisted business researchers often go on "fishing expeditions," cross-tabulating every question on a survey with every other question. Every possible response becomes a possible explanatory variable. All too often this activity provides only reams of extra computer output of no value to management. To avoid this, the number of cross-tabulations should be predetermined when the research objectives are stated.

Quadrant Analysis

quadrant analysis
A variation of the cross-tabulation table in which responses to two rating scale questions are plotted in four quadrants on a two-dimensional table.

Quadrant analysis is a variation of the cross-tabulation table that has grown increasingly popular as a component of total quality management programs. Quadrant analysis plots responses to two rating scale questions into four quadrants on a two-dimensional table. Most quadrant analysis in business research portrays or plots the relationship between the average responses about a product attribute's importance and average ratings of a company's (or brand's) performance with respect to that product feature. Sometimes the term *importance-performance analysis* is used because consumers rate perceived importance of several attributes and then rate the company's brand (and competitors' brands) in relation to that attribute.

Exhibit 20.2 shows a quadrant analysis matrix for a gourmet microwave food product that was evaluated using two seven-point scales.[6] The upper-left quadrant (high importance/low rating) shows importance ratings above 4.0 and performance ratings of 4.0 or below.[7] This exhibit shows that consumers believe a microwave meal should be easy to prepare, but this new product is rated low on this attribute. Consumers know what they want, but they are not getting it. The upper-right quadrant (high importance/high rating) shows importance ratings above 4.0 and performance ratings above 4.0. Microwave meals should taste good, and this product scores high on this attribute. Managers often look to this quadrant for attributes that are "hot buttons" that will be useful in positioning the product. The lower quadrants show attributes of low importance to consumers, with either low or high product ratings. This microwave product could be eaten as a late night snack, but this attribute is not important to consumers.

EXHIBIT 20.2 QUADRANT ANALYSIS FOR A MICROWAVE MEAL

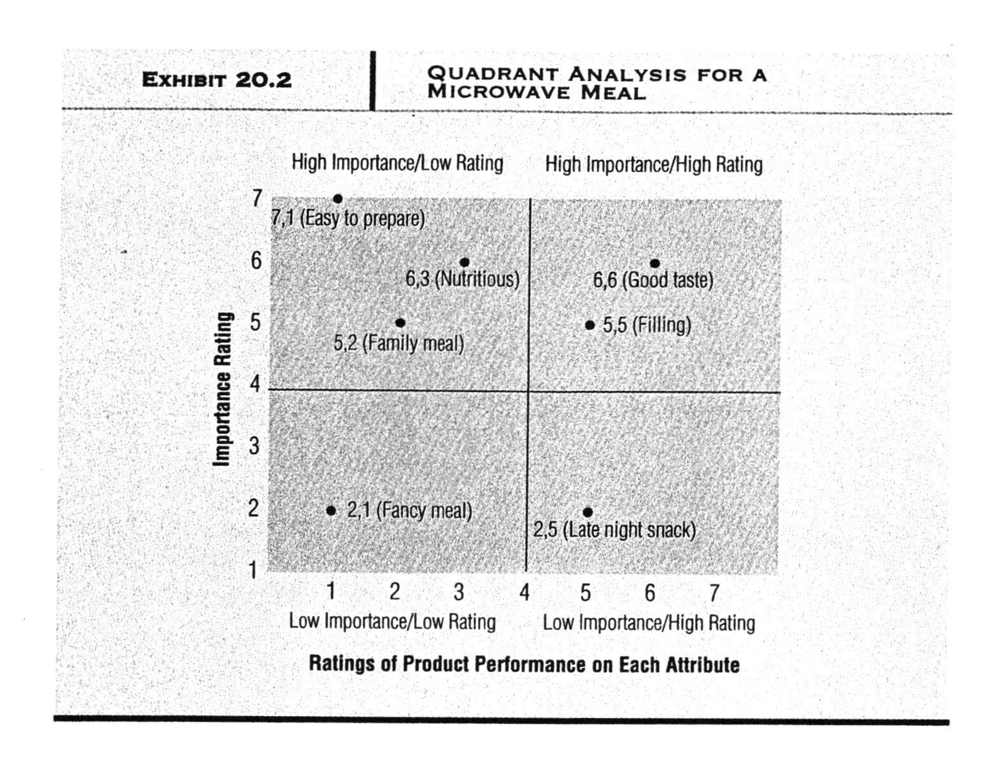

DATA TRANSFORMATION

data transformation
The process of changing data from their original form to a format that better supports data analysis to achieve research objectives. Also called data conversion.

TO THE POINT

All that we do is done with an eye to something else.

ARISTOTLE

Data transformation is the process of changing data from their original form to a format that is more suitable to perform a data analysis that will achieve the research objectives. Researchers often modify the values of scalar data or create new variables. For example, many researchers believe that response bias will be less if interviewers ask consumers for their year of birth rather than their age, even though the objective of the data analysis is to investigate respondents' ages in years. This does not present a problem for the research analyst, because a simple data transformation is possible. The raw data coded as birth year can be easily transformed to age by subtracting the birth year from the current year.

Collapsing or combining adjacent categories of a variable is a common data transformation that reduces the number of categories. Exhibit 20.3 shows an example of a Likert scale item that has been collapsed. The "strongly agree" and the "agree" response categories have been combined. The "strongly disagree" and the "disagree" response categories have also been combined into a single category. The result is the collapsing of the five-category scale down to three.

Creating new variables by respecifying the data with numeric or logical transformations is another important data transformation. For example, Likert summated scales reflect the combination of scores (raw data) from various attitudinal statements. The summative score for an attitude scale with three statements is calculated as follows:

$$\text{Summative Score} = \text{Variable 1} + \text{Variable 2} + \text{Variable 3}$$

This calculation can be accomplished by using simple arithmetic or by programming a computer with a data transformation equation that creates the new variable "summative score."

EXHIBIT 20.3 | **COLLAPSING A FIVE-CATEGORY LIKERT SCALE**

Likert Scale as It Appeared on the Questionnaire

Increased foreign investment in the United States poses a threat to our economic independence.

Strongly Agree *Agree* *Neither Agree or Disagree* *Disagree* *Strongly Disagree*

Tabulation of Responses in Original and Collapsed Versions

5-Point Scale	Percentage	Collapsed Scale	Percentage
Strongly Agree	3	Strongly Agree/Agree	15
Agree	12		
Neither Agree nor Disagree	30	Neither Agree nor Disagree	30
Disagree	45	Strongly Disagree/Disagree	55
Strongly Disagree	10		

In many cases, however, the establishment of categories requires careful thought. For example, how does one categorize women on their orientation toward the feminist movement? The first rule for identifying categories, as in other aspects of research, is that the categories should be related to the research problem and purpose.

Index Numbers

index number
Data summary values based on data for some base period to facilitate comparisons over time.

The consumer price index and the wholesale price index are secondary data sources frequently used by business researchers. These price indexes, like other **index numbers,** allow researchers to compare a variable or set of variables in a given time period with another variable or set of variables in another time period. Scores or observations are recalibrated so that they may be related to a certain base period or base number.

Consider the information in Table 20.6 on weekly television viewing (hours:minutes) by household size. Index numbers are computed in the following manner. First, a base number is selected—in this case, the U.S. average of 52 hours and 36 minutes. The index numbers are computed by dividing the

TABLE 20.6 | **HOURS OF TELEVISION USAGE PER WEEK**

Household Size	Hours:Minutes
1	41:01
2	47:58
3+	60:49
Total U.S. average	52:36

score for each category and multiplying by 100. The index shows percentage changes from a base number; for example:

$$\text{1 person:} \quad \frac{41{:}01}{52{:}36} = .7832 \times 100 = 78.32$$

$$\text{2 people:} \quad \frac{47{:}58}{52{:}36} = .9087 \times 100 = 90.87$$

$$\text{3+ people:} \quad \frac{60{:}49}{52{:}36} = 1.1553 \times 100 = 115.53$$

$$\text{Total U.S. average:} \quad \frac{52{:}36}{52{:}36} = 1.0000 \times 100 = 100.00$$

If the data are time-related, a base year is chosen. The index numbers are then computed by dividing each year's activity by the base year activity and multiplying by 100. Index numbers require a ratio scale of measurement.

Calculating Rank Order

Respondents often indicate a rank ordering of brand preference or some other variable of interest to researchers. To summarize these data for all respondents, analysts perform a data transformation by multiplying the frequency times the rank (score) to develop a new scale that represents the summarized rank ordering.

For example, suppose the president of a company had ten executives rank their preferences for "dream destinations" that would be the prize in a productivity contest. Table 20.7 shows how 10 executives ranked each of four locations: Hawaii, Paris, Greece, and China. Table 20.8 tabulates the frequencies of these rankings. To calculate a summary rank ordering, the destination with the first (highest) preference was given the lowest number (1) and the least preferred destination (lowest preference) was given the highest number (4). The summarized rank ordering is obtained with the following calculations:

$$\text{Hawaii:} \quad (3 \times 1) + (5 \times 2) + (1 \times 3) + (1 \times 4) = 20$$

$$\text{Paris:} \quad (3 \times 1) + (1 \times 2) + (3 \times 3) + (3 \times 4) = 26$$

$$\text{Greece:} \quad (2 \times 1) + (2 \times 2) + (4 \times 3) + (2 \times 4) = 26$$

$$\text{China:} \quad (2 \times 1) + (2 \times 2) + (2 \times 3) + (4 \times 4) = 28$$

TABLE 20.7 INDIVIDUAL RANKING OF DREAM DESTINATIONS

Person	Hawaii	Paris	Greece	China
1	1	2	4	3
2	1	3	4	2
3	2	1	3	4
4	2	4	3	1
5	2	1	3	4
6	3	4	1	2
7	2	3	1	4
8	1	4	2	3
9	4	3	2	1
10	2	1	3	4

TABLE 20.8 FREQUENCY TABLE OF DREAM DESTINATION RANKINGS

	PREFERENCE RANKINGS			
Destination	**1st**	**2nd**	**3rd**	**4th**
Hawaii	3	5	1	1
Paris	3	1	3	3
Greece	2	2	4	2
China	2	2	2	4

The lowest total score indicates the first (highest) preference ranking. The results show the following rank ordering: (1) Hawaii, (2) Paris, (3) Greece, and (4) China.

TABULAR AND GRAPHIC METHODS OF DISPLAYING DATA

Tables and graphs (pictorial representations of data) may simplify and clarify the research data. Tabular and graphic representations of data may take a number of forms, ranging from computer printouts to elaborate pictographs. The purpose of each table or graph, however, is to facilitate the summarization and communication of the meaning of the data. For example, Table 20.9 illustrates the relationship among education, income, and expenditures on regional airline usage for vacation/pleasure trips. Note that the shaded area emphasizes a

TABLE 20.9 REGIONAL AIRLINE USAGE FOR VACATION/PLEASURE BY INCOME AND EDUCATION

	Total	**Under $20,000**	**$20,000–$39,000**	**$40,000–$59,000**	**$60,000 and Over**
All Consumers					
Expenditures (%)	100	10	7	16	67
Consumer units (%)	100	42	19	16	23
Index	100	26	36	100	291
Non–High School Grad					
Expenditures (%)	8	1	2	1	4
Consumer units (%)	35	21	6	4	4
Index	21	5	33	25	100
High School Grad					
Expenditures (%)	29	4	2	8	15
Consumer units (%)	30	11	6	6	7
Index	96	36	33	133	214
Attended/graduated College					
Expenditures (%)	63	5	3	7	48
Consumer units (%)	35	10	6	6	13
Index	180	50	50	116	369
				% Pop. 32	= % Expen. 78

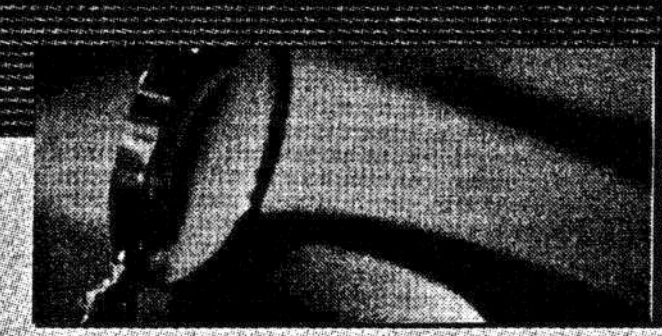

RESEARCH INSIGHT

FLORENCE NIGHTINGALE: INVENTOR OF THE PIE CHART

Florence Nightingale is remembered as a pioneering nurse and hospital reformer.[8] Less well known is her equally pioneering use of statistics. In advocating medical reform Nightingale also promoted statistical description; she developed a uniform procedure for hospitals to report statistical information. She also invented the pie chart, in which proportions are represented as wedges of a circular diagram. Finally, she struggled to get the study of statistics introduced into higher education.

One of Nightingale's analyses compared the peacetime death rates of British soldiers and civilians. She discovered and showed that the soldiers who lived in barracks under unhealthy conditions were twice as likely to die as civilians of the same age and sex. She then used the soldiers' 2 percent death rate to persuade the Queen and the Prime Minister to establish a Royal Commission on the Health of the Army. It is just as criminal, she wrote, for the Army to have a mortality of 20 per 1,000 "as it would be to take 1,100 men per annum out upon Salisbury Plain and shoot them."

key conclusion with respect to market share: The information indicates that 32 percent of the population makes 78 percent of the expenditures. This form of presentation simplifies interpretation.

Although there are a number of standardized forms for presenting data in tables or graphs, the creative researcher can increase the effectiveness of a particular presentation. Bar charts, pie charts, curve diagrams, pictograms, and other graphic forms of presentation create a strong visual impression. (See Chapter 25.)

For example, Exhibit 20.4 shows how a line graph can show comparisons over time. Exhibit 20.5 shows how pie charts and bar charts can enhance information from a survey.

COMPUTER PROGRAMS FOR ANALYSIS

The proliferation of computer technology in businesses and universities has greatly facilitated tabulation and statistical analysis. Commercial statistical packages eliminate the need to write a new program every time you want to tabulate and analyze data with a computer. SAS, Statistical Package for the Social Sciences (SPSS), SYSTAT, and MINITAB are commonly used statistical packages. These user-friendly packages emphasize statistical calculations

EXHIBIT 20.4 | **LINE GRAPHS HIGHLIGHTING COMPARISONS OVER TIME[9]**

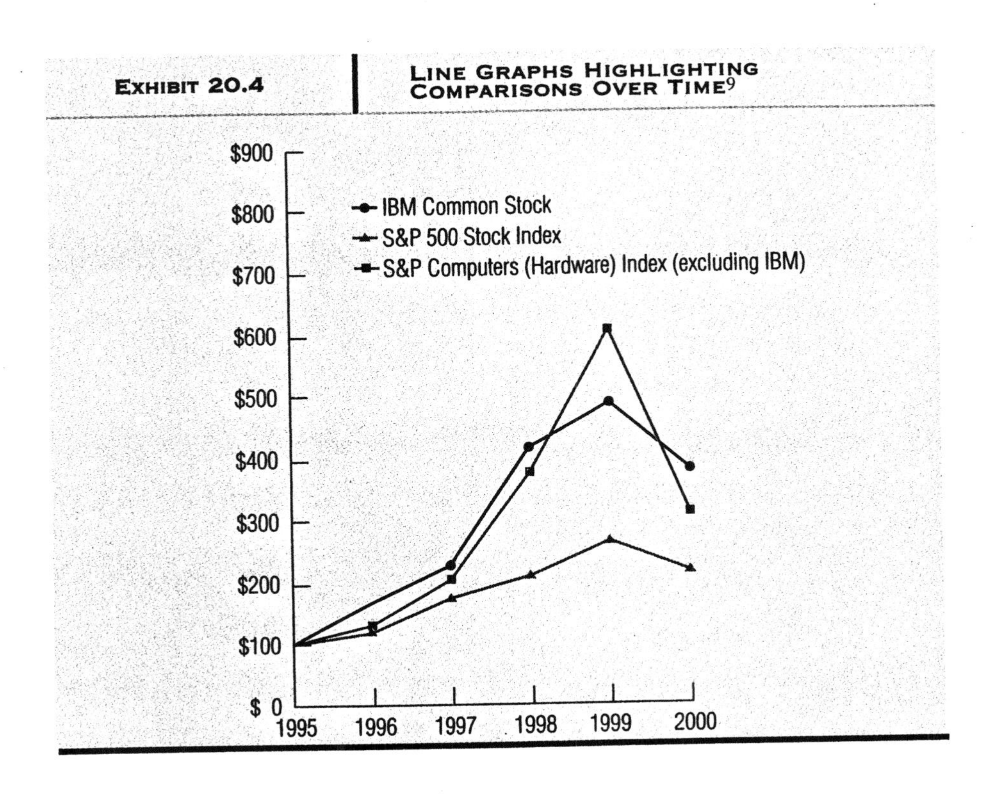

and hypothesis testing for varied types of data. They also provide programs for entering and editing data. Most of these packages contain sizable arrays of programs for descriptive analysis and univariate, bivariate, and multivariate statistical analysis. Several examples will be given in this section to illustrate how easy it is to use these statistical packages.

EXHIBIT 20.5 | **PIE CHARTS AND BAR GRAPHS ENHANCE VISUAL IMPACT[10]**

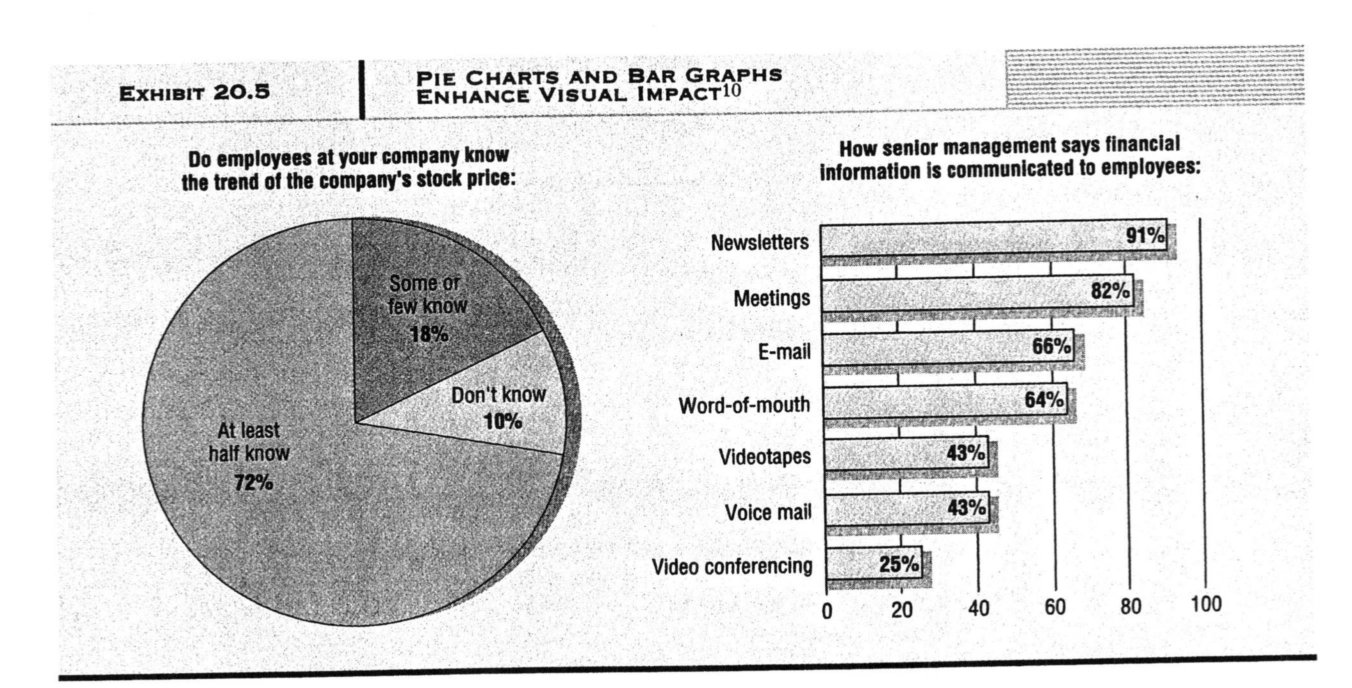

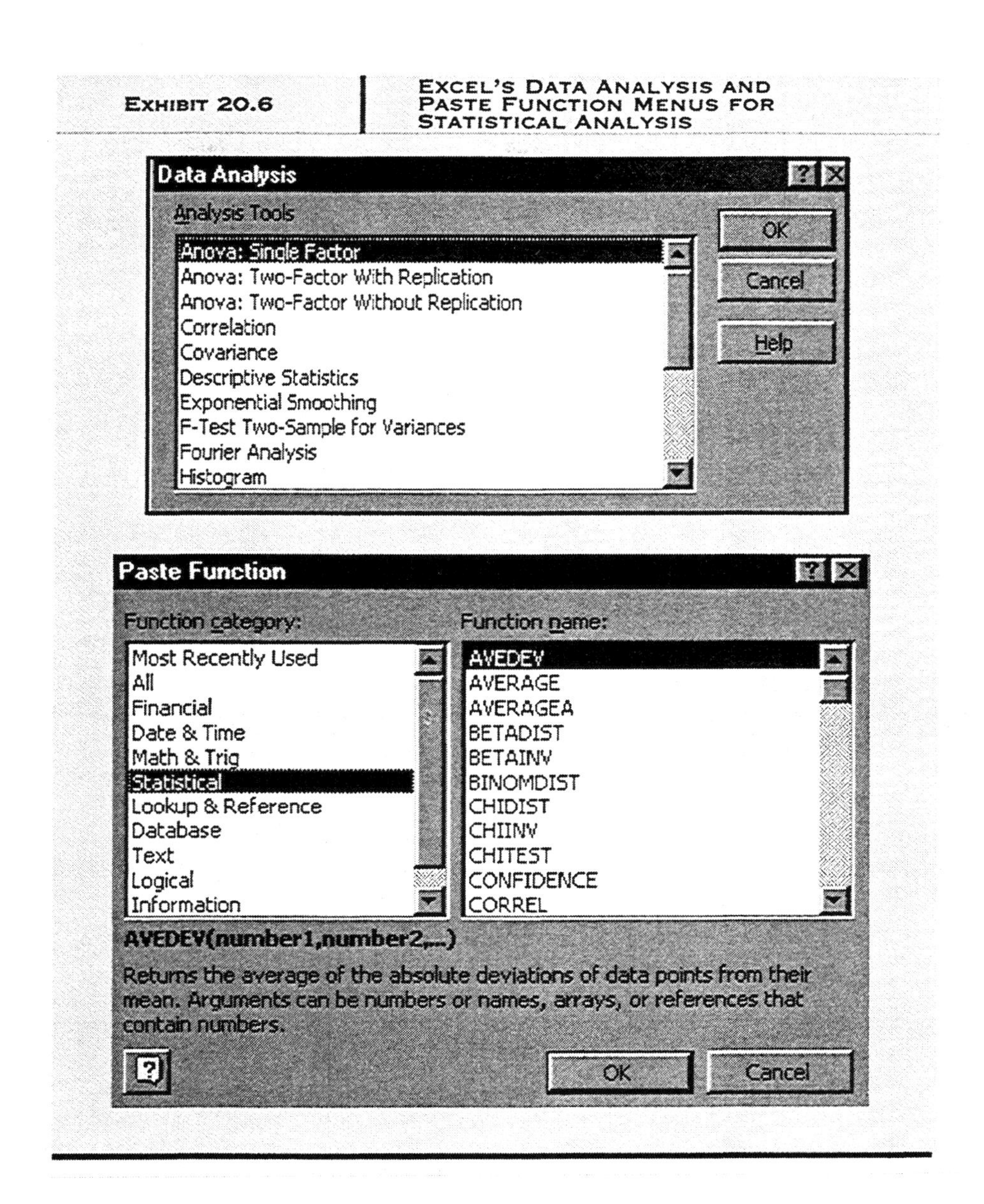

Exhibit 20.6 Excel's Data Analysis and Paste Function Menus for Statistical Analysis

Microsoft Excel, Lotus 1-2-3, and Quatro Pro are spreadsheet packages that emphasize database management and allow a user to enter and edit data with minimal effort. They also incorporate some programs for descriptive analysis, graphic analysis, and limited statistical analysis. In Excel, statistical calculations can be performed using the Data Analysis and Paste Function menus shown in Exhibit 20.6. (Note: Depending on the version of Excel you have, you may have to add-in the statistical software applications. You will then find the enhanced functions by clicking on the Tools menu and then on Data Analysis.)

Exhibit 20.7 shows an SAS computer printout of descriptive statistics for two variables: EMP (number of employees working in an MSA, or Metropolitan Statistical Area) and SALES (sales volume in dollars in an MSA). The numbers of data elements (*N*), the mean, the standard deviation, and other descriptive statistics are displayed.

EXHIBIT 20.7 | **SAS OUTPUT OF DESCRIPTIVE STATISTICS**

State = NY

Variable	N	Mean	Standard Deviation	Minimum Value	Maximum Value	STD Error of Mean	Sum	Variance	C.V.
EMP	10	142.930	232.665	12.8000	788.800	73.575	1429.300	54133.0	162.782
SALES	10	5807.800	11905.127	307.0000	39401.000	3764.732	58078.000	141732049.1	204.985

Key: EMP = Number of employees (000)
SALES = Sales (000)

Exhibit 20.8 presents output from the SPSS package showing the results of a question about confidence in the stock market in a frequency table. This SPSS output gives the absolute frequency of observations, the relative frequency as a percentage of all observations, the valid percentage (the adjusted frequency as a percentage of the number of respondents who provided a recorded answer rather than answering "don't know" or leaving the question blank), and the cumulative percentage.

A histogram is similar to a bar chart. Exhibit 20.9 shows an SPSS histogram plot of purchase price data from a survey. In this histogram, each bar indicates the number of purchasers.

Exhibit 20.10 shows an SPSS cross-tabulation of two variables: gender (GENDER) and satisfaction with daycare (DAYCARE), with the column total used as a basis for percentages.

As you can see, statistical software programs are quite versatile, and they are widely used in business research.

EXHIBIT 20.8 | **SPSS COMPUTER OUTPUT SHOWING FREQUENCIES**

STOCK Confidence in Stock Market

Value Label	Value	Frequency	Percent	Valid Percent	Cum Percent
Yes	1.00	319	59.1	59.4	59.4
No	2.00	218	40.4	40.6	100.0
	.	3	.6	Missing	
	Total	540	100.0	100.0	

Valid cases 537 Missing cases 3

COMPUTER GRAPHICS/COMPUTER MAPPING

Graphic aids prepared by computers are rapidly replacing graphic aids drawn by artists. Computer graphics are extremely useful for descriptive analysis of information stored in databases. Computer-generated graphics and charts may be created inexpensively and quickly with easy-to-use computer software programs such as Power Point or Astound. These software programs are both user-friendly and versatile. Their versatility allows researchers to explore many alternative ways of visually communicating their findings.

EXHIBIT 20.9 | **SPSS HISTOGRAM OUTPUT**[11]

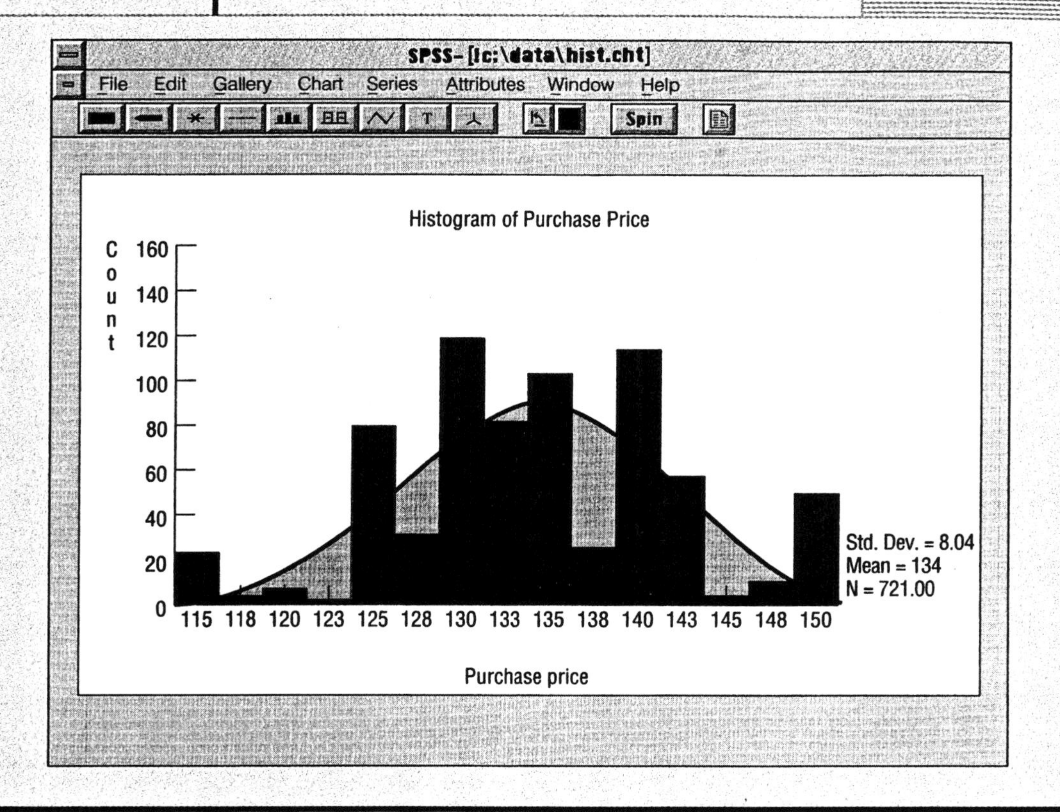

EXHIBIT 20.10 | **SPSS CROSS-TABULATION OUTPUT**

SPSS/PC Cross-Tabulation with Column and Total Percents

Satisfaction with DAYCARE * GENDER Cross-Tabulation

			GENDER		
			women	men	Total
Satisfaction with Daycare	high	Count	9	17	26
		% within GENDER	10.6%	9.2%	9.6%
		% of Total	3.3%	6.3%	9.6%
	low	Count	45	70	115
		% within GENDER	52.9%	37.8%	42.6%
		% of Total	16.7%	25.9%	42.6%
	middle	Count	31	98	129
		% within GENDER	36.5%	53.0%	47.8%
		% of Total	11.5%	36.3%	47.8%
Total		Count	85	185	270
		% within GENDER	100.0%	100.0%	100.0%
		% of Total	31.5%	68.5%	100.0%

computer map
A computer-generated map that portrays a variable, such as demographic data, in two or three dimensions.

Decision support systems can portray data for sales, demographics, lifestyles, production activity, retail activity, and other variables on two- or three-dimensional **computer maps.** For example, in Exhibit 20.11 a computer map displays wiretap surveillance.

Geographic information systems and computer maps have many other uses. When a 911 emergency call comes in, a fire department may use its computer to locate the fire hydrant nearest the fire's location. A city's water department might get a call reporting a water leak near a given intersection and use the geographic information system to map all the water lines and pumps in the area. The information system could also generate a detailed maintenance history on any segment of the water system.[12]

EXHIBIT 20.11 | COMPUTER GRAPHIC ILLUSTRATING WIRETAP SURVEILLANCE INTERCEPTION BY STATE[13]

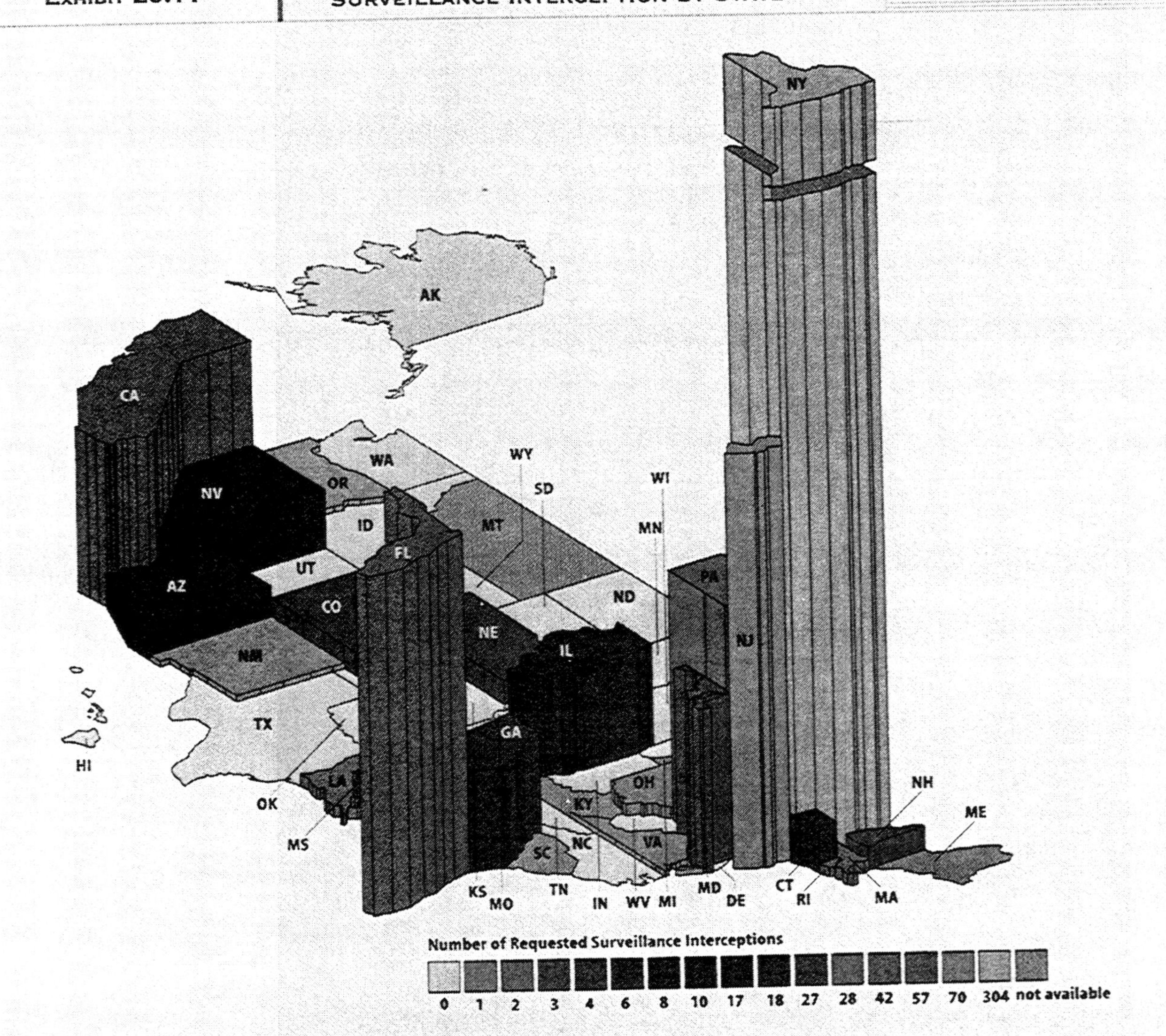

box and whisker plot
A graphic device that represents central tendencies, percentiles, variability, and frequency distributions.

interquartile range
The part of a data distribution between the 25th and 75th percentiles; also called the midspread.

outlier
A value that lies outside the normal range of a set of data.

Many computer programs can draw **box and whisker plots** that graphically represent central tendencies, percentiles, variability, and frequency distributions. Exhibit 20.12 shows a computer-drawn box and whisker plot for 100 responses to a question involving a 10-point scale.[14] The response categories are shown on the vertical axis. The box inside the plot represents 50 percent of the responses; it extends from the 25th percentile to the 75th percentile. This shows a measure of variability sometimes called the **interquartile range,** though the term *midspread* is less complex and more descriptive.[15] The location of the line within the box indicates the median. The dashed lines extending from the top and bottom of the box are the whiskers. Each whisker extends either the length of the box (the midspread in our example is 2 scale points) or to the most extreme observation in that direction. An **outlier** is a value that lies outside the normal range of the data. In Exhibit 20.12, outliers are indicated by either 0s or asterisks. Box and whisker plots are particularly useful for comparing group categories (e.g., men versus women) or several variables (e.g., relative importance levels of product attributes).

INTERPRETATION

An interpreter at the United Nations translates a foreign language into another language to explain the meaning of a foreign diplomat's speech. In business research the purpose of the interpretation process is to explain the meaning of the data. After the statistical analysis of the data, researchers and

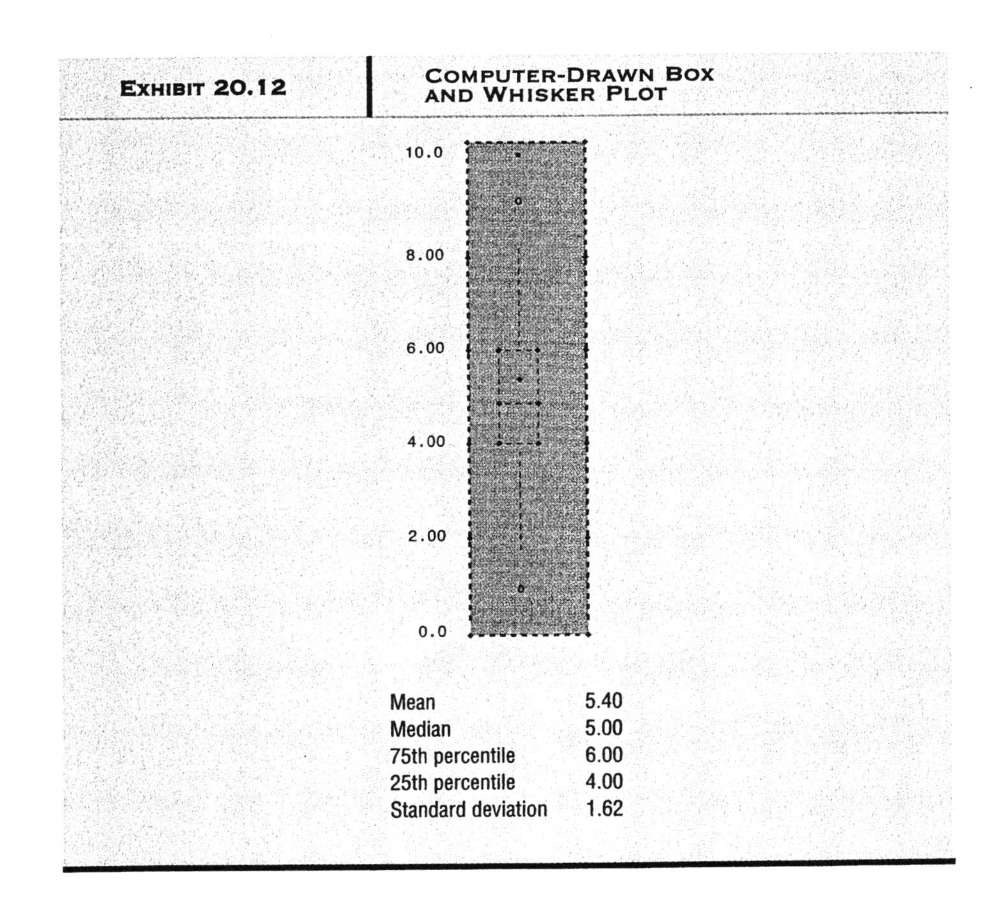

EXHIBIT 20.12 COMPUTER-DRAWN BOX AND WHISKER PLOT

Mean	5.40
Median	5.00
75th percentile	6.00
25th percentile	4.00
Standard deviation	1.62

managers begin to make inferences and formulate conclusions about their meaning.

interpretation
The process of making inferences and drawing conclusions concerning the meaning and implications of a research investigation.

A distinction can be made between *analysis* and *interpretation*. **Interpretation** refers to making inferences pertinent to the meaning and implications of the research investigation and drawing conclusions about the managerial implications of its variables. Of course, the logical interpretation of the data and statistical analysis are closely intertwined. Researchers interpret and analyze at the same time—that is, when a researcher calculates, say, a *t*-test of two means, he or she almost immediately infers group differences or the existence of a relationship. Almost automatically researchers seek out the significance of the statistical analysis for the research problem as they order, break down, and manipulate the data.[16]

The more we study, the more we discover our ignorance.
PERCY BYSSHE SHELLEY

From a management perspective, however, the qualitative meaning of the data and the managerial implications are important aspects of the interpretation. Consider the crucial role interpretation of the research results played in investigating a new product: a lip stain that could color the lips a desired shade semipermanently and last for a month at a time:

> The lip stain idea, among lipstick wearers, received very high scores on a rating scale ranging from "excellent" to "poor," presumably because it would not wear off. However, it appeared that even among routine wearers of lipstick the idea was being rated highly more for its interesting, even ingenious, nature than for its practical appeal to the consumer's personality. They liked the idea, but for someone else, not themselves. . . . [Careful interpretation of the data] revealed that not being able to remove the stain for that length of time caused most women to consider the idea irrelevant in relation to their own personal needs and desires. Use of the product seems to represent more of a "permanent commitment" than is usually associated with the use of a particular cosmetic. In fact, women attached overtly negative meaning to the product concept, often comparing it with hair dyes instead of a long-lasting lipstick.[17]

This example shows that interpretation is crucial. However, the process is difficult to explain in a textbook because there is no one best way to interpret data. Many possible interpretations of data may be derived from a number of thought processes. Experience with selected cases will help students develop their own interpretative ability.

In all too many instances data are merely reported and not interpreted. Research firms may provide reams of computer output that do not state what the data mean. At the other extreme there are researchers who tend to analyze every possible relationship between each and every variable in the study; they usually have not defined the problem during the earlier stages of research. Researchers who have a clear sense of the purpose of the research do not request statistical analysis of data that may have little or nothing to do with the primary purpose of the research.

SUMMARY

Descriptive analysis refers to the transformation of raw data into an understandable form so that their interpretation will not be difficult. Descriptive information is obtained by summarizing, categorizing, rearranging, and other forms of analysis.

Tabulation refers to the orderly arrangement of data in a table or other summary format. It is useful for indicating percentages and cumulative percentages as well as frequency distributions. The data may be described by measures of central tendency, such as the mean, median, or mode. Cross-tabulation shows how one variable relates to another, revealing differences between groups. Cross-tabulations should be limited to categories related to the research problem and purpose. It is also useful to put the results into percentage form to facilitate intergroup comparisons.

Performing the basic cross-tabulation within various subgroups of the sample is a common form of elaboration analysis. Elaboration analysis often identifies moderator variables or spurious relationships. A moderator variable is a third variable that, when introduced into the analysis, alters or has a contingent effect on the relationship between an independent variable and a dependent variable. A spurious relationship is an apparent relationship between two variables that turns out not to be authentic when a third variable is added to the analysis. Quadrant analysis is a variation of the cross-tabulation table that plots two rating scale questions into four quadrants on a two-dimensional table.

Tables and graphs help to simplify and clarify research data. Computer software greatly facilitates descriptive analysis. Many programs are available that facilitate the construction of graphs and charts. Data transformation is the process of changing data from their original form to a format that is more suitable for data analysis. Index numbers relate data for a particular time period to data for a base year.

Computer mapping portrays demographic, sales, and other data on two- or three-dimensional maps that aid interpretation of descriptive data.

The interpretation of data uses the results of descriptive analysis. Interpretation involves making inferences about the real world and drawing conclusions about the data's managerial implications.

Key Terms

descriptive analysis
simple tabulation
frequency table
percentage
cumulative percentage
frequency distribution
cross-tabulation
contingency table
base (base number)
elaboration analysis
moderator variable
spurious relationship
quadrant analysis
data transformation
index number
computer map
box and whisker plot
interquartile range
outlier
interpretation

Questions for Review and Critical Thinking

1. In a survey respondents were asked to respond to a statement asking if their work was interesting. Interpret the frequency distribution in the SPSS output below.

"My work is interesting."

Category Label	Code	Absolute Frequency	Relative Frequency (Percent)	Adjusted Frequency (Percent)	Cum. Frequency (Percent)
Very true	1	650	23.9	62.4	62.4
Somewhat true	2	303	11.2	29.1	91.5
Not very true	3	61	2.2	5.9	97.3
Not at all true	4	28	1.0	2.7	100.0
		1,673	61.6	Missing	
	Total	2,715	100.0	100.0	

Valid cases 1,042 Missing cases 1,673

2. Use the data in the table below to
   (a) prepare a frequency distribution of respondents' ages and
   (b) cross-tabulate the respondents' genders with cola preference.

Individual	Sex	Age	Cola Preference	Weekly Unit Purchases
John	M	19	Coke	2
Al	M	17	Pepsi	5
Bill	M	20	Pepsi	7
Mary	F	20	Coke	2
Jim	M	18	Coke	4
Bobbie	F	16	Coke	4
Tom	M	17	Pepsi	8
Dawn	F	19	Pepsi	1

3. Data on the average size of a soda (in ounces) at all 30 major league baseball parks are as follows: 14, 18, 20, 16, 16, 12, 14, 16, 14, 16, 16, 16, 14, 14, 16, 20, 12, 16, 20, 12, 16, 16, 24, 16, 16, 14, 14, 12, 14, 20. The results of an Excel Descriptive Statistics analysis of these data are shown on the next page. Interpret the output.

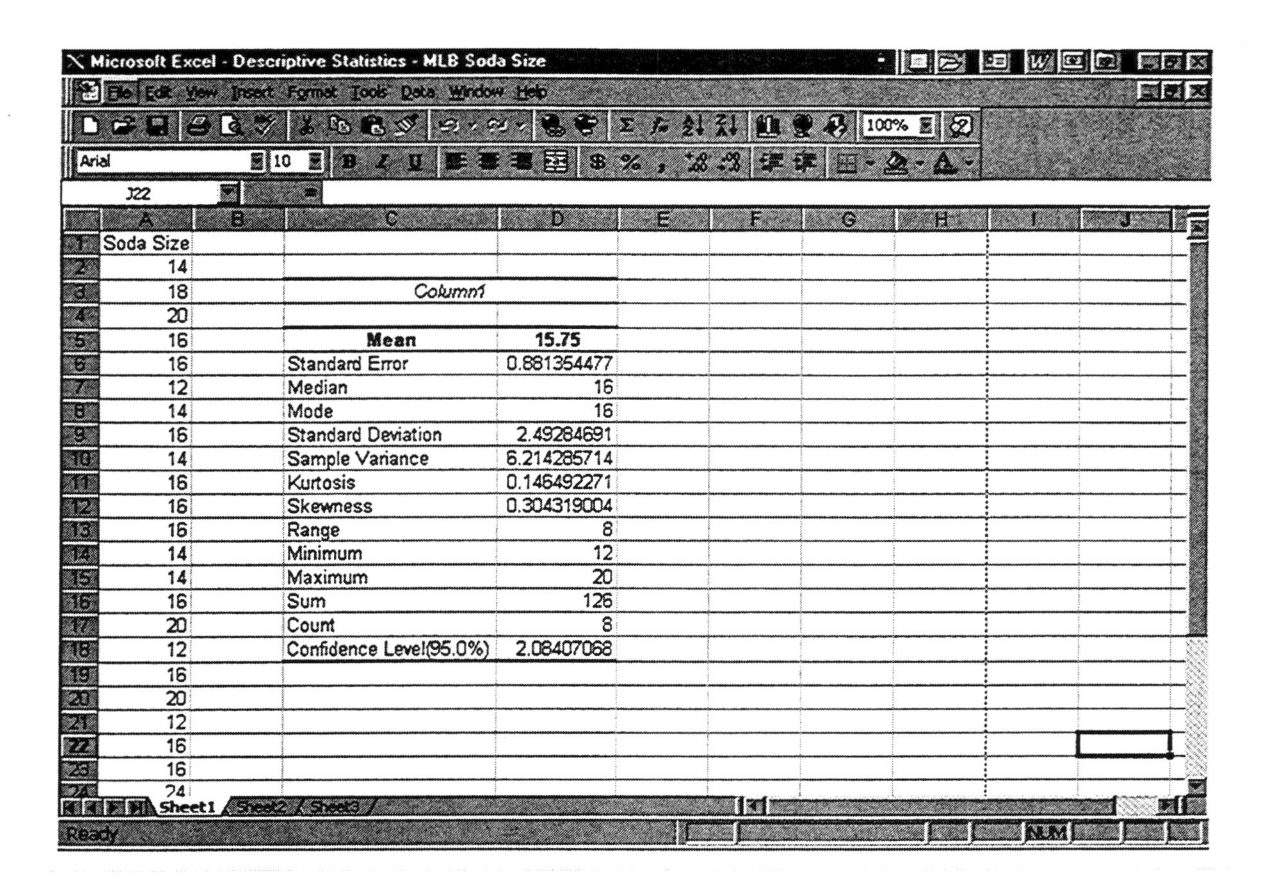

Microsoft Excel - Descriptive Statistics - MLB Soda Size

	A	B	C	D
1	Soda Size			
2	14			
3	18		*Column1*	
4	20			
5	16		**Mean**	**15.75**
6	16		Standard Error	0.881354477
7	12		Median	16
8	14		Mode	16
9	16		Standard Deviation	2.49284691
10	14		Sample Variance	6.214285714
11	16		Kurtosis	0.146492271
12	16		Skewness	0.304319004
13	16		Range	8
14	14		Minimum	12
15	14		Maximum	20
16	16		Sum	126
17	20		Count	8
18	12		Confidence Level(95.0%)	2.08407068
19	16			
20	20			
21	12			
22	16			
23	16			
24	24			

4. Interpret the following table showing the percentage of individuals on a low-fat or low-cholesterol diet by gender and age.

Age Group	Women	Men	Total
16–24	29%	13%	21%
25–34	43	25	34
35–44	46	28	37
45–54	54	32	43
55+	49	35	43

5. Visit your school's computer center and find out if it has SPSS, SAS, or SYSTAT computer packages.
6. What types of scalar data (that is, nominal, ordinal, interval, or ratio) are typically utilized in cross-tabulation analysis?
7. It has been argued that analysis and interpretation of data are managerial arts. Comment.
8. The data in the following tables are some of the results of an Internal Revenue Service survey of taxpayers. Analyze and interpret the data.

The last year you filed an income tax return, did you get any suggestions or information that was especially helpful to you in filing?

	Absolute Frequency	Relative Frequency (Percent)	Adjusted Frequency (Percent)
Yes	156	29.5	29.8
No	368	69.7	70.2
Don't know	1	.2	Missing
Not ascertained	1	.2	Missing
Blank	2	.4	Missing
	528	100.0	100.0

What kind of information was it?

	Absolute Frequency	Relative Frequency (Percent)	Adjusted Frequency (Percent)
Learned about energy credit	8	1.5	5.4
Learned about another deduction	46	8.7	31.3
Obtained info. about forms to use	9	1.7	6.1
Received pamphlets/forms	40	7.6	27.2
Other	44	8.3	29.9
Don't know	6	1.1	Missing
Not ascertained	2	.4	Missing
Blank	373	70.6	Missing
	528	100.0	100.0

9. A data processing analyst for a research supplier finds that preliminary computer runs of survey results show that consumers love a client's new product. The data processor buys a large block of the client's stock. Is this ethical?

Exploring the Internet

1. The Megapenny Project is located at http://www.kokogiak.com/megapenny/default.asp. Visit this site to get an insight into what large numbers mean.
2. Go to http://www.spss.com and click on Industries and Market Research. What services does the company provide?
3. To see descriptive data analysis in a report on smokeless tobacco, go to the Federal Trade Commission's Bureau of Consumer Protection at http://www.ftc.gov/bcp/reports/smokeless97.htm.
4. Economagic.com's Economic Time Series Page provides links to charts and data for over 68,000 series at http://www.economagic.com.

WebSurveyor Activities

The WebSurveyor Desktop software allows you to control how results are displayed using the Chart Toolbox. Results can be displayed in the following formats: Bar, Horizontal Bar, Pie, Area, Line, Scatter, and Text.

Run the WebSurveyor Desktop software, and click Example Internet Usage Survey under the heading "Open a sample survey with real data" from the Getting Started Wizard. (If the Getting Started Wizard does not appear, click on Tools and then Options from the main menu, make sure "Display the Getting Started Wizard for new surveys" is checked, and then click OK. Next click File and then New from the main menu, and then click Example Internet Usage Survey under the heading "Open a sample survey with real data.")

Using the Chart Toolbox, view the results for question 1 in each format. Which one do you prefer? Why?

Cross Tabulation Analysis

WebSurveyor's cross-tabulation feature allows you to evaluate relationships between responses to two different questions. The Cross Tabs feature of WebSurveyor Desktop is accessed through the Chart Toolbox. First click on Chart Toolbox. You can perform a Cross Tab analysis by selecting a chart type of Text Only on questions of the following types: Select Only One, Select All That Apply, Numeric Values, and Date Values. As soon as you change the chart type to text only, you should see a "Cross Tab" tab appear in the Chart Toolbox.

The Example Internet Usage Survey (Sample3.ws3) was used to create the cross-tabulation shown below.

Using question 1: "How long have you been using the Internet?" from the Example Internet Usage Survey opened above, perform cross-tabulations on gender, marital status, and income.

Filter

Using a filter is a great way to temporarily isolate parts of your data—for example, to view only the responses from those who answered "Male" to the question of gender and "Between 35 and 45" to the question of age.

When a filter is applied, it affects all of the analysis, reports, and data exports. You can create a filter by clicking the Set Filter . . . button in the Analysis window. Use question 6 and view only the female answers. If you understand the operation, use the filter to view the answers of divorced females.

Old School or New School

As mentioned in Chapter 14, three academic researchers investigated the idea that, in America in sports, there are two segments with opposing views on what constitutes the goal of competition (i.e., winning versus self-actualization) and the acceptable/desirable way of achieving this goal.[18] People who believe in "winning at any cost" are proponents of sports success as a product and can be labeled "new school" (NS) individuals. The new school is founded on notions of the player before the team, loyalty to the highest bidder, and high-tech production and consumption of professional sports. On the other hand, people who value the process of sports and believe that "how you play the game matters" can be labeled "old school" (OS) individuals. The old school emerges from old-fashioned American notions of the team before the player, sportsmanship and loyalty above all else, and competition simply for "love of the game." The sample was drawn from attendees at a university spring season football intra-squad scrimmage.

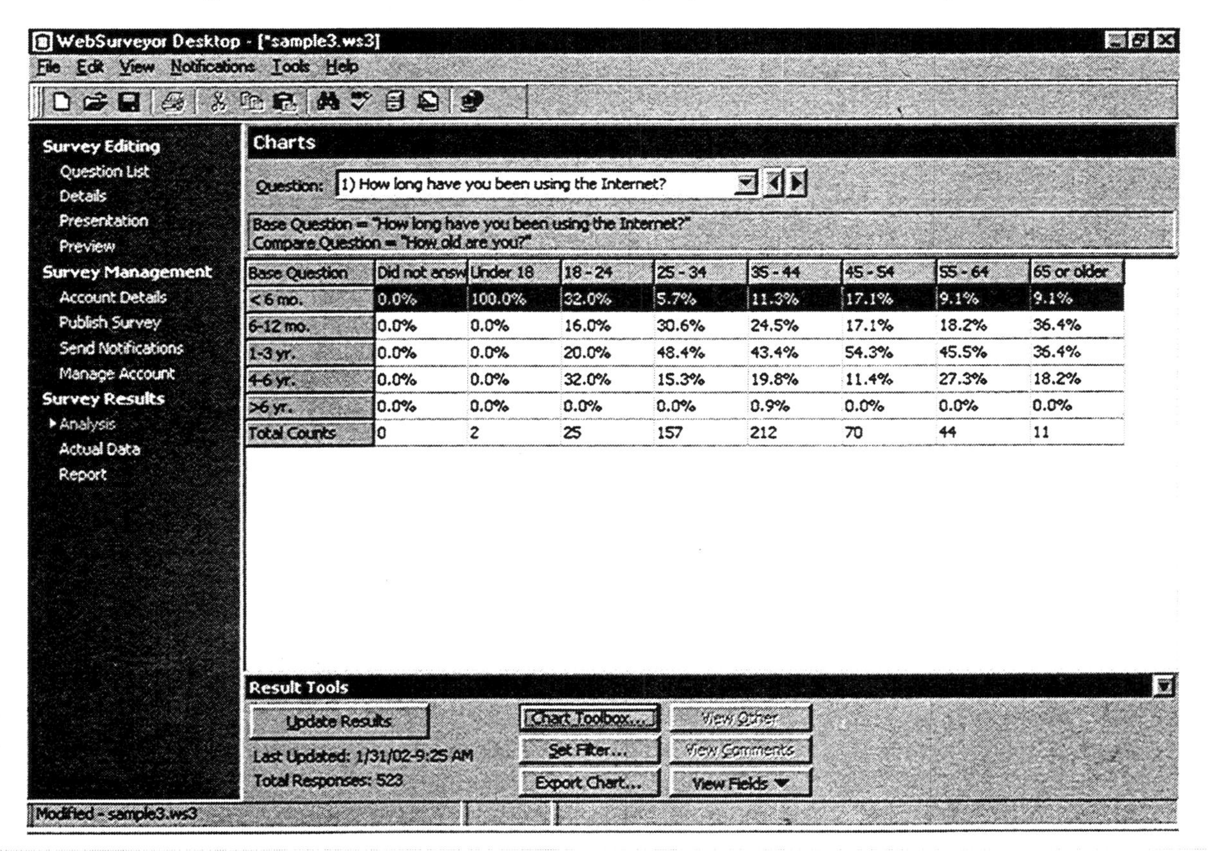

Base Question	Did not answ	Under 18	18 - 24	25 - 34	35 - 44	45 - 54	55 - 64	65 or older
<6 mo.	0.0%	100.0%	32.0%	5.7%	11.3%	17.1%	9.1%	9.1%
6-12 mo.	0.0%	0.0%	16.0%	30.6%	24.5%	17.1%	18.2%	36.4%
1-3 yr.	0.0%	0.0%	20.0%	48.4%	43.4%	54.3%	45.5%	36.4%
4-6 yr.	0.0%	0.0%	32.0%	15.3%	19.8%	11.4%	27.3%	18.2%
>6 yr.	0.0%	0.0%	0.0%	0.0%	0.9%	0.0%	0.0%	0.0%
Total Counts	0	2	25	157	212	70	44	11

Open the survey using the WebSurveyor Desktop software by selecting File and then Open from the main menu, select the file named "Sports.ws3" and go to Analysis. Select three questions (perhaps "most professional athletes have become too materialistic," "have no sense of loyalty to the team," and "are more interested in making money than playing the game"). Prepare a frequency distribution for each question and write a short report.

2001 Marketing Professionals Salary Survey Open the 2001 Marketing Professionals Salary Survey using the WebSurveyor Desktop software. Click Analysis and go to the question "How did you find your last job?" What conclusions can you draw from the answers to this question?

Case Suggestions

Case 25: The Multiplex Company
Case 26: Survey on Americans and Dietary Supplements
Case 29: LastDance Health Care
Case 30: Sunbelt Energy Corporation
Case 31: Employees Federal Credit Union

8

Estimation with Single Samples

Learning Objectives

The overall learning objective of Chapter 8 is to help you understand estimating parameters of single populations, thereby enabling you to:

1. Know the difference between point and interval estimation.
2. Estimate a population mean from a sample mean for large sample sizes.
3. Estimate a population mean from a sample mean for small sample sizes.
4. Estimate a population proportion from a sample proportion.
5. Estimate the minimum sample size necessary to achieve given statistical goals.

The central limit theorem presented in Chapter 7 states that certain statistics of interest, such as the sample mean and the sample proportion, are approximately normally distributed for large sample sizes regardless of the shape of the population distribution. The Z formulas for each statistic that were developed and discussed have the potential for use in parametric estimation, hypothesis testing, and determination of sample size. This chapter describes how these Z formulas for large statistics can be manipulated algebraically into a format that can be used to estimate population parameters and to determine the size of samples necessary to conduct research. In addition, mechanisms are introduced for estimation with small sample sizes.

8.1

Estimating the Population Mean with Large Sample Sizes

On many occasions estimating the population mean is useful in business research. For example, the manager of human resources in a company might want to estimate the average number of days of work an employee misses per year because of illness. If the firm has thousands of employees, direct calculation of a population mean such as this may be practically impossible. Instead, a random sample of employees can be taken, and the sample mean number of sick days can be used to estimate the population mean. Suppose another company has developed a new process for prolonging the shelf life of a loaf of bread. The company wants to be able to date each loaf for freshness, but company officials do not know exactly how long the bread will stay fresh. By taking a random sample and determining the sample mean shelf life, they can estimate the average shelf life for the population of bread.

As the cellular telephone industry matures, a cellular telephone company is rethinking its pricing structure. Users appear to be spending more time on the phone and are shopping around for the best deals. To do better planning, the cellular company wants to ascertain the average number of minutes of time used per month by each of its residential users but does not have the resources available to examine all monthly bills and extract the information. The company decides to take a sample of customer bills and estimate the population mean from sample data. A business analyst for the company takes a random sample of 85 bills for a recent month and from these bills computes a sample mean of 153 minutes. This sample mean, which is a statistic, is being used to estimate the population mean, which is a parameter. If the company uses the sample mean of 153 minutes as an estimate for the population mean, then the sample mean is being used as a *point estimate.*

Point estimate
An estimate of a population parameter constructed from a statistic taken from a sample.

Interval estimate
A range of values within which it is estimated with some confidence the population parameter lies.

A **point estimate** is *a statistic taken from a sample and is used to estimate a population parameter.* However, a point estimate is only as good as the representativeness of its sample. If other random samples are taken from the population, the point estimates derived from those samples are likely to vary. Because of variation in sample statistics, estimating a population parameter with an interval estimate is often preferable to using a point estimate. An **interval estimate** (confidence interval) is *a range of values within which the analyst can declare with some confidence the population parameter lies.* Confidence intervals can be two sided or one sided. This text presents only two-sided confidence intervals. How are confidence intervals constructed?

As a result of the central limit theorem, the following Z formula for sample means can be used when sample sizes are large, regardless of the shape of the population distribution, or for smaller sizes if the population is normally distributed.

$$Z = \frac{\overline{X} - \mu}{\frac{\sigma}{\sqrt{n}}}$$

Rearranging this formula algebraically to solve for μ gives

$$\mu = \bar{X} - Z\frac{\sigma}{\sqrt{n}}.$$

Because a sample mean can be greater than or less than the population mean, Z can be positive or negative. Thus the preceding expression takes the following form.

$$\bar{X} \pm Z\frac{\sigma}{\sqrt{n}}$$

Rewriting this expression yields the confidence interval formula for estimating μ with large sample sizes.

100(1 – α)% CONFIDENCE INTERVAL TO ESTIMATE μ

$$\bar{X} \pm Z_{\alpha/2}\frac{\sigma}{\sqrt{n}}$$

or

(8.1) $$\bar{X} - Z_{\alpha/2}\frac{\sigma}{\sqrt{n}} \le \mu \le \bar{X} + Z_{\alpha/2}\frac{\sigma}{\sqrt{n}}$$

where:

α = the area under the normal curve outside the confidence interval area

$\alpha/2$ = the area in one end (tail) of the distribution outside the confidence interval

Alpha (α) is the area under the normal curve in the tails of the distribution outside the area defined by the confidence interval. We will focus more on α in Chapter 9. Here we use α to locate the Z value in constructing the confidence interval as shown in Figure 8.1. Because the standard normal table is based on areas between a Z of 0 and $Z_{\alpha/2}$, the table Z value is found by locating the area of $.5000 - \alpha/2$, which is the part of the normal curve between the middle of the curve and one of the tails. Another way to locate this Z value is to change the confidence level from percentage to proportion, divide it in half, and go to the table with this value. The results are the same.

The confidence interval formula (8.1) yields a range (interval) within which we feel with some confidence the population mean is located. It is not certain that the population mean is in the interval unless we have a 100% confidence interval that is infinitely wide.

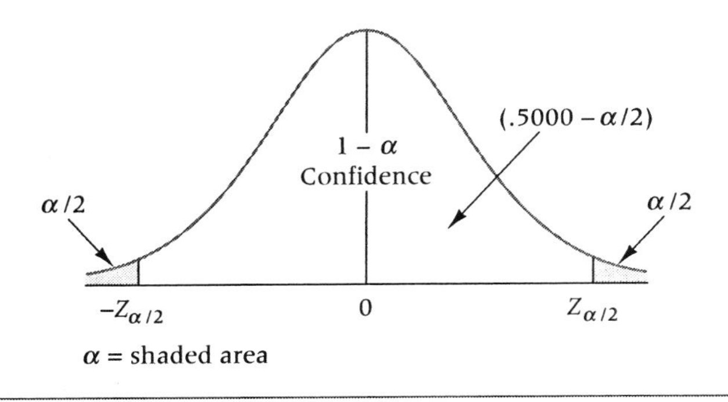

Figure 8.1

Z scores for confidence intervals in relation to α

However, we can assign a probability that the parameter (in this case, μ) is located within the interval. Formula 8.1 can be presented as a probability statement.

$$\text{Prob}\left[\bar{X} - Z_{\alpha/2}\frac{\sigma}{\sqrt{n}} \leq \mu \leq \bar{X} + Z_{\alpha/2}\frac{\sigma}{\sqrt{n}}\right] = 1 - \alpha$$

If we want to construct a 95% confidence interval, the level of confidence is 95% or .95. The probability statement shown tells us there is a .95 probability that the population mean is in this interval. If 100 such intervals are constructed by taking random samples from the population, it is likely that 95 of the intervals would include the population mean and five would not. The probability tells us the likelihood that a particular interval is one that does include the population mean.

As an example, in the cellular telephone company problem of estimating the population mean number of minutes called per residential user per month, from the sample of 85 bills it was determined that the sample mean is 153 minutes. Using this sample mean, a confidence interval can be calculated within which the researcher is relatively confident the actual population mean is located. To do this using Formula 8.1, the value of the population standard deviation and the value of Z (in addition to the sample mean, 153, and the sample size, 85) must be known. Suppose past history and similar studies indicate that the population standard deviation is 46 minutes.

The value of Z is determined by the level of confidence desired. An interval with 100% confidence is so wide that it is meaningless. Some of the more common levels of confidence used by business analysts are 90%, 95%, 98%, and 99%. Why would a business analyst not just select the highest confidence and always use that level? The reason is that trade-offs between sample size, interval width, and level of confidence must be considered. For example, as the level of confidence is increased, the interval gets wider, provided the sample size and standard deviation remain constant.

For the cellular telephone problem, suppose the business analyst decided on a 95% confidence interval for the results. Figure 8.2 shows a normal distribution of sample means about the population mean. When using a 95% level of confidence, he is selecting an interval centered on μ within which 95% of all sample mean values will fall and then using the width of that interval to create an interval around the *sample mean* within which he has some confidence the population mean will fall.

For 95% confidence, $\alpha = .05$ and $\alpha/2 = .025$. The value of $Z_{\alpha/2}$ or $Z_{.025}$ is found by looking in the standard normal table under $.5000 - .0250 = .4750$. This area in the table is associated with a Z value of 1.96. There is another way to locate the table Z value. Because the distribution is symmetric and the intervals are equal on each side of the population mean, (1/2)(95%), or .4750, of the area is on each side of the mean. Table A.5 yields a Z value of 1.96 for this portion of the normal curve. Thus the Z value for a 95% confidence interval is always 1.96. In other words, of all the possible $\bar{X}$ values along the horizontal axis of the diagram, 95% of them should be within a Z score of 1.96 from the population mean.

Figure 8.2

Distribution of sample means for 95% confidence

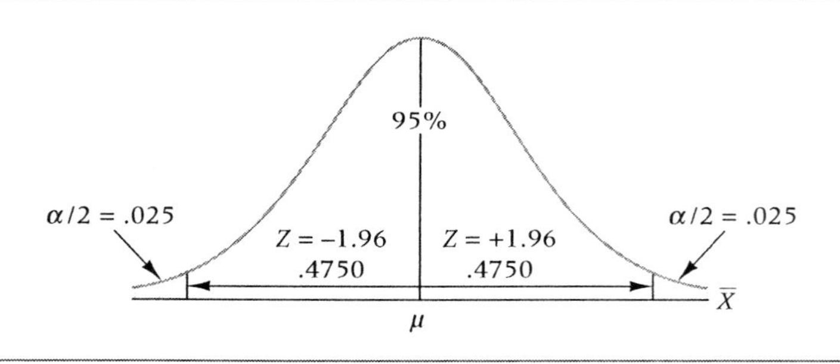

The business analyst can now complete the cellular telephone problem. To determine a 95% confidence interval for $\overline{X} = 153$, $\sigma = 46$, $n = 85$, and $Z = 1.96$, he estimates the average call length by including the value of Z in Formula 8.1.

$$153 - 1.96\frac{46}{\sqrt{85}} \leq \mu \leq 153 + 1.96\frac{46}{\sqrt{85}}$$

$$153 - 9.78 \leq \mu \leq 153 + 9.78$$

$$143.22 \leq \mu \leq 162.78$$

The confidence interval is constructed from the point estimate, which in this problem is 153 minutes, and the error of this estimate, which is ±9.78 minutes. The resulting confidence interval is $143.22 \leq \mu \leq 162.78$. The cellular telephone company business analyst is 95% confident that the average length of a call for the population is between 143.22 and 162.78 minutes.

What does being 95% confident that the population mean is in an interval actually indicate? It indicates that, if the company researcher were to randomly select 100 samples of 85 calls and use the results of each sample to construct a 95% confidence interval, approximately 95 of the 100 intervals would contain the population mean. It also indicates that 5% of the intervals would not contain the population mean. The company business analyst is likely to take only a single sample and compute the confidence interval from that sample information. That interval either contains the population mean or it does not. The odds are in his favor.

Figure 8.3 depicts the meaning of a 95% confidence interval for the mean. Note that if 20 random samples are taken from the population, 19 of the 20 are likely to contain the

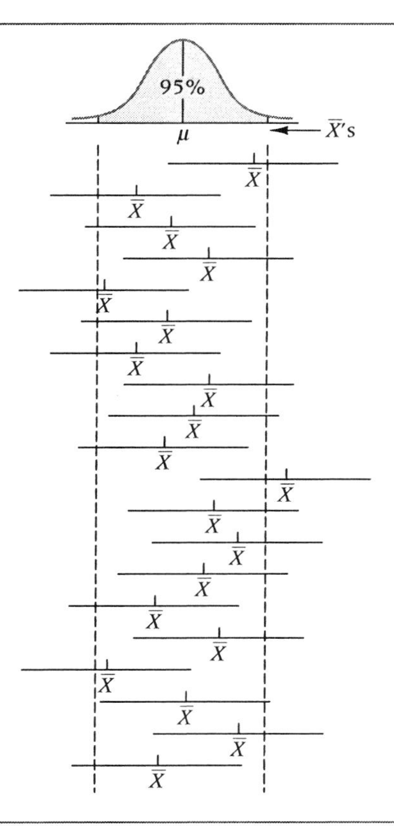

Figure 8.3

Twenty 95% confidence intervals of μ

population mean if a 95% confidence interval is used (19/20 = 95%). If a 90% confidence interval is constructed, only 18 of the 20 intervals are likely to contain the population mean.

DEMONSTRATION PROBLEM 8.1

A survey was taken of U.S. companies that do business with firms in India. One of the questions on the survey was: Approximately how many years has your company been trading with firms in India? A random sample of 44 responses to this question yielded a mean of 10.455 years. Suppose the population standard deviation for this question is 7.7 years. Using this information, construct a 90% confidence interval for the mean number of years that a company has been trading in India for the population of U.S. companies trading with firms in India.

SOLUTION

Here, $n = 44$, $\bar{X} = 10.455$, and $\sigma = 7.7$. To determine the value of $Z_{\alpha/2}$, divide the 90% confidence in half or take $.5000 - \alpha/2 = .5000 - .0500$. The Z distribution of $\bar{X}$ around μ contains .4500 of the area on each side of μ, or (1/2)(90%). Table A.5 yields a Z value of 1.645 for the area of .4500 (interpolating between .4495 and .4505). The confidence interval is

$$\bar{X} - Z\frac{\sigma}{\sqrt{n}} \le \mu \le \bar{X} + Z\frac{\sigma}{\sqrt{n}}$$

$$10.455 - 1.645\frac{7.7}{\sqrt{44}} \le \mu \le 10.455 + 1.645\frac{7.7}{\sqrt{44}}$$

$$10.455 - 1.91 \le \mu \le 10.455 + 1.91$$

$$8.545 \le \mu \le 12.365$$

$$\text{Prob}[8.545 \le \mu \le 12.365] = .90.$$

That is, the analyst is 90% confident that if a census of all U.S. companies trading with firms in India were taken at the time of this survey, the actual population mean number of years a company would have been trading with firms in India would be between 8.545 and 12.365. The point estimate is 10.455 years.

Finite Correction Factor

Recall from Chapter 7 that if the sample is taken from a finite population, a finite correction factor may be used to increase the accuracy of the solution. In the case of interval estimation, the finite correction factor is used to reduce the width of the interval. As stated in Chapter 7, if the sample size is less than 5% of the population, the finite correction factor does not significantly alter the solution. If Formula 8.1 is modified to include the finite correction factor, the result is Formula 8.2.

CONFIDENCE INTERVAL TO ESTIMATE μ USING THE FINITE CORRECTION FACTOR

$$\bar{X} - Z_{\alpha/2}\frac{\sigma}{\sqrt{n}}\sqrt{\frac{N-n}{N-1}} \le \mu \le \bar{X} + Z_{\alpha/2}\frac{\sigma}{\sqrt{n}}\sqrt{\frac{N-n}{N-1}} \qquad (8.2)$$

Demonstration Problem 8.2 shows how the finite correction factor can be used.

DEMONSTRATION PROBLEM 8.2

A study is being conducted in a company that has 800 engineers. A random sample of 50 of these engineers reveals that the average sample age is 34.3 years. Historically, the population standard deviation of the age of the company's engineers is approximately 8 years. Construct a 98% confidence interval to estimate the average age of all the engineers in this company.

SOLUTION

This problem has a finite population. The sample size, 50, is greater than 5% of the population, so the finite correction factor may be helpful. In this case $N = 800$, $n = 50$, $\bar{X} = 34.3$, and $\sigma = 8$. The Z value for a 98% confidence interval is 2.33 (.98 divided into two equal parts yields .4900; the Z value is obtained from Table A.5 by using .4900). Substituting into Formula 8.2 and solving for the confidence interval gives

$$34.3 - 2.33\frac{8}{\sqrt{50}}\sqrt{\frac{750}{799}} \leq \mu \leq 34.3 + 2.33\frac{8}{\sqrt{50}}\sqrt{\frac{750}{799}}$$

$$34.3 - 2.55 \leq \mu \leq 34.3 + 2.55$$

$$31.75 \leq \mu \leq 36.85.$$

Without the finite correction factor, the result would have been

$$34.3 - 2.64 \leq \mu \leq 34.3 + 2.64$$

$$31.66 \leq \mu \leq 36.94$$

The finite correction factor takes into account the fact that the population is only 800 instead of being infinitely large. The sample, $n = 50$, is a greater proportion of the 800 than it would be of a larger population, and thus the width of the confidence interval is reduced.

Confidence Interval to Estimate μ When σ Is Unknown

In the formulas and problems presented so far in this section, the population standard deviation was known. Estimating the population mean when the population standard deviation is known may seem strange. Sometimes the population standard deviation is estimated from past records or from industry standards. However, the reality is that in most instances, the population standard deviation is unknown. For example, in the cellular telephone example, the average length of a call is unknown. The likelihood is high that the population standard deviation also is unknown. So how does the business analyst get around this dilemma?

When samples sizes are large ($n \geq 30$), the sample standard deviation is a good estimate of the population standard deviation and can be used as an acceptable approximation of the population standard deviation in the Z formula for a mean. Because formulas based on the central limit theorem require large samples for nonnormal populations, it makes sense to modify Formula 8.1 to use the sample standard deviation, S. Beware, however, not to use this modified formula for small samples when the population standard deviation is unknown, even when the population is normally distributed. Section 8.2 presents techniques for handling the case of the small samples when the population standard deviation is unknown and X is normally distributed.

Shown next is the confidence interval formula to estimate μ with large samples when using the sample standard deviation.

CONFIDENCE INTERVAL TO ESTIMATE μ WHEN POPULATION STANDARD DEVIATION IS UNKNOWN AND n IS LARGE

$$\bar{X} \pm Z_{\alpha/2} \frac{S}{\sqrt{n}}$$

or

$$\bar{X} - Z_{\alpha/2} \frac{S}{\sqrt{n}} \le \mu \le \bar{X} + Z_{\alpha/2} \frac{S}{\sqrt{n}} \tag{8.3}$$

As an example, suppose a U.S. car rental firm wants to estimate the average number of miles traveled per day by each of its cars rented in California. A random sample of 110 cars rented in California reveals that the sample mean travel distance per day is 85.5 miles, with a sample standard deviation of 19.3 miles. Compute a 99% confidence interval to estimate μ.

Here, $n = 110$, $\bar{X} = 85.5$, and $S = 19.3$. For a 99% level of confidence, a Z value of 2.575 is obtained. The confidence interval is

$$\bar{X} - Z_{\alpha/2} \frac{S}{\sqrt{n}} \le \mu \le \bar{X} + Z_{\alpha/2} \frac{S}{\sqrt{n}}$$

$$85.5 - 2.575 \frac{19.3}{\sqrt{110}} \le \mu \le 85.5 + 2.575 \frac{19.3}{\sqrt{110}}$$

$$85.5 - 4.7 \le \mu \le 85.5 + 4.7$$

$$80.8 \le \mu \le 90.2.$$

The point estimate indicates that the average number of miles traveled per day by a rental car in California is 85.5. With 99% confidence, we estimate that the population mean is somewhere between 80.8 and 90.2 miles per day.

For convenience, Table 8.1 contains some of the more common levels of confidence and their associated Z values.

TABLE 8.1
Values of Z for Some of the More Common Levels of Confidence

CONFIDENCE LEVEL	Z VALUE
90%	1.645
95%	1.96
98%	2.33
99%	2.575

Analysis Using Excel

Confidence intervals for a population mean with the normal distribution can be constructed using three statistical functions and one mathematical function from Excel. However to simplify the process, **FAST⧹STAT** has a macro procedure for constructing such a confidence interval. In addition, the procedure performs the computations necessary for conducting a hypothesis test as discussed in Chapter 9. This feature is available from FAST⧹STAT's pull-down menu with the name **1 Mean Using *Z* Dist.** The dialog box for it is shown in Figure 8.4.

As you may note from the figure, the inputs are grouped into three segments. The first group is for the sample itself. This input is the worksheet cell range for the sample values. The second grouping also has just one input. It is the level of confidence for the confidence interval. It is to be given as a percentage such as 99%, 95%, 90%, and so on.

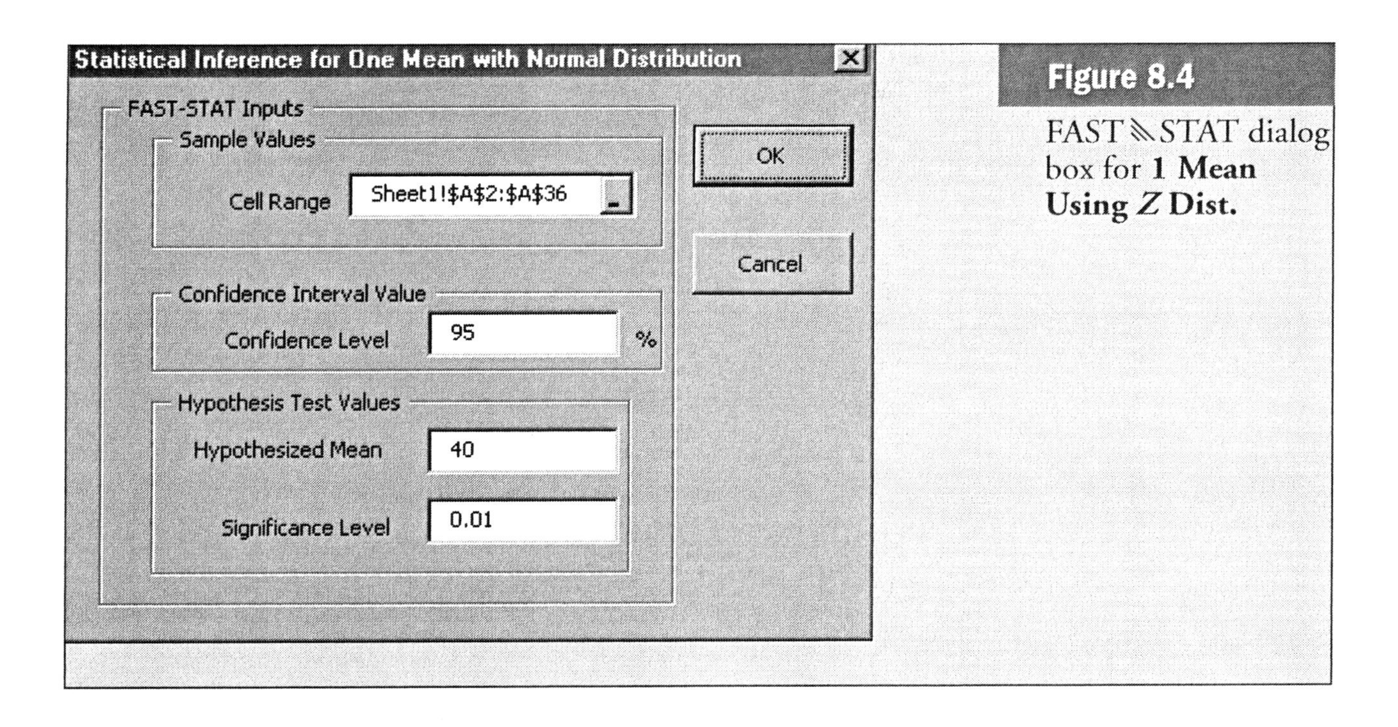

Figure 8.4

FAST⧹STAT dialog box for **1 Mean Using *Z* Dist.**

The third grouping includes two inputs for conducting a hypothesis test. These will be discussed later in Section 9.2 of Chapter 9. If you only wish to compute a confidence interval, enter *any number* for the *hypothesized mean* and *a number between 0 and 100* for the *significance level.* We should note, however, if these two values are left blank or are zero, Excel will indicate the ***#NUM!*** error condition. This doesn't invalidate the confidence interval results, but some users may find this error message distracting. To avoid the message, enter a number that is greater than zero and less than one for the significance level.

To demonstrate this FAST⧹STAT feature, consider this example. A newly organized dot-com company wishes to construct a 95% confidence interval for the age of their employees. A sample of 35 employees produces the following ages.

44	37	49	30	56	48	53
42	51	38	39	45	47	52
59	50	46	34	39	46	27
35	52	51	46	45	58	51
37	45	52	51	54	39	48

These values are entered into an Excel worksheet in cells A2 through A36. Figure 8.5 shows the results for this example.

In column A you will find the sample values. In columns C through G, the values for the four dialog box inputs are repeated. The outputs that follow are in four parts: sample statistic values, the point estimate, the confidence interval, and the hypothesis test for the sample. The sample statistic values include the sample mean, standard deviation, and sample size. The confidence interval results include the *Z* value for the specified confidence level and the standard error of the mean. In addition, it includes the error of estimation (sometimes termed the interval half width), the endpoints of the interval, and the complete interval.

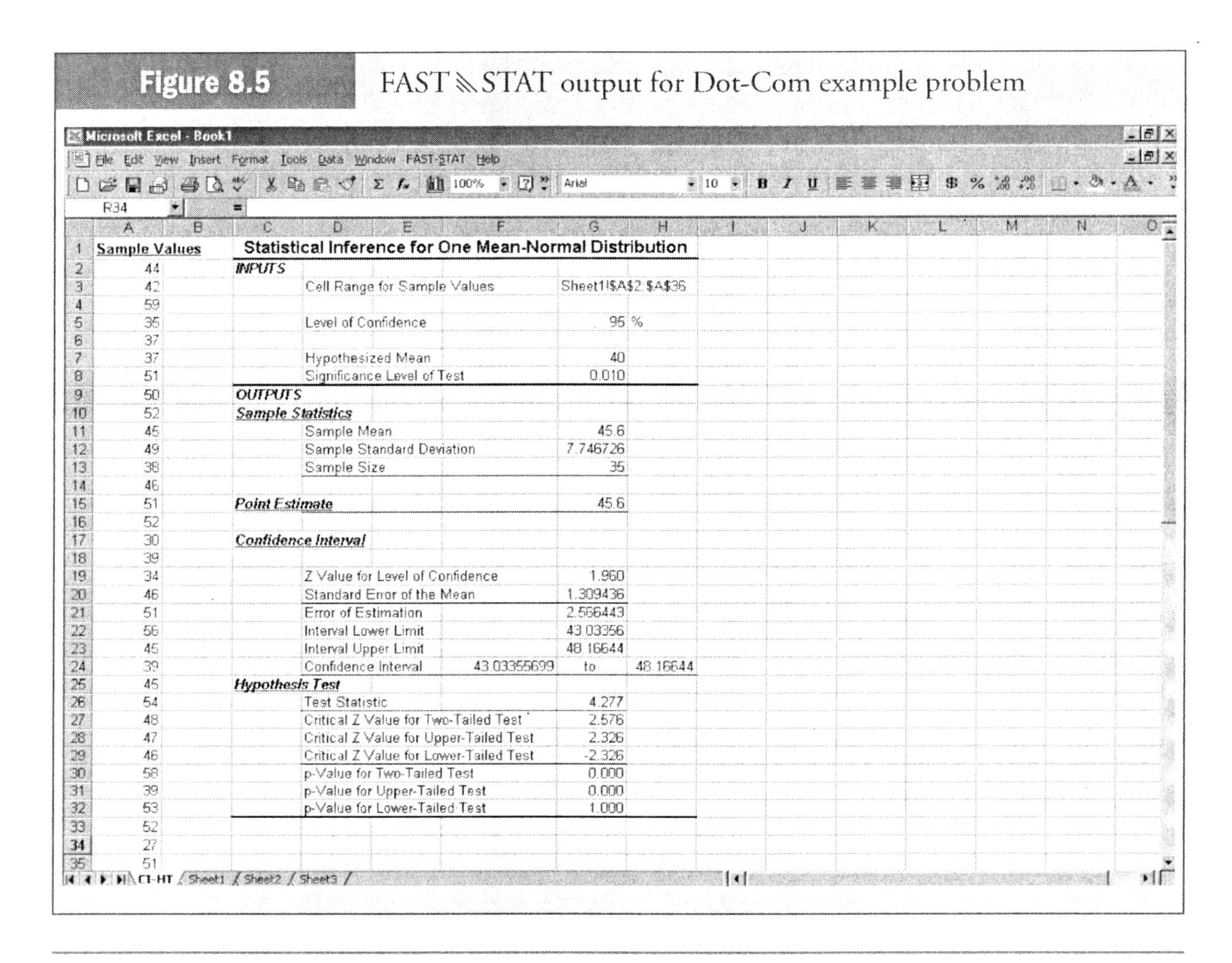

Figure 8.5 FAST\STAT output for Dot-Com example problem

8.1

Problems

8.1 Use the following information to construct the confidence intervals specified to estimate μ.

a. 95% confidence; $\overline{X} = 25$, $\sigma = 3.5$, and $n = 60$

b. 98% confidence; $\overline{X} = 119.6$, $S = 23.89$, and $n = 75$

c. 90% confidence; $\overline{X} = 3.419$, $S = 0.974$, and $n = 32$

d. 80% confidence; $\overline{X} = 56.7$, $\sigma = 12.1$, $N = 500$, and $n = 47$

8.2 For a random sample of 36 items and a sample mean of 211, compute a 95% confidence interval for μ if the population standard deviation is 23.

8.3 A random sample of 81 items is taken, producing a sample mean of 47 and a sample standard deviation of 5.89. Construct a 90% confidence interval to estimate the population mean.

8.4 A candy company fills a 20-ounce package of Halloween candy with individually wrapped pieces of candy. The number of pieces of candy per package varies because the package is sold by weight. The company wants to estimate the number of pieces per package. Inspectors randomly sample 120 packages of this candy and count the number of pieces in each package. They find that the sample mean number of pieces is 18.72, with a sample standard deviation of .8735. What is the point estimate of the number of pieces per package? Construct a 99% confidence interval to estimate the mean number of pieces per package for the population.

8.5 A small lawnmower company produced 1500 lawnmowers in 1990. In an effort to determine how maintenance-free these units were, the company decided to conduct a multi-year study of the 1990 lawnmowers. A sample of 200 owners of these lawnmowers was drawn randomly from company records and contacted. The owners were given an 800 number and asked to call the company when the first major repair was required for the lawnmowers. Owners who no longer used the lawnmower to cut their grass were disqualified. After many years, 187 of the owners had reported. The other 13 disqualified themselves. The average number of years until the first major repair was 5.3 for the 187 owners reporting, and the sample standard deviation was 1.28 years. If the company wants to advertise an average number of years of repair-free lawnmowing for this lawnmower, what is the point estimate? Construct a 95% confidence interval for the average number of years until the first major repair.

8.6 The average total dollar purchase at a convenience store is less than that at a supermarket. Despite smaller-ticket purchases, convenience stores can still be profitable because of the size of operation, volume of business, and the markup. A researcher is interested in estimating the average purchase amount for convenience stores in suburban Long Island. To do so, she randomly sampled 32 purchases from several convenience stores in suburban Long Island and tabulated the amounts to the nearest dollar. Use the following data to construct a 90% confidence interval for the population average amount of purchases.

$2	$11	$8	$7	$9	$3	$3	$6
5	4	2	1	10	8	5	4
14	7	6	3	7	2	3	6
4	1	3	6	8	4	7	12

8.7 A community health association is interested in estimating the average number of maternity days women stay in the local hospital. A random sample is taken of 36 women who had babies in the hospital during the past year. The following numbers of maternity days each woman was in the hospital are rounded to the nearest day.

3	3	4	3	2	5	3	1	4	3	4	2
3	5	3	2	4	3	2	4	1	6	3	4
3	3	5	2	3	2	3	5	4	3	5	4

Use these data to construct a 98% confidence interval to estimate the average maternity stay in the hospital for all women who have babies in this hospital.

8.8 A meat-processing company in the Midwest produces and markets a package of eight small sausage sandwiches. The product is nationally distributed, and the company is interested in knowing the average retail price charged for this item in stores across the country. The company cannot justify a national census to generate this information. The company information system produces a list of all retailers who carry the product. A researcher for the company contacts 36 of these retailers and ascertains the selling prices for the product. Use the following price data to determine a point estimate for the national retail price of the product. Construct a 90% confidence interval to estimate this price.

$2.23	$2.11	$2.12	$2.20	$2.17	$2.10
2.16	2.31	1.98	2.17	2.14	1.82
2.12	2.07	2.17	2.30	2.29	2.19
2.01	2.24	2.18	2.18	2.32	2.02
1.99	1.87	2.09	2.22	2.15	2.19
2.23	2.10	2.08	2.05	2.16	2.26

8.9 According to the U.S. Bureau of the Census, the average travel time to work in Philadelphia is 27.4 minutes. Suppose a researcher wants to estimate the average travel time to work in Cleveland using a 95% level of confidence. A random sample of 45 Cleveland commuters is taken and the travel time to work is obtained from each. The data are entered into an Excel spreadsheet with a population standard deviation of 5.1 minutes. Excel calculates the mean as 25 and then computes the error of the interval around the mean. Excel yielded 1.49 as the error of the confidence estimation around the mean. The data used in the calculation follow. Compute a 95% confidence interval on the data. How do your calculations compare with Excel's figures?

27	25	19	21	24	27	29	34	18	29	16	28
20	32	27	28	22	20	14	15	29	28	29	33
16	29	28	28	27	23	27	20	27	25	21	18
26	14	23	27	27	21	25	28	30			

8.2

Estimating the Population Mean: Small Sample Sizes, σ Unknown

In Section 8.1 we learned how to estimate the population mean by using the sample mean. The central limit theorem, presented in Chapter 7, guarantees that the sample means are normally distributed when sample size is large. These procedures can still be used when the sample size is small if the population is normally distributed and if σ is known.

When the population standard deviation is unknown, the sample standard deviation is an acceptable estimate of and substitute for the population standard deviation and can be used in the confidence interval, along with the sample mean, to estimate the population mean if sample size is *large*. A value of $n \geq 30$ is generally considered a lower limit for large sample size.

On the other hand, in many real-life situations, sample sizes of less than 30 are the norm. For example, a researcher is interested in studying the average flying time of a DC-10 from New York to Los Angeles, but a sample of only 21 flights is available. Another researcher is studying the impact of movie video advertisements on consumers, but the group used in the study contains only 11 people.

If the population is known to be normally distributed and the population standard deviation is known, the Z values computed from the sample means are normally distributed regardless of sample size. Thus, by assuming that the *population* is normally distributed (many phenomena are normally distributed) and that the population standard deviation is known, a researcher could theoretically continue to use the techniques presented in Section 8.1 for confidence interval estimation, even with small samples. This formula for sample means is

$$\bar{X} - Z\frac{\sigma}{\sqrt{n}} \leq \mu \leq \bar{X} + Z\frac{\sigma}{\sqrt{n}}.$$

In many research situations, the population standard deviation is not known and must be estimated by using the sample standard deviation. In these situations, S is substituted into the preceding formula.

$$\bar{X} - Z\frac{S}{\sqrt{n}} \leq \mu \leq \bar{X} + Z\frac{S}{\sqrt{n}}$$

However, the sample standard deviation, S, is only a good approximation for the population standard deviation, σ, for large samples. The Z formulas that use S therefore are not applicable to small-sample analysis. This problem was considered and solved by a British statistician, William S. Gosset.

Gosset was born in 1876 in Canterbury, England. He studied chemistry and mathematics and in 1899 went to work for the Guinness Brewery in Dublin, Ireland. Gosset was involved in quality control at the brewery, studying variables such as raw materials and temperature. Because of the circumstances of his experiments, Gosset conducted many studies with small samples. He discovered that using the standard Z test with a *sample* standard deviation produced inexact and incorrect distributions for small sample sizes. This finding led to his development of the distribution of the sample standard deviation and the t test.

Gosset was a student and close personal friend of Karl Pearson. When Gosset's first work on the t test was published, he used the pen name "Student." As a result, the t test is sometimes referred to as the Student's t test. Gosset's contribution was significant because it led to more exact statistical tests, which some scholars say marked the beginning of the modern era in mathematical statistics.*

The t Distribution

Gosset developed the ***t* distribution,** which *describes the sample data in small samples when the population standard deviation is unknown and the population is normally distributed.* The formula for the ***t* value** is

$$t = \frac{\overline{X} - \mu}{\frac{S}{\sqrt{n}}}$$

t **distribution**
A distribution that describes the sample data in small samples when the standard deviation is unknown and the population is normally distributed.

This formula is essentially the same as the Z formula, but the distribution table values are different. The t distribution values are contained in Table A.6 and, for convenience, inside the front cover of the text.

t **value**
The computed value of t used to reach statistical conclusions regarding the null hypothesis in small-sample analysis.

The t distribution actually is a series of distributions because every sample size has a different distribution, thereby creating the potential for many t tables. To make these t values more manageable, only select key values are presented; each line in the table contains values from a different t distribution. *The assumption underlying the use of the techniques discussed in this chapter for small sample sizes is that the population is normally distributed.* If the population distribution is not normal or is unknown, nonparametric techniques should be used.

Robustness

Most statistical techniques have one or more underlying assumptions. If a statistical technique *is relatively insensitive to minor violations in one or more of its underlying assumptions,* the technique is said to be **robust** to that assumption. The t statistic for estimating a population mean is relatively robust to the assumption that the population is normally distributed.

Robust
Describes a statistical technique that is relatively insensitive to minor violations in one or more of its underlying assumptions.

Some statistical techniques are not robust, and a business analyst should exercise extreme caution to be certain that the assumptions underlying a technique are being met

*ADAPTED FROM: Arthur L. Dudycha and Linda W. Dudycha, "Behavioral Statistics: An Historical Perspective," in *Statistical Issues: A Reader for the Behavioral Sciences,* edited by Roger Kirk (Monterey, CA: Brooks/Cole, 1972).

Figure 8.6

Comparison of two t distributions to the standard normal curve

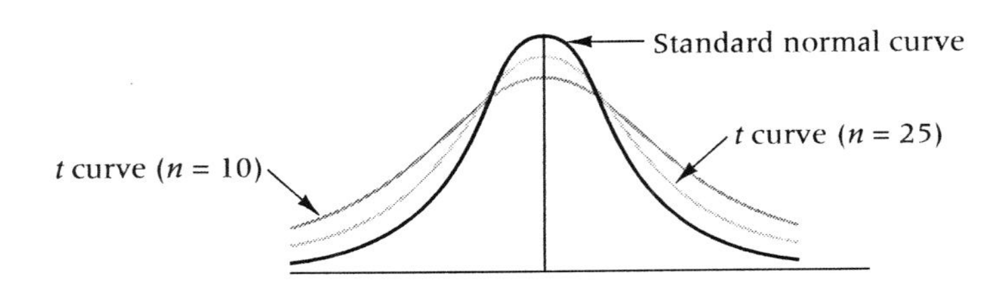

before using it or interpreting statistical output resulting from its use. A business analyst should always beware of statistical assumptions and the robustness of techniques being used in an analysis.

Characteristics of the t Distribution

Figure 8.6 displays two t distributions superimposed on the standard normal distribution. Like the normal curve, t distributions are symmetric, unimodal, and a family of curves. The t distributions are flatter in the middle and have more area in their tails than the standard normal distribution.

An examination of t distribution values reveals that the t distribution approaches the standard normal curve as n becomes large. The t distribution is the appropriate distribution to use any time the population variance or standard deviation is unknown, regardless of sample size. However, because the difference between the table values for Z and t becomes negligible for large samples, many researchers use the Z distribution for large-sample analysis even when the standard deviation or variance is unknown. In this text, the t distribution is reserved for use with small sample size problems ($n < 30$) because, as n nears size 30, the t table values approach the Z table values.

Reading the t Distribution Table

Degrees of freedom
A mathematical adjustment made to the size of the sample; used along with α to locate values in statistical tables.

To find a value in the t distribution table requires knowing the sample size. The t distribution table is a compilation of many t distributions, with each line of the table representing a different sample size. However, the sample size must be converted to **degrees of freedom (df)** before a table value can be determined. The degrees of freedom vary according to which t formula is being used, so a df formula is given along with each t formula. The concept of degrees of freedom is difficult and beyond the scope of this text. A brief explanation is that t formulas are used because the population variance or standard deviation, which is part of the Z formula, is unknown and must be estimated by a sample standard deviation or variance. For every parameter (such as variance or standard deviation) of a statistical formula that is unknown and must be estimated by a statistic (e.g., sample variance or standard deviation) in the formula, one degree of freedom is lost.

In Table A.6 the degrees of freedom are located in the left column. The t distribution table in this text does not use the area between the statistic and the mean as does the Z distribution (standard normal distribution). Instead, the t table uses the area in the tail of the distribution. The emphasis in the t table is on α, and each tail of the distribution contains $\alpha/2$ of the area under the curve when confidence intervals are constructed. (In Chapter 9, sometimes a single tail of the distribution will contain α proportion of the area.) For confidence intervals, the table t value is in the column under the value of $\alpha/2$ at the intersection of the df value.

For example, if a 90% confidence interval is being computed, the total area in the two tails is 10%. Thus, α is .10 and $\alpha/2$ is .05, as indicated in Figure 8.7. The t distribution

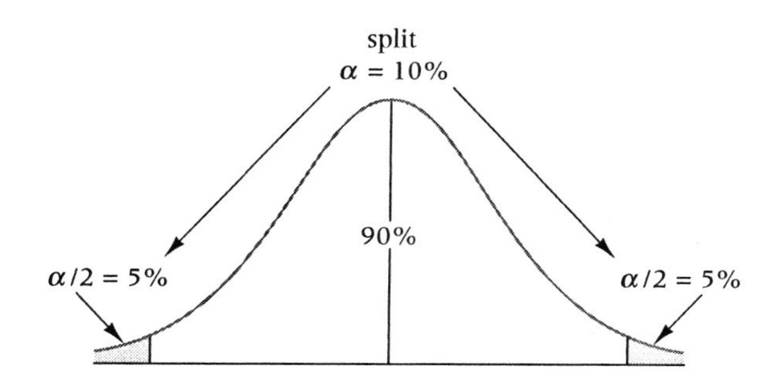

Figure 8.7

Distribution with alpha for 90% confidence

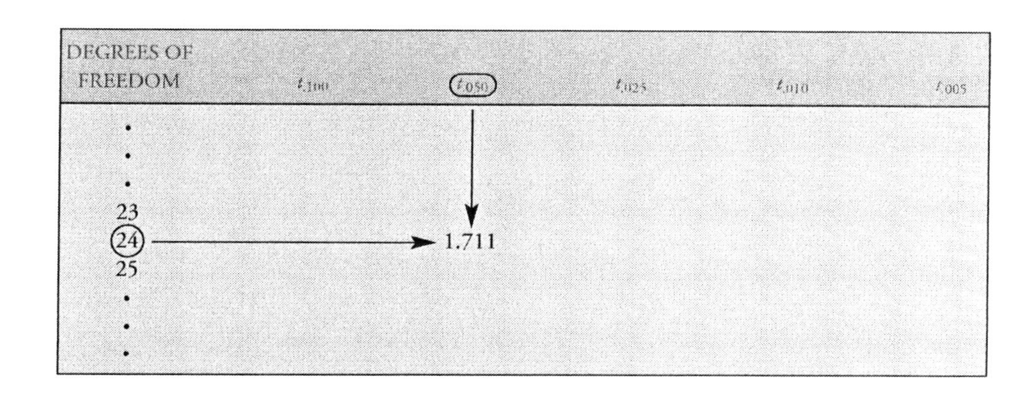

TABLE 8.2
t Distribution

table shown in Table 8.2 contains only five values of $\alpha/2$ (.10, .05, .025, .01, .005). The t value is located at the intersection of the df value and the selected $\alpha/2$ value. So if the degrees of freedom for a given t statistic are 24 and the desired $\alpha/2$ value is .05, the t value is 1.711.

Confidence Intervals to Estimate μ When σ Is Unknown and Sample Size Is Small

The t formula,

$$t = \frac{\bar{X} - \mu}{\frac{S}{\sqrt{n}}},$$

can be manipulated algebraically to produce a formula for estimating the population mean using small samples when σ is unknown and the population is normally distributed. The result is the formulas given next.

CONFIDENCE INTERVAL TO ESTIMATE μ: SMALL SAMPLES AND POPULATION STANDARD DEVIATION UNKNOWN

$$\bar{X} \pm t_{\alpha/2,n-1} \frac{S}{\sqrt{n}}$$

$$\bar{X} - t_{\alpha/2,n-1} \frac{S}{\sqrt{n}} \le \mu \le \bar{X} + t_{\alpha/2,n-1} \frac{S}{\sqrt{n}} \qquad (8.4)$$

$$\text{df} = n - 1$$

Formula 8.4 can be used in a manner similar to methods presented in Section 8.1 for constructing a confidence interval to estimate μ. For example, in the aerospace industry some companies allow their employees to accumulate extra working hours beyond their 40-hour week. These extra hours sometimes are referred to as *green* time, or *comp* time. Many managers work longer than the 8-hour workday, preparing proposals, overseeing crucial tasks, and taking care of paperwork. Recognition of such overtime is important. Most managers are usually not paid extra for this work, but a record is kept of this time and occasionally the manager is allowed to use some of this comp time as extra leave or vacation time.

Suppose a researcher wants to estimate the average amount of comp time accumulated per week for managers in the aerospace industry. He randomly samples 18 managers and measures the amount of extra time they work during a specific week and obtains the results shown (in hours).

6	21	17	20	7	0	8	16	29
3	8	12	11	9	21	25	15	16

He constructs a 90% confidence interval to estimate the average amount of extra time per week worked by a manager in the aerospace industry. He assumes that comp time is normally distributed in the population. The sample size is 18, so df = 17. A 90% level of confidence results in an $\alpha/2 = .05$ area in each tail. The table t value is

$$t_{.05,17} = 1.740.$$

The subscripts in the t value denote to other researchers the area in the right tail of the t distribution (for confidence intervals $\alpha/2$) and the number of degrees of freedom. The sample mean is 13.56 hours, and the sample standard deviation is 7.8 hours. The confidence interval is computed from this information as

$$\overline{X} \pm t_{\alpha/2,n-1} \frac{S}{\sqrt{n}}$$

$$13.56 \pm 1.740 \frac{7.8}{\sqrt{18}} = 13.56 \pm 3.20$$

$$10.36 \leq \mu \leq 16.76$$

$$\text{Prob}[10.36 \leq \mu \leq 16.76] = .90.$$

The point estimate for this problem is 13.56 hours, with an error of ±3.20 hours. The researcher is 90% confident that the average amount of comp time accumulated by a manager per week in this industry is between 10.36 and 16.76 hours.

From these figures, aerospace managers could attempt to build a reward system for such extra work or evaluate the regular 40-hour week to determine how to use the normal work hours more effectively and thus reduce comp time.

DEMONSTRATION PROBLEM 8.3

The owner of a large equipment rental company wants to make a rather quick estimate of the average number of days a piece of ditchdigging equipment is rented out per person per time. The company has records of all rentals, but the amount of time required to conduct an audit of *all* accounts would be prohibitive. The owner decides to take a random sample of rental invoices. Fourteen different rentals of ditchdiggers are selected randomly from the files, yielding the following data. She uses these data to construct a 99% confidence interval to estimate the average number of days that a ditchdigger is rented and assumes that the number of days per rental is normally distributed in the population.

3 1 3 2 5 1 2 1 4 2 1 3 1 1

SOLUTION

As $n = 14$, the df = 13. The 99% level of confidence results in $\alpha/2 = .005$ area in each tail of the distribution. The table t value is

$$t_{.005,13} = 3.012.$$

The sample mean is 2.14 and the sample standard deviation is 1.29. The confidence interval is

$$\bar{X} \pm t\frac{S}{\sqrt{n}}$$

$$2.14 \pm 3.012\frac{1.29}{\sqrt{14}} = 2.14 \pm 1.04$$

$$1.10 \le \mu \le 3.18$$

$$\text{Prob}[1.10 \le \mu \le 3.18] = .99.$$

The point estimate of the average length of time per rental is 2.14 days, with an error of ± 1.04. With a 99% level of confidence, the company's owner can estimate that the average length of time per rental is between 1.10 and 3.18 days. Combining this figure with variables such as frequency of rentals per year can help the owner estimate potential profit or loss per year for such a piece of equipment.

Analysis Using Excel

Confidence intervals for a population mean with the t distribution can be constructed using a combination of statistical and mathematical functions from Excel. However to simplify the process, **FAST⧹⧹STAT** has a macro procedure for constructing such a confidence interval. In addition, the procedure performs the computations necessary for conducting a hypothesis test as discussed in Chapter 9. This feature is available from FAST⧹⧹STAT's pull-down menu with the name **1 Mean Using *t* Dist.** The dialog box for it is shown in Figure 8.8

As you may note from the figure, the inputs are grouped into three segments. The first group is for the sample itself. This input is the worksheet cell range for the sample values. The second grouping also has just one input. It is the level of confidence for the confidence interval. It is to be given as a percentage such as 99%, 95%, 90%, and so on.

The third grouping includes two inputs for conducting a hypothesis test. These will be discussed later in Section 9.3 of Chapter 9. If you only wish to compute a confidence interval, enter *any number* for the *hypothesized mean* and *a number between 0 and 100* for the *significance level.*

Figure 8.9 presents the **1 Mean Using *t* Dist.** results for Demonstration Problem 8.3.

In column A you will find the sample values. In columns C through G, the values for the four dialog box inputs are repeated. The outputs that follow are in four parts: sample statistic values, the point estimate, the confidence interval, and the hypothesis test for the sample. The sample statistic values include the sample mean, standard deviation, and sample size. The confidence interval results include the t value for the specified confidence

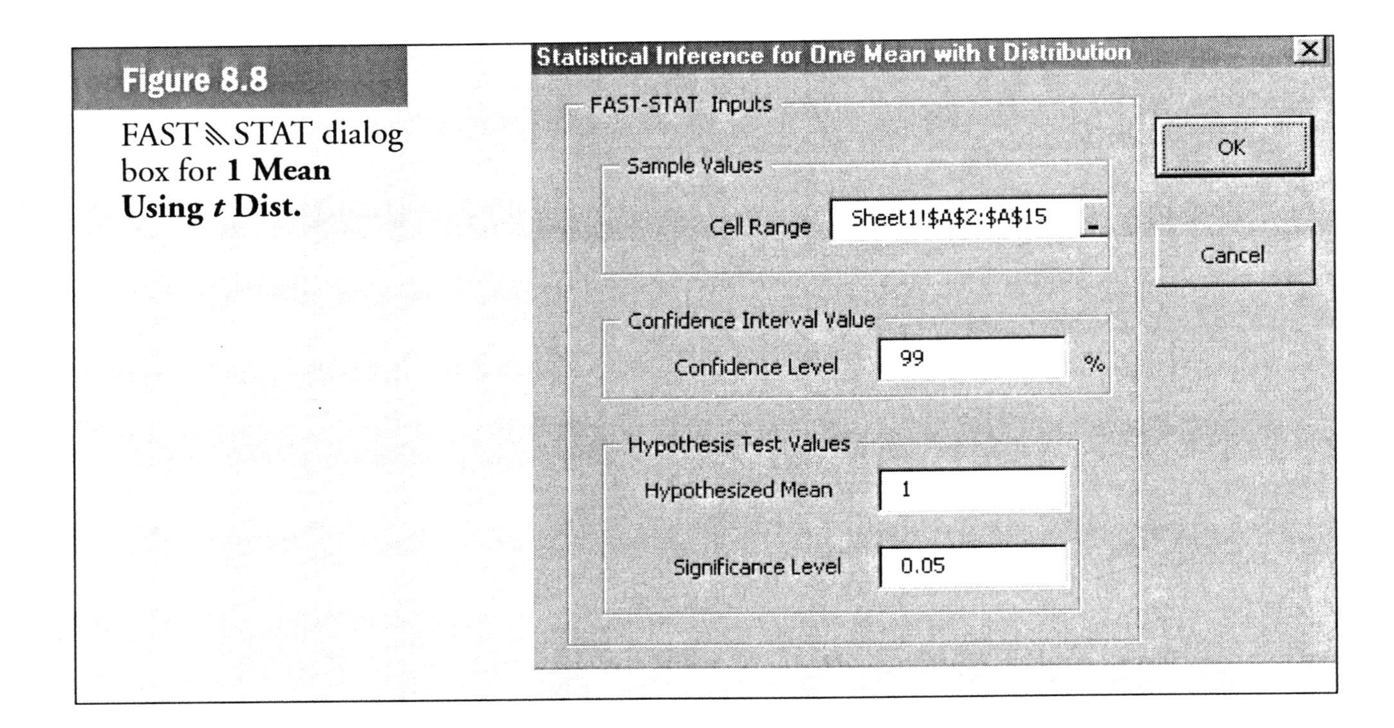

Figure 8.8

FAST⧵STAT dialog box for **1 Mean Using *t* Dist.**

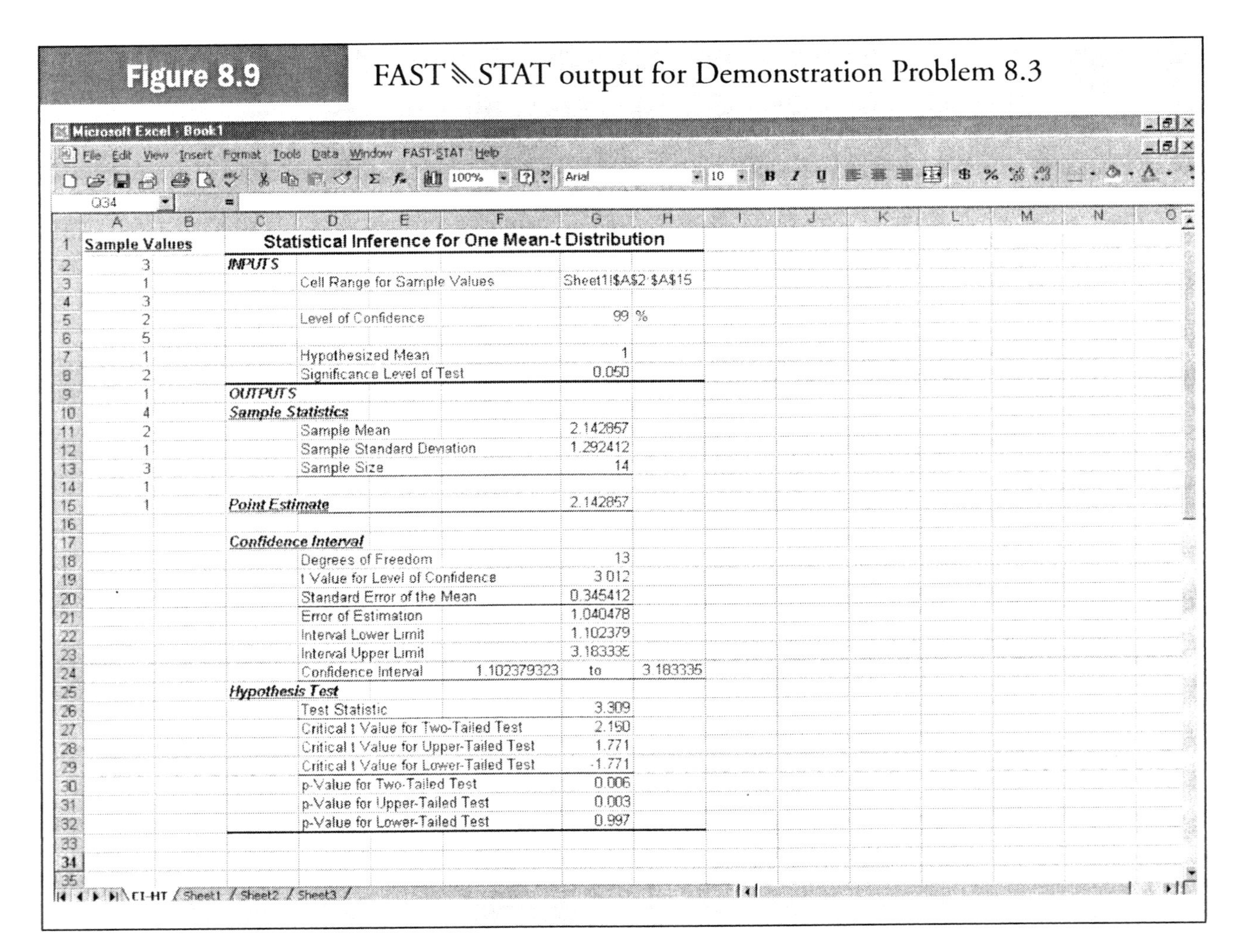

Figure 8.9

FAST⧵STAT output for Demonstration Problem 8.3

Row	A	C–E	F	G	H
1	Sample Values	Statistical Inference for One Mean-t Distribution			
2	3	INPUTS			
3	1	Cell Range for Sample Values		Sheet1!$A$2:$A$15	
4	3				
5	2	Level of Confidence		99	%
6	5				
7	1	Hypothesized Mean		1	
8	2	Significance Level of Test		0.050	
9	1	OUTPUTS			
10	4	Sample Statistics			
11	2	Sample Mean		2.142857	
12	1	Sample Standard Deviation		1.292412	
13	3	Sample Size		14	
14	1				
15	1	Point Estimate		2.142857	
16					
17		Confidence Interval			
18		Degrees of Freedom		13	
19		t Value for Level of Confidence		3.012	
20		Standard Error of the Mean		0.345412	
21		Error of Estimation		1.040478	
22		Interval Lower Limit		1.102379	
23		Interval Upper Limit		3.183335	
24		Confidence Interval	1.102379323	to	3.183335
25		Hypothesis Test			
26		Test Statistic		3.309	
27		Critical t Value for Two-Tailed Test		2.160	
28		Critical t Value for Upper-Tailed Test		1.771	
29		Critical t Value for Lower-Tailed Test		-1.771	
30		p-Value for Two-Tailed Test		0.006	
31		p-Value for Upper-Tailed Test		0.003	
32		p-Value for Lower-Tailed Test		0.997	

level and the standard error of the mean. In addition, it includes the error of estimation (sometimes termed the interval half width), the endpoints of the interval, and the complete interval.

8.2

Problems

8.10 Suppose the following data are selected randomly from a population of normally distributed values.

40	51	43	48	44	57	54
39	42	48	45	39	43	

Construct a 95% confidence interval to estimate the population mean value.

8.11 Assuming X is normally distributed, use the following information to compute a 90% confidence interval to estimate μ.

313	320	319	340
325	310	321	329
317	311	307	318

8.12 If a random sample of 27 items produces $\overline{X} = 128.4$ and $S = 20.6$, what is the 98% confidence interval for μ? Assume X is normally distributed for the population. What is the point estimate?

8.13 Use the following data to construct a 99% confidence interval for μ.

16.4	17.1	17.0	15.6	16.2
14.8	16.0	15.6	17.3	17.4
15.6	15.7	17.2	16.6	16.0
15.3	15.4	16.0	15.8	17.2
14.6	15.5	14.9	16.7	16.3

Assume X is normally distributed. What is the point estimate for μ?

8.14 According to Runzheimer International, the average cost of a domestic trip for business travelers in the financial industry is \$1250. Suppose another travel industry research company takes a random sample of 22 business travelers in the financial industry and determines that the sample average cost of a domestic trip is \$1192, with a sample standard deviation of \$279. Construct a 98% confidence interval for the population mean from these sample data. Assume that the data are normally distributed in the population. Now go back and examine the \$1250 figure published by Runzheimer International. Does it fall into the confidence interval computed from the sample data? What does that tell you?

8.15 A valve manufacturer produces a butterfly valve composed of two semicircular plates on a common spindle and is used to permit flow in one direction only. The semicircular plates are supplied by a vendor with specifications that the plates be 2.37 mm thick and have a tensile strength of 5 lb/mm. A random sample of 20 such plates is taken. Electronic calipers are used to measure the thickness of each plate; the measurements are given here. Assuming that the thicknesses of such plates are normally distributed, use the data to construct a 95% level of confidence for the population mean thickness of these plates. What is the point estimate? How much is the error of the interval?

2.4066	2.4579	2.6724	2.1228	2.3238
2.1328	2.0665	2.2738	2.2055	2.5267
2.5937	2.1994	2.5392	2.4359	2.2146
2.1933	2.4575	2.7956	2.3353	2.2699

8.16 Some fast-food chains have been offering a lower-priced combination meal in an effort to attract budget-conscious customers. One chain test marketed an offer of a burger, fries, and a drink for \$1.71. The weekly sales volume for these meals was impressive. Suppose the chain wants to estimate the average amount its customers spent on a meal at their restaurant while this offer was in effect. An analyst gathers data from 28 randomly selected customers. The following data represent the sample meal totals.

\$3.21	\$5.40	\$3.50	\$4.39	\$5.60	\$8.65	\$5.02
4.20	1.25	7.64	3.28	5.57	3.26	3.80
5.46	9.87	4.67	5.86	3.73	4.08	5.47
4.49	5.19	5.82	7.62	4.83	8.42	9.10

Use these data to construct a 90% confidence interval to estimate the population mean value. Assume the amounts spent are normally distributed.

8.17 The marketing director of a large department store wants to estimate the average number of customers who enter the store every 5 minutes. She has a research assistant randomly select 5-minute intervals and count the number of arrivals at the store. The assistant obtains the figures 58, 32, 41, 47, 56, 80, 45, 29, 32, and 78. The analyst assumes the number of arrivals is normally distributed. Using these data, the analyst computes a 95% confidence interval to estimate the mean value for all 5-minute intervals. What interval values does she get?

8.18 Runzheimer International publishes results of studies on overseas business travel costs. Suppose as a part of one of these studies the following per diem travel accounts (in dollars) are obtained for 14 business travelers staying in Johannesburg, South Africa. Use these data to construct a 98% confidence interval to estimate the average per diem expense for business people traveling to Johannesburg. What is the point estimate? Assume per diem rates for any locale are approximately normally distributed.

142.59	148.48	159.63	171.93	146.90	168.87	141.94
159.09	156.32	142.49	129.28	151.56	132.87	178.34

8.3

Estimating the Population Proportion

Business decision makers and researchers often need to be able to estimate the population proportion. For most businesses, estimating market share (their proportion of the market) is important because many company decisions evolve from market share information. Political pollsters are interested in estimating the proportion of the vote that their candidates will receive. Companies spend thousands of dollars estimating the proportion of produced goods that are defective. Market segmentation opportunities come from a knowledge of the proportion of various demographic characteristics among potential customers or clients.

Methods similar to those in Section 8.1 can be used to estimate the population proportion. The central limit theorem for sample proportions led to the following formula in Chapter 7.

$$Z = \frac{\hat{p} - P}{\sqrt{\frac{P \cdot Q}{n}}}$$

where $Q = 1 - P$. Recall that this formula can be applied only when $n \cdot P$ and $n \cdot Q$ are greater than 5.

Algebraically manipulating this formula to estimate P involves solving for P. However, P is in both the numerator and the denominator, which complicates the resulting formula. For this reason—for confidence interval purposes only and for large sample sizes—$\hat{p}$ is substituted for P in the denominator, yielding

$$Z = \frac{\hat{p} - P}{\sqrt{\frac{\hat{p}\hat{q}}{n}}}$$

where $\hat{q} = 1 - \hat{p}$. Solving for P results in the confidence interval in Formula 8.5*

(8.5) $$\hat{p} - Z_{\alpha/2}\sqrt{\frac{\hat{p}\hat{q}}{n}} \leq P \leq \hat{p} + Z_{\alpha/2}\sqrt{\frac{\hat{p}\hat{q}}{n}}$$

CONFIDENCE INTERVAL TO ESTIMATE P

where:
$\hat{p}$ = sample proportion
$\hat{q} = 1 - \hat{p}$
P = population proportion
n = sample size

In this formula, $\hat{p}$ is the point estimate and $\pm Z_{\alpha/2}\sqrt{\frac{\hat{p}\hat{q}}{n}}$ is the error of the estimation.

As an example, a study of 87 randomly selected companies with a telemarketing operation revealed that 39% of the sampled companies had used telemarketing to assist them in order processing. Using this information, how could a researcher estimate the *population* proportion of telemarketing companies that use their telemarketing operation to assist them in order processing?

The sample proportion, $\hat{p} = .39$, is the *point estimate* of the population proportion, P. For $n = 87$ and $\hat{p} = .39$, a 95% confidence interval can be computed to determine the interval estimation of P. The Z value for 95% confidence is 1.96. The value of $\hat{q} = 1 - \hat{p} = 1 - .39 = .61$. The confidence interval estimate is

$$.39 - 1.96\sqrt{\frac{(.39)(.61)}{87}} \leq P \leq .39 + 1.96\sqrt{\frac{(.39)(.61)}{87}}$$

$$.39 - .10 \leq P \leq .39 + .10$$

$$.29 \leq P \leq .49$$

$$\text{Prob}[.29 \leq P \leq .49] = .95.$$

This interval suggests a .95 probability that the population proportion of telemarketing firms that use their operation to assist order processing is somewhere between .29 and .49. There is a point estimate of .39 with an error of ±.10. This result has a 95% level of confidence.

*Because we are not using the true standard deviation of $\hat{p}$, the correct divisor of the standard error of $\hat{p}$ is $n - 1$. However, for large sample sizes, the effect is negligible. Although technically the minimal sample size for the techniques presented in this section is $n \cdot P$ and $n \cdot Q$ greater than 5, in actual practice sample sizes of several hundred are more commonly used. As an example, for $\hat{p}$ and $\hat{q}$ of .50 and $n = 300$, the standard error of $\hat{p}$ is .02887 using n and .02892 using $n - 1$, a difference of only .00005.

DEMONSTRATION PROBLEM 8.4

Coopers & Lybrand surveyed 210 chief executives of fast-growing small companies. Only 51% of these executives had a management-succession plan in place. A spokesman for Cooper & Lybrand said that many companies do not worry about management succession unless it is an immediate problem. However, the unexpected exit of a corporate leader can disrupt and unfocus a company for long enough to cause it to lose its momentum.

Use the data given to compute a 92% confidence interval to estimate the proportion of *all* fast-growing small companies that have a management-succession plan.

SOLUTION

The point estimate is the sample proportion given to be .51. It is estimated that .51, or 51% of all fast-growing small companies have a management-succession plan. Realizing that the point estimate might change with another sample selection, we calculate a confidence interval.

The value of n is 210; $\hat{p}$ is .51 and $\hat{q} = 1 - \hat{p} = .49$. Because the level of confidence is 92%, the value of $Z_{.04} = 1.75$. The confidence interval is computed as

$$.51 - 1.75\sqrt{\frac{(.51)(.49)}{210}} \le P \le .51 + 1.75\sqrt{\frac{(.51)(.49)}{210}}$$

$$.51 - .06 \le P \le .51 + .06$$

$$.45 \le P \le .57$$

$$\text{Prob}[.45 \le P \le .57] = .92.$$

It is estimated with 92% confidence that the proportion of the population of fast-growing small companies that have a management-succession plan is between .45 and .57.

DEMONSTRATION PROBLEM 8.5

A clothing company produces men's jeans. The jeans are made and sold with either a regular cut or a boot cut. In an effort to estimate the proportion of their men's jeans market in Oklahoma City that is for boot-cut jeans, the analyst takes a random sample of 212 jeans sales from the company's two Oklahoma City retail outlets. Only 34 of the sales were for boot-cut jeans. Construct a 90% confidence interval to estimate the proportion of the population in Oklahoma City who prefer boot-cut jeans.

SOLUTION

The sample size is 212, and the number preferring boot-cut jeans is 34. The sample proportion is $\hat{p} = 34/212 = .16$. A point estimate for boot-cut jeans in the population is .16, or 16%. The Z value for a 90% level of confidence is 1.645, and the value of $\hat{q} = 1 - \hat{p} = 1 - .16 = .84$. The confidence interval estimate is

$$.16 - 1.645\sqrt{\frac{(.16)(.84)}{212}} \le P \le .16 + 1.645\sqrt{\frac{(.16)(.84)}{212}}$$

$$.16 - .04 \le P \le .16 + .04$$

$$.12 \le P \le .20$$

$$\text{Prob}[.12 \le P \le .20] = .90.$$

The analyst estimates with a probability of .90 that the population proportion of boot-cut jeans purchases is between .12 and .20. The level of confidence in this result is 90%.

Analysis Using Excel

Excel itself does not have a feature for computing a confidence interval for a population proportion. However, a confidence interval to estimate a population proportion can be constructed using the **FAST⩓ STAT** feature, **1 Proportion C.I. and H.T.**, which is available from FAST⩓ STAT's pull-down menu. The dialog box for **1 Proportion C.I. and H.T.** is shown in Figure 8.10.

As you may note from the figure, the inputs are grouped into three segments. The first group is for the sample itself. It includes the sample size and the number of items in the sample that have the characteristic of interest. For some situations, the business analyst may know the proportion of the items that have the characteristic instead of the number. For such instances, the number with the characteristic can be found by multiplying the known proportion times the sample size.

The second grouping has just one input. It is the level of confidence for the confidence interval. It is to be given as a percentage such as 99%, 95%, 90%, and so on.

The third grouping includes two inputs for conducting a hypothesis test. These will be discussed in Section 9.4 of Chapter 9. If you wish to compute a confidence interval, enter a number greater than zero and less than one for these two entries.

Figure 8.11 gives the **1 Proportion** results for Demonstration Problem 8.5. At the top of the figure, the values for the five inputs are repeated. The outputs are in three parts: the point estimate, the confidence interval, and the hypothesis test for the sample. The confidence interval results include the Z value for the specified confidence level and the standard error of the proportion. In addition, it includes the error of estimation (sometimes termed the interval half width), the endpoints of the interval, and the complete interval.

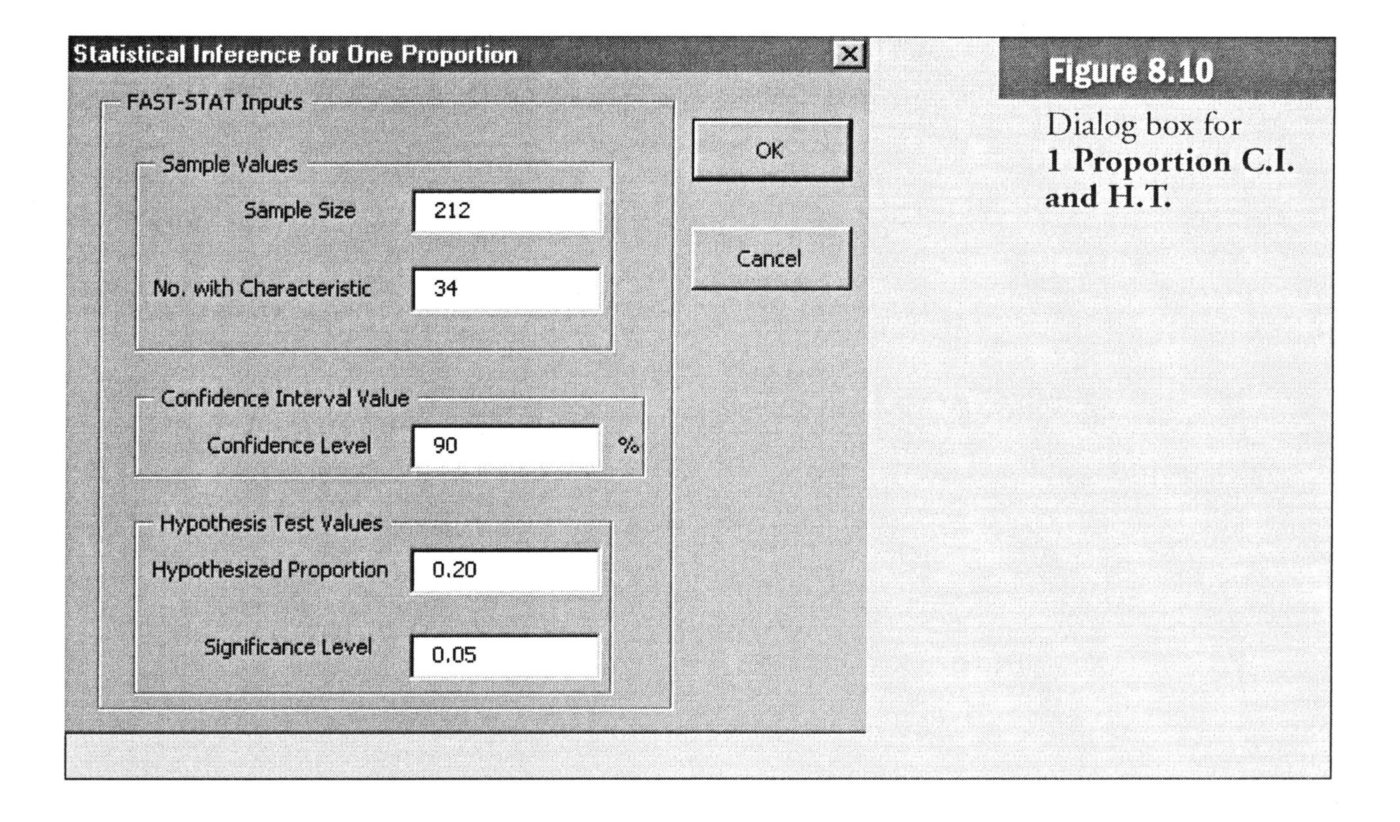

Figure 8.10

Dialog box for **1 Proportion C.I. and H.T.**

Figure 8.11 FAST⧹STAT output for Demonstration Problem 8.5

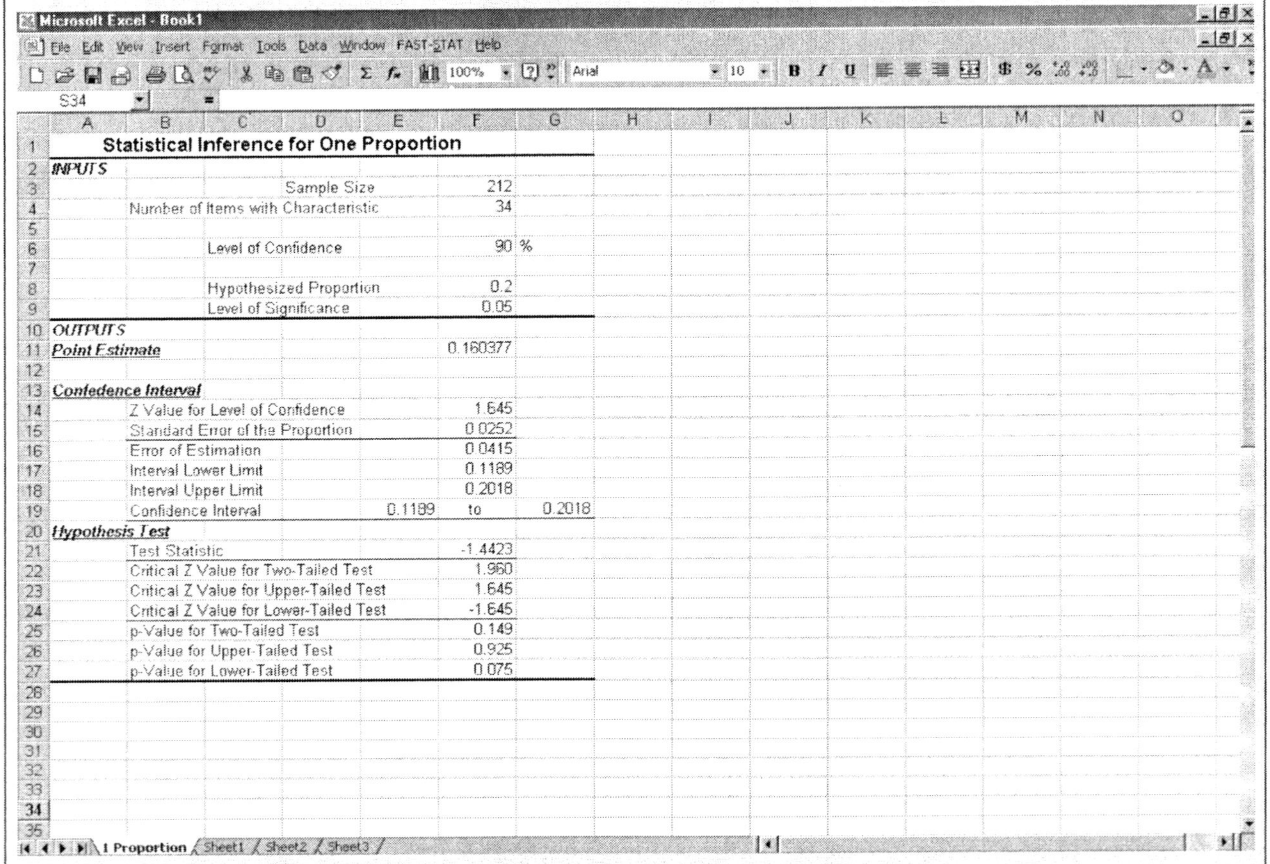

Microsoft Excel - Book1

Statistical Inference for One Proportion

INPUTS				
	Sample Size		212	
	Number of Items with Characteristic		34	
	Level of Confidence		90	%
	Hypothesized Proportion		0.2	
	Level of Significance		0.05	
OUTPUTS				
Point Estimate			0.160377	
Confedence Interval				
	Z Value for Level of Confidence		1.645	
	Standard Error of the Proportion		0.0252	
	Error of Estimation		0.0415	
	Interval Lower Limit		0.1189	
	Interval Upper Limit		0.2018	
	Confidence Interval	0.1189	to	0.2018
Hypothesis Test				
	Test Statistic		-1.4423	
	Critical Z Value for Two-Tailed Test		1.960	
	Critical Z Value for Upper-Tailed Test		1.645	
	Critical Z Value for Lower-Tailed Test		-1.645	
	p-Value for Two-Tailed Test		0.149	
	p-Value for Upper-Tailed Test		0.925	
	p-Value for Lower-Tailed Test		0.075	

1 Proportion / Sheet1 / Sheet2 / Sheet3

8.3
Problems

8.19 Use the information about each of the following samples to compute the confidence interval to estimate P.

a. $n = 44$ and $\hat{p} = .51$; compute a 99% confidence interval.
b. $n = 300$ and $\hat{p} = .82$; compute a 95% confidence interval.
c. $n = 1{,}150$ and $\hat{p} = .48$; compute a 90% confidence interval.
d. $n = 95$ and $\hat{p} = .32$; compute a 88% confidence interval.

8.20 Use the following sample information to calculate the confidence interval to estimate the population proportion. Let X be the number of items in the sample having the characteristic of interest.

a. $n = 116$ and $X = 57$, with 99% confidence
b. $n = 800$ and $X = 479$, with 97% confidence
c. $n = 240$ and $X = 106$, with 85% confidence
d. $n = 60$ and $X = 21$, with 90% confidence

8.21 Suppose a random sample of 85 items has been taken from a population and 40 of the items contain the characteristic of interest. Use this information to calculate a 90% confidence interval to estimate the proportion of the population that has the characteristic of interest. Calculate a 95% confidence interval. Calculate a 99%

confidence interval. As the level of confidence changes and the other sample information stays constant, what happens to the confidence interval?

8.22 A study released by Scoop Marketing early in 1999 showed that Universal/PolyGram held a 24.5% share of the music CD market. Suppose this figure is actually a point estimate obtained by interviewing 1003 people who purchased a music CD in January of 1999. Use this information to compute a 99% confidence interval for the proportion of the market that is held by Universal/PolyGram. Suppose the figure was obtained from a survey of 10,000 people. Recompute the confidence interval and compare your results with the first confidence interval. How did they differ? What might you conclude about sample size and confidence intervals?

8.23 According to the Stern Marketing Group, 9 out of 10 professional women say that financial planning is more important today than it was 5 years ago. Where do these women go for help in financial planning? Forty-seven percent use a financial advisor (broker, tax consultant, financial planner). Twenty-eight percent use written sources such as magazines, books, and newspapers. Suppose these figures were obtained by taking a sample of 560 professional women who said that financial planning is more important today than it was 5 years ago. Construct a 95% confidence interval for the proportion who use a financial advisor. Use the percentage given in this problem as the point estimate. Construct a 90% confidence interval for the proportion who use written sources. Use the percentage given in this problem as the point estimate.

8.24 What proportion of pizza restaurants that are primarily for walk-in business have a salad bar? Suppose that, in an effort to determine this figure, a random sample of 1250 of these restaurants across the U.S. based on the Yellow Pages is called. If 997 of the restaurants sampled have a salad bar, what is the 98% confidence interval for the population proportion?

8.25 The highway department wants to estimate the proportion of vehicles on Interstate 25 between the hours of midnight and 5:00 A.M. that are 18-wheel tractor trailers. The estimate will be used to determine highway repair and construction considerations and in highway patrol planning. Suppose researchers for the highway department counted vehicles at different locations on the interstate for several nights during this time period. Of the 3481 vehicles counted, 927 were 18-wheelers.

a. Determine the point estimate for the proportion of vehicles traveling Interstate 25 during this time period that are 18-wheelers.

b. Construct a 99% confidence interval for the proportion of vehicles on Interstate 25 during this time period that are 18-wheelers.

8.26 What proportion of commercial airline pilots are more than 40 years of age? Suppose a researcher has access to a list of all pilots who are members of the Commercial Airline Pilots Association. If this list is used as a frame for the study, she can randomly select a sample of pilots, contact them, and ascertain their ages. From 89 of these pilots so selected, she learns that 48 are more than 40 years of age. Construct an 85% confidence interval to estimate the population proportion of commercial airline pilots who are more than 40 years of age.

8.27 According to Runzheimer International, in a survey of relocation administrators 63% of all workers who rejected relocation offers did so for family considerations. Suppose this figure was obtained by using a random sample of the files of 672 workers who had rejected relocation offers. Use this information to construct a 95% confidence interval to estimate the population proportion of workers who reject relocation offers for family considerations.

8.4

Estimating Sample Size

Sample-size estimation An estimate of the size of sample necessary to fulfill the requirements of a particular level of confidence and to be within a specified amount of error.

In most business research that uses sample statistics to infer about the population, being able to *estimate the size of sample necessary to accomplish the purposes of the study* is important. The need for this **sample-size estimation** is the same for the large corporation investing tens of thousands of dollars in a massive study of consumer preference and for students undertaking a small case study and wanting to send questionnaires to local business people. In either case, such things as level of confidence, sampling error, and width of estimation interval are closely tied to sample size. If the large corporation is undertaking a market study, should it sample 40 people or 4000 people? The question is an important one. In most cases, because of cost considerations, researchers do not want to sample any more units or individuals than necessary.

Sample Size When Estimating μ

In research studies when μ is being estimated, the size of sample can be determined by using the Z formula for sample means to solve for n.

$$Z = \frac{\bar{X} - \mu}{\frac{\sigma}{\sqrt{n}}}$$

Error of estimation The difference between the statistic computed to estimate a parameter and the parameter.

The difference between $\bar{X}$ and μ is the **error of estimation** resulting from the sampling process. Let $E = (\bar{X} - \mu) =$ the error of estimation. Substituting E into the preceding formula yields

$$Z = \frac{E}{\frac{\sigma}{\sqrt{n}}}.$$

Solving for n produces the sample size.

SAMPLE SIZE WHEN ESTIMATING μ

$$n = \frac{Z^2_{\alpha/2}\sigma^2}{E^2} = \left(\frac{Z_{\alpha/2}\sigma}{E}\right)^2 \quad (8.6)$$

Sometimes in estimating sample size the population variance is known or can be determined from past studies. Other times, the population variance is unknown and must be estimated to determine the sample size. In such cases, it is acceptable to use the following estimate to represent σ.

$$\sigma = \frac{1}{4}(\text{range})$$

This estimate is derived from the empirical rule (Chapter 3) stating that approximately 95% of the values in a normal distribution are within $\pm 2\sigma$ of the mean, giving a range within which most of the values are located.

Using Formula 8.6, the researcher can estimate the sample size needed to achieve the goals of the study before gathering data. For example, suppose a researcher wants to estimate the average monthly expenditure on bread by a family in Chicago. She wants to be 90% confident of her results. How much error is she willing to tolerate in the results? Suppose she wants the estimate to be within \$1.00 of the actual figure and the standard deviation of average monthly bread purchases is \$4.00. What is the sample size estimation for this problem? The value of Z for a 90% level of confidence is 1.645. Using Formula 8.6 with $E = \$1.00$, $\sigma = \$4.00$, and $Z = 1.645$ gives

$$n = \frac{Z^2_{\alpha/2}\sigma^2}{E^2} = \frac{(1.645)^2(4)^2}{1^2} = 43.30.$$

That is, at least $n = 43.3$ must be sampled randomly to attain a 90% level of confidence and produce an error within \$1.00 for a standard deviation of \$4.00. Sampling 43.3 units is impossible, so this result should be rounded up to $n = 44$ units.

In this approach to estimating sample size, we view the error of the estimation as the amount of difference between the statistic (in this case, $\bar{X}$) and the parameter (in this case, μ). The error could be in either direction, that is, the statistic could be over or under the parameter. Thus, the error, E, is actually $\pm E$ as we view it. So when a problem states that the researcher wants to be within \$1.00 of the actual monthly family expenditure for bread, it means that the researcher is willing to allow a tolerance within $\pm\$1.00$ of the actual figure. Another name for this error is the **bounds** of the interval. Some business analysts prefer to view the error of the confidence interval in terms of the total distance across the interval (width of the interval). In such a case, the value of E is equal to one-half this distance.

Bounds
The error portion of the confidence interval that is added and/or subtracted from the point estimate to form the confidence interval.

DEMONSTRATION PROBLEM 8.6

Suppose you want to estimate the average age of all Boeing 727 airplanes now in active domestic U.S. service. You want to be 95% confident, and you want your estimate to be within 2 years of the actual figure. The 727 was first placed in service about 30 years ago, but you believe that no active 727s in the U.S. domestic fleet are more than 25 years old. How large a sample should you take?

SOLUTION

Here, $E = 2$ years, the Z value for 95% is 1.96, and σ is unknown, so it must be estimated by using $\sigma \approx (1/4) \cdot (\text{range})$. As the range of ages is 0 to 25 years, $\sigma = (1/4)(25) = 6.25$. Use Formula 8.6.

$$n = \frac{Z^2\sigma^2}{E^2} = \frac{(1.96)^2(6.25)^2}{2^2} = 37.52$$

Because you cannot sample 37.52 units, the required sample size is 38. If you randomly sample 38 units, you have an opportunity to estimate the average age of active 727s within 2 years and be 95% confident of the results. If you want to be within 1 year for the estimate ($E = 1$), the sample-size estimate changes to

$$n = \frac{Z^2\sigma^2}{E^2} = \frac{(1.96)^2(6.25)^2}{1^2} = 150.1.$$

Note that cutting the error by a factor of ½ increases the required sample size by a factor of 4. The reason is the squaring factor in Formula 8.6. If you want to reduce the error to one-half of what you used before, you must be willing to incur the cost of a sample that is four times larger, for the same level of confidence.

Note: Sample-size estimates for the population mean with small samples where σ is unknown using the t distribution are not shown here. Because a sample size must be known to determine the table value of t, which in turn is used to estimate the sample size, this procedure usually involves an iterative process.

Determining Sample Size When Estimating P

Determining the sample size required to estimate the population proportion, P, also is possible. The process begins with the Z formula for sample proportions.

$$Z = \frac{\hat{p} - P}{\sqrt{\frac{P \cdot Q}{n}}}$$

where $Q = 1 - P$.

As various samples are taken from the population, $\hat{p}$ will rarely equal the population proportion, P, resulting in an error of estimation. That is, the difference between $\hat{p}$ and P is the error of estimation, so $E = \hat{p} - P$.

$$Z = \frac{E}{\sqrt{\frac{P \cdot Q}{n}}}$$

Solving for n yields the sample size.

SAMPLE SIZE WHEN ESTIMATING P

$$n = \frac{Z^2 PQ}{E^2} \qquad (8.7)$$

where:
P = population proportion
$Q = 1 - P$
E = error of estimation
n = sample size

TABLE 8.3
PQ for Various Selected Values of *P*

P	PQ
.5	.25
.4	.24
.3	.21
.2	.16
.1	.09

How can the value of n be determined prior to a study if the formula requires the value of P and the study is being done to estimate P? Although the actual value of P is not known prior to the study, similar studies might have generated a good approximation for P. If no previous value is available for use in estimating P, some possible P values, as shown in Table 8.3, might be considered.

Note that, as PQ is in the numerator of the sample-size formula, $P = .5$ will result in the largest sample sizes. Often *if P is unknown, business analysts use .5 as an estimate of P* in Formula 8.7. This selection results in the largest sample size that could be determined from Formula 8.7 for a given Z value and a given error value.

DEMONSTRATION PROBLEM 8.7

Hewitt Associates conducted a national survey to determine the extent to which employers are promoting health and fitness among their employees. One of the questions asked was, Does your company offer on-site exercise classes? Suppose it was estimated before the study that no more than 40% of the companies would answer yes. How large a sample would Hewitt Associates have to take in estimating the population proportion to ensure a 98% confidence in the results and to be within .03 of the true population proportion?

SOLUTION

The value of E for this problem is .03. Because it is estimated that no more than 40% of the companies would say yes, $P = .40$ can be used. A 98% confidence interval results in a Z value of 2.33. Inserting these values into Formula 8.9 yields

$$n = \frac{(2.33)^2(.40)(.60)}{(.03)^2} = 1447.7.$$

Hewitt Associates would have to sample 1448 companies to be 98% confident in the results and maintain an error of .03.

DEMONSTRATION PROBLEM 8.8

The Packer, a produce industry trade publication, reports on American produce-eating habits. One result of a survey published in the journal showed that about two-thirds of all Americans tried a new type of produce in the past 12 months. Suppose a produce industry organization wants to survey Americans and ask whether they are eating more fresh fruit and vegetables than they did 1 year ago. The organization wants to be 90% confident in its results and maintain an error within .05. How large a sample should it take?

SOLUTION

The value of E is .05. Because no approximate figure has been given as to what proportion of people might answer yes to the question of eating more fresh fruit and vegetables, we shall use $P = .50$. The Z value for a 90% confidence interval is ± 1.645. Solving for n gives

$$n = \frac{Z^2PQ}{E^2} = \frac{(1.645)^2(.50)(.50)}{(.05)^2} = 270.6.$$

The organization should sample at least 271 consumers to achieve 90% confidence and have an error within .05.

Analysis Using Excel

Excel can determine the sample size needed to estimate a population mean through the use of a statistical and a mathematical function. This process has been implemented in **FAST⧹STAT** in a macro procedure entitled **Sample Size for 1 Mean.** The procedure is selected from FAST⧹STAT's pull-down menu. The resulting dialog box is as shown in Figure 8.12.

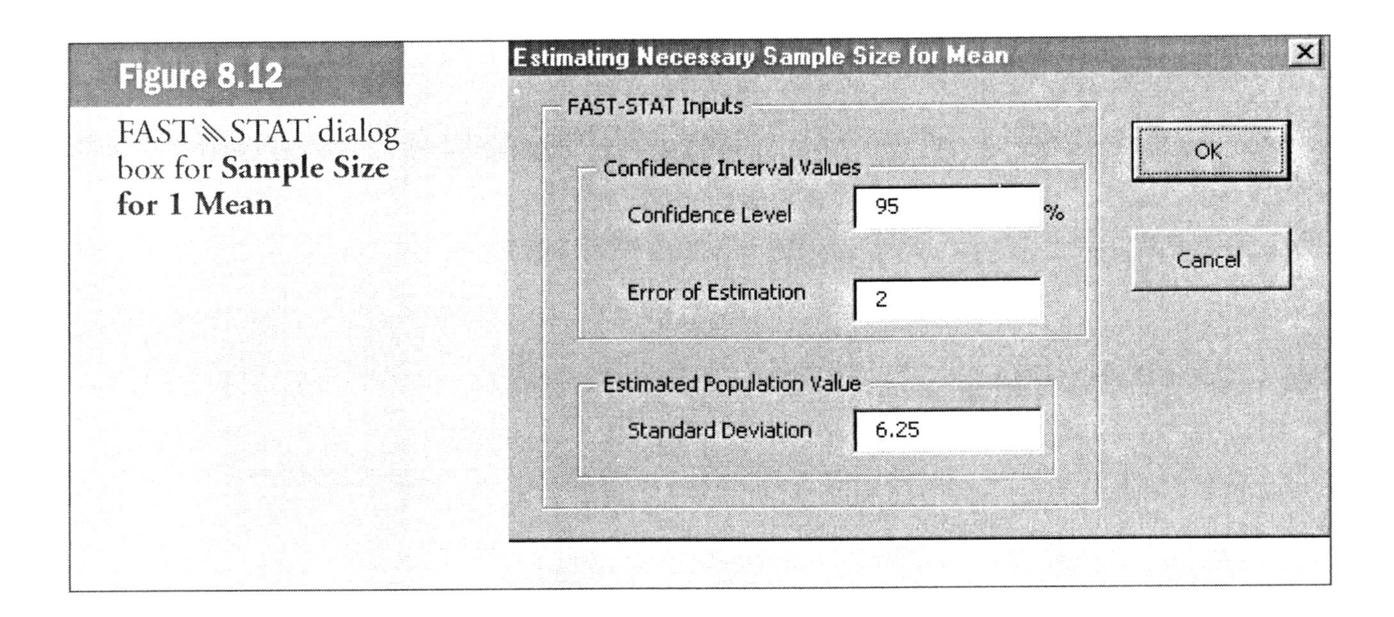

Figure 8.12

FAST⋱STAT dialog box for **Sample Size for 1 Mean**

The **Sample Size for 1 Mean** procedure requires three inputs. The first two specify the desired confidence interval through the value for the confidence level and the value for the error of estimation or bounds for the interval (E). The remaining input is an estimation of the standard deviation for the population. This estimate could come from a prior study or sample or could be set equal to ¼ the range as previously discussed.

Figure 8.13 presents the results of this procedure for Demonstration Problem 8.6. The results include a summary of the input values together with the minimal recommended sample size. The procedure always rounds the sample size up to the next higher integer.

To use **FAST⋱STAT** to determine sample size when estimating a population proportion, select **Sample Size—1 Proportion** from the FAST⋱STAT pull-down menu. The dialog box for this procedure, which is quite similar to that for the mean, is displayed in Figure 8.14.

The **Sample Size—1 Proportion** procedure requires three inputs. The first two specify the desired confidence interval with the values for the confidence level and the error of estimation or bounds for the interval (E). The remaining input is an estimation of the population proportion. This estimate could come from a prior study or sample. If no such estimate is available, a value of 0.50 is oftentimes used for the estimate as previously mentioned.

Figure 8.15 presents the results of this procedure for Demonstration Problem 8.7. As you will note, the results include a summary of the input values together with the minimal recommended sample size. The procedure always rounds the sample size up to the next higher integer.

You may have noted that the sample size computed by Excel in Figure 8.15 differs slightly from the hand-calculated value given for Demonstration Problem 8.7. The difference results from the value used for Z. When computing by hand we use the value 2.33 from the normal table. When computing with Excel we use the statistical function **NORMSINV.** The resulting computer-generated Z value is not limited to two decimal places, but has 14 places to the right of the decimal point. Specifically, the value is 2.32634192798286. Obviously not all these digits are meaningful. However, it does differ slightly from 2.33. As a result, when computing necessary sample sizes for proportions that usually are in the neighborhood of 1000 or more, a small difference in the Z value results in a small, but noticeable, difference in values for n. If you had to choose between the answers, most persons would elect the computer-generated value.

Figure 8.13 FAST\STAT output for Demonstration Problem 8.6

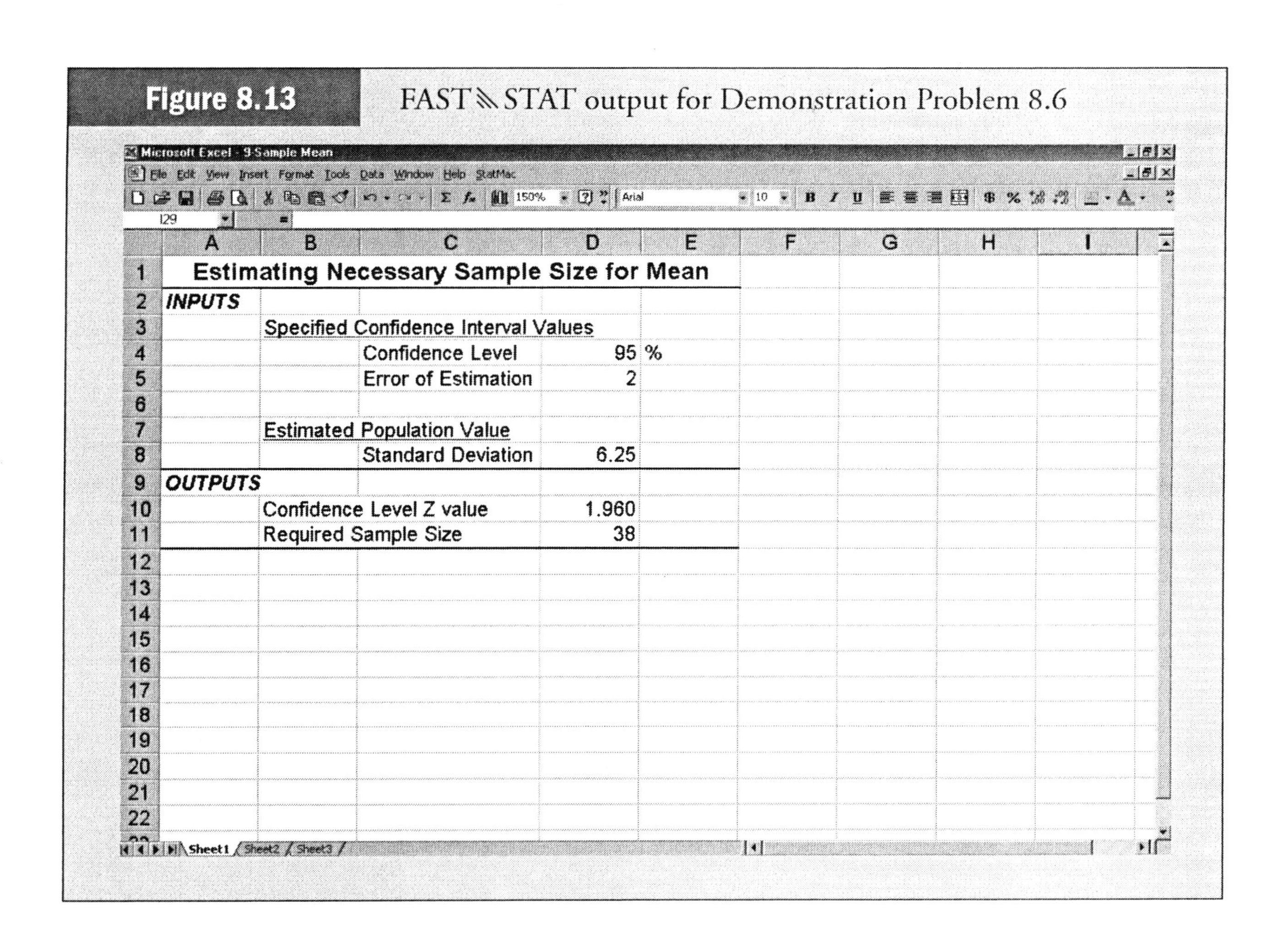

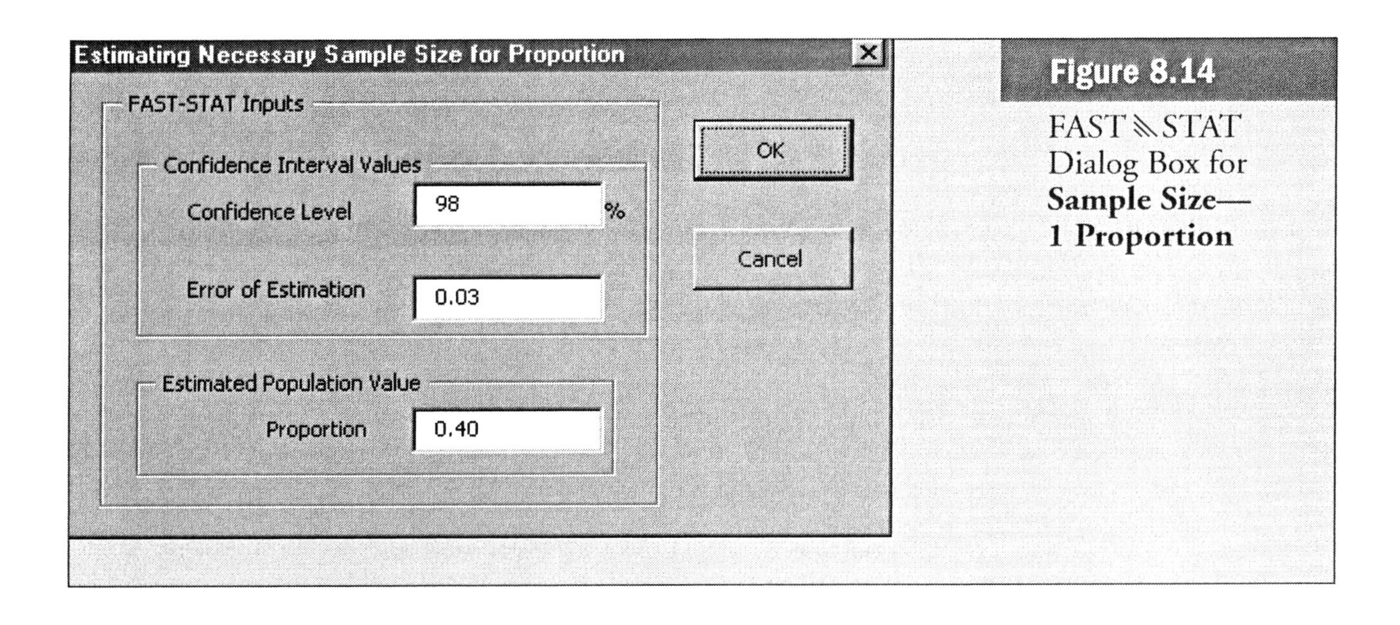

Figure 8.14 FAST\STAT Dialog Box for **Sample Size—1 Proportion**

Figure 8.15 FAST\STAT output for Demonstration Problem 8.7

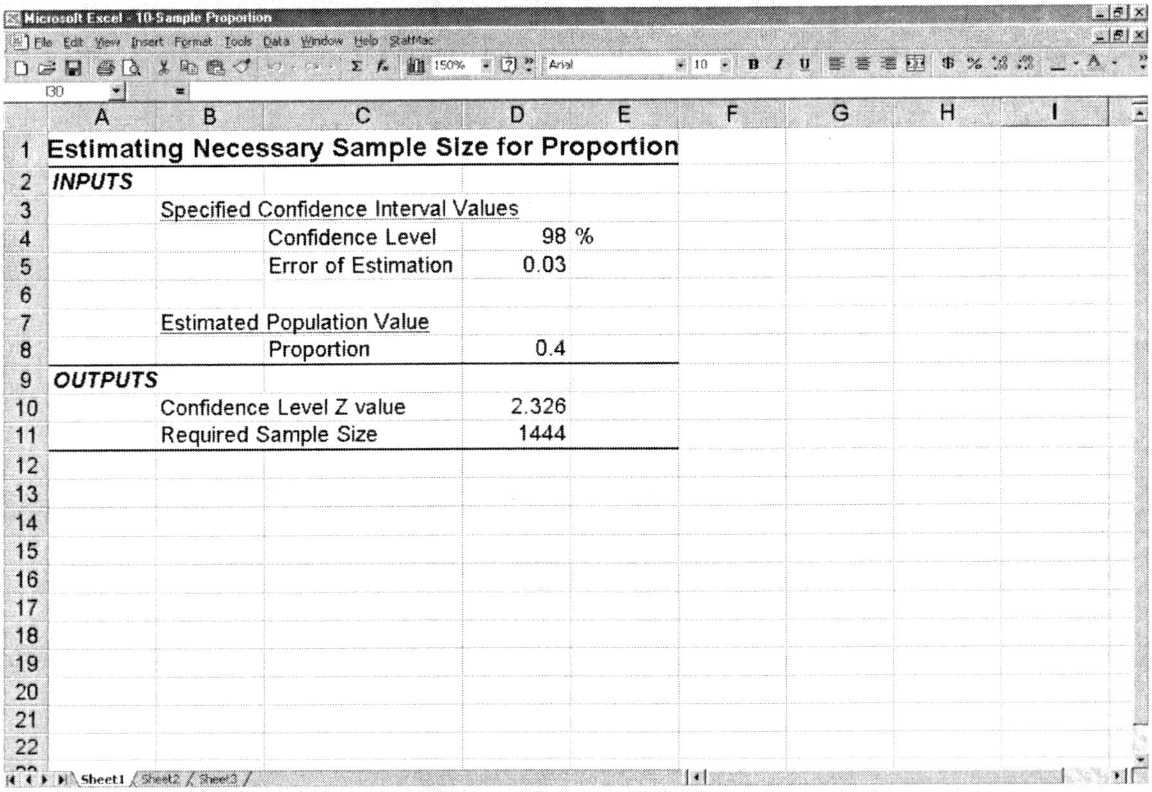

Microsoft Excel - 10-Sample Proportion

	A	B	C	D	E
1	**Estimating Necessary Sample Size for Proportion**				
2	***INPUTS***				
3		Specified Confidence Interval Values			
4			Confidence Level	98 %	
5			Error of Estimation	0.03	
6					
7		Estimated Population Value			
8			Proportion	0.4	
9	***OUTPUTS***				
10		Confidence Level Z value		2.326	
11		Required Sample Size		1444	

8.4

Problems

8.28 Determine the sample size necessary to estimate μ for the following information.

a. $\sigma = 36$ and $E = 5$ at 95% confidence

b. $\sigma = 4.13$ and $E = 1$ at 99% confidence

c. Values range from 80 to 500, error is to be within 10, and the confidence level is 90%

d. Values range from 50 to 108, error is to be within 3, and the confidence level is 88%

8.29 Determine the sample size necessary to estimate P for the following information.

a. $E = .02$, P is approximately .40, and confidence level is 96%

b. E is to be within .04, P is unknown, and confidence level is 95%

c. E is to be within 5%, P is approximately 55%, and confidence level is 90%

8.30 A bank officer wants to determine the amount of the average total monthly deposits per customer at the bank. He believes an estimate of this average amount using a confidence interval is sufficient. How large a sample should he take to be within \$200 of the actual average with 99% confidence? He assumes the standard deviation of total monthly deposits for all customers is about \$1000.

8.31 Suppose you have been following a particular airline stock for many years. You are interested in determining the average daily price of this stock in a 10-year period and you have access to the stock reports for these years. However, you do not want to average all the daily prices over 10 years because of the more than 2500 data points, so you decide to take a random sample of the daily prices and estimate the average. You want to be 90% confident of your results, you want the estimate to be within $2.00 of the true average, and you believe the standard deviation of the price of this stock is about $12.50 over this period of time. How large a sample should you take?

8.32 A group of investors wants to develop a chain of fast-food restaurants. In determining potential costs for each facility, they must consider, among other expenses, the average monthly electric bill. They decide to sample some fast-food restaurants currently operating to estimate the monthly cost of electricity. They want to be 90% confident of their results and want the error of the interval estimate to be no more than $100. They estimate that such bills range from $600 to $2500. How large a sample should they take?

8.33 Suppose a production facility purchases a particular component part in large lots from a supplier. The production manager wants to estimate the proportion of defective parts received from this supplier. She believes the proportion defective is no more than .20 and wants to be within .02 of the true proportion of defective parts with a 90% level of confidence. How large a sample should she take?

8.34 What proportion of secretaries of *Fortune 500* companies has a personal computer at his or her work station? You want to answer this question by conducting a random survey. How large a sample should you take if you want to be 95% confident of the results and you want the error of the confidence interval to be no more than .05? Assume no one has any idea of what the proportion actually is.

8.35 What proportion of shoppers at a large appliance store actually make a large-ticket purchase? To estimate this proportion within 10% and be 95% confident of the results, how large a sample should you take? Assume that no more than 50% of all shoppers actually make a large-ticket purchase.

Summary

Techniques for estimating population parameters from sample statistics are important tools for business research. These tools include techniques for estimating population means by using both large- and small-sample statistics, techniques for estimating the population proportion, and methodology for determining how large a sample to take is presented.

At times in business research a product is new and/or untested or information about the population is unknown. In such cases, gathering data from a sample and making estimates about the population is useful and can be done with a point estimate or an interval estimate. A point estimate is the use of a statistic from the sample as an estimate for a parameter of the population. The problem with point estimates is that they are likely to change with every sample taken. An interval estimate is a range of values computed from the sample within which the researcher believes with some confidence that the population parameter lies. Certain levels of confidence seem to be used more than others: 90%, 95%, 98%, and 99%.

In estimating the population mean when sample size is large, it is permissible to use the sample standard deviation as an approximation for the population standard deviation when the population standard deviation is unknown.

However, if sample size is small and the population standard deviation is unknown, the t distribution should be used instead of the Z distribution. It is assumed when using the t distribution that the population from which the samples are drawn is normally distributed. However, the technique for estimating a population mean by using the t test is robust, which means it is relatively insensitive to minor violations to the assumption.

The formulas in Chapter 7 resulting from the central limit theorem can be manipulated to produce formulas for estimating sample size for large samples. Determining the sample size necessary to estimate a population mean, if the population standard deviation is unavailable, can be based on one-fourth the range as an estimate of the population standard deviation. Estimating the population proportion calls for the value of the population proportion. The population proportion is the parameter to be estimated, so it is unknown. A value of the population proportion from a similar study can be used in sample-size estimation. If none is available, using a value of .50 will result in the largest sample-size estimation for the problem if other variables are held constant. Sample-size estimation is used mostly to provide a ballpark figure to give researchers some guidance. Costs are associated with research, and larger sample sizes usually result in greater costs.

Key Terms

bounds
degrees of freedom (df)
error of estimation
interval estimate
point estimate
robust
sample-size estimation
t distribution
t value

SUPPLEMENTARY PROBLEMS

8.36 In planning both market opportunity and production levels, being able to estimate the size of a market can be important. Suppose a diaper manufacturer wants to know how many diapers a 1-month-old baby uses during a 24-hour period. To determine this, the manufacturer's analyst randomly selects 17 parents of 1-month-olds and asks them to keep track of diaper usage for 24 hours. The results are shown. Construct a 99% confidence interval to estimate the average daily diaper usage of a 1-month-old baby. Assume diaper usage is normally distributed.

12	8	11	9	13	14	10
10	9	13	11	8	11	15
10	7	12				

8.37 Suppose you want to estimate the proportion of cars that are sport utility vehicles (SUVs) being driven in Kansas City, Missouri, at rush hour by standing on the corner of I-70 and I-470 and counting SUVs. You believe the figure is no higher than .40. If you want the error of the confidence interval to be no greater than .03, how many cars should you randomly sample? Use a 90% level of confidence.

8.38 What is the average length of a company's policy book? Suppose policy books are sampled from 45 medium-size companies. The average number of pages in the sample books is 213, with a sample standard deviation of 48. Use this information to construct a 98% confidence interval to estimate the mean number of pages for the population of medium-size company policy books.

8.39 A random sample of small-business managers was given a leadership style questionnaire. The results were scaled so that each manager received a score for initiative. Suppose the following data are a random sample of these scores.

37	42	40	39	38	31	40
37	35	45	30	33	35	44
36	37	39	33	39	40	41
33	35	36	41	33	37	38
40	42	44	35	36	33	38
32	30	37	42			

Use these data to construct a 90% confidence interval to estimate the average score on initiative for all small-business managers.

8.40 A national beauty salon chain wants to estimate the number of times per year a woman has her hair done at a beauty salon if she uses one at least once a year. The chain's researcher estimates that, of those women who use a beauty salon at least once a year, the standard deviation of number of times of usage is approximately 6. The national chain wants the estimate to be within one time of the actual mean value. How large a sample should the researcher take to obtain a 98% confidence level?

8.41 Is the environment a major issue with Americans? To answer that question, a researcher conducts a survey of 1255 randomly selected Americans. Suppose 714 of the sampled people replied that the environment is a major issue with them. Construct a 95% confidence interval to estimate the proportion of Americans who feel that the environment is a major issue with them. What is the point estimate of this proportion?

8.42 According to a survey by Topaz Enterprises, a travel auditing company, the average error by travel agents is $128. Suppose this figure was obtained from a random sample of 25 travel agents and the sample standard deviation is $21. What is the point estimate of the national average error for all travel agents? Compute a 98% confidence interval for the national average error based on these sample results. Assume the travel agent errors are normally distributed in the population. How wide is the interval? Interpret the interval.

8.43 A national survey on telemarketing was undertaken. One of the questions asked was: How long has your organization had a telemarketing operation? Suppose the following data represent some of the answers received to this question. Suppose further that only 300 telemarketing firms comprised the population when this survey was taken. Use the following data to compute a 98% confidence interval to estimate the average number of years a telemarketing organization has had a telemarketing operation.

5	5	6	3	6	7	5
5	6	8	4	9	6	4
10	5	10	11	5	14	7
5	9	6	7	3	4	3
7	5	9	3	6	8	16
12	11	5	4	3	6	5
8	3	5	9	7	13	4
6	5	8	3	5	8	7
11	5	14	4			

8.44 An entrepreneur wants to open an appliance service repair shop. She would like to know about what the average home repair bill is, including the charge for the service call for appliance repair in the area. She wants the estimate to be within $20 of the actual figure. She believes the range of such bills is between $30 and $600. How large a sample should the entrepreneur take if she wants to be 95% confident of the results?

8.45 A national survey of insurance offices was taken, resulting in a random sample of 245 companies. Of these 245 companies, 189 responded that they were going to purchase new software for their offices in the next year. Construct a 90% confidence interval to estimate the population proportion of insurance offices that intend to purchase new software during the next year.

8.46 A national survey of companies included a question that asked whether the company had at least one bilingual telephone operator. The sample results of 90 companies follow (y denotes that the company does have at least one bilingual operator; n denotes that it does not).

n	n	n	n	y	n	y	n	n
y	n	n	n	y	y	n	n	n
n	n	y	n	y	n	y	n	y
y	y	n	y	n	n	n	y	n
n	y	n	n	n	n	n	n	n
y	n	y	y	n	n	y	n	y
n	n	y	y	n	n	n	n	n
y	n	n	n	n	y	n	n	n
y	y	y	n	n	y	n	n	n
n	n	n	y	y	n	n	y	n

Use this information to estimate with 95% confidence the proportion of the population that does have at least one bilingual operator.

8.47 A movie theater has had a poor accounting system. The manager has no idea how many large containers of popcorn are sold per movie showing. She knows that the amounts vary by day of the week and hour of the day. However, she wants to estimate the overall average per movie showing. To do so, she randomly selects 12 movie performances and counts the number of large containers of popcorn sold between 1/2 hour before the movie showing and 15 minutes after the movie showing. The sample average was 43.7 containers, with a variance of 228. Construct a 95% confidence interval to estimate the mean number of large containers of popcorn sold during a movie showing. Assume the number of large containers of popcorn sold per movie is normally distributed in the population.

8.48 According to a survey by Runzheimer International, the average cost of a fast-food meal (quarter-pound cheeseburger, large fries, medium soft drink, excluding taxes) in Seattle is $4.82. Suppose this was based on a sample of 27 different establishments and the standard deviation was $0.37. Construct a 95% confidence interval for the population mean cost for all fast-food meals in Seattle. Assume the costs of a fast-food meal in Seattle are normally distributed. Using the interval as a guide, is it likely that the population mean is really $4.50? Why or why not?

8.49 A survey of 77 commercial airline flights of under 2 hours resulted in a sample average late time for a flight of 2.48 minutes. The sample standard deviation was 12 minutes. Construct a 95% confidence interval for the average time that a commercial flight of under 2 hours is late. What is the point estimate? What does the interval tell about whether the average flight is late?

8.50 A regional survey of 560 companies asked the vice president of operations how satisfied he or she was with the software support being received from the computer staff of the company. Suppose 33% of the 560 vice presidents said they were satisfied. Construct a 99% confidence interval for the proportion of the population of vice presidents who would have said they were satisfied with the software support if a census had been taken.

8.51 A research firm has been asked to determine the proportion of all restaurants in the state of Ohio that serve alcoholic beverages. The firm wants to be 98% confident of its results but has no idea of what the actual proportion is. The firm would like to report an error of no more than .05. How large a sample should it take?

8.52 A national magazine marketing firm attempts to win subscribers with a mail campaign that involves a contest using magazine stickers. Often when people subscribe to magazines in this manner they sign up for multiple magazine subscriptions. Suppose the marketing firm wants to estimate the average number of subscriptions per customer of those who purchase at least one subscription. To do so, the marketing firm's researcher randomly selects 65 returned contest entries. Twenty-seven contain subscription requests. Of the 27, the average number of subscriptions is 2.10, with a standard deviation of .86. The researcher uses this information to compute a 98% confidence interval to estimate μ and assumes that X is normally distributed. What does he find?

8.53 Suppose a national survey of 23 retail outlets of Hillshire Farm Deli Select cold cuts was taken to estimate the price per pound. If the data below represent these prices, what is a 90% confidence interval for the population mean of these prices? Assume prices are normally distributed in the population.

5.18	5.22	5.25	5.19	5.30
5.17	5.15	5.28	5.20	5.14
5.05	5.19	5.26	5.23	5.19
5.22	5.08	5.21	5.24	5.33
5.22	5.19	5.19		

8.54 The price of a head of iceberg lettuce varies greatly with the season and the geographic location of a store. During February a researcher contacts a random sample of 39 grocery stores across the United States and asks the produce manager of each to state the current price charged for a head of iceberg lettuce. Using the researcher's results that follow, construct a 99% confidence interval to estimate the mean price of a head of iceberg lettuce in February in the United States.

\$1.59	\$1.25	\$1.65	\$1.40	\$0.89
1.19	1.50	1.49	1.30	1.39
1.29	1.60	0.99	1.29	1.19
1.20	1.50	1.49	1.29	1.35
1.10	0.89	1.10	1.39	1.39
1.50	1.50	1.55	1.20	1.15
0.99	1.00	1.30	1.25	1.10
1.00	1.55	1.29	1.39	

ANALYZING THE DATABASES

1. Construct a 95% confidence interval for the population mean number of production workers using the manufacturing database as a sample. What is the point estimate? How much is the error of the estimation? Comment on the results.
2. Construct a 90% confidence interval to estimate the average census for hospitals using the hospital database. State the point estimate and the error of the estimation. Change the level of confidence to 99%. What happened to the interval? Did the point estimate change?
3. The financial database contains financial data on 100 companies. Use this database as a sample and estimate the earnings per share for all corporations from these data. Select several levels of confidence and compare the results.
4. Using the tally or frequency feature of the computer software, determine the sample proportion of the hospital database under the variable "service" that are "general medical" (category 1). From this statistic, construct a 95% confidence interval to estimate the population proportion of hospitals that are "general medical." What is the point estimate? How much error is there in the interval?

CASE

THERMATRIX

In 1985, a company called In-Process Technology was set up to produce and sell a thermal oxidation process that could be used to reduce industrial pollution. The initial investors had acquired the rights to technology that had been developed at a federal government laboratory. However, for years the company performed dismally and by 1991 was still only earning $264,000 annually.

In 1992, current CEO John Schofield was hired to turn things around. Under his tutelage, the company was reorganized and renamed Thermatrix. Schofield realized the potential of the technology in the environmental marketplace. He was able to raise more than $20 million in private equity offerings over several years to produce, market, and distribute the product. In June of 1996, there was a successful public offering of Thermatrix in the financial markets.

Thermatrix's philosophy was to give customers more than competitors gave without charging more. The company targeted large corporations as customers, hoping to use its client list as a selling tool. In addition, realizing that they were a small, thinly capitalized company, Thermatrix partnered with many of its clients in developing solutions to the clients' specific environment problems.

Eventually, Schofield located the Thermatrix operations group in Knoxville, Tennessee because of the low cost of living and the large pool of highly trained professional workers. Thermatrix was able to attract good employees using stock options and other competitive compensation. There are presently 60 employees in the company, and annual sales have risen to around $15 million.

Thermatrix also has become a player in the international marketplace. In 1997, 35% of company revenue came from overseas business. By 1998, it was expected that over 60% of its revenues would be derived from overseas customers. One of the main keys to the company's success has been its customer satisfaction.

DISCUSSION

1. Thermatrix has grown and flourished because of its good customer relationships, which include partnering, delivering a quality product on time, and listening to the customer's needs. Suppose company management wants to formally measure customer satisfaction at least once a year and develops a brief survey that includes the following four questions. Suppose 115 customers participated in this survey with the results shown. Use techniques presented in this chapter to analyze the data to estimate population responses to these questions.

Question	Yes	No
1. In general, were deliveries on time?	63	52
2. Were the contact people at Thermatrix helpful and courteous?	86	29
3. Was the pricing structure fair to your company?	101	14
4. Would you recommend Thermatrix to other companies?	105	10

2. Now suppose Thermatrix officers want to ascertain employee satisfaction with the company. To do this, they randomly sample nine employees and ask them to complete a satisfaction survey under the supervision of an independent testing organization. As part of this survey, employees are asked to respond to questions on a 5-point scale where 1 is low satisfaction and 5 is high satisfaction. Assume the data are at least interval and that the overall responses on questions are normally distributed. The questions and the results of the survey are shown here. Analyze the results by using techniques from this chapter.

QUESTION	MEAN	STANDARD DEVIATION
1. Are you treated fairly as an employee?	3.79	.86
2. Has the company given you the training you need to do the job adequately?	2.74	1.27
3. Does management seriously consider your input in making decisions about production?	4.18	.63
4. Is your physical work environment acceptable?	3.34	.81
5. Is the compensation for your work adequate and fair?	3.95	.21

ADAPTED FROM: "Thermatrix: Selling Products, Not Technology," *Insights and Inspiration: How Businesses Succeed.* Published by *Nation's Business* on behalf of MassMutual—The Blue Chip Company and the U.S. Chamber of Commerce in association with The Blue Chip Enterprise Initiative, 1997; and Thermatrix, Inc. website accessed by http://www.thermatrix.com under the title "Company Background."

9

Hypothesis Testing with Single Samples

Learning Objectives

The main objective of Chapter 9 is to help you to learn how to test hypotheses on single populations, thereby enabling you to:

1. Understand the logic of hypothesis testing and know how to establish null and alternative hypotheses.
2. Understand Type I and Type II errors.
3. Use large samples to test hypotheses about a single population mean and about a single population proportion.
4. Test hypotheses about a single population mean using small samples when σ is unknown and the population is normally distributed.

The concept of hypothesis testing lies at the very heart of inferential statistics, and the use of statistics to "prove" or "disprove" claims hinges on it. Applications of statistical hypothesis testing run the gamut from determining whether a production line process is out of control to providing conclusive evidence that a new medicine is significantly more effective than the old. The process of hypothesis testing is used in the legal system to provide evidence in civil suits. Hypotheses are tested in virtually all areas of life, including education, psychology, marketing, science, law, and medicine. How does the hypothesis testing process begin?

9.1

Introduction to Hypothesis Testing

Hypothesis testing
A process of testing hypotheses about parameters by setting up null and alternative hypotheses, gathering sample data, computing statistics from the samples, and using statistical techniques to reach conclusions about the hypotheses.

One of the foremost statistical mechanisms for decision making is the *hypothesis test.* With **hypothesis testing,** business analysts are able to structure problems in such a way that they can use statistical evidence to test various theories about business phenomena. For example, a U.S. Bureau of Labor Statistics report published in March 1994 stated that the average number of vacation days awarded to manufacturing workers in Germany was 30. Suppose international business analysts hypothesize that the figure is not the same this year. How do they go about testing this hypothesis? If they have the necessary resources, they might choose to interview every manufacturing worker in Germany at the end of the year and compute the national mean number of vacation days from the census. However, the business analysts are likely to take a random sample of German workers, gather sample data, and attempt to reach some conclusion about the population from the sample data. They would probably use a hypothesis-testing approach. Hypothesis testing is a process that consists of several steps.

Steps in Hypothesis Testing

Most business analysts take the following steps when testing hypotheses.

1. Establish the hypotheses; state the null and alternative hypotheses.
2. Determine the appropriate statistical test and sampling distribution.
3. Specify the Type I error rate.
4. State the decision rule.
5. Gather sample data.
6. Calculate the value of the test statistic.
7. State the statistical conclusion.
8. Make a managerial decision.

After stating the null and alternative hypotheses, the business analyst selects the appropriate statistical test and sampling distribution. This selection involves matching the level of data collected and the type of statistic being analyzed with the statistical tests available. In this chapter and Chapter 10, various statistical tests and their associated sampling distribution are presented, along with their applicability to specific situations. Particular statistical tests have certain assumptions that must be met for the tests to be valid.

The next step is for the business analyst to specify the Type I error rate, α. Alpha, sometimes referred to as the amount of risk, is the probability for committing a Type I error and is discussed later. The fourth step is to state a decision rule. In conjunction with alpha and the type of statistical test and sampling distribution being used, a critical value is established. The critical value is obtained from tables and is used as a standard against which gathered data are compared to reach a statistical decision about whether to reject the null hypothesis or not. *The business analyst should not gather data before taking the first four hypothesis-testing steps.* Too often, the business analyst gathers the data first and then tries to determine what to do with them.

In gathering data, the business analyst is cautioned to recall the proper techniques of random sampling (presented in Chapter 7). Care should be taken in establishing a frame, determining the sampling technique, and constructing the measurement device. A strong effort should be made to avoid all nonsampling errors. After the data are gathered, the value of the test statistic can be calculated by using both the data from the study and the hypothesized value of the parameter(s) being studied (mean, proportion, etc.). Using the previously established decision rule and the value of the test statistic, the business analyst can draw a statistical conclusion. In *all* hypothesis tests, the business analyst needs to conclude whether the null hypothesis is rejected or cannot be rejected. From this information, a managerial decision about the phenomenon being studied can be reached. For example, if the hypothesis-testing procedure results in a conclusion that train passengers are significantly older today than they were in the past, the manager may decide to cater to these older customers or to draw up a strategy to make ridership more appealing to younger people.

Null and Alternative Hypotheses

The first step in testing a hypothesis is to establish a **null hypothesis** and an **alternative hypothesis.** The null hypothesis is represented by H_0 and the alternative hypothesis by H_a. Establishing null and alternative hypotheses can be a frustrating and confusing process.

Null hypothesis The hypothesis that assumes the status quo—that the old theory, method, or standard is still true, the complement of the alternative hypothesis.

Alternative hypothesis The hypothesis that complements the null hypothesis; usually it is the hypothesis that the business analyst is interested in proving.

The null and alternative hypotheses are set up in opposition to each other. The alternative hypothesis often contains the research question and the null hypothesis can be seen as the negation of the alternative hypothesis. The hypothesis-testing process is structured so that either the null hypothesis is true or the alternative hypothesis is true, but not both. The null hypothesis initially is assumed to be true. The data are gathered and examined to determine whether the evidence is strong enough away from the null hypothesis to reject it. When the business analyst is testing an industry standard or a widely accepted value, the standard or accepted value is assumed true in the null hypothesis. *Null* in this sense means that nothing is new, or there is no new value or standard. The burden is then placed on the business analyst to demonstrate through gathered data that the null hypothesis is false. This task is analogous to the courtroom ideal of innocent until proven guilty. In the courtroom the accused is assumed to be innocent before the trial (null is assumed true). Evidence is presented during the trial (data are gathered). If there is enough evidence against innocence, the accused is found guilty (null is rejected). If there is not enough evidence to prove guilt, the prosecutors have failed to prove the accused guilty. However, they have not "proven" the accused innocent. Typically, what the business analyst is interested in "proving" is formulated into the alternative hypothesis, although in some cases it is not.

As an example, suppose a soft-drink company is filling 12-ounce cans with cola. Recognizing that only under perfect conditions would all cans have exactly 12 ounces of cola, the company hopes that the cans are averaging that amount. A quality controller is worried that a machine is out of control and wants to conduct a hypothesis test to help determine whether that is true. The quality controller hopes the machine is functioning properly, but is really interested in determining whether the machine is malfunctioning with the result that cans are over- or underfilled. The null hypothesis is that there is no problem and the mean value is 12 ounces. The alternative hypothesis is that there is some kind of problem and the cans are not averaging 12 ounces of cola. The null and alternative hypothesis for this problem follow.

$$H_0: \mu = 12 \text{ ounces}$$
$$H_a: \mu \neq 12 \text{ ounces}$$

In testing these hypotheses, the null hypothesis is assumed to be true; that is, the assumption is that the average fill of the cans is 12 ounces. The quality controller randomly selects and tests cans. If there is enough evidence (a sample average fill that is too low or too high), the null hypothesis is rejected. A rejection of the null hypothesis results in the acceptance of the alternative hypothesis.

All statistical conclusions reached in the hypothesis-testing process are stated in reference to the null hypothesis. We either *reject the null hypothesis or fail to reject the null hypothesis.* When we fail to reject the null hypothesis, we never say that we "accept the null hypothesis" because we have not proven that the null hypothesis is true. The null hypothesis is assumed to be true at the beginning of the hypothesis-testing procedure. Failure to attain evidence to reject the null hypothesis in favor of the alternative hypothesis does not equate to "proof" that the null hypothesis is true. It merely means that we did not have enough evidence to reject the null hypothesis and thereby failed to reject the null hypothesis.

Recall the scenario of an international business analyst who wants to test the hypothesis that manufacturing workers in Germany no longer receive an average of 30 vacation days per year. The null hypothesis is that the mean is 30 days (as before, nothing new). The alternative hypothesis is that the mean is not still 30 days.

$$H_0: \mu = 30 \text{ days}$$
$$H_a: \mu \neq 30 \text{ days}$$

The assumption is that the mean number of vacation days is 30 days. Data are gathered. If enough evidence shows that the average is less than or more than 30 days, the conclusion is that the null hypothesis is rejected. If there is not enough evidence, the conclusion is that the null hypothesis cannot be rejected. In such a case, we have not proven that the mean number of vacation days is still 30; rather, we have failed to disprove it.

Note that in establishing the null and alternative hypotheses, the equality point *must* be assigned to the null hypothesis. In addition, one of the two hypotheses must *exactly* match the research question being stated in the problem. In both of the preceding examples, the equality is in the null hypothesis. If the research question for the soft-drink company example is whether the process is out of control, the alternative hypothesis contains this question. In the vacation days problem, the alternative hypothesis states the research question that the mean number of vacation days is not 30.

Acceptance and Rejection Regions

After establishing the null and alternative hypotheses, the business analyst can set up decision rules to determine whether the null hypothesis is going to be rejected or not. In the can-filling problem, suppose the business analyst decides to test the null hypothesis by randomly sampling cans and measuring the fills. How much fill would the business analyst have to find in the 12-ounce cans to reject the null hypothesis? Common sense says that expecting all cans to be filled with exactly 12 ounces of fluid is unrealistic. More reasonable is to expect that the cans *average* 12 ounces. In this way the hypotheses are structured around the mean value, not individual fills. Would the null hypothesis be rejected if a sample mean of 11.99 ounces is obtained? In testing a hypothesis, the business analyst should establish a **rejection region** after determining the null and alternative hypotheses. Figure 9.1 shows a normal distribution from the soft-drink can example with the mean in the middle and rejection regions in the tails. In this case, the mean of the distribution is 12 ounces. The rejection regions are established in the tails of the distribution because the only way to reject a null hypothesis of H_0: $\mu = 12$ ounces is to get a result in the region of $\mu \neq 12$ ounces.

Rejection region
If a computed statistic lies in this portion of a distribution, the null hypothesis will be rejected.

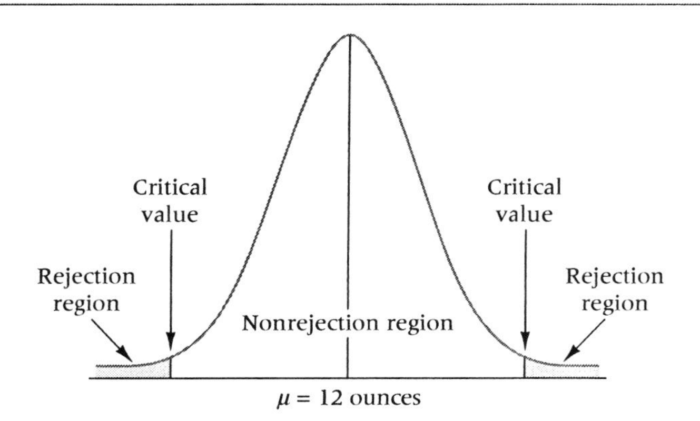

Figure 9.1

Rejection and nonrejection regions

Each rejection region is divided from the rest of the distribution by a point called the **critical value.** If results obtained from the data yield a computed value in a rejection region beyond the critical value, the null hypothesis is rejected. The *rest of the distribution, which is not in a rejection region, is called the* **nonrejection region.**

Critical value
The value that divides the nonrejection region from the rejection region.

Nonrejection region
Any portion of a distribution that is not in the rejection region. If the observed statistic falls in this region, the decision is to fail to reject the null hypothesis.

Type I and Type II Errors

Occasionally, the sample data gathered in the research process lead to a decision to reject a null hypothesis when actually it is true. This is called **Type I error**—an error committed *when a true null hypothesis is rejected.* In drawing random samples from a population, there is always a possibility of selecting a sample from the fringe of the distribution by chance. In the soft-drink can example, the business analyst could randomly select 50 of the cans with the smallest amounts of fluid or 50 with the largest amounts, causing rejection of the null hypothesis even when the company actually is filling the cans with an average of 12 ounces. In that case, the business analyst would incorrectly conclude that the company is not filling the cans with an average of 12 ounces and commit a Type I error.

Type I error
An error committed by rejecting a true null hypothesis.

An analogy of the Type I error can be found in manufacturing. Suppose a production line worker hears some unusual noises and on that evidence decides to push the red button that shuts down the production line. If the null hypothesis is that there is no problem on the production line, the worker has just rejected that null hypothesis by taking action. Suppose an investigation shows there really is no problem with the production line (perhaps the noise was coming from outside). The worker has just committed a Type I error. In manufacturing, a significant cost usually is involved in shutting down the production line (production ceases, but labor costs and fixed costs are still incurred). As another example, suppose a manager suspects a worker is cheating the company. The manager starts accumulating evidence until he is convinced the worker is guilty. The manager fires the worker for cheating. But suppose the worker was not really cheating the company and the data gathered were merely coincidental occurrences that cast the worker in a bad light. The manager has committed a Type I error. The cost to the company is the loss of a qualified and trained worker along with the potential for a lawsuit. In a court of law, a Type I error is committed when an innocent person is convicted.

Alpha (α) or the **level of significance** is *the probability of committing a Type I error.* Alpha is the proportion of the area of the curve occupied by the rejection region. The most commonly used values of alpha are .001, .01, .05, and .10. Recall that determination of alpha is step 3 in the hypothesis-testing procedure. It is sometimes referred to as the amount of *risk* taken in an experiment. The larger the area of the rejection region, the greater is the risk of committing a Type I error.

alpha (α) or Level of significance
The probability of committing a Type I error.

Type II error
An error committed by failing to reject a false null hypothesis.

A **Type II error** is *committed by failing to reject a false null hypothesis.* In some instances the null hypothesis is not true, but the data gathered yield a computed value that is the nonrejection region. For example, suppose a consumer advocate is testing a null hypothesis of $\mu = 12$ ounces and the soft-drink company actually is filling the cans with an average of 11.85 ounces. She could select a random batch of cans from this distribution of fills and get a sample average of 11.95 ounces. If the mean of 11.95 is in the nonrejection region of the null hypothesis, she incorrectly fails to reject the null hypothesis.

We can view the Type II error in light of the preceding manufacturing example as well. Suppose the production line worker hears unusual noises and is concerned about them but is not convinced enough that there is a problem to shut down the line. He abstains from pushing the red button and fails to reject the null hypothesis. Suppose, however, that a major belt on one of the machines is coming unraveled and there really is a production line problem. The worker has committed a Type II error. Such an error in manufacturing might result in poor-quality products being shipped, which can lead to loss of sales, increased cost of warranty judgments, and/or increased cost of rework or scrap. What about the worker who was suspected of cheating? Suppose the manager gathers evidence but feels it is not sufficient to justify firing the person. If the worker really is cheating the company, the manager has committed a Type II error. The cost to the company is continued cheating by the worker, which can result in low morale and lost revenue. In a court of law, a Type II error is committed when a guilty person is declared not guilty and set free.

beta (β)
The probability of committing a Type II error.

The *probability of committing a Type II error* is represented by **beta (β).** The value of beta varies within an experiment, depending on various alternative values of the parameter (in this case, the mean). Whereas alpha is determined before the experiment, beta is computed by using alpha, the hypothesized parameter, and various theoretical alternatives to the null hypothesis.

There is an inverse relationship between α and β. That is, for a given sample size, β increases as the business analyst decreases α and vice versa. Thus, there are trade-offs in the two errors. Suppose a plant manager really wants to protect against having the production line shut down for no reason (Type I error). The manager will either create a climate that makes shutting down the line difficult or create test standards for rejection that are so difficult to attain that the line is rarely shut down without real reason. The result is likely to be a decrease in Type I errors (a reduction in α). However, when there really is a production line problem, workers will be less apt to act on data collected and less inclined to shut down the line. The result is likely to be an increase in Type II errors (β). Consider the case of the potentially cheating worker. Suppose company policy dictates that managers act to fire potential cheaters more quickly and on less evidence. The result could be a reduction in Type II errors. However, there is more potential for an innocent worker to be fired (a Type I error). In a court of law, making it harder to convict innocent people (reducing Type I error) increases the possibility of not convicting guilty people (increases Type II error).

Ideally, managers and decision makers want to reduce both types of error simultaneously. One way to accomplish that statistically is to use larger sample sizes. If larger samples are not possible, one strategy is for the business analyst to establish an alpha value that is the largest possible value he or she is willing to tolerate. Thus, the probability of beta will be minimized for the business analyst's hypothesis-testing process.

Power
The probability of rejecting a false null hypothesis.

Power, which is equal to $1 - \beta$, is *the probability of a test rejecting the null hypothesis when the null hypothesis is false.* Figure 9.2 shows the relationship between α, β, and power.

Two-Tailed and One-Tailed Tests

Two-tailed test
A statistical test wherein the business analyst is interested in testing both sides of the distribution.

Statistical hypothesis testing can be done with either two-tailed or one-tailed tests. The two preceding problems are examples of **two-tailed tests.** Recall that in testing to determine whether cola cans were filled with an average of 12 ounces, the alternative hypothe-

		State of nature	
		Null true	Null false
Action	Fail to reject null	Correct decision	Type II error (β)
	Reject null	Type I error (α)	Correct decision (power)

Figure 9.2

Alpha, beta, and power

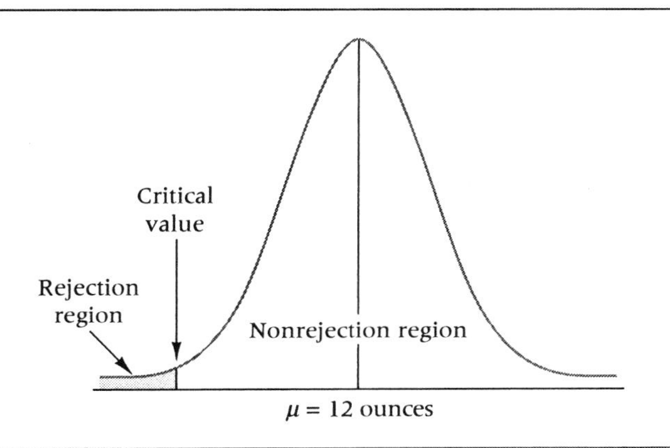

Figure 9.3

Rejection region for the soft-drink example with a one-tailed test

sis was $\mu \neq 12$ ounces. The alternative hypothesis does not state whether the business analyst believes the cans are overfilled or underfilled. Figure 9.1 showed rejection regions in both tails that cover both possibilities. In two-tailed tests, the alternative hypothesis is always stated with a does-not-equal sign ($\neq$), and there is a rejection region in *both* tails of the distribution.

At times the business analyst is interested in only one direction of the test. For example, if a consumer group is concerned that the soft-drink company is "short-changing" purchasers of the drink by underfilling the cans, the consumer group may be interested in testing only the alternative hypothesis

$$H_a\text{: } \mu < 12 \text{ ounces.}$$

That is, they are interested only in determining whether the consumer is being cheated by the company (by underfill). They are not interested in or worried about whether the company overfills the cans. This is an example of a **one-tailed test.** Figure 9.3 shows the rejection region, the critical value, and the nonrejection region for this one-tailed test. Notice that only the lower tail is shaded. Any time hypotheses are established so that the alternative hypothesis is directional (less than or greater than), the test is one-tailed. With a one-tailed test, α is concentrated at one end of the sampling distribution. Figure 9.4 shows the sampling distribution for the soft-drink can example.

One-tailed test
A statistical test wherein the business analyst is interested only in testing one side of the distribution.

Setting up the null and alternative hypotheses is more difficult with one-tailed tests than with two-tailed tests because the direction of the inequality must be determined. To use a one-tailed test, the business analyst must have some knowledge of the subject matter being studied to determine the direction of the hypotheses.

Figure 9.4

Sampling distribution with alpha for the soft-drink example

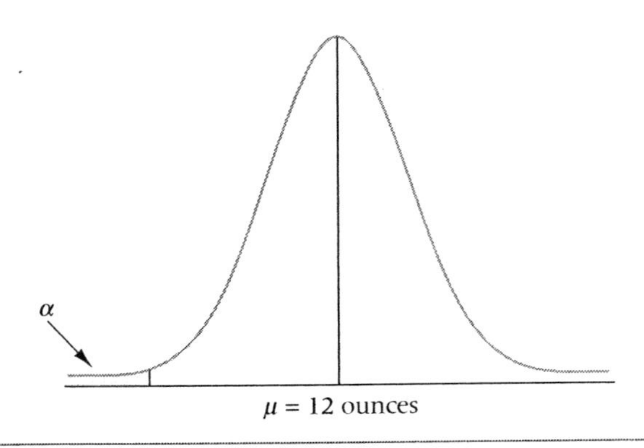

Figure 9.5

Rejection regions for a two-tailed test for the soft-drink example

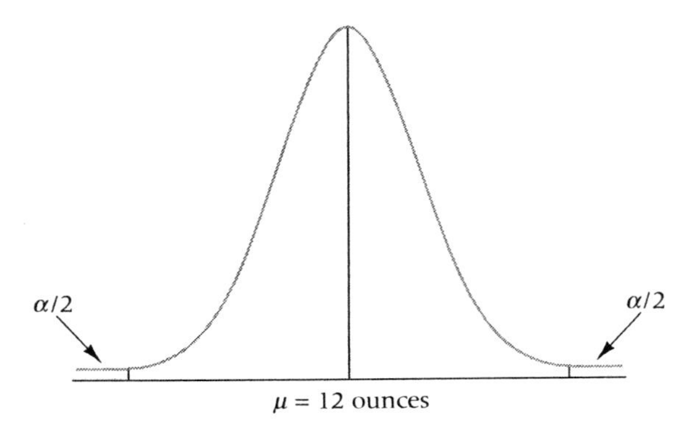

A two-tailed test is nondirectional. In a two-tailed test, the null hypothesis has an equals sign and the alternative hypothesis has a does-not-equal sign. A two-tailed test is used when the business analyst either has no idea which direction the study will go or is interested in testing both directions. If a new technique, theory, or product is being developed, a two-tailed test might be used because the business analyst does not have enough knowledge of the phenomena to perform a directional test. At other times, a two-tailed test might be used because the business analyst is interested in both ends of the distribution.

In the case of the two-tailed test, α is divided in half, and $\alpha/2$ is the probability of the mean being in the rejection region at either end of the distribution by chance, as depicted in Figure 9.5. For any value of alpha, a two-tailed test causes the critical value to be farther from the center of the distribution than a one-tailed test because the two-tailed test splits the α and results in a smaller area in the tail.

In most situations, a two-tailed test is recommended. One-tailed tests are appropriate only when the outcome of the opposite tail is of no interest to and is completely meaningless to the business analyst. Even when the business analyst is fairly certain of the direction the research will take, unexpected and surprising results can occur. If the business analyst chooses to conduct a study with a one-tailed test, the null hypothesis is still the equality and the alternate hypothesis contains the direction of interest.

For example, one-tailed hypotheses for the soft-drink problem from the consumer group's perspective are

$$H_0: \mu = 12 \text{ ounces}$$

$$H_a: \mu < 12 \text{ ounces}.$$

Notice that the greater-than sign (>) is not in the hypotheses. If the data justify rejection of the null hypothesis in favor of the alternative hypothesis, then certainly any values greater than 12 ounces are rejected. It is generally standard practice to state the null hypothesis as the equality. However, because a rejection of such a null hypothesis in favor of the alternative would include a rejection of values greater than 12 (which are farther away), some business analysts would write the null hypothesis as

$$H_0: \mu \geq 12 \text{ ounces.}$$

In this text, we will use only the equality sign in the null hypothesis.

9.2

Testing Hypotheses about a Single Mean Using Large Samples

One of the most basic hypothesis tests is a test about a population mean. A business analyst might be interested in testing to determine whether an established or accepted mean value for an industry is still true. Or a business analyst might be interested in testing a mean value for a new theory or product. The test of a single population mean can be used to accomplish either objective. Formula 9.1 can be used to test hypotheses about a single population mean if the sample size is large ($n \geq 30$). The same formula can also be used for small samples ($n < 30$) if X is normally distributed *and* σ is known.

Z TEST FOR A SINGLE MEAN

$$Z = \frac{\bar{X} - \mu}{\frac{\sigma}{\sqrt{n}}} \quad (9.1)$$

Using the Observed Value to Reach a Decision

A survey of CPAs across the United States found that the average net income for sole proprietor CPAs is \$74,914.* Since this survey is now over 5 years old, suppose an accounting business analyst wants to test this figure by taking a random sample of 112 sole proprietor accountants in the United States to determine whether the net income figure has changed since the survey was taken. The business analyst could use the eight steps of hypothesis testing to do so. Assume the population standard deviation of net incomes for sole proprietor CPAs is \$14,530.

At step 1, the hypotheses must be established. As the business analyst is testing to determine whether the figure has changed, the alternative hypothesis is that the mean net income is not \$74,914. The null hypothesis is that the mean still equals \$74,914. These hypotheses follow.

$$H_0: \mu = \$74{,}914$$
$$H_a: \mu \neq \$74{,}914$$

Step 2 is to determine the appropriate statistical test and sampling distribution. Because sample size is large ($n = 112$) and the business analyst is using the sample mean as the statistic, the Z test in Formula 9.1 is the appropriate test statistic.

$$Z = \frac{\bar{X} - \mu}{\frac{\sigma}{\sqrt{n}}}$$

*ADAPTED FROM: Daniel J. Flaherty, Raymond A. Zimmerman, and Mary Ann Murray, "Benchmarking Against the Best," *Journal of Accountancy*, July 1995, 85–88.

Figure 9.6

CPA net income example

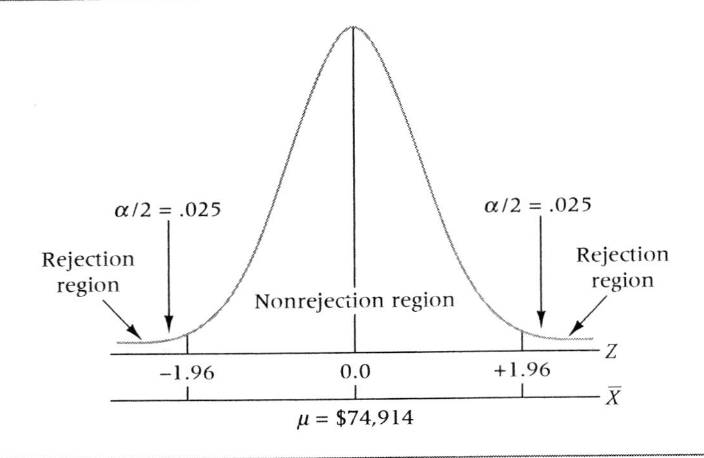

Step 3 is to specify the Type I error rate, or alpha, which is .05 in this problem. Step 4 is to state the decision rule. Because the test is two-tailed and alpha is .05, there is an $\alpha/2$ or .025 area in each of the tails of the distribution. Thus, the rejection region is the two ends of the distribution with 2.5% of the area in each. There is a .4750 area between the mean and each of the critical values that separate the tails of the distribution (the rejection region) from the nonrejection region. By using this .4750 area and Table A.5, the critical Z value can be obtained.

$$Z_{\alpha/2} = \pm 1.96$$

Figure 9.6 displays the problem with the rejection regions and the critical values of Z. The decision rule is that if the data gathered produce a Z value greater than 1.96 or less than −1.96, the test statistic is in one of the rejection regions and the decision is to reject the null hypothesis. If the Z value calculated from the data is between −1.96 and +1.96, the decision is to not reject the null hypothesis because the calculated Z value is in the nonrejection region.

Step 5 is to gather the data. Suppose the 112 CPAs who respond produce a sample mean of $78,695. At step 6, the value of the test statistic is calculated by using $\overline{X}$ = $78,695, $n = 112$, σ = $14,530, and a hypothesized μ = $74,914.

$$Z = \frac{78{,}695 - 74{,}914}{\frac{14{,}530}{\sqrt{112}}} = 2.75$$

Because this test statistic, $Z = 2.75$, is greater than the critical value of Z in the upper tail of the distribution, $Z = +1.96$, the statistical conclusion reached at step 7 of the hypothesis-testing process is the reject the null hypothesis.

Step 8 is to make a managerial decision. What does this result mean? Statistically, the business analyst has enough evidence to reject the figure of $74,914 as the true national average net income for sole proprietor CPAs. Although the business analyst conducted a two-tailed test, the evidence gathered indicates that the national average may have increased. The sample mean of $78,695 is $3781 higher than the national mean being tested. The business analyst can conclude that the national average is more than before, but because the $78,695 is only a sample mean, there is no guarantee that the national average for all sole proprietor CPAs is $3781 more. If a confidence interval were constructed with the sample data, $78,695 would be the point estimate. Other samples might produce different sample means. Managerially, this statistical finding may mean that CPAs will be more expensive to hire either as full-time employees or as consultants. It may mean that consulting services have gone up in price. For new accountants, it may mean the potential for greater earning power. Such a finding could serve as a motivation for CPAs in multiowner firms to strike out on their own.

Using a Sample Standard Deviation

In many real-life situations, the population value for the standard deviation is unavailable. With large sample sizes ($n \geq 30$), use of the sample standard deviation as a good approximate substitute for the population standard deviation, σ, is permitted.

(9.2)

$$Z = \frac{\bar{X} - \mu}{\frac{S}{\sqrt{n}}}$$

Z FORMULA TO TEST A MEAN WITH σ UNKNOWN—LARGE SAMPLES ONLY

Formula 9.2 can be used only for *large* sample sizes, regardless of the shape of the distribution of X. In the example involving CPA sole proprietorship net incomes, the sample standard deviation was 14,543. This approximation of σ could have been used to calculate the Z value.

Testing the Mean with a Finite Population

If the hypothesis test for the population mean is being conducted with a known finite population, the population information can be incorporated into the hypothesis-testing formula. Doing so can increase the potential for rejecting the null hypothesis. Formula 9.1 can be amended to include the population information.

(9.3)

$$Z = \frac{\bar{X} - \mu}{\frac{\sigma}{\sqrt{n}}\sqrt{\frac{N-n}{N-1}}}$$

FORMULA TO TEST HYPOTHESES ABOUT μ WITH A FINITE POPULATION

In the CPA net income example, suppose there are only 600 sole proprietor CPAs in the United States. A sample of 112 CPAs taken from a population of only 600 CPAs is 18.67% of the population and therefore is much more likely to be representative of the population than a sample of 112 CPAs taken from a population of 20,000 CPAs (.56% of the population). The finite correction factor takes this into consideration and allows for an increase in the calculated value of Z. The calculated Z value would change to

$$Z = \frac{\bar{X} - \mu}{\frac{\sigma}{\sqrt{n}}\sqrt{\frac{N-n}{N-1}}} = \frac{78,695 - 74,914}{\frac{14,530}{\sqrt{112}}\sqrt{\frac{600-112}{600-1}}} = \frac{3781}{1,239.2} = 3.05$$

Use of the finite correction factor increased the calculated Z value from 2.75 to 3.05. The decision to reject the null hypothesis does not change with this new information. However, on occasion, the finite correction factor can make the difference between rejecting and failing to reject the null hypothesis.

Using the Critical Value Method to Test Hypotheses

Critical value method
A method of testing hypotheses in which the sample statistic is compared to a critical value in order to reach a conclusion about rejecting or failing to reject the null hypothesis.

One alternative method of testing hypotheses is the **critical value method.** In the preceding example, the null hypothesis was rejected because the computed value of Z was in the rejection zone. What mean income would it take to cause the calculated Z value to be in the rejection zone? The critical value method determines the critical mean value required for Z to be in the rejection region and uses it to test the hypotheses.

This method also uses Formula 9.1. However, instead of a calculated Z, a critical $\overline{X}$ value, $\overline{X}_c$, is determined. The critical table value of Z_c is inserted into the formula, along with μ and σ. Thus,

$$Z_c = \frac{\overline{X}_c - \mu}{\frac{\sigma}{\sqrt{n}}}$$

Substituting values from the preceding example gives

$$\pm 1.96 = \frac{\overline{X}_c - 74{,}914}{\frac{14{,}530}{\sqrt{112}}}$$

or

$$\overline{X}_c = 74{,}914 \pm 1.96\frac{14{,}530}{\sqrt{112}} = 74{,}914 \pm 2691$$

$$\text{lower } \overline{X}_c = 72{,}223 \quad \text{and} \quad \text{upper } \overline{X}_c = 77{,}605.$$

Figure 9.7 depicts graphically the rejection and nonrejection regions in terms of means instead of Z scores.

Figure 9.7

Rejection and nonrejection regions for critical value method

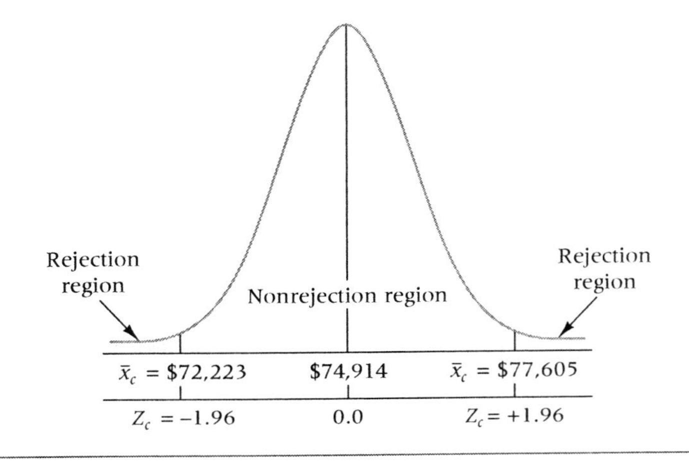

With the critical value method, most of the computational work is done ahead of time unless the sample standard deviation is being used as an estimate for σ. In this problem, before the sample means are computed, the analyst knows that a sample mean value of greater than \$77,605 or less than \$72,223 must be attained to reject the hypothesized population mean. Because the sample mean for this problem was \$78,695, which is greater than \$77,605, the analyst rejects the null hypothesis. This method is particularly attractive in industrial settings where standards can be set ahead of time and then quality control technicians can gather data and compare actual measurements of products to specifications.

Using the p-Value Method to Test Hypotheses

Another way to reach statistical conclusions in hypothesis testing problems is by the ***p*-value method,** sometimes referred to as **observed significance level.** The *p*-value method is growing in importance with the increasing use of statistical computer packages to test hypotheses. There is no preset value of α in the *p*-value method. Instead, the probability of getting a test statistic at least as extreme as the observed test statistic (computed from the data) is computed under the assumption that the null hypothesis is true. Virtually every statistical computer program yields this probability (p value). The p value defines the smallest value of alpha for which the null hypothesis can be rejected. For example, if the p value of a test is .038, the null hypothesis cannot be rejected at $\alpha = .01$ because .038 is the smallest value of alpha for which the null hypothesis can be rejected. However, the null hypothesis can be rejected for $\alpha = .05$.

***p*-value method, or Observed significance level**
A method of testing hypotheses in which there is no preset level of α. The probability of getting a test statistic at least as extreme as the observed test statistic is computed under the assumption that the null hypothesis is true. This probability is called the p value, and it is the smallest value of α for which the null hypothesis can be rejected.

Suppose a business analyst is conducting a one-tailed test with a rejection region in the upper tail and obtains an observed test statistic of $Z = 2.04$ from the sample data. Using the standard normal table, Table A.5, we find that the probability of randomly obtaining a Z value this great or greater by chance is $.5000 - .4793 = .0207$. The p value is .0207. Using this information, the business analyst would reject the null hypothesis for $\alpha = .05$ or .10 or any value more than .0207. The business analyst would not reject the null hypothesis for any alpha value less than or equal to .0207 (in particular, $\alpha = .01$, .001, etc.).

For a two-tailed test, recall that we have been splitting alpha to determine the critical value of the test statistic. With the *p*-value method and a two-tailed test, the probability of getting a test statistic at least as extreme as the observed value is computed, doubled, and then reported as the p value.

As an example of using p values with a two-tailed test, consider the CPA net income problem. The observed test statistic for this problem is $Z = 2.75$. Using Table A.5, we know that the probability of obtaining a test statistic at least this extreme if the null hypothesis is true is $.5000 - .4970 = .0030$. To reach a statistical conclusion from this p value, the business analyst must either double it to .0060 and compare it to α or compare it (.0030) to $\alpha/2$.

DEMONSTRATION PROBLEM 9.1

In an attempt to determine why customer service is important to managers in the United Kingdom, business analysts surveyed managing directors of manufacturing plants in Scotland.* One of the reasons proposed was that customer service is a means of retaining customers. On a scale from 1 to 5, with 1 being low and 5 being high, the survey respondents rated this reason more highly than any of the others, with a mean response of 4.30. Suppose U.S. business analysts believe American manufacturing managers would not rate this reason as highly and conduct a hypothesis test to prove their theory. Alpha is set at .05. Data are gathered and the following results are obtained. Use these

*ADAPTED FROM: William G. Donaldson, "Manufacturers Need to Show Greater Commitment to Customer Service," *Industrial Marketing Management*, 24, October 1995, 421–430. The 1-to-5 scale has been reversed here for clarity of presentation.

data and the eight steps of hypothesis testing to determine whether U.S. managers rate this reason significantly lower than the 4.30 mean ascertained in the United Kingdom.

3	4	5	5	4	5	5	4	4	4	4
4	4	4	4	5	4	4	4	3	4	4
4	3	5	4	4	5	4	4	4	5	

SOLUTION

STEP **1.** Establish hypotheses. Because the U.S. business analysts are interested only in "proving" that the mean figure is lower in the United States, the test is one-tailed. The alternative hypothesis is that the population mean is lower than 4.30. The null hypothesis states the equality case.

$$H_0: \mu = 4.30$$
$$H_a: \mu < 4.30$$

STEP **2.** Determine the appropriate statistical test. The test statistic is

$$Z = \frac{\bar{X} - \mu}{\frac{S}{\sqrt{n}}}$$

STEP **3.** Specify the Type I error rate.

$$\alpha = .05$$

STEP **4.** State the decision rule. As this is a one-tailed test, the critical Z value is found by looking up .5000 − .0500 = .4500 as the area in Table A.5. The critical value of the test statistic is $Z_{.05} = -1.645$. An observed test statistic must be less than −1.645 to reject the null hypothesis. The rejection region and critical value can be depicted as in the following diagram.

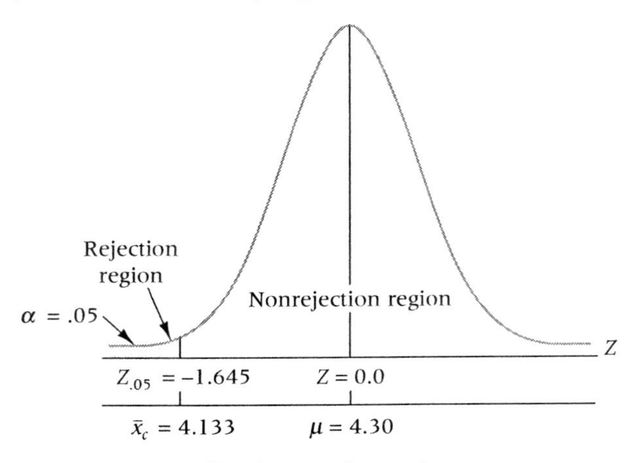

STEP **5.** Gather the sample data. The data are shown above.

STEP **6.** Calculate the value of the test statistic.

$$\bar{X} = 4.156 \qquad S = .574$$

$$Z = \frac{4.156 - 4.30}{\frac{.574}{\sqrt{32}}} = -1.42$$

STEP **7.** State the statistical conclusion. Because the observed test statistic is not less than the critical value and is not in the rejection region, the statistical conclusion is that the null hypothesis cannot be rejected.

STEP **8.** Make a managerial decision. There is not enough evidence to conclude that U.S. managers think it is less important to use customer service as a means of retaining customers than do United Kingdom managers. Customer service is an important tool for retaining customers in both countries according to managers.

Using the critical value method: For what sample mean (or more extreme) value would the null hypothesis be rejected? This critical sample mean can be determined by using the critical Z value associated with alpha, $Z_{.05} = -1.645$. Because the decision rule must be set before data are gathered, a population standard deviation or an estimate of one from previous studies is needed. For illustration purposes, we will use the sample standard deviation computed above in this calculation (let $\sigma = .574$).

$$Z_c = \frac{\bar{X}_c - \mu}{\frac{\sigma}{\sqrt{n}}}$$

$$-1.645 = \frac{\bar{X}_c - 4.30}{\frac{.574}{\sqrt{32}}}$$

$$\bar{X}_c = 4.133$$

The decision rule is that a sample mean less than 4.133 would be necessary to reject the null hypothesis. As the mean obtained from the sample data is 4.156, the business analysts fail to reject the null hypothesis. The diagram above includes a scale with the critical sample mean and the rejection region for the critical value method.

Using the p-value method: The calculated observed test statistic is $Z = -1.42$. From Table A.5, the probability of getting a Z value at least this extreme when the null hypothesis is true is $.5000 - .4222 = .0778$. Hence, the null hypothesis cannot be rejected at $\alpha = .05$ because the smallest value of alpha for which the null hypothesis can be rejected is .0778.

Analysis Using Excel

In Section 8.1 of the prior chapter, we introduced the **FAST⑊STAT** macro procedure called **1 Mean Using *Z* Dist.** In that chapter we used the procedure to compute confidence intervals for one mean with the normal distribution. This procedure also computes the statistics for conducting a hypothesis test for one mean with the normal distribution. The input dialog box for this procedure is shown in Figure 9.8.

To conduct a hypothesis test, you first enter the sample values into an Excel worksheet. Next click on **FAST⑊STAT** on the menu bar and select **1 Mean Using *Z* Dist.** from the subsequent pull-down menu. Now drag through the sample values to enter the cell range in the first box of the dialog box. If the confidence interval is not of interest, the entry for the confidence level may be set equal to any value between 0 and 100. Then enter values for the hypothesized mean and the significance level. When the data for Demonstration Problem 9.1 are entered as in Figure 9.8, a click on the **OK** command button yields the results of Figure 9.9.

In this figure in Column A you will find the sample values. In Columns C through G, the four dialog box inputs are repeated. The output values that follow include four parts. The first part displays the values for the sample mean, standard deviation, and sample size. The second and third parts provide the point estimate and confidence interval values as discussed

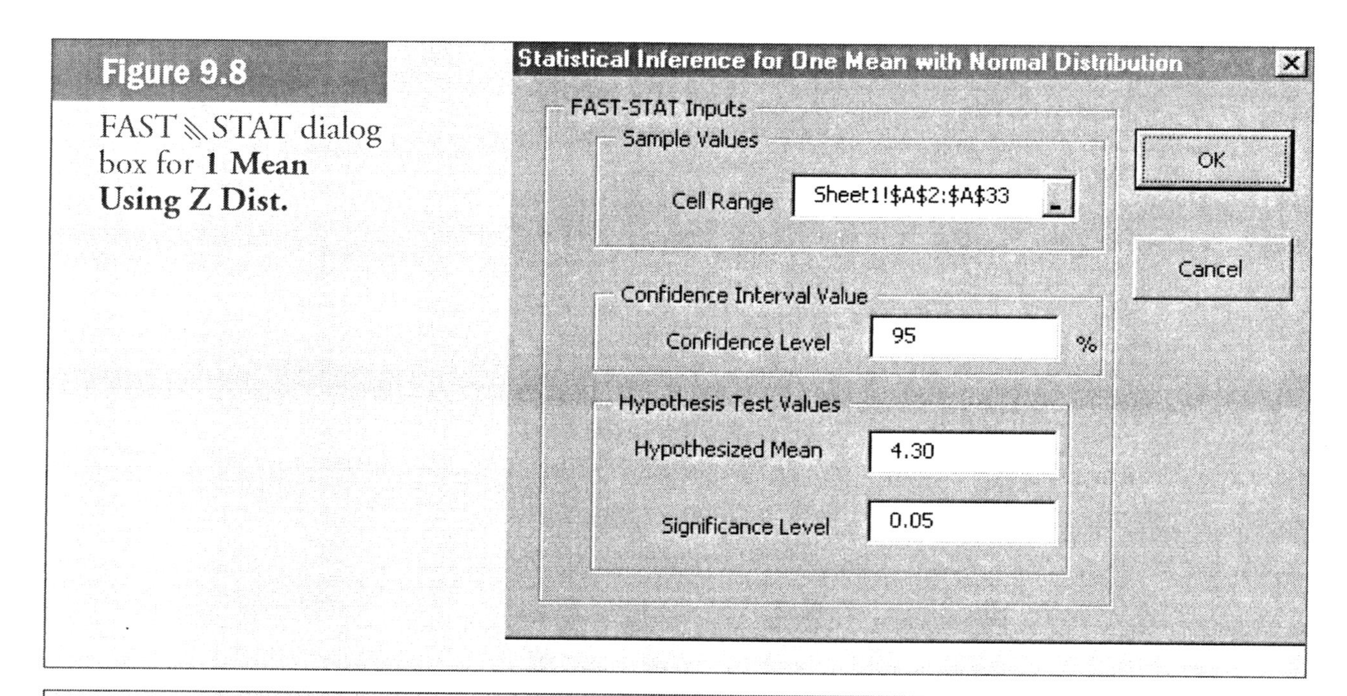

Figure 9.8

FAST\STAT dialog box for **1 Mean Using Z Dist.**

Figure 9.9

FAST\STAT output for Demonstration Problem 9.1

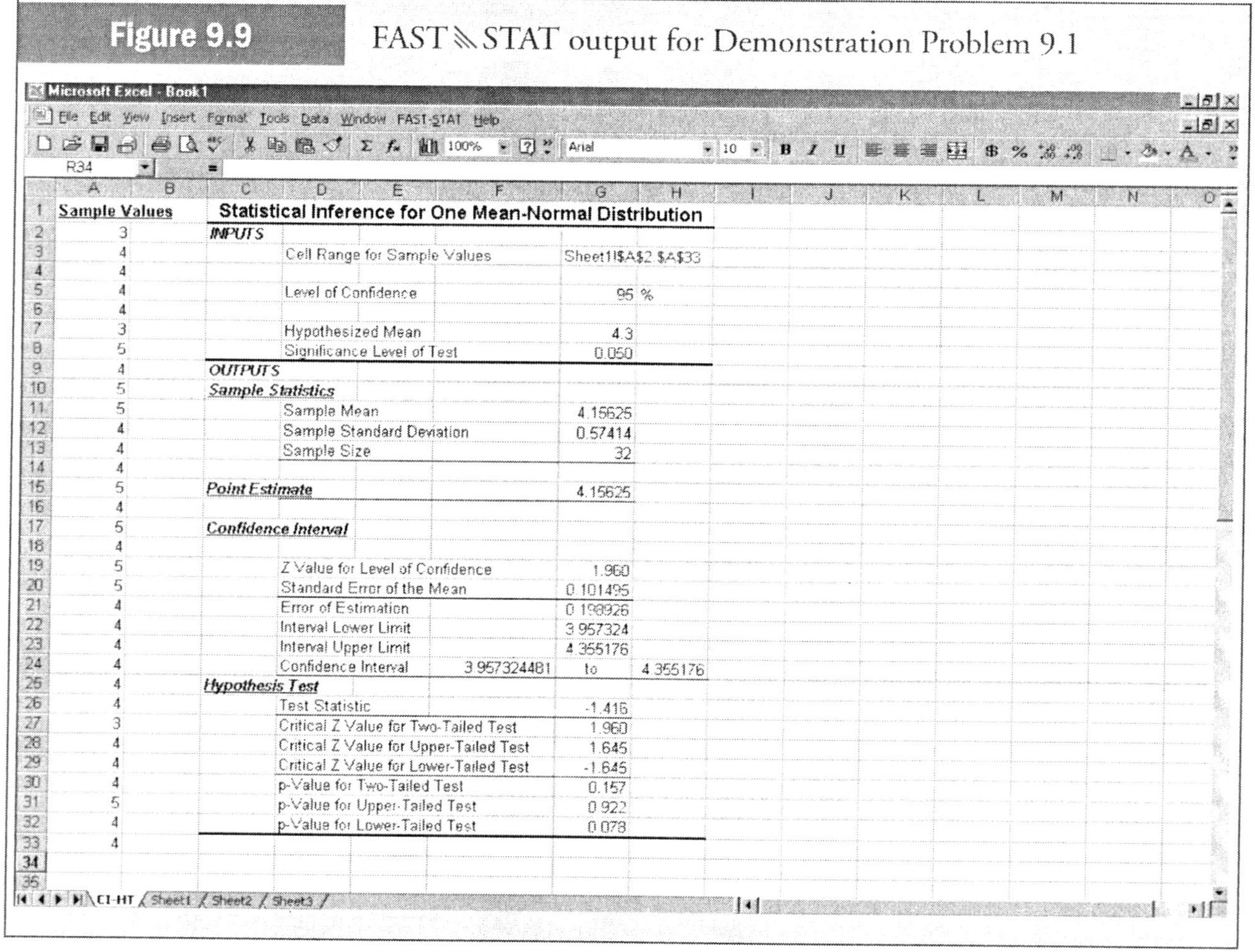

	A	C	D	F	G	H
1	**Sample Values**	**Statistical Inference for One Mean-Normal Distribution**				
2	3	*INPUTS*				
3	4		Cell Range for Sample Values		Sheet1!$A$2 $A$33	
4	4					
5	4		Level of Confidence		95	%
6	4					
7	3		Hypothesized Mean		4.3	
8	5		Significance Level of Test		0.050	
9	4	*OUTPUTS*				
10	5	***Sample Statistics***				
11	5		Sample Mean		4.15625	
12	4		Sample Standard Deviation		0.57414	
13	4		Sample Size		32	
14	4					
15	5	***Point Estimate***			4.15625	
16	4					
17	5	***Confidence Interval***				
18	4					
19	5		Z Value for Level of Confidence		1.960	
20	5		Standard Error of the Mean		0.101495	
21	4		Error of Estimation		0.198926	
22	4		Interval Lower Limit		3.957324	
23	4		Interval Upper Limit		4.355176	
24	4		Confidence Interval	3.957324481	to	4.355176
25	4	***Hypothesis Test***				
26	4		Test Statistic		-1.416	
27	3		Critical Z Value for Two-Tailed Test		1.960	
28	4		Critical Z Value for Upper-Tailed Test		1.645	
29	4		Critical Z Value for Lower-Tailed Test		-1.645	
30	4		p-Value for Two-Tailed Test		0.157	
31	5		p-Value for Upper-Tailed Test		0.922	
32	4		p-Value for Lower-Tailed Test		0.078	
33	4					

in Chapter 8. The fourth part presents the hypothesis test values. Here you will note the calculated Z test statistic value and the three critical Z values for conducting the three possible forms of the hypothesis test. In addition, three p-values are given, one for each possible form of the hypothesis test.

Consider the results of Figure 9.9. Since this is a lower-tailed test, a comparison of the calculated Z value of -1.416 to the critical Z of -1.645 results in failure to reject the null hypothesis. In like manner, a comparison of the p-value of 0.078 to the significance level of 0.05 results in the same conclusion as it must.

9.2 Problems

9.1 The Environmental Protection Agency releases figures on urban air soot in selected cities in the United States. For the city of St. Louis, the EPA claims that the average number of micrograms of suspended particles per cubic meter of air is 82. Suppose St. Louis officials have been working with businesses, commuters, and industries to reduce this figure. These city officials hire an environmental company to take random measures of air soot over a period of several weeks. The resulting data follow. Use these data to determine whether the urban air soot in St. Louis is significantly lower than it was when the EPA conducted its measurements. Let $\alpha = .01$.

81.6	66.6	70.9	82.5	58.3	71.6	72.4
96.6	78.6	76.1	80.0	73.2	85.5	73.2
68.6	74.0	68.7	83.0	86.9	94.9	75.6
77.3	86.6	71.7	88.5	87.0	72.5	83.0
85.8	74.9	61.7	92.2			

9.2 According to the U.S. Bureau of Labor Statistics, the average weekly earnings of a production worker in 1997 were \$424.20. Suppose a labor business analyst wants to test to determine whether this figure is still accurate today. The business analyst randomly selects 54 production workers from across the United States and obtains a representative earnings statement for one week from each. The resulting sample average is \$432.69, with a standard deviation of \$33.90. Use these data and hypothesis-testing techniques along with a 5% level of significance to determine whether the mean weekly earnings of a production worker have changed.

9.3 Thirty-eight percent of all U.S. households own a wireless phone according to Personal Communications Industry Association. They report that the average wireless phone user earns \$62,600 per year. Suppose a business analyst believes that the average annual earnings of a wireless phone user are higher than that now, and he sets up a study in an attempt to prove his theory. He randomly samples 48 wireless phone users and finds out that the average annual salary for this sample is \$64,820, with a standard deviation of \$7810. Use $\alpha = .01$ to test the business analyst's theory.

9.4 A manufacturing company produces valves in various sizes and shapes. One particular valve plate is supposed to have a tensile strength of 5 lb/mm. The company tests a random sample of 42 such valve plates from a lot of 650 valve plates. The sample mean is a tensile strength of 5.0611 lb/mm, with a standard deviation of .2803 lb/mm. Use $\alpha = .10$ and test to determine whether the lot of valve plates has an average tensile strength of 5 lb/mm.

9.5 A manufacturing firm has been averaging 18.2 orders per week for several years. However, during a recession, orders appear to have slowed. Suppose the firm's production manager randomly samples 32 weeks and finds a sample mean of 15.6 orders, with a sample standard deviation of 2.3 orders. Test to determine whether the average number of orders is down by using $\alpha = .10$.

9.6 A study conducted by Runzheimer International showed that Paris is the most expensive place to live of the 12 European Community cities. Paris ranks second in housing expense, with a rental unit of six to nine rooms costing an average of $4292 a month. Suppose a company's CEO believes this figure is too high and decides to conduct her own survey. Her assistant contacts the owners of 55 randomly selected rental units of six to nine rooms and finds that the sample average cost is $4008, with a standard deviation of $386. Using the sample results and $\alpha = .01$, test to determine whether the figure published by Runzheimer International is too high.

9.7 The American Water Works Association estimates that the average person in the United States uses 123 gallons of water per day. Suppose some business analysts believe that the actual figure is lower than this and want to test to determine whether this is so. They randomly select a sample of Americans and carefully keep track of the water used by each sample member for a day. The data from this sample are shown below. Use $\alpha = .05$ to test this hypothesis.

105	80	119	146	144	158	56	107
141	85	95	69	65	88	93	58
98	102	117	103	104	103	148	111
108	100	164	136	175	96	156	71
127	136	163	111	99	131	103	133

9.3

Testing Hypotheses about a Single Mean Using Small Samples: σ Unknown

There are times when a business analyst is testing hypotheses about a single population mean and, for reasons such as time, money, convenience, or availability, is able to gather only a small random sample ($n < 30$) of data. In such cases, if the data are normally distributed in the population and σ is known, the Z test can be used. However, in reality the sample standard deviation is often used as an estimate for the population standard deviation in hypothesis testing about the population mean because the population standard deviation is unknown. Thus, the Z test has limited usage for small-sample analysis of single population means.

Chapter 8 presented the t distribution, which can be used to analyze hypotheses about a single population mean for small sample sizes when σ is unknown *if* the population is normally distributed for the measurement being studied. In this section, we will examine the t test for a single population mean. In general, this t test is applicable whenever the business analyst is drawing a single random sample to test the value of a population mean (μ) when using small samples, when the population standard deviation is unknown, and when the population is normally distributed for the measurement of interest. The formula for testing such hypotheses follows.

t TEST FOR μ

$$t = \frac{\overline{X} - \mu}{\frac{S}{\sqrt{n}}} \qquad (9.4)$$

$$\text{df} = n - 1$$

The U.S. Farmers' Production Company builds large harvesters. For a harvester to be properly balanced when operating, a 25-pound plate is installed on its side. The machine that produces these plates is set to yield plates that average 25 pounds. The distribution of plates produced from the machine is normal. However, the shop supervisor is worried that the machine is out of adjustment and is producing plates that do not average 25 pounds. To test this concern, he randomly selects 20 of the plates produced the day

22.6	22.2	23.2	27.4	24.5
27.0	26.6	28.1	26.9	24.9
26.2	25.3	23.1	24.2	26.1
25.8	30.4	28.6	23.5	23.6

$\bar{X} = 25.51, S = 2.1933, n = 20$

TABLE 9.1
Weights in Pounds of a Sample of 20 Plates

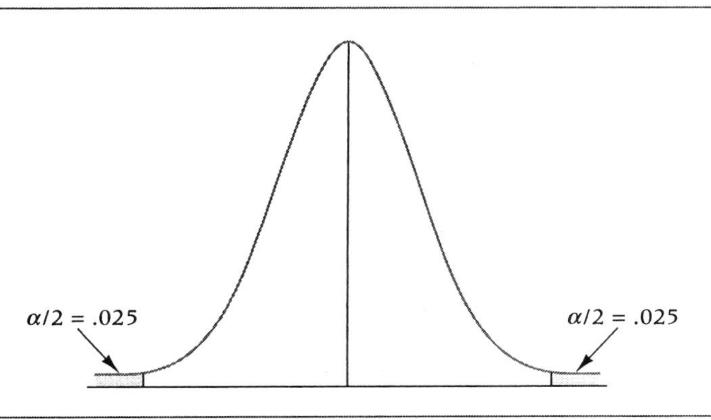

Figure 9.10

Rejection regions for the machine plate example

before and weighs them. Table 9.1 shows the weights obtained, along with the computed sample mean and sample standard deviation.

The test is to determine whether the machine is out of control, and the shop supervisor has not specified whether he believes the machine is producing plates that are too heavy or too light. Thus a two-tailed test is appropriate. The following hypotheses are tested.

$$H_0: \mu = 25 \text{ pounds}$$
$$H_a: \mu \neq 25 \text{ pounds}$$

An α of .05 is used. Figure 9.10 shows the rejection regions.

Because $n = 20$, the degrees of freedom for this test are 19 (20 – 1). The t distribution table is a one-tailed table but the test for this problem is two-tailed, so alpha must be split, which yields $\alpha/2 = .025$, the value in each tail. (To obtain the table t value when conducting a two-tailed test, always split alpha and use $\alpha/2$.) The table t value for this example is 2.093. Table values such as this one are often written in the following form:

$$t_{.025,19} = 2.093.$$

Figure 9.11 depicts the t distribution for this example, along with the critical values, the calculated t value, and the rejection regions. In this case, the decision rule is to reject the null hypothesis if the calculated value of t is less than –2.093 or greater than +2.093 (in the tails of the distribution). Computation of the test statistic yields

$$Z = \frac{\bar{X} - \mu}{\frac{S}{\sqrt{n}}} = \frac{25.51 - 25.0}{\frac{2.1933}{\sqrt{20}}} = 1.04 \text{ (Calculated } t\text{)}$$

Because the calculated value is +1.04, the null hypothesis is not rejected. There is not enough evidence in this sample to reject the hypothesis that the population mean is 25 pounds.

Figure 9.12 presents the FAST⧹⧹STAT output for the machine plate example. The FAST⧹⧹STAT results provide the calculated t value, the critical t values, and the p-values

Figure 9.11

Graph of calculated and critical t values for the machine plate example

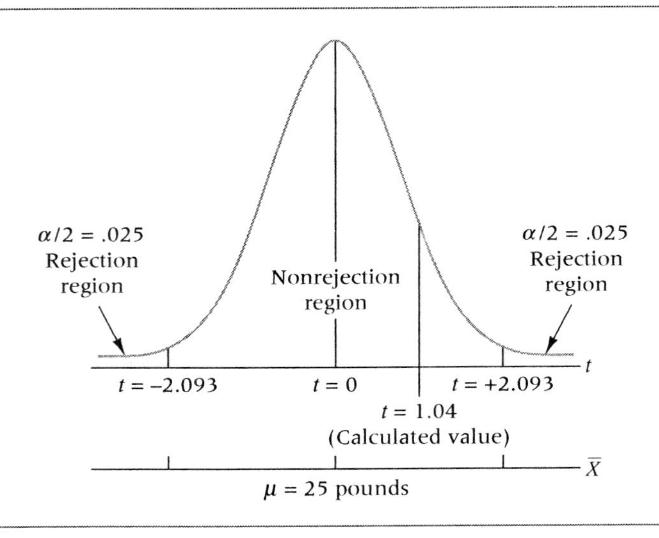

Figure 9.12 FAST\STAT output for the machine plate example

Microsoft Excel - Book1

R34

	A	C	D	F	G	H
1	**Sample Values**	**Statistical Inference for One Mean-t Distribution**				
2	22.6	*INPUTS*				
3	27		Cell Range for Sample Values		Sheet2!$A$2:$A$21	
4	26.2					
5	25.8		Level of Confidence		95	%
6	22.2					
7	26.6		Hypothesized Mean		25	
8	25.3		Significance Level of Test		0.050	
9	30.4	*OUTPUTS*				
10	23.2	***Sample Statistics***				
11	28.1		Sample Mean		25.51	
12	23.1		Sample Standard Deviation		2.193267	
13	28.6		Sample Size		20	
14	27.4					
15	26.9	***Point Estimate***			25.51	
16	24.2					
17	23.5	***Confidence Interval***				
18	24.5		Degrees of Freedom		19	
19	24.9		t Value for Level of Confidence		2.093	
20	26.1		Standard Error of the Mean		0.490429	
21	23.6		Error of Estimation		1.026481	
22			Interval Lower Limit		24.48352	
23			Interval Upper Limit		26.53648	
24			Confidence Interval	24.48351903	to	26.53648
25		***Hypothesis Test***				
26			Test Statistic		1.040	
27			Critical t Value for Two-Tailed Test		2.093	
28			Critical t Value for Upper-Tailed Test		1.729	
29			Critical t Value for Lower-Tailed Test		-1.729	
30			p-Value for Two-Tailed Test		0.311	
31			p-Value for Upper-Tailed Test		0.156	
32			p-Value for Lower-Tailed Test		0.844	

CI-HT / Sheet1 / Sheet2 / Sheet3

for all three possible forms of the hypothesis test. Since this is a two-tailed test, a comparison of the calculated t value of 1.040 to the critical t value of 2.093 results in a failure to reject the null hypothesis. In like manner, a comparison of the p-value of 0.311 (p-value for a two-tailed test) to the significance level of 0.05 results in the same conclusion.

DEMONSTRATION PROBLEM 9.2

Figures released by the U.S. Department of Agriculture show that the average size of farms has been increasing since 1940. In 1940, the mean size of a farm was 174 acres; by 1997, the average size was 471 acres. Between those years the number of farms decreased but the amount of tillable land remained relatively constant, so there are now bigger farms. This trend might be explained, in part, by the inability of small farms to compete with the prices and costs of large-scale operations and to produce a level of income necessary to support the farmers' desired standard of living. Suppose an agri-business analyst believes the average size of farms has increased from the 1997 mean figure of 471 acres. To test this notion, she randomly sampled 23 farms across the United States and ascertained the size of each farm from county records. The data she gathered follow. Use a 5% level of significance to test her hypothesis.

445	489	474	505	553	477	454	463	466
557	502	449	438	500	466	477	557	433
545	511	590	561	560				

SOLUTION

STEP **1.** The business analyst's hypothesis is that the average size of a U.S. farm is more than 471 acres. Because this is an unproven theory, it is the alternate hypothesis. The null hypothesis is that the mean is still 471 acres.

$$H_0: \mu = 471$$
$$H_a: \mu > 471$$

STEP **2.** The statistical test to be used is

$$t = \frac{\bar{X} - \mu}{\frac{S}{\sqrt{n}}}$$

STEP **3.** The value of alpha is .05.

STEP **4.** With 23 data points, df $= n - 1 = 23 - 1 = 22$. This test is one-tailed, and the critical table t value is

$$t_{.05,22} = 1.717.$$

The decision rule is to reject the null hypothesis if the observed test statistic is greater than 1.717.

STEP **5.** The gathered data are shown above.

STEP **6.** The sample mean is 498.78 and the sample standard deviation is 46.94. The computed t value is

$$t = \frac{\bar{X} - \mu}{\frac{S}{\sqrt{n}}} = \frac{498.78 - 471}{\frac{46.94}{\sqrt{23}}} = 2.84$$

STEP **7.** The computed t value of 2.84 is greater than the table t value of 1.717, so the business analyst rejects the null hypothesis. She accepts the alternative hypothesis and concludes that the average size of a U.S. farm is now more than 471 acres. The following graph represents this analysis pictorially.

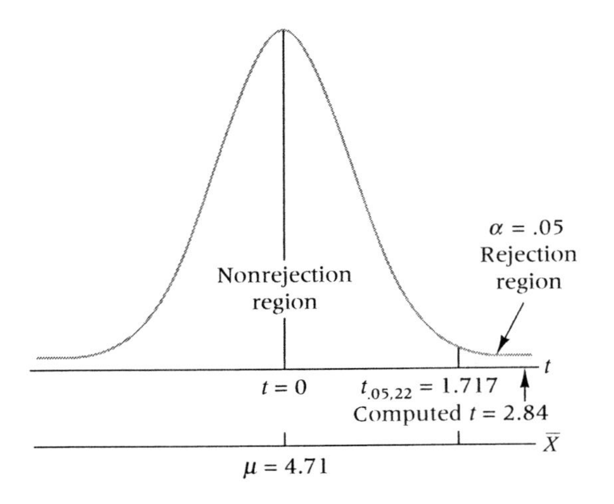

STEP **8.** Agri-business analysts can speculate about what it means to have larger farms. It could mean that small farms are not financially viable. It might mean that corporations are buying out small farms and that large company farms are on the increase. Such a trend might spark legislative movements to protect the small farm. Larger farm sizes might also affect commodity trading.

Analysis Using Excel

In Section 8.2 of the prior chapter, we introduced the **FAST⧹STAT** macro procedure called **1 Mean Using *t* Dist.** In that chapter we used the procedure to compute confidence intervals for one mean with the t distribution. This procedure also computes the statistics for conducting a hypothesis test for one mean with the t distribution. The input dialog box for this procedure is shown in Figure 9.13.

To conduct the hypothesis test, first enter the sample values into an Excel worksheet. Next click on **FAST⧹STAT** on the menu bar and select **1 Mean Using *t* Dist.** from the subsequent pull-down menu. Then drag through the sample values to enter the cell range into the first box of the dialog box. If the confidence interval is not of interest, the entry for the confidence level may be set equal to any value between 0 and 100. Now enter the hypothesized mean and the significance level. When the data for Demonstration Problem 9.2 are entered as in Figure 9.13, a click on the **OK** command button yields the results of Figure 9.14.

Figure 9.14 for the t distribution looks just like Figure 9.9 for the normal distribution with one exception. Row 18 of the worksheet of Figure 9.14 includes the additional entry for degrees of freedom for the hypothesis test.

The FAST⧹STAT results provide the calculated t value, the critical t values and the p-values for all three possible forms of the hypothesis test. Since this is an upper-tailed test, a comparison of the calculated t value of 2.838 to the critical t value of 1.717 results in the rejection of the null hypothesis. Similarly, a comparison of the p-value of 0.0096 to the significance level of 0.05 results in the same conclusion.

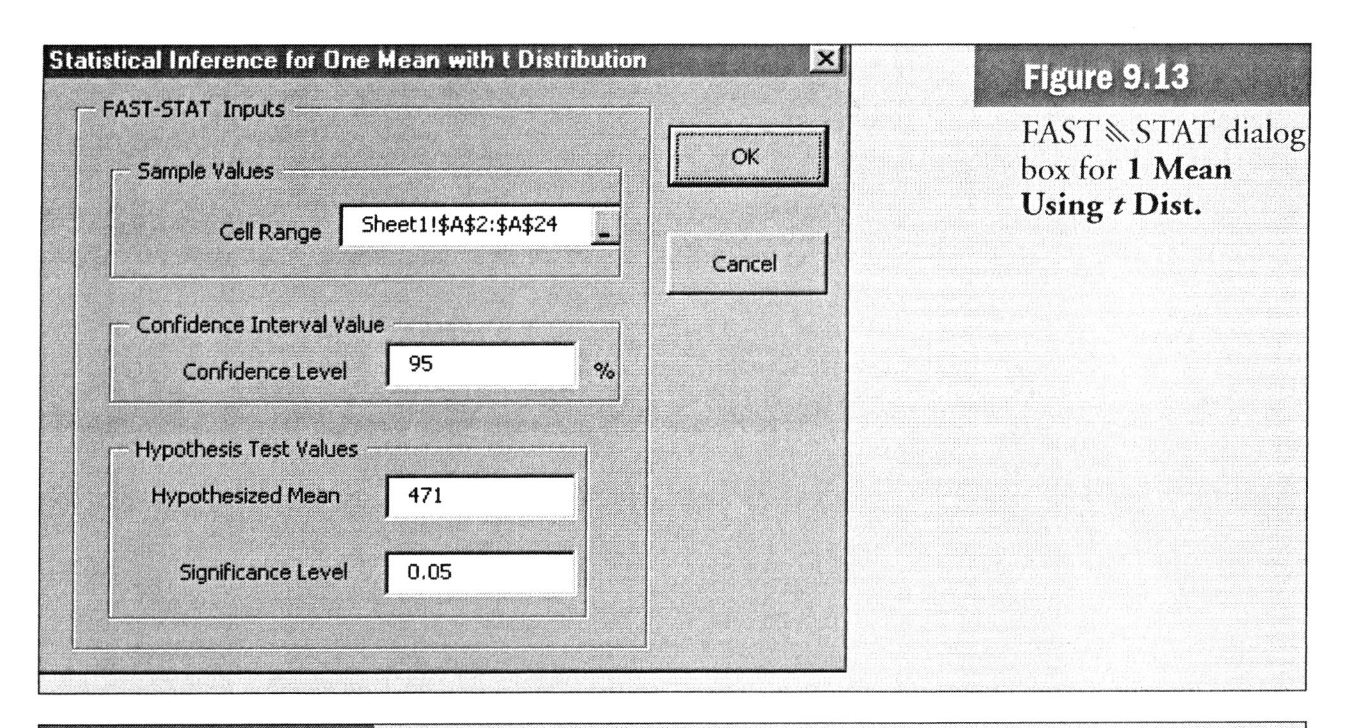

Figure 9.13 FAST⧹STAT dialog box for **1 Mean Using *t* Dist.**

Figure 9.14 FAST⧹STAT output for Demonstration Problem 9.2

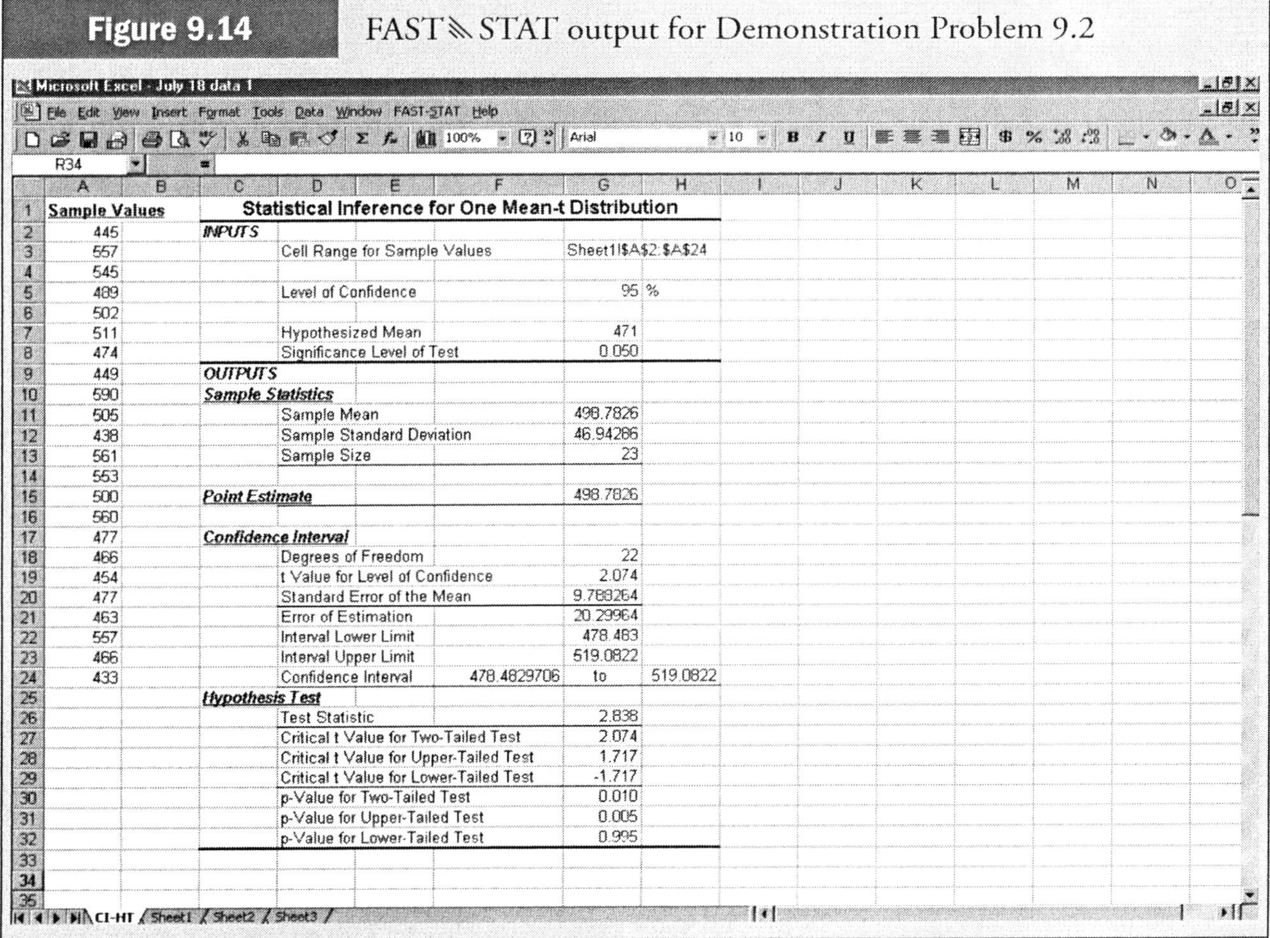

Row	Sample Values		Statistical Inference for One Mean-t Distribution		
2	445	*INPUTS*			
3	557		Cell Range for Sample Values	Sheet1!$A$2:$A$24	
4	545				
5	489		Level of Confidence	95	%
6	502				
7	511		Hypothesized Mean	471	
8	474		Significance Level of Test	0.050	
9	449	*OUTPUTS*			
10	590	***Sample Statistics***			
11	505		Sample Mean	498.7826	
12	438		Sample Standard Deviation	46.94286	
13	561		Sample Size	23	
14	553				
15	500	***Point Estimate***		498.7826	
16	560				
17	477	***Confidence Interval***			
18	466		Degrees of Freedom	22	
19	454		t Value for Level of Confidence	2.074	
20	477		Standard Error of the Mean	9.788264	
21	463		Error of Estimation	20.29964	
22	557		Interval Lower Limit	478.483	
23	466		Interval Upper Limit	519.0822	
24	433		Confidence Interval 478.4829706	to	519.0822
25		***Hypothesis Test***			
26			Test Statistic	2.838	
27			Critical t Value for Two-Tailed Test	2.074	
28			Critical t Value for Upper-Tailed Test	1.717	
29			Critical t Value for Lower-Tailed Test	-1.717	
30			p-Value for Two-Tailed Test	0.010	
31			p-Value for Upper-Tailed Test	0.005	
32			p-Value for Lower-Tailed Test	0.995	

9.3
Problems

9.8 The following data were gathered from a random sample of 11 items.

1200	1175	1080	1275	1201	1387
1090	1280	1400	1287	1225	

Use these data and a 5% level of significance to test the following hypotheses, assuming that the data come from a normally distributed population.

$$H_0: \mu = 1160 \qquad H_a: \mu > 1160$$

9.9 The following data (in pounds), which were selected randomly from a normally distributed population of values, represent measurements of a machine part that is supposed to weigh, on average, 8.3 pounds.

8.1	8.4	8.3	8.2	8.5	8.6	8.4	8.3	8.4	8.2
8.8	8.2	8.2	8.3	8.1	8.3	8.4	8.5	8.5	8.7

Use these data and $\alpha = .01$ to test the hypothesis that the parts average 8.3 pounds.

9.10 A hole-punch machine is set to punch a hole 1.84 cm in diameter in a strip of sheet metal in a manufacturing process. The strip of metal is then creased and sent on to the next phase of production, where a metal rod is slipped through the hole. It is important that the hole be punched to the specified diameter of 1.84 cm. To test punching accuracy, technicians have randomly sampled 12 punched holes and measured the diameters. The data (in cm) follow. Use an alpha of .10 to determine whether the holes are being punched an average of 1.84 cm. Assume the punched holes are normally distributed in the population.

1.81	1.89	1.86	1.83
1.85	1.82	1.87	1.85
1.84	1.86	1.88	1.85

9.11 Suppose a study reports that the average price for a gallon of self-serve regular unleaded gasoline is \$1.16. You believe that the figure is higher in your area of the country. You decide to test this claim for your part of the United States by randomly calling gasoline stations. Your random survey of 25 stations produces the following prices.

\$1.27	\$1.29	\$1.16	\$1.20	\$1.37
1.20	1.23	1.19	1.20	1.24
1.16	1.07	1.27	1.09	1.35
1.15	1.23	1.14	1.05	1.35
1.21	1.14	1.14	1.07	1.10

Assume gasoline prices for a region are normally distributed. Do the data you obtained provide enough evidence to reject the claim? Use a 1% level of significance.

9.12 Suppose that in past years the average price per square foot for warehouses in the United States has been \$32.28. A national real estate investor wants to determine whether that figure has changed now. The investor hires a business analyst who randomly samples 19 warehouses that are for sale across the United States and finds that the mean price per square foot is \$31.67, with a standard deviation of \$1.29. If the business analyst uses a 5% level of significance, what statistical conclusion can be reached? What are the hypotheses?

9.13 According to a National Public Transportation survey, the average commuting time for people who commute to a city with a population of 1 to 3 million is 19.0 minutes. Suppose a business analyst lives in a city with a population of 2.4 million and wants to test to determine if commuting time has increased. She takes a random sample of 26 commuters and gathers the data shown below. Using an alpha of .05 and assuming that commuting time is normally distributed, what did she find?

19	16	20	23	23
24	13	19	23	16
17	15	14	27	17
23	18	18	20	18
18	18	23	19	19
28				

9.4 Testing Hypotheses about a Proportion

The formula for proportions based on the central limit theorem makes possible the testing of hypotheses about the population proportion in a manner similar to that of the formula used to test sample means. A proportion is a value between 0 and 1 that expresses the part of the whole that has a given characteristic. For example, according to Forrester Research, Inc., .41 of all companies offer payment confirmation on their Website. Whereas means are computed by averaging measurements, proportions are calculated by counting or tallying the number of items in a population that have a characteristic and then dividing that number by the total. Recall that $\hat{p}$ denotes a sample proportion and P denotes the population proportion.

The central limit theorem applied to sample proportions states that $\hat{p}$ values are approximately normally distributed. It has been shown that the mean of the distribution of a set of $\hat{p}$ values is P and the standard deviation is $\sqrt{(P \cdot Q)/n}$ when $n \cdot P \geq 5$ and $n \cdot Q \geq 5$. A Z test is used to test hypotheses about P.

Z TEST OF A POPULATION PROPORTION

$$Z = \frac{\hat{p} - P}{\sqrt{\frac{P \cdot Q}{n}}} \tag{9.5}$$

where:
$\hat{p}$ = sample proportion
P = population proportion
$Q = 1 - P$

A manufacturer believes exactly 8% of its products contain at least one minor flaw. Suppose a company business analyst wants to test this belief. The null and alternative hypotheses are

$$H_0\text{: } P = .08$$
$$H_a\text{: } P \neq .08.$$

This is a two-tailed test because the hypothesis being tested is whether or not the proportion of products with at least one minor flaw is .08. Alpha is selected to be .10. Figure 9.15 shows the distribution, with the rejection regions and $Z_{.05}$. Because α is divided for a two-tailed test, the table value for an area of $(1/2)(.10) = .05$ is $Z_{.05} = \pm 1.645$.

For the business analyst to reject the null hypothesis, the calculated Z value must be greater than 1.645 or less than −1.645. The business analyst randomly selects a sample of

Figure 9.15

Distribution with rejection regions for flawed-product example

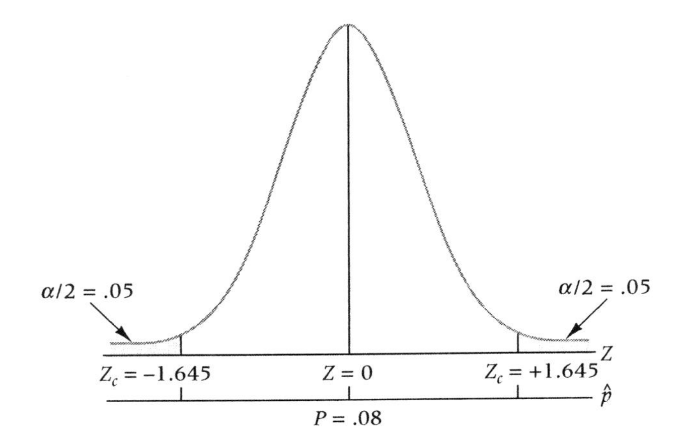

200 products, inspects each item for flaws, and determines that 33 items have at least one minor flaw. Calculating the sample proportion gives

$$\hat{p} = \frac{33}{200} = .165.$$

The calculated Z value is

$$Z = \frac{\hat{p} - P}{\sqrt{\frac{P \cdot Q}{n}}} = \frac{.165 - .080}{\sqrt{\frac{(.08)(.92)}{200}}} = \frac{.085}{.019} = 4.43.$$

Note that the denominator of the Z formula contains the population proportion. Although the business analyst does not actually know the population proportion, he is testing a population proportion value. Hence he uses the hypothesized population value in the denominator of the formula as well as in the numerator. This method contrasts with the confidence interval formula, where the sample proportion is used in the denominator.

The calculated value of Z is in the rejection region (calculated $Z = 4.43 >$ table $Z_{.05} = +1.645$), so the business analyst rejects the null hypothesis. He concludes that the proportion of items with at least one minor flaw in the population from which the sample of 200 was drawn is not .08. With $\alpha = .10$, the risk of committing a Type I error in this example is .10.

The calculated value of $Z = 4.43$ is outside the range of most values in virtually all Z tables. Thus if the business analyst were using the p-value method to arrive at a decision about the null hypothesis, the probability would be .0000, and he would reject the null hypothesis.

Suppose the business analyst wanted to use the critical value method. He would enter the table value of $Z_{.05} = 1.645$ in the Z formula for single sample proportions, along with the hypothesized population proportion and n, and solve for the critical value of $\hat{p}$, $\hat{p}_c$. The result is

$$Z_{\alpha/2} = \frac{\hat{p}_c - P}{\sqrt{\frac{P \cdot Q}{n}}}$$

$$\pm 1.645 = \frac{\hat{p}_c - .08}{\sqrt{\frac{(.08)(.92)}{200}}}$$

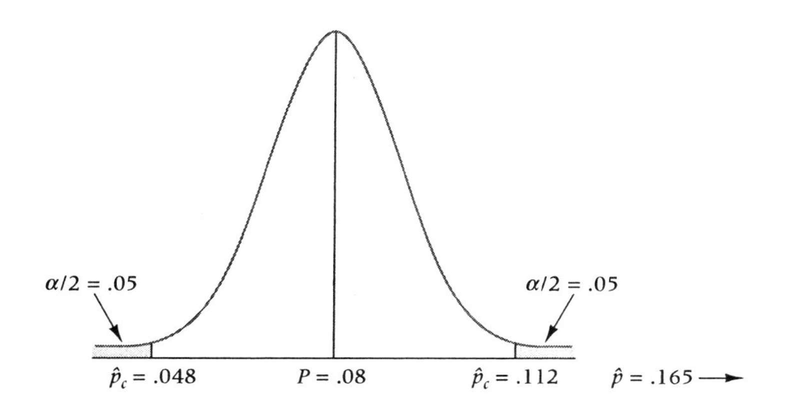

Figure 9.16

Distribution using critical value method for the flawed-product example

and

$$\hat{p}_c = .08 \pm 1.645\sqrt{\frac{(.08)(.92)}{200}} = .08 \pm .032$$
$$= .048 \text{ and } .112.$$

Examination of the sample proportion, $\hat{p} = .165$, and Figure 9.16 clearly shows that the sample proportion is in the rejection region. The statistical conclusion is to reject the null hypothesis. The proportion of products with at least one flaw is not .08.

DEMONSTRATION PROBLEM 9.3

A survey of the morning beverage market has shown that the primary breakfast beverage for 17% of Americans is milk. A milk producer in Wisconsin, where milk is plentiful, believes the figure is higher for Wisconsin. To test this idea, she contacts a random sample of 550 Wisconsin residents and asks which primary beverage they consumed for breakfast that day. Suppose 115 replied that milk was the primary beverage. Using a level of significance of .05, test the idea that the milk figure is higher for Wisconsin.

SOLUTION

STEP **1.** The milk producer's theory is that the proportion of Wisconsin residents who drink milk for breakfast is higher than the national proportion, which is the alternative hypothesis. The null hypothesis is that the proportion in Wisconsin does not differ from the national average. That is, the hypotheses for this problem are

$$H_0: P = .17$$
$$H_a: P > .17.$$

STEP **2.** The test statistic is

$$Z = \frac{\hat{p} - P}{\sqrt{\frac{P \cdot Q}{n}}}.$$

STEP **3.** The Type I error rate is .05.

STEP **4.** This is a one-tailed test, and the table value is $Z_{.05} = +1.645$. The sample results must yield an observed Z value greater than 1.645 for the milk producer to reject the null hypothesis. The following diagram shows $Z_{.05}$ and the rejection region for this problem.

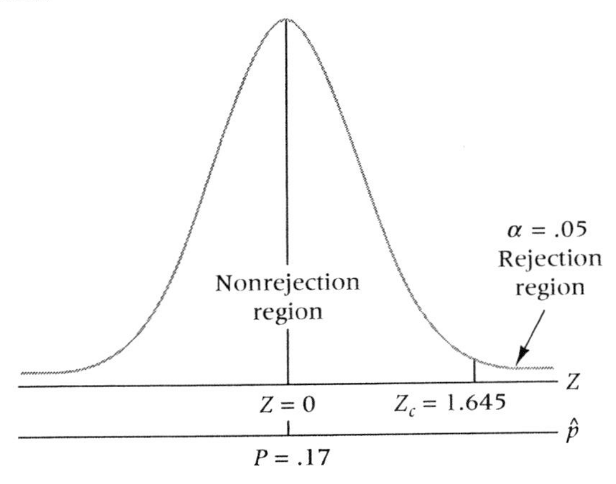

STEP **5.** $n = 550$ and $X = 115$

$$\hat{p} = \frac{115}{550} = .209$$

STEP **6.**

$$Z = \frac{\hat{p} - P}{\sqrt{\frac{P \cdot Q}{n}}} = \frac{.209 - .17}{\sqrt{\frac{(.17)(.83)}{550}}} = \frac{.039}{.016} = 2.44$$

STEP **7.** As $Z = 2.44$ is beyond $Z_{.05} = 1.645$ in the rejection region, the milk producer rejects the null hypothesis. On the basis of the random sample, the producer is ready to conclude that the proportion of Wisconsin residents who drink milk as the primary beverage for breakfast is higher than the national proportion.

STEP **8.** If the proportion of residents who drink milk for breakfast is higher in Wisconsin than in other parts of the United States, milk producers might have a market opportunity in Wisconsin that is not available in other parts of the country. Perhaps Wisconsin residents are being loyal to home-state products, in which case marketers of other Wisconsin products might be successful in appealing to residents to support their products. The fact that more milk is sold in Wisconsin might mean that if Wisconsin milk producers appealed to markets outside Wisconsin in the same way they do their own, they might increase their market share of the breakfast beverage market in other states.

The probability of obtaining a $Z \geq 2.44$ by chance is .0073. As this probability is less than $\alpha = .05$, the null hypothesis is also rejected with the p-value method.

A critical proportion can be solved for by

$$Z_{.05} = \frac{\hat{p} - P}{\sqrt{\frac{P \cdot Q}{n}}};$$

$$1.645 = \frac{\hat{p}_c - .17}{\sqrt{\frac{(.17)(.83)}{550}}};$$

$$\hat{p}_c = .17 + .026 = .196.$$

With the critical value method, a sample proportion greater than .196 must be obtained to reject the null hypothesis. The sample proportion for this problem is .209, so the null hypothesis is also rejected with the critical value method.

Analysis Using Excel

In Section 8.3 of the prior chapter, we introduced the **FAST⧵STAT** macro procedure called **1 Proportion C.I. and H.T.** In that chapter we used the procedure to compute confidence intervals for one proportion with the normal distribution. This procedure also computes the statistics for conducting a hypothesis test for one proportion with the normal distribution. The input dialog box for this procedure is shown in Figure 9.17.

To conduct a hypothesis test, first enter the sample size and number of items in the sample having the characteristic of interest in the first grouping of FAST⧵STAT inputs. If the confidence interval is not of interest, the entry for the confidence level may be set equal to any value between 0 and 100. Next enter the hypothesized proportion and the significance level of the test in the third grouping of inputs. When the data for Demonstration Problem 9.3 are entered as in Figure 9.17, a click on the **OK** command button yields the results of Figure 9.18.

Figure 9.18 for the 1 proportion is quite similar to the prior figures demonstrating the statistical inference computations for 1 mean: Figures 9.9, 9.12, and 9.14. The hypothesis test output of Figure 9.18 includes the calculated Z value, the critical Z values and the p-values for all three possible forms of the hypothesis test. Since this is an upper-tailed test, a comparison of the calculated Z value of 2.441 to the critical Z value of 1.645 results in the rejection of the null hypothesis. Similarly, a comparison of the p-value of 0.007 to the significance level of 0.05 results in the same conclusion.

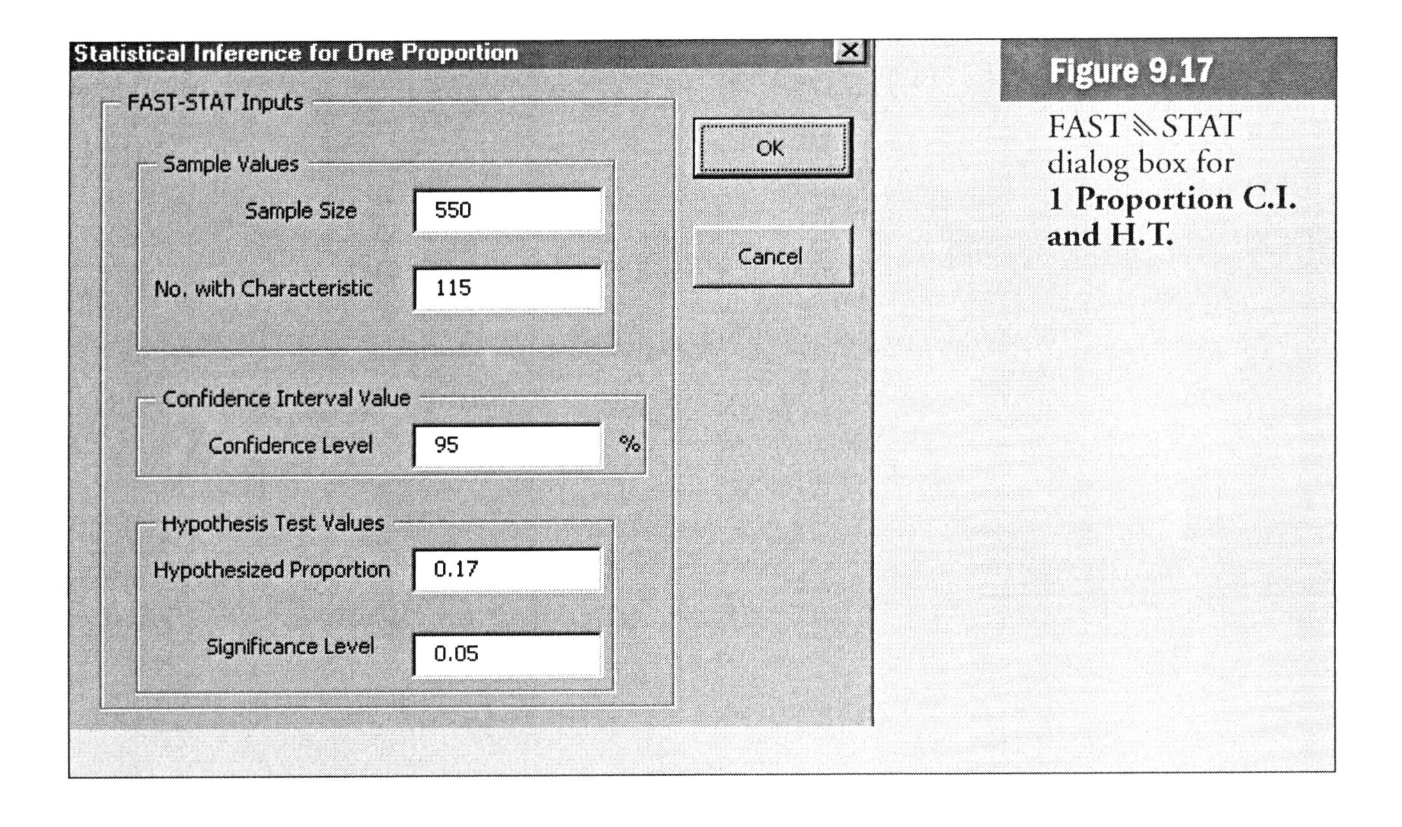

Figure 9.17

FAST⧵STAT dialog box for **1 Proportion C.I. and H.T.**

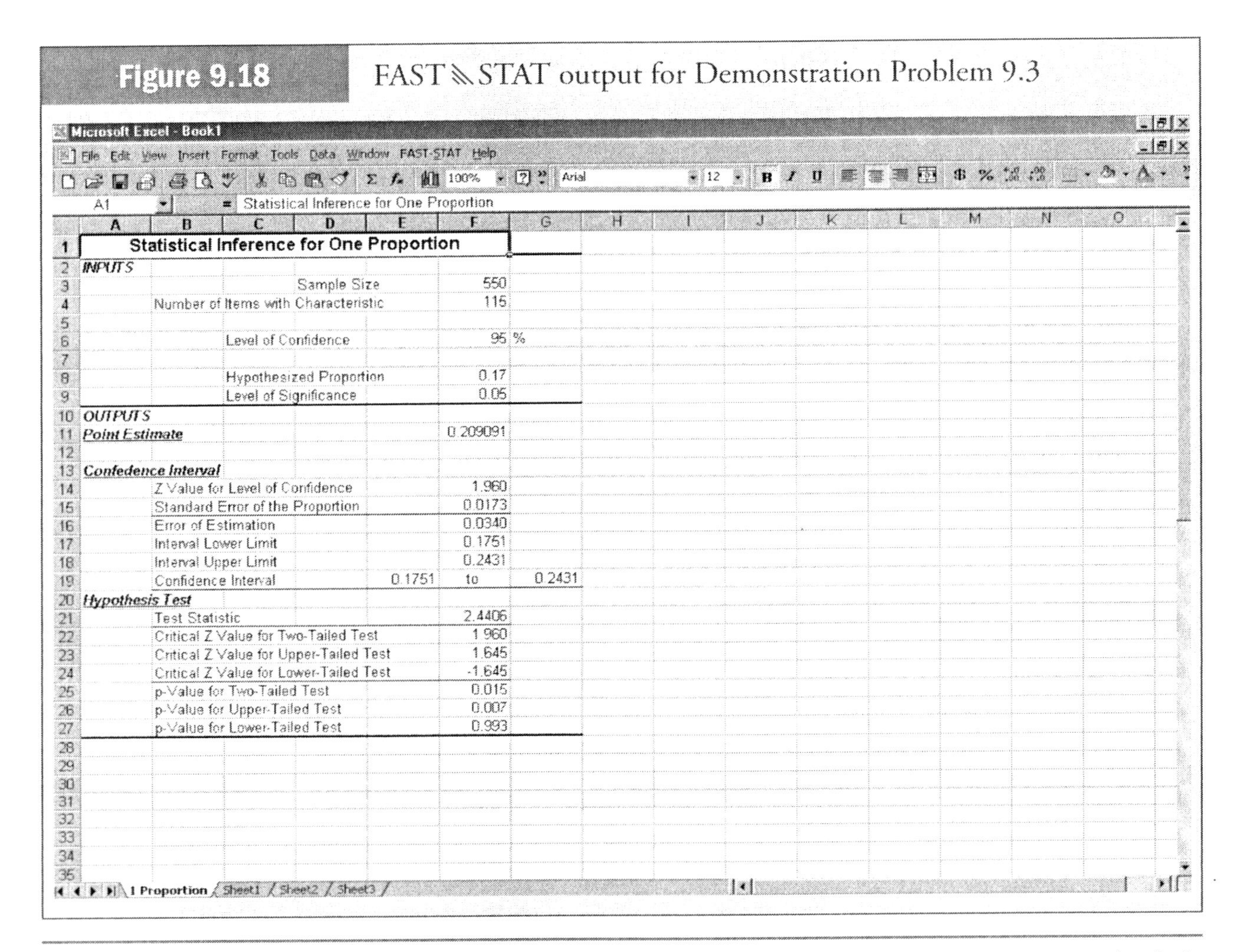

	A–E	F	G
1	**Statistical Inference for One Proportion**		
2	*INPUTS*		
3	Sample Size	550	
4	Number of Items with Characteristic	115	
5			
6	Level of Confidence	95	%
7			
8	Hypothesized Proportion	0.17	
9	Level of Significance	0.05	
10	*OUTPUTS*		
11	*Point Estimate*	0.209091	
12			
13	*Confedence Interval*		
14	Z Value for Level of Confidence	1.960	
15	Standard Error of the Proportion	0.0173	
16	Error of Estimation	0.0340	
17	Interval Lower Limit	0.1751	
18	Interval Upper Limit	0.2431	
19	Confidence Interval 0.1751	to	0.2431
20	*Hypothesis Test*		
21	Test Statistic	2.4406	
22	Critical Z Value for Two-Tailed Test	1.960	
23	Critical Z Value for Upper-Tailed Test	1.645	
24	Critical Z Value for Lower-Tailed Test	-1.645	
25	p-Value for Two-Tailed Test	0.015	
26	p-Value for Upper-Tailed Test	0.007	
27	p-Value for Lower-Tailed Test	0.993	

Figure 9.18 FAST\STAT output for Demonstration Problem 9.3

9.4
Problems

9.14 Suppose you are testing H_0: $P = .29$ versus H_a: $P \neq .29$. A random sample of 740 items shows that 207 have this characteristic. With a .05 probability of committing a Type I error, test the hypothesis. If you had used the critical value method, what would the two critical values be? How do the sample results compare with the critical values? For the p-value method, what is the probability of the calculated Z value for this problem?

9.15 The Independent Insurance Agents of America conducted a survey of insurance consumers and discovered that 48% of them always reread their insurance policies, 29% sometimes do, 16% rarely do, and 7% never do. Suppose a large insurance company invests considerable time and money in rewriting policies so that they will be more attractive and easy to read and understand. After using the new policies for a year, company managers want to determine whether rewriting the policies has significantly changed the proportion of policyholders who always reread their insurance policy. They contact 380 of the company's insurance consumers who have purchased a policy in the past year and ask them whether they always reread their insurance policies. One hundred and sixty-four respond that they do. Use a 1% level of significance to test the hypothesis.

9.16 A study by Hewitt Associates showed that 79% of companies offer employees flexible scheduling. Suppose a business analyst believes that in accounting firms this figure is lower. The business analyst randomly selects 415 accounting firms and through interviews determines that 303 of these firms have flexible scheduling. With a 1% level of significance, is there enough evidence to conclude that a significantly lower proportion of accounting firms offer employees flexible scheduling?

9.17 A survey was undertaken by Bruskin/Goldring Research for Quicken to determine how people plan to meet their financial goals in the next year. Respondents were allowed to select more than one way to meet their goals. Thirty-one percent said that they were using a financial planner to help them meet their goals. Twenty-four percent were using family/friends to help them meet their financial goals followed by broker/accountant (19%), computer software (17%), and books (14%). Suppose another business analyst takes a similar survey of 600 people to test these results. If 200 people respond that they are going to use a financial planner to help them meet their goals, is this enough evidence to reject the 31% figure generated in the Bruskin/Goldring survey using $\alpha = .10$? If 130 respond that they are going to use family/friends to help them meet their financial goals, is this enough evidence to declare that the proportion is significantly lower than Bruskin/Goldring's figure of .24 if $\alpha = .05$?

9.18 Eighteen percent of U.S.-based multinational companies provide an allowance for personal long-distance calls for executives living overseas, according to the Institute for International Human Resources and the National Foreign Trade Council. Suppose a business analyst thinks that U.S.-based multinational companies are having a more difficult time recruiting executives to live overseas and that an increasing number of these companies are providing an allowance for personal long-distance calls to these executives to ease the burden of living away from home. To test this, a new study is conducted by contacting 376 multinational companies. Twenty-two percent of these surveyed companies are providing an allowance for personal long-distance calls to executives living overseas. Is this enough evidence to declare that a significantly higher proportion of multinational companies are doing this? Let $\alpha = .01$.

9.19 A large manufacturing company investigated the service it has received from suppliers and discovered that, in the past, 32% of all materials shipments have been received late. However, the company recently installed a just-in-time system in which suppliers are linked more closely to the manufacturing process. A random sample of 118 deliveries since the just-in-time system was installed reveals that 22 deliveries were late. Use this sample information to test whether the proportion of late deliveries has been reduced significantly. Let $\alpha = .05$.

9.20 Where do CFOs get their money news? According to Robert Half International, 47% get their money news from newspapers, 15% get it from communication/colleagues, 12% get it from television, 11% from the Internet, 9% from magazines, 5% from radio, and 1% don't know. Suppose a business analyst wants to test these results. She randomly samples 67 CFOs and finds that 40 of them get their money news from newspapers. Is this enough evidence to reject the findings of Robert Half International? Use $\alpha = .05$.

Summary

Hypothesis testing is a very important tool for business statisticians and is used to test statistical hypotheses. The process begins with the selection of a null hypothesis and an alternative hypothesis. The null and alternative hypotheses are structured so that either one or the other is true but not both. In testing hypotheses, the business analyst assumes that the null hypothesis is true. By examining the sampled data, the business analyst either rejects or does nor reject the null hypothesis. If the sample data are significantly in opposition to the null hypothesis, the business analyst rejects the null hypothesis and accepts the alternative hypothesis by default.

Hypothesis tests can be one-tailed or two-tailed. Two-tailed tests always utilize = and ≠ in the null and alternative hypotheses. These tests are nondirectional in that significant deviations from the hypothesized value that are either greater than or less than the value are in rejection regions. The one-tailed test is directional, and the alternative hypothesis contains < or > signs. In these tests, only one end or tail of the distribution contains a rejection region. In a one-tailed test, the business analyst is interested only in deviations from the hypothesized value that are either greater than or less than the value but not both.

When a business analyst makes a decision about the null hypothesis, it can involve an error. If the null hypothesis is true, the business analyst can make a Type I error by rejecting the null hypothesis. The probability of making a Type I error is alpha (α). Alpha is usually set by the business analyst when establishing the hypotheses. Another expression sometimes used for the value of α is level of significance.

If the null hypothesis is false and the business analyst fails to reject it, a Type II error has been committed. Beta (β) is the probability of committing a Type II error. Type II errors must be computed from the hypothesized value of the parameter, α, and a specific alternative value of the parameter being examined. There are as many possible Type II errors in a problem as there are possible alternative statistical values.

If a null hypothesis is true and the business analyst fails to reject it, no error has been committed, and the business analyst has made a correct decision. Similarly, if a null hypothesis is false and it is rejected, no error has been committed. Power $(1 - \beta)$ is the probability of a statistical test rejecting the null hypothesis when the null hypothesis is false.

Included in this chapter were hypothesis tests for a single mean for both large and small sample sizes and a test of a single population proportion. Three different analytic approaches were presented: (1) standard method, (2) critical value method, and (3) the p-value method.

Key Terms

alpha (α)
alternative hypothesis
beta (β)
critical value
critical value method
hypothesis testing
level of significance
nonrejection region
null hypothesis
observed significance level
one-tailed test
p-value method
power
rejection region
two-tailed test
Type I error
Type II error

SUPPLEMENTARY PROBLEMS

9.21 According to a survey by ICR for Vienna Systems, a majority of American households have tried to cut long-distance phone bills. Of those who have tried to cut the bills, 32% have done so by switching long-distance companies. Suppose that lately there has been a frenzy of "slamming" (where the customer's long-distance provider is switched without the customer's knowledge or approval) and long-distance company solicitation and advertising. Because of this, ICR conducts another survey by randomly contacting 80 American households who have tried to cut long-distance phone bills. If 39% of the contacted households say they have tried to cut their long-distance phone bills by switching long-distance companies, is this enough evidence to state that a significantly higher proportion of American households are trying to cut long-distance phone bills by switching companies? Let $\alpha = .01$.

9.22 According to Zero Population Growth, the average urban U.S. resident uses 3.3 pounds of food per day. Is this figure accurate for rural U.S. residents? Suppose 64 rural U.S. residents are identified by a random procedure and their average consumption per day is 3.45 pounds of food. Assume a population variance of 1.31 pounds of food per day. Use a 5% level of significance to determine whether the Zero Population Growth figure for urban U.S. residents also is true for rural U.S. residents on the basis of the sample data.

9.23 Brokers generally agree that bonds are a better investment during times of low interest rates than during times of high interest rates. A survey of executives during a time of low interest rates showed that 57% of them had some retirement funds invested in bonds. Assume this percentage is constant for bond market investment by executives with retirement funds. Suppose interest rates have risen lately and the proportion of executives with retirement investment money in the bond market may have dropped. To test this idea, a business analyst randomly samples 210 executives who have retirement funds. Of these, 93 now have retirement funds invested in bonds. For $\alpha = .10$, is this enough evidence to declare that the proportion of executives with retirement fund investments in the bond market is significantly lower than .57?

9.24 Highway engineers in Ohio are painting white stripes on a highway. The stripes are supposed to be approximately 10 feet long. However, because of the machine, the operator, and the motion of the vehicle carrying the equipment, there is considerable variation among the stripe lengths. Shown below are a sample of 12 measured stripe lengths from a recent highway painting. Using these data, test to determine if stripe lengths are averaging 10 feet. Assume stripe length is normally distributed. Let $\alpha = .05$.

STRIPE LENGTHS IN FEET

10.3	9.4	9.8	10.1
9.2	10.4	10.7	9.9
9.3	9.8	10.5	10.4

9.25 A computer manufacturer estimates that its line of minicomputers has, on average, 8.4 days of downtime per year. To test this claim, a business analyst contacts seven companies that own one of these computers and is allowed to access company computer records. It is determined that, for the sample, the average number of downtime days is 5.6, with a sample standard deviation of 1.3 days. Assuming that number of downtime days is normally distributed, test to determine whether these minicomputers actually average 8.4 days of downtime in the entire population. Let $\alpha = .01$.

9.26 A life insurance salesperson claims the average worker in the city of Cincinnati has no more than $25,000 of personal life insurance. To test this claim, you randomly sample 100 workers in Cincinnati. You find that this sample of workers has an average of $26,650 of personal life insurance and that the standard deviation is $12,000.

Determine whether there is enough evidence to reject the null hypothesis posed by the salesperson. Assume the probability of committing a Type I error is .05.

9.27 A study of MBA graduates by Universum for The American Graduate Survey 1999 revealed that MBA graduates have several expectations from prospective employers beyond their base pay. In particular, according to the study 46% expect a performance-related bonus, 46% expect stock options, 42% expect a signing bonus, 28% expect profit sharing, 27% expect extra vacation/personal days, 25% expect tuition reimbursement, 24% expect health benefits, and 19% expect guaranteed annual bonuses. Suppose a study is conducted in an ensuing year to see if these expectations have changed. If 125 MBA graduates are randomly selected and if 66 expect stock options, is this enough evidence to declare that a significantly higher proportion of MBAs expect stock options? Let $\alpha = .05$.

9.28 Suppose the number of beds filled per day in a medium-size hospital is normally distributed. A hospital administrator has been quoted as having told the board of directors that, on the average, at least 185 beds are filled on any given day. One of the board members believes this figure is inflated, and she manages to secure a random sample of figures for 16 days. The data are shown here. Use $\alpha = .05$ and the sample data to test whether the hospital administrator's statement is false. Assume the number of filled beds per day is normally distributed in the population.

NUMBER OF BEDS OCCUPIED PER DAY

173	149	166	180
189	170	152	194
177	169	188	160
199	175	172	187

9.29 According to the International Data Corporation, Compaq Computers holds a 16% share of the personal computer market in the United States and a 12.7% share of the worldwide market. Suppose a market business analyst believes that Compaq holds a higher share of the market in the southwestern region of the United States. To verify this theory, he randomly selects 428 people who have purchased a personal computer in the last month in the southwestern region of the United States. Eighty-four of these purchases were Compaq Computers. Using a 1% level of significance, test the market business analyst's theory. What is the probability of making a Type I error?

9.30 A national publication reported that a college student living away from home spends, on average, no more than $15 per month on laundry. You believe this figure is too low and want to disprove this claim. To conduct the test, you randomly select 35 college students and ask them to keep track of the amount of money they spend during a given month for laundry. The sample produces an average expenditure on laundry of $19.34, with a standard deviation of $4.52. Use these sample data to conduct the hypothesis test. Assume you are willing to take a 10% risk of making a Type I error.

9.31 A study of pollutants showed that certain industrial emissions should not exceed 2.5 parts per million. You believe a particular company may be exceeding this average. To test this supposition, you randomly take a sample of nine air tests. The sample average is 3.4 parts per million, with a sample standard deviation of .6. Is this enough evidence for you to conclude that the company has been exceeding the safe limit? Use $\alpha = .01$. Assume emissions are normally distributed.

9.32 The average cost per square foot for office rental space in the central business district of Philadelphia is $23.58, according to Cushman & Wakefield, Inc. A large real estate company wants to confirm this figure. The firm conducts a telephone survey of 95 offices in the central business district of Philadelphia and asks the office managers how much they pay in rent per square foot. Suppose the sample average is $22.83 per square foot, with a standard deviation of $5.11.

Conduct a hypothesis test using $\alpha = .05$ to determine whether the cost per square foot reported by Cushman & Wakefield, Inc. should be rejected.

9.33 The American Water Works Association reports that, on average, men use between 10 and 15 gallons of water daily to shave when they leave the water running. Suppose the following data are the numbers of gallons of water used in a day to shave by 12 randomly selected men and the data come from a normal distribution of data. Use these data and a 5% level of significance to test to determine whether the population mean for such water usage is less than 12.5 gallons.

10	8	13	17	13	9
12	13	5	8	9	7

ANALYZING THE DATABASES

1. Suppose the average number of employees per industry group in the manufacturing database is believed to be less than 150 (1000s). Test this belief as the alternative hypothesis by using the 140 SIC code industries given in the database as the sample. Let $\alpha = .01$. What did you decide and why?
2. Examine the hospital database. Suppose you want to "prove" that the average hospital in the United States has an average of more than 700 births per year. Use the hospital database as your sample and test this hypothesis. Let alpha be .01. On average, do hospitals in the United States have fewer than 800 personnel? Use the hospital database as your sample and an alpha of .10 to test this as the alternative hypothesis.
3. Consider the financial database. Is the average earnings per share for companies in the stock market more than $2.50? Use the sample of companies represented by this database to test that hypothesis. Let $\alpha = .05$. Test to determine whether the average return on equity for all companies is equal to 21. Use this database as the sample and $\alpha = .10$.
4. Fifteen years ago, the average production in the United States for green beans was 166,770 per month. Use the 12 months in 1997 (the last 12 months in the database) in the agriculture database as a sample to test to determine whether the mean monthly production figure for green beans in the United States is now different from the old figure. Let $\alpha = .01$.

CASE

FRITO-LAY TARGETS THE HISPANIC MARKET

Frito Company was founded in 1932 in San Antonio, Texas, by Elmer Doolin. H. W. Lay & Company was founded in Atlanta, Georgia, by Herman W. Lay in 1938. In 1961, the two companies merged to form Frito-Lay, Inc., with headquarters in Texas. Frito-Lay, Inc. produced, distributed, and marketed snack foods with particular emphasis on various types of chips. In 1965, the company merged with Pepsi-Cola to form PepsiCo, Inc. Three decades later, Pepsi-Cola combined its domestic and international snack food operations into one business unit called Frito-Lay Company. According to data released by Information Resources, Inc., Frito-Lay brands account for over 60% of the share of the snack chip market.

One problem facing Frito-Lay has been its general lack of appeal to the Hispanic market, which is a growing segment of the U.S. population. In an effort to better penetrate that market, Frito-Lay hired various market analysts to determine why Hispanics do not purchase their products as often as company officials had hoped and what could be done about the problem.

Driving giant RVs through Hispanic neighborhoods and targeting Hispanic women (who tend to buy most of the groceries for their families), the business analysts tested various brands and discovered several things. Hispanics thought Frito-Lay products were too bland, not spicy enough. Hispanics also were relatively unaware of Frito-Lay advertising. In addition, they tended to purchase snacks in small bags rather than in large family-style bags and at small local grocery stores rather than at large supermarkets.

After the "road test," focus groups composed of male teens and male young adults—a group that tends to consume a lot of chips—were formed. The business analysts determined that while many of the teens spoke English at school, they spoke Spanish at home with their family. From this, it was concluded that Spanish advertisements would be needed to reach Hispanics. In addition, it was discovered that the use of Spanish rock music, a growing movement in the Hispanic youth culture, would be effective in some ads.

Business analysts also found that using a "Happy Face" logo, which is an icon of Frito-Lay's sister company in Mexico, was effective. Because it reminded the 63% of all Hispanics in the United States who are Mexican-American of snack foods from home, the logo increased product familiarity.

As a result of this research, Frito-Lay launched its first Hispanic products in San Antonio in 1997. Since that time, sales of the Doritos brand improved 32% in Hispanic areas and Doritos Salsa Verde sales have grown to represent 15% of all sales. Frito-Lay since has expanded its line of products into other areas of the United States with large Hispanic populations.

DISCUSSION

In the research process for Frito-Lay Company, many different numerical questions were raised regarding Frito-Lay products, advertising techniques, and purchase patterns among Hispanics. In each of these areas, statistics—in particular, hypothesis testing—plays a central role. Using the case information and the concepts of statistical hypothesis testing, discuss the following:

1. Many proportions were generated in the focus groups and market research that were conducted for this project, including the proportion of the market that is Hispanic, the proportion of Hispanic grocery shoppers that are women, the proportion of chip purchasers that are teens, and so on. Use techniques presented in this chapter to analyze each of the following and discuss how the results might affect marketing decision makers about the Hispanic market.
   a. The case information stated that 63% of all U.S. Hispanics are Mexican-American. How might we test that figure? Suppose 850 U.S. Hispanics are randomly selected using U.S. Bureau of the Census information. Suppose 575 state that they are Mexican-Americans. Test the 63% percentage using an alpha of .05.
   b. Suppose that in the past 94% of all Hispanic grocery shoppers are women. Perhaps due to changing cultural values, we believe that more Hispanic men are now grocery shopping. We randomly sample 689 Hispanic grocery shoppers from around the United States and 606 are women. Is this enough evidence to conclude that a lower proportion of Hispanic grocery shoppers now are women?
   c. What proportion of Hispanics listen primarily to advertisements in Spanish? Suppose one source says that in the past the proportion has been about .83. We want to test to determine whether this figure is true. A random sample of 438 Hispanics is selected, and 347 listened primarily in Spanish. Use $\alpha = .05$ and any appropriate calculations to reach some conclusions from these data.
2. The statistical mean can be used to measure various aspects of the Hispanic culture and the Hispanic market, including size of purchase, frequency of purchase, age of consumer, size of store, and so on. Use techniques presented in this chapter to analyze each of the following and discuss how the results might affect marketing decisions.
   a. What is the average age of a purchaser of Doritos Salsa Verde? Suppose initial tests indicate that the mean age is 31. Is this really correct? To test this, a business analyst randomly contacts 24 purchasers of Doritos Salsa Verde and asks their age with results shown below. Discuss the output in terms of a hypothesis test to determine whether the mean age is actually 31. Let α be .01.

$$\bar{X} = 27.61415$$
$$t = -1.8557$$
$$p\text{-value (two-tailed)} = .07635$$

   b. What is the average expenditure of a Hispanic customer on chips per year? Suppose it is hypothesized that the figure is \$45 per year. A business analyst who knows the Hispanic market believes that this figure is too high and wants to prove her case. She randomly selects 18 Hispanics, has them keep a log of grocery purchases for one year, and obtains the following figures. Analyze the data using techniques from this chapter and an alpha of .05.

$55	37	59	57	27	28
16	46	34	62	9	34
4	25	38	58	3	50

ADAPTED FROM: "From Bland to Brand," *American Demographics*, March 1999, 57; the Frito-Lay website at http://www.fritolay.com; and Alsop, Ronald J., Editor. *The Wall Street Journal Almanac 1999*. New York: Ballantine Books, 1998 by Dow Jones & Company, Inc., 202.

10

Hypothesis Testing with Two Samples

Learning Objectives

Chapter 10 focuses on hypothesis testing about parameters from two populations, thereby enabling you to:

1. Test hypotheses about the difference in two population means using data from large independent samples.
2. Test hypotheses about the difference in two population means using data from small independent samples when the populations are normally distributed.
3. Test hypotheses about the population mean difference in two related populations when the populations are normally distributed.
4. Test hypotheses about the difference in two population proportions.
5. Test hypotheses about two population variances when the populations are normally distributed.

The presentation of hypothesis testing in Chapter 9 was centered on drawing a single sample from one population. Included in Chapter 9 were hypothesis tests about a population mean and a population proportion. In Chapter 10, we examine a number of hypothesis testing techniques that utilize two samples in an effort to test inferences about two populations. Some examples of such tests are:

- Testing the hypothesis that there was an increase in annual consumer expenditures on automobile insurance from the year 1991 to the year 2001 using a random sample from each year.
- Testing the hypothesis that there is a difference in the mean tensile strength of metal rods produced on two machines by taking a random sample of rods from each machine.
- Testing the hypothesis that female managers score higher on sensitivity ratings than males by taking a random sample of male and female managers matched on age, experience, and level of responsibility from each of several companies.
- Testing the hypothesis that there is a difference in the market shares of a given product in two markets using a sample from each market.
- Testing the hypothesis that there is a greater variance in the thickness of plastic bottles produced at manufacturing plant A than there is at manufacturing plant B by taking a random sample of bottles at each plant.

Independent samples Two or more samples in which the selected items are related only by chance.

Dependent samples, or Related samples Two or more samples selected in such a way as to be dependent or related; each item or person in one sample has a corresponding matched or related item in the other samples.

In this chapter, we will consider several different techniques for analyzing data that come from two samples. One technique is used with proportion, one is used with variances, and the others are used with means. The techniques for analyzing means are separated into those used with large samples and those used with small samples. In four of the five techniques presented in this chapter, the two samples are assumed to be **independent samples.** The samples are independent because *the items or people sampled in each group are in no way related to those in the other group.* Any similarity between items or people in the two samples is coincidental and due to chance. One of the techniques presented in the chapter is for analyzing data from two **dependent** or **related samples,** which are *samples selected in such a way as to be dependent or related.* In this case, *items or persons in one sample are matched in some way with items or persons in the other sample.* We begin with techniques for analyzing the difference in two independent large samples by using means.

10.1 Hypothesis Testing about the Difference in Two Means: Large, Independent Samples

In certain research designs, the sampling plan calls for selecting two different, independent samples. If the business analyst selects the mean as the statistic and if *two* samples are randomly chosen, the business analyst has *two* sample means to compare. This type of analysis is particularly useful in business when the business analyst is attempting to determine, for example, whether there is a difference in the effectiveness of two brands of toothpaste or the difference in wear of two brands of tires. Research might be conducted to study the difference in the productivity of men and women on an assembly line under certain conditions. An engineer might want to determine differences in the strength of aluminum produced under two different temperatures. Is there a difference in the average cost of a two-bedroom, one-story house between Boston and Seattle? If so, how much is the difference? These and many other interesting questions can be researched by comparing results obtained from two random samples.

How does a business analyst approach the analysis of the difference of two samples by using sample means? The central limit theorem states that the difference in two sample means, $\overline{X}_1 - \overline{X}_2$, is normally distributed for large sample sizes (both n_1 and $n_2 \geq 30$) regardless of the shape of the populations. It can also be shown that

$$\mu_{\bar{X}_1-\bar{X}_2} = \mu_1 - \mu_2$$

$$\sigma_{\bar{X}_1-\bar{X}_2} = \sqrt{\frac{\sigma_1^2}{n_1} + \frac{\sigma_2^2}{n_2}}$$

These expressions lead to a test statistic for the difference in two sample means.

(10.1)

$$Z = \frac{(\bar{X}_1 - \bar{X}_2) - (\mu_1 - \mu_2)}{\sqrt{\frac{\sigma_1^2}{n_1} + \frac{\sigma_2^2}{n_2}}}$$

where:

μ_1 = the mean of population 1
μ_2 = the mean of population 2
n_1 = size of sample 1
n_2 = size of sample 2
σ_1^2 = the variance of population 1
σ_2^2 = the variance of population 2
$\bar{X}_1$ = the mean of sample 1
$\bar{X}_2$ = the mean of sample 2

Z FORMULA FOR THE DIFFERENCE IN TWO SAMPLE MEANS FOR n_1 AND $n_2 \geq 30$ (INDEPENDENT SAMPLES)

This formula makes possible the solution of problems involving two random independent samples and their means.

Note: If two populations are known to be normally distributed on the measurement being studied and if the population variances are known, Formula 10.1 can be used for small sample sizes (n_1 or $n_2 < 30$).

In addition, sample variances can be used in Formula 10.1 in place of population variances when population variances are unknown and sample sizes are large (n_1, $n_2 \geq 30$) because the sample variances are good approximations of the population variances for large sample sizes.

Hypothesis Testing

In many instances, a business analyst wants to test the differences in the mean values of two populations. One example might be to test the difference between the mean values of men and women for achievement, intelligence, or other characteristics. A consumer organization might want to test two brands of light bulbs to determine whether one burns longer than the other. A company wanting to relocate might want to determine whether there is a significant difference in the average price of a home between Newark, New Jersey, and Cleveland, Ohio. Formula 10.1 can be used to test the difference between two population means.

As a specific example, suppose we want to conduct a hypothesis test to determine if the average annual wage for an advertising manager is different from the average annual wage of an auditing manager. Because we are testing to determine if the means are different, it might seem logical that the null and alternative hypotheses would be:

$$H_0: \mu_1 = \mu_2$$
$$H_a: \mu_1 \neq \mu_2$$

where: advertising managers are population 1
auditing managers are population 2

However, statisticians generally construct these hypotheses as:

$$H_0: \mu_1 - \mu_2 = \delta$$
$$H_a: \mu_1 - \mu_2 \neq \delta$$

This allows the business analyst not only to test if the population means are equal, but also affords her the opportunity to hypothesize about a particular difference in the means (δ). Generally speaking, most business analysts are only interested in testing whether or not there is a zero difference in the means. Thus, δ is set equal to zero resulting in the following hypotheses which we will use for this problem (and many others):

$$H_0: \mu_1 - \mu_2 = 0$$
$$H_a: \mu_1 - \mu_2 \neq 0$$

A random sample of 32 advertising managers from across the United States is taken. The advertising managers are contacted by telephone and asked what is their annual salary. A similar random sample is taken of 34 auditing managers. The resulting salary data are listed in Table 10.1, along with the sample means, the sample standard deviations, and the sample variances.

In this problem, the business analyst is testing to determine whether there is a difference in the average wage of an advertising manager and an auditing manager; and therefore, the test is two-tailed. If the business analyst had hypothesized that one type of manager was paid more than the other (or less than the other), the test would have been one-tailed.

Suppose $\alpha = .05$. Because this is a two-tailed test, each of the two rejection regions has an area of .025, leaving .475 of the area in the distribution between each critical value and the mean of the distribution. The associated critical table $Z_{\alpha/2}$ value for this area is $Z_{.025} = \pm 1.96$. Figure 10.1 shows the critical table Z value along with the rejection regions.

Note that the population variances are not available in this problem. So long as the sample size is large, S^2 is a good approximation of σ^2. Hence, the following formula is equivalent to Formula 10.1 for large samples.

Z FORMULA TO TEST THE DIFFERENCE IN POPULATION MEANS WITH σ_1^2, σ_2^2 UNKNOWN AND n_1, n_2 LARGE; INDEPENDENT SAMPLES

$$Z = \frac{(\bar{X}_1 - \bar{X}_2) - (\mu_1 - \mu_2)}{\sqrt{\frac{S_1^2}{n_1} + \frac{S_2^2}{n_2}}} \quad (10.2)$$

Formula 10.2 and the data in Table 10.1 yield a Z value to complete the hypothesis test.

$$Z = \frac{(70.700 - 62.187) - (0)}{\sqrt{\frac{264.164}{32} + \frac{166.411}{34}}} = 2.35$$

The observed value of 2.35 is greater than the critical value obtained from the Z table, 1.96. The business analyst rejects the null hypothesis and can say that there is a significant difference between the average annual wage of an advertising manager and the average an-

TABLE 10.1
Wages for Advertising Managers and Auditing Managers ($1,000)

ADVERTISING MANAGER	AUDITING MANAGER
74.256	69.962
96.234	55.052
89.807	57.828
93.261	63.362
103.030	37.194
74.195	99.198
75.932	61.254
80.742	73.065
39.672	48.036
45.652	60.053
93.083	66.359
63.384	61.261
57.791	77.136
65.145	66.035
96.767	54.335
77.242	42.494
67.056	83.849
64.276	67.160
74.194	37.386
65.360	59.505
73.904	72.790
54.270	71.351
59.045	58.653
68.508	63.508
71.115	43.649
67.574	63.369
59.621	59.676
62.483	54.449
69.319	46.394
35.394	71.804
86.741	72.401
57.351	56.470
	67.814
	71.492
$n_1 = 32$	$n_2 = 34$
$\overline{X}_1 = 70.700$	$\overline{X}_2 = 62.187$
$S_1 = 16.253$	$S_2 = 12.900$
$S_1^2 = 264.164$	$S_2^2 = 166.411$

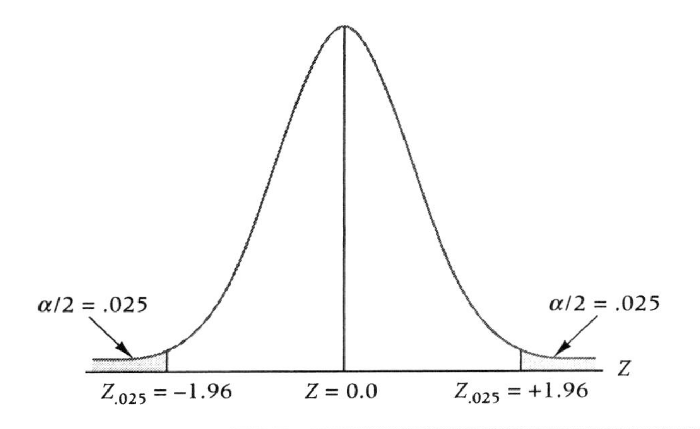

Figure 10.1

Critical values and rejection regions for the wage example

Figure 10.2

Location of calculated Z value for the wage example

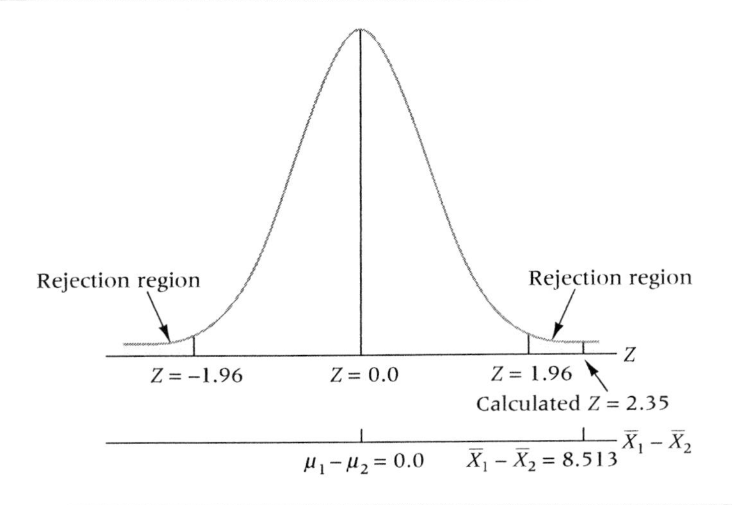

nual wage of an auditing manager. The business analyst then examines the sample means (70.700 for advertising managers and 62.187 for auditing managers) and uses common sense to conclude that advertising managers earn more, on the average, than do auditing managers. Figure 10.2 shows the relationship between the observed Z (2.35) and the critical Z (1.96).

This conclusion could have been reached by using the p-value method. Looking up the probability of $Z \geq 2.35$ in the Z distribution table in Appendix A.5 yields an area of $.5000 - .4906 = .0094$. This value is less than $\alpha/2 = .025$. The decision is to reject the null hypothesis.

Analysis Using Excel

Excel has the capability of testing hypotheses between two means from large samples using the Z test if the population variances are known. In most cases, business analysts do not know the values of the population variances. However, as pointed out earlier, for large sample sizes the sample variances are close enough approximations of the population variances to suffice. Thus, we can use the Excel ***z*-Test: Two Sample for Means** data analysis tool by first computing the sample variances and substituting these for the unknown population variances*. After obtaining the sample variances, the Z test for two sample means can be accomplished by selecting **Tools** from the menu bar and **Data Analysis** from the subsequent drop-down menu. ***z*-Test: Two Sample for Means** is one of the options in the **Data Analysis** scrolling list box. The subsequent dialog box for ***z*-Test: Two Sample for Means** is shown in Figure 10.3. Note that the dialog box requires the locations of the data for each of the two variables, the hypothesized difference of the means (in most cases this is zero), the variances of each variable, and the value of alpha, the significance level of the test.

Observe that the Excel dialog box displayed in Figure 10.3 contains the locations of the two columns of data for the advertising manager and auditing manager problem, the hypothesized mean difference (zero), each of the values of the sample variances, and the value of alpha.

The Excel output for this problem is shown in Figure 10.4. The results include the means, variances, and sample sizes of the two samples along with the hypothesized difference.

---

*Sample variances can be computed in Excel using the **Descriptive Statistics** function of the Data Analysis tool or by using selecting the **VAR** function from the **Statistics** category of the Paste Function

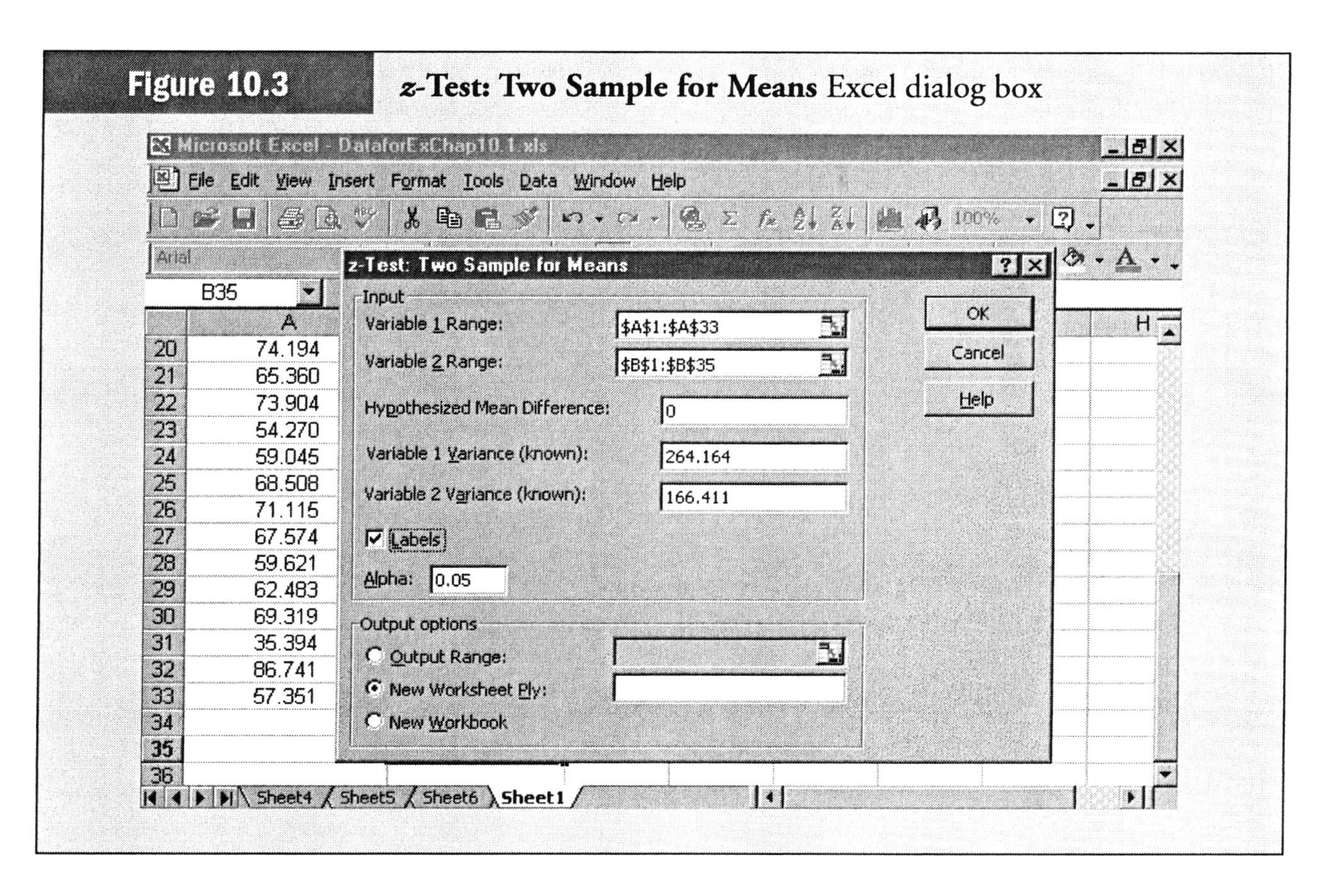

Figure 10.3 *z*-**Test: Two Sample for Means** Excel dialog box

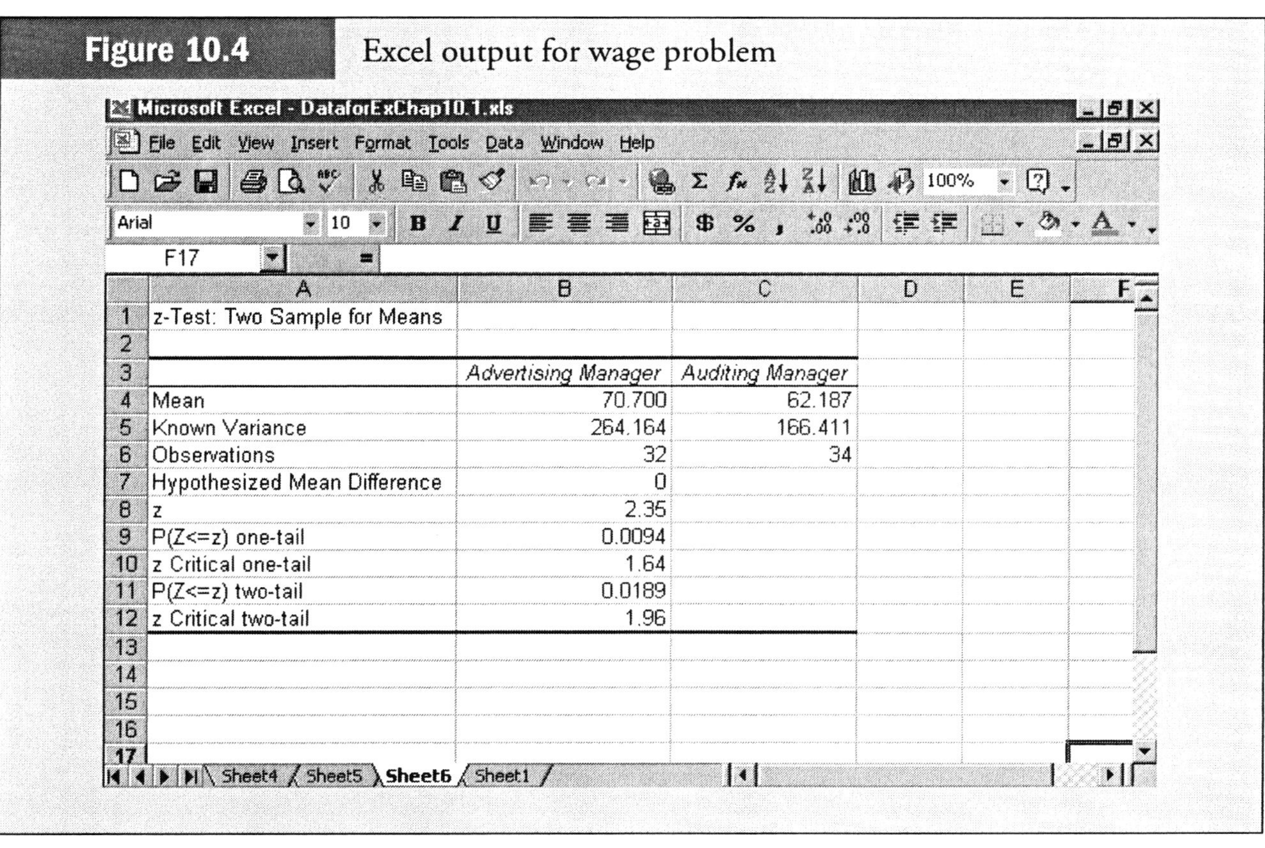

	A	B	C
1	z-Test: Two Sample for Means		
2			
3		*Advertising Manager*	*Auditing Manager*
4	Mean	70.700	62.187
5	Known Variance	264.164	166.411
6	Observations	32	34
7	Hypothesized Mean Difference	0	
8	z	2.35	
9	P(Z<=z) one-tail	0.0094	
10	z Critical one-tail	1.64	
11	P(Z<=z) two-tail	0.0189	
12	z Critical two-tail	1.96	

Figure 10.4 Excel output for wage problem

In addition, the output includes the observed Z value, $Z = 2.35$, and its associated p-value of .0189 for a two-tail test indicating statistical significance at $\alpha = .05$. The p-value for a one-tail test, .0094, is also given and can be used in the wage problem to compare against $\alpha/2$ (one-tail) = .025. The Excel output also includes critical table values for business analysts who prefer using the table rather than using p-values. The critical table Z value is 1.96. Since the observed Z value of 2.35 is greater than the critical table Z value of 1.96, the decision is to reject the null hypothesis, which is consistent with the conclusion reached using p-values.

DEMONSTRATION PROBLEM 10.1

A sample of 87 professional working women showed that the average amount paid annually into a private pension fund per person was $3343, with a sample standard deviation of $1226. A sample of 76 professional working men showed that the average amount paid annually into a private pension fund per person was $5568, with a sample standard deviation of $1716. A women's activist group wants to "prove" that women do not pay as much per year as men into private pension funds. If they use $\alpha = .001$ and these sample data, will they be able to reject a null hypothesis that women annually pay the same as or more than men into private pension funds? Use the eight-step hypothesis-testing process.

SOLUTION

STEP **1.** This test is one-tailed. Because the women's activist group wants to prove that women pay less than men into private pension funds annually, the alternative hypothesis should be $\mu_w - \mu_m < 0$, and the null hypothesis is that women pay the same as or more than men, $\mu_w - \mu_m = 0$.

STEP **2.** The test statistic is

$$Z = \frac{(\bar{X}_1 - \bar{X}_2) - (\mu_1 - \mu_2)}{\sqrt{\frac{S_1^2}{n_1} + \frac{S_2^2}{n_2}}}.$$

STEP **3.** Alpha has been specified as .001.

STEP **4.** By using this value of alpha, a critical $Z_{.001} = -3.08$ can be determined. The decision rule is to reject the null hypothesis if the observed calculated value of the test statistic, Z, is less than −3.08.

STEP **5.** The sample data follow.

WOMEN	MEN
$\bar{X}_1 = 3343$	$\bar{X}_2 = 5568$
$S_1 = 1226$	$S_2 = 1716$
$n_1 = 87$	$n_2 = 76$

STEP **6.** Solving for Z gives

$$\frac{(3343 - 5568) - (0)}{\sqrt{\frac{1226^2}{87} + \frac{1716^2}{76}}} = -9.40.$$

STEP **7.** The observed calculated Z value of -9.40 is deep in the rejection region, well past the table value of $Z_c = -3.08$. Even with the small $\alpha = .001$, the null hypothesis is rejected.

STEP **8.** The evidence is substantial that women, on average, pay less than men into private pension funds annually. The following diagram displays these results.

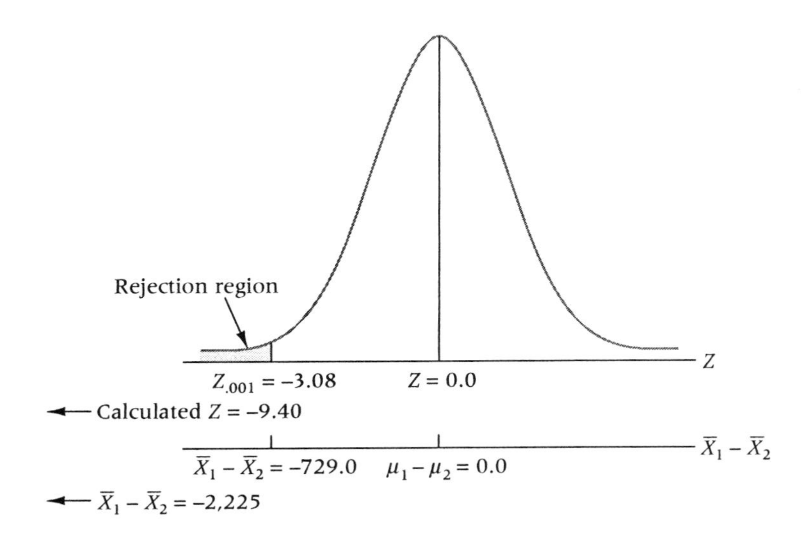

The probability of obtaining a calculated Z value of -9.40 by chance is virtually zero, because the value is beyond the limits of the Z table. By the p-value method, the null hypothesis is rejected because the probability is .0000, or less than $\alpha = .001$.

If this problem were worked by the critical value method, what critical value of the difference in the two means would have to be surpassed to reject the null hypothesis for a table Z value of -3.08? The answer is

$$(\bar{X}_1 - \bar{X}_2)_c = (\mu_1 - \mu_2) - Z\sqrt{\frac{S_1^2}{n_1} + \frac{S_2^2}{n_2}}$$

$$= 0 - 3.08(236.7) = -729.0.$$

The difference in sample means would need to be at least 729.0 to reject the null hypothesis. The actual sample difference in this problem was -2225, which is considerably larger than the critical value of difference. Thus, with the critical value method also, the null hypothesis is rejected.

Shown on the next page is the Excel output for Demonstration Problem 10.1. Note that the observed $Z = -9.40$ has an associated p-value of 0 confirming the conclusion reached above to reject the null hypothesis. The one-tail critical table Z value is reported by Excel to be -3.09. Since the observed $Z = -9.40$ is less than the critical table Z value of -3.09, the decision is to reject the null hypothesis.

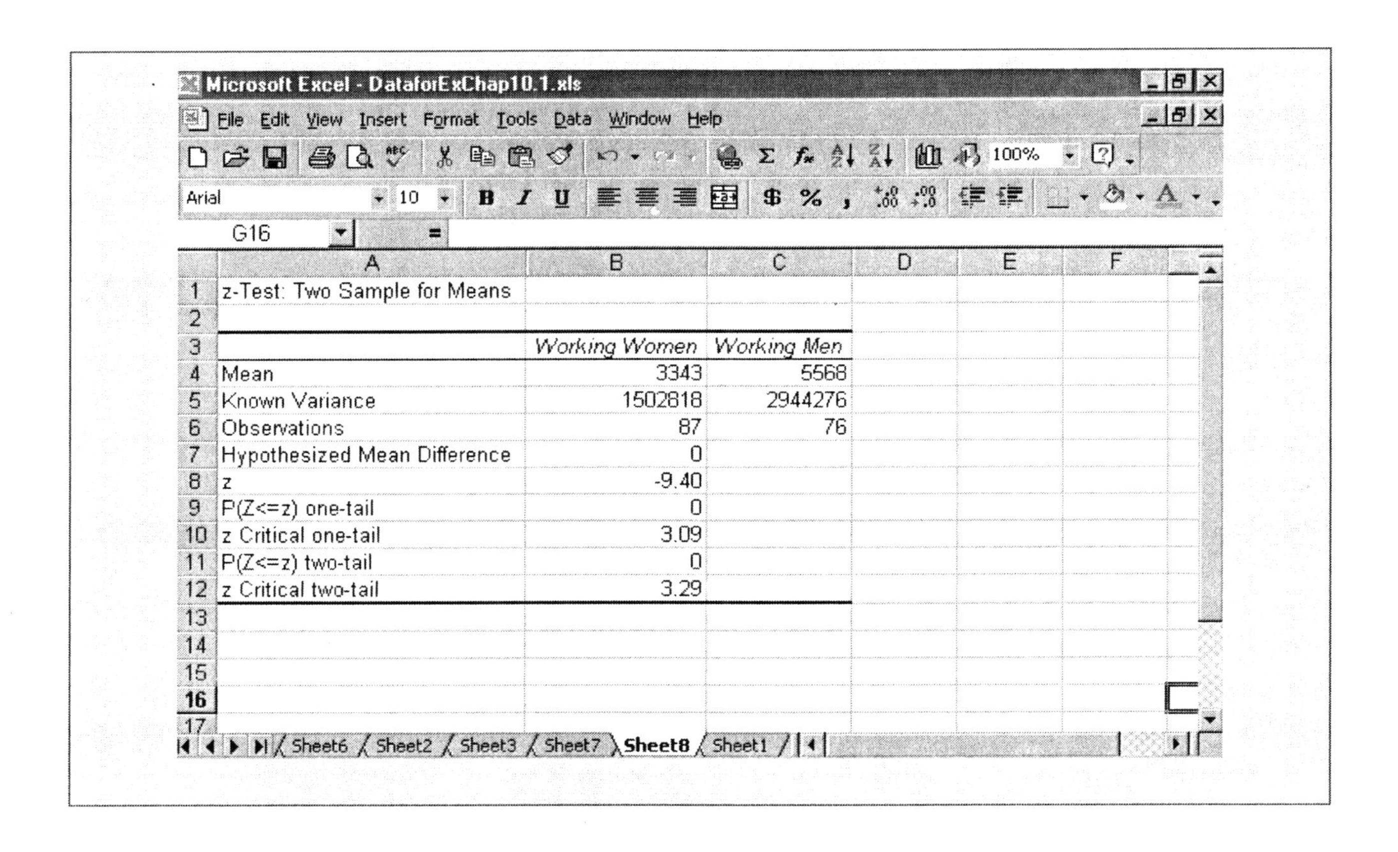

Microsoft Excel - DataforExChap10.1.xls

	A	B	C
1	z-Test: Two Sample for Means		
2			
3		*Working Women*	*Working Men*
4	Mean	3343	5568
5	Known Variance	1502818	2944276
6	Observations	87	76
7	Hypothesized Mean Difference	0	
8	z	-9.40	
9	P(Z<=z) one-tail	0	
10	z Critical one-tail	3.09	
11	P(Z<=z) two-tail	0	
12	z Critical two-tail	3.29	

10.1

Problems

10.1 Consider the data given below.

SAMPLE 1					SAMPLE 2				
58	50	47	43	53	47	47	63	55	52
60	46	60	55	52	50	45	48	52	53
60	46	59	49	57	47	48	58	61	57
67	50	49	55	59	47	59	62	54	63
46	46	42	61	53	52	62	45	49	57
48	54	52	46	50	55	50	49	57	55
65					61	57			

a. Test the following hypotheses of the difference in population means on these data with $\alpha = .10$

$$H_0: \mu_1 - \mu_2 = 0 \quad H_a: \mu_1 - \mu_2 < 0$$

b. Use the critical value method to find the critical difference in the mean values required to reject the null hypothesis.

c. What is the p-value for this problem?

10.2 Examine the following data. Use the data to test the following hypotheses ($\alpha = .02$).

$$H_0: \mu_1 - \mu_2 = 0 \quad H_a: \mu_1 - \mu_2 \neq 0$$

SAMPLE 1			SAMPLE 2		
90	88	80	78	85	82
88	87	91	90	80	76
81	84	84	77	75	79
88	90	91	82	83	88
89	95	97	80	90	74
88	83	94	81	75	76
81	83	88	83	88	77
87	87	93	86	90	75
88	84	83	80	80	74
95	93	97	89	84	79

10.3 The Trade Show Bureau conducted a survey to determine why people go to trade shows. The respondents were asked to rate a series of reasons on a scale from 1 to 5, with 1 representing little importance and 5 representing great importance. Shown below are the responses for 50 people from the computers/electronics industry and 50 people from the food/beverage industry. Use these data and $\alpha = .01$ to determine whether there is a significant difference between people in these two industries on this question.

COMPUTERS/ELECTRONICS										FOOD/BEVERAGE									
1	2	1	3	2	0	3	3	2	1	3	3	2	4	3	4	5	2	4	3
3	3	1	2	2	3	2	2	2	2	3	2	3	2	3	4	3	3	3	3
1	2	3	2	1	1	1	3	3	2	2	4	2	3	3	2	4	4	4	4
2	1	4	1	4	2	3	0	1	0	3	5	3	3	2	2	0	2	2	5
3	3	2	2	3	2	1	0	2	3	4	3	3	2	3	4	3	3	3	2

10.4 A company's auditor believes the per diem cost in Nashville, Tennessee, rose significantly between 1995 and 2001. To test this belief, the auditor samples 33 business trips from the company's records for 1995 and 36 business trips for 2001. The data are shown below. Test to determine if the average per diem cost rose significantly from 1995 to 2001. Let the risk of committing a Type I error be .01.

1995						2001					
176	164	206	183	184	193	188	181	194	198	189	205
217	182	180	177	181	196	207	189	213	208	167	208
194	209	192	206	177	156	213	209	182	200	212	197
199	169	186	203	202	189	158	217	188	191	191	182
185	214	185	172	207	193	204	190	194	224	186	202
220	168	189				159	189	192	178	201	196

10.5 Suppose a market analyst wants to determine the difference in the average price of a gallon of whole milk in Seattle and Atlanta. To do so, he takes a telephone survey of 31 randomly selected consumers in Seattle. He first asks whether they have purchased a gallon of milk during the past 2 weeks. If they say no, he continues to select consumers until he selects $n = 31$ people who say yes. If they say yes, he asks them how much they paid for the milk. The analyst undertakes a similar survey in Atlanta with 31 respondents. Using the resulting sample information that follows, use $\alpha = .05$ to test to determine if there is a significant difference in the mean price of a gallon of milk between the two cities.

SEATTLE			ATLANTA		
\$2.55	\$2.36	\$2.43	\$2.25	\$2.40	\$2.39
2.67	2.54	2.43	2.30	2.33	2.40
2.50	2.54	2.38	2.19	2.29	2.23
2.61	2.80	2.49	2.41	2.18	2.29
3.10	2.61	2.57	2.39	2.59	2.53
2.86	2.56	2.71	2.26	2.38	2.19
2.50	2.64	2.97	2.19	2.25	2.45
2.47	2.72	2.65	2.42	2.61	2.33
2.76	2.73	2.80	2.60	2.25	2.51
2.65	2.83	2.69	2.38	2.29	2.36
		2.71			2.44

10.6 Employee suggestions can provide useful and insightful ideas for management. Some companies solicit and receive employee suggestions more than others; and company culture influences the use of employee suggestions. Suppose a study is conducted to determine whether there is a significantly higher mean number of suggestions annually per employee at the Johnson Corporation than at the Davison Corporation. Random samples of employees are selected from each Corporation and the resulting data are given below. Use these data and $\alpha = .10$ to test the hypothesis.

JOHNSON										DAVISON									
6	6	7	6	9	4	8	4	6	6	7	5	4	6	4	6	6	7	5	6
8	8	7	7	5	7	4	5	5	3	6	6	7	6	3	4	5	6	3	5
6	5	5	3	5	5	5	9	6	4	4	5	4	5	4	7	5	3	5	4
3	2	8	4	6	9					4	3	8	4	5	5	5	6	4	6
										6	8	4	3	4					

10.2 Hypothesis Testing about the Difference in Two Population Means: Small Independent Samples

The techniques presented in Section 10.1 are for use whenever sample sizes are large or the population variances are known. There are many occasions when business analysts wish to test hypotheses about the difference in two population means and the population variances are not known. If the sample sizes are small, the Z methodology is not appropriate. This section presents methodology for handling the small-sample situation when the population variances are unknown.

Hypothesis Testing

The hypothesis test presented in this section is a test that compares the means of two samples to determine whether there is a difference in the two population means from which the samples come. An assumption underlying this technique is that the measurement or characteristic being studied is normally distributed for both populations. This technique is used whenever sample size is small (n_1, $n_2 < 30$), the population variances are unknown (and hence the sample variances must be used), and the samples are independent (not related an any way). In Section 10.1, the difference in large sample means was analyzed by Formula 10.1:

$$Z = \frac{(\overline{X}_1 - \overline{X}_2) - (\mu_1 - \mu_2)}{\sqrt{\dfrac{\sigma_1^2}{n_1} + \dfrac{\sigma_2^2}{n_2}}}.$$

If $\sigma_1^2 = \sigma_2^2$, Formula 10.1 algebraically reduces to

$$Z = \frac{(\overline{X}_1 - \overline{X}_2) - (\mu_1 - \mu_2)}{\sigma\sqrt{\frac{1}{n_1} + \frac{1}{n_2}}}.$$

If σ is unknown, it can be estimated by *pooling* the two sample variances and computing a pooled sample standard deviation.

$$\sigma \approx S = \sqrt{\frac{S_1^2(n_1 - 1) + S_2^2(n_2 - 1)}{n_1 + n_2 - 2}}$$

Substituting this expression for σ and changing Z to t produces a formula to test the difference in means.

(10.3)

$$t = \frac{(\overline{X}_1 - \overline{X}_2) - (\mu_1 - \mu_2)}{\sqrt{\frac{S_1^2(n_1 - 1) + S_2^2(n_2 - 1)}{n_1 + n_2 - 2}}\sqrt{\frac{1}{n_1} + \frac{1}{n_2}}}$$

$$\text{df} = n_1 + n_2 - 2$$

t FORMULA TO TEST THE DIFFERENCE IN MEANS ASSUMING $\sigma_1^2 = \sigma_2^2$

Formula 10.3 is constructed by assuming that the two population variances, σ_1^2 and σ_2^2, are equal. Thus, when using Formula 10.3 to test hypotheses about the difference in two means for small independent samples when the population variances are unknown, we must assume that the two samples come from populations in which the variances are essentially equal. If that is not possible, the following formula should be used.

(10.4)

$$t = \frac{\overline{X}_1 - \overline{X}_2}{\sqrt{\frac{S_1^2}{n_1} + \frac{S_2^2}{n_2}}}$$

$$\text{df} = \frac{\left[\frac{S_1^2}{n_1} + \frac{S_2^2}{n_2}\right]^2}{\frac{\left(\frac{S_1^2}{n_1}\right)^2}{n_1 - 1} + \frac{\left(\frac{S_2^2}{n_2}\right)^2}{n_2 - 1}}$$

t FORMULA TO TEST THE DIFFERENCE IN MEANS ASSUMING $\sigma_1^2 \neq \sigma_2^2$

In Formula 10.4, the population variances are not assumed to be equal. Since this formula has a more complex degrees-of-freedom component, it may be unattractive to some users. Excel offers the user a choice of the "equal variances" formula or the "unequal variances" formula. The "equal variances" formula in Excel is Formula 10.3, in which equal population variances are assumed. The "unequal variances" formula is Formula 10.4 and is used when population variances cannot be assumed to be equal. Again, in each of these

TABLE 10.2
Test Scores for New Employees After Training

TRAINING METHOD A					TRAINING METHOD B			
56	50	52	44	52	59	54	55	65
47	47	53	45	48	52	57	64	53
42	51	42	43	44	53	56	53	57

formulas, the populations from which the two samples are drawn are assumed to be normally distributed for the phenomenon being measured.

At the Hernandez Manufacturing Company, an application of the test of the difference in small sample means arises. New employees are expected to attend a 3-day seminar to learn about the company. At the end of the seminar, they are tested to measure their knowledge about the company. The traditional training method has been lecture and a question and answer session. Management has decided to experiment with a different training procedure, which processes new employees in 2 days by using videocassettes and having no question and answer session. If this procedure works, it could save the company thousands of dollars over a period of several years. However, there is some concern about the effectiveness of the 2-day method, and company managers would like to know whether there is any difference in the effectiveness of the two training methods.

To test the difference in the two methods, the managers randomly select one group of 15 newly hired employees to take the 3-day seminar (method A) and a second group of 12 new employees for the 2-day videocassette method (method B). Table 10.2 shows the test scores of the two groups. Using $\alpha = .05$, the managers want to determine whether there is a significant difference in the mean scores of the two groups. They assume that the scores for this test are normally distributed and that the population variances are approximately equal.

STEP **1.** The hypotheses for this test follow.

$$H_0: \mu_1 - \mu_2 = 0$$
$$H_a: \mu_1 - \mu_2 \neq 0$$

STEP **2.** The statistical test to be used is Formula 10.3.

STEP **3.** The value of alpha is .05.

STEP **4.** Because the hypotheses are = and ≠, this test is two-tailed. The degrees of freedom are 25 (15 + 12 − 2 = 25) and alpha is .05. The t table requires an alpha value for one tail only, and, as this test is two-tailed, alpha is split from .05 and .025 to obtain the table t value: $t_{.025,25} = \pm 2.060$.

The null hypothesis will be rejected if the observed t value is less than −2.060 or greater than +2.060.

STEP **5.** The sample data are given in Table 10.2. From these data, we can calculate the sample statistics. The sample means and variances follow.

METHOD A	METHOD B
$\bar{X}_1 = 47.73$	$\bar{X}_2 = 56.50$
$S_1^2 = 19.495$	$S_2^2 = 18.273$
$n_1 = 15$	$n_2 = 12$

STEP **6.** The calculated value of t is

$$t = \frac{(47.73 - 56.50) - 0}{\sqrt{\frac{(19.495)(14) + (18.273)(11)}{(15 + 12 - 2)}}\sqrt{\frac{1}{15} + \frac{1}{12}}} = -5.20.$$

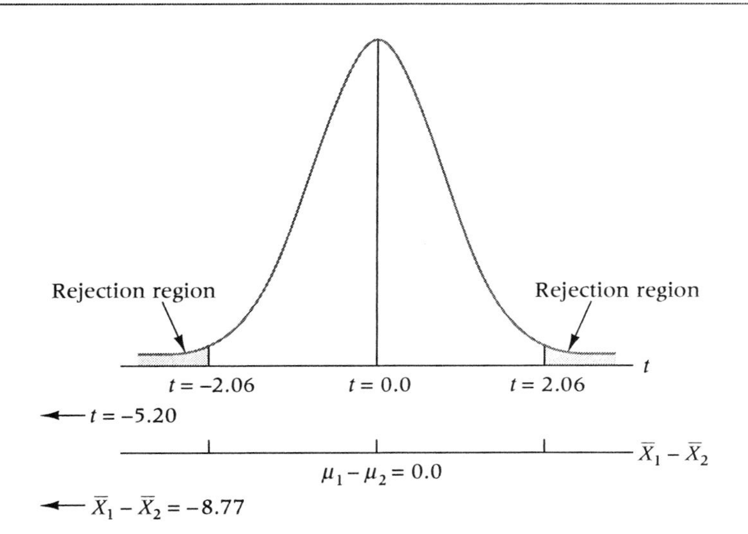

Figure 10.5

t Values for the training methods example

STEP **7.** Because the calculated value, $t = -5.20$, is less than the lower critical table value, $t = -2.06$, the calculated value of t is in the rejection region. The null hypothesis is rejected. There *is* a significant difference in the mean scores of the two tests.

STEP **8.** Figure 10.5 shows the critical areas, the calculated t value, and the decision for this test. Note that the computed t value is -5.20, which is enough to cause the managers of the Hernandez Manufacturing Company to reject the null hypothesis. Their conclusion is that there is a significant difference in the effectiveness of the training methods. Upon examining the sample means, they realize that method B (the 2-day videocassette method) actually produced an average score that was more than eight points higher than that for the group trained with method A.

In a test of this sort, which group is group 1 and which is group 2 is an arbitrary decision. If the two samples had been designated in reverse, the calculated t value would have been $t = +5.20$ (same magnitude but different sign), and the decision would have been the same.

Analysis Using Excel

Excel can test hypotheses about the difference in two means for independent samples using the t test for both the equal and the unequal variance cases using two separate **Data Analysis** tools. The equal variance t test of two means is ***t*-Test: Two-Sample Assuming Equal Variances,** and the dialog box for this test is shown in Figure 10.6. The t test of two means assuming unequal variances is ***t*-Test: Two-Sample Assuming Unequal Variances,** and the dialog box for this test is shown in Figure 10.7. Each of these dialog boxes requires the locations of the data for the two variables being analyzed, along with the hypothesized difference in means (usually zero) and the value of alpha.

The Hernandez Company training method problem can be analyzed using Excel, and the results are displayed in Figure 10.8. Note that the two-sample *t*-test assuming equal variances was used for this analysis. The output includes the mean, variance, and size of each sample, along with the hypothesized mean difference and the degrees of freedom for the test. The observed t value is -5.20, which is the same as that obtained previously using Formula 10.3. Since this problem involves a two-tail test, the critical table values are ± 2.06, even though Excel also lists the critical table value for a one-tail test (1.71). Since

Figure 10.6 Excel dialog box for the **Two-Sample *t*-Test Assuming Equal Variances**

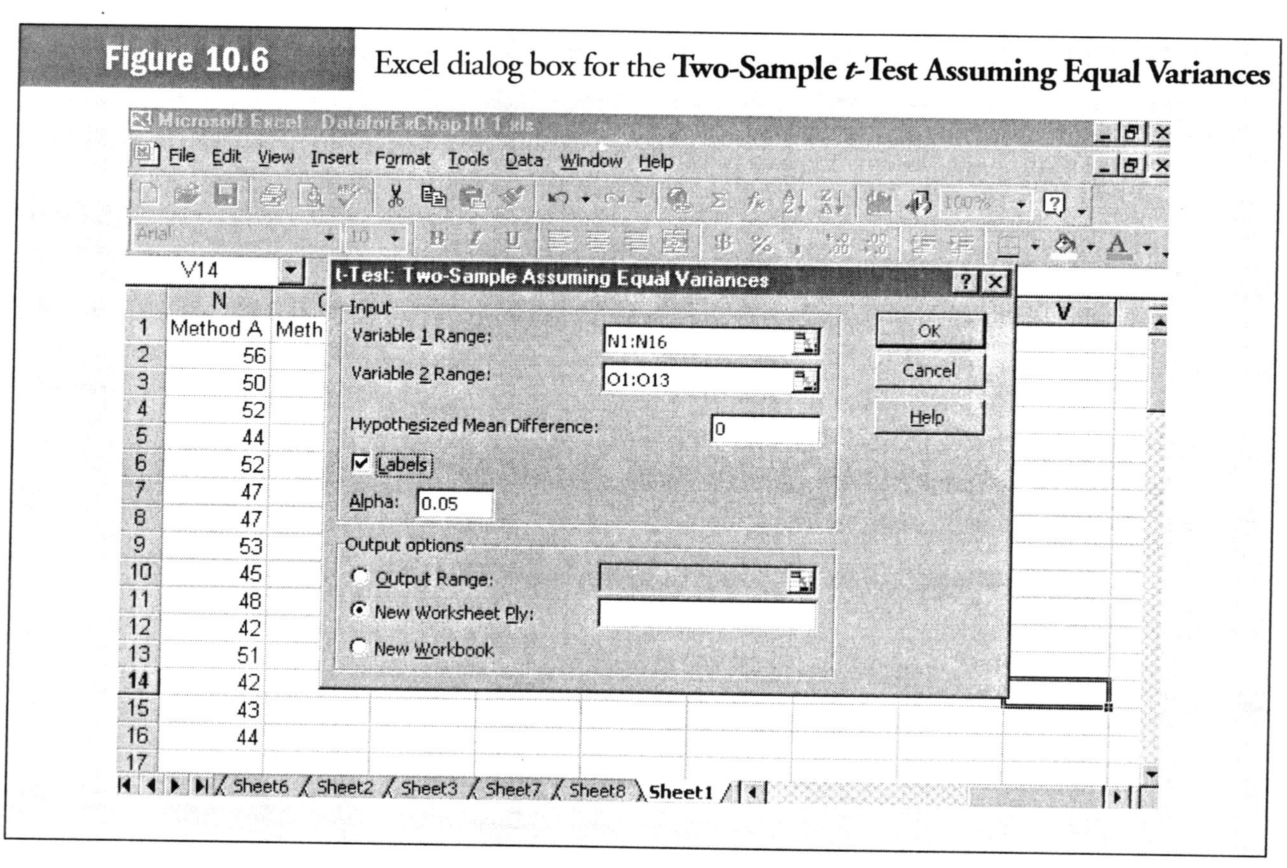

Figure 10.7 Excel dialog box for the **Two-Sample *t*-Test Assuming Unequal Variances**

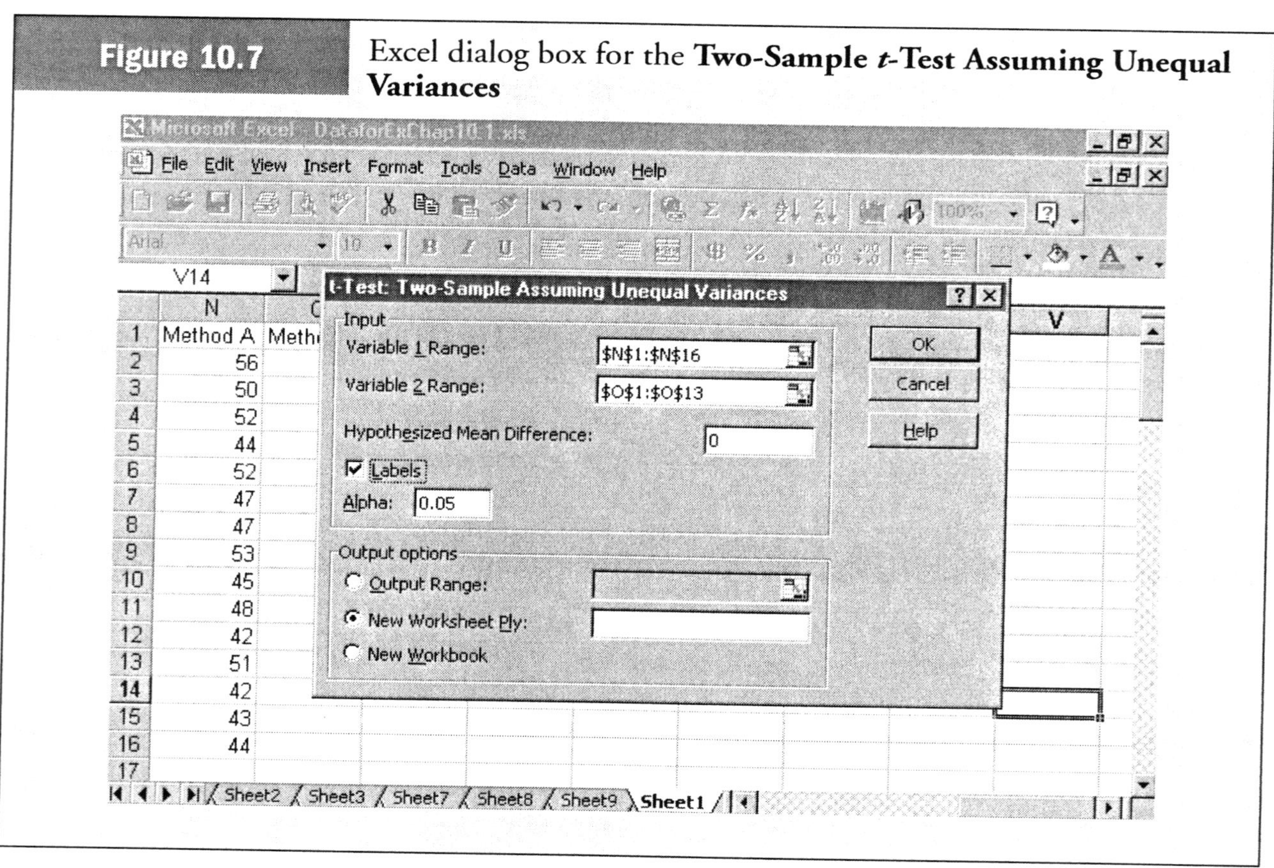

Figure 10.8 Excel output for the Hernandez Company problem

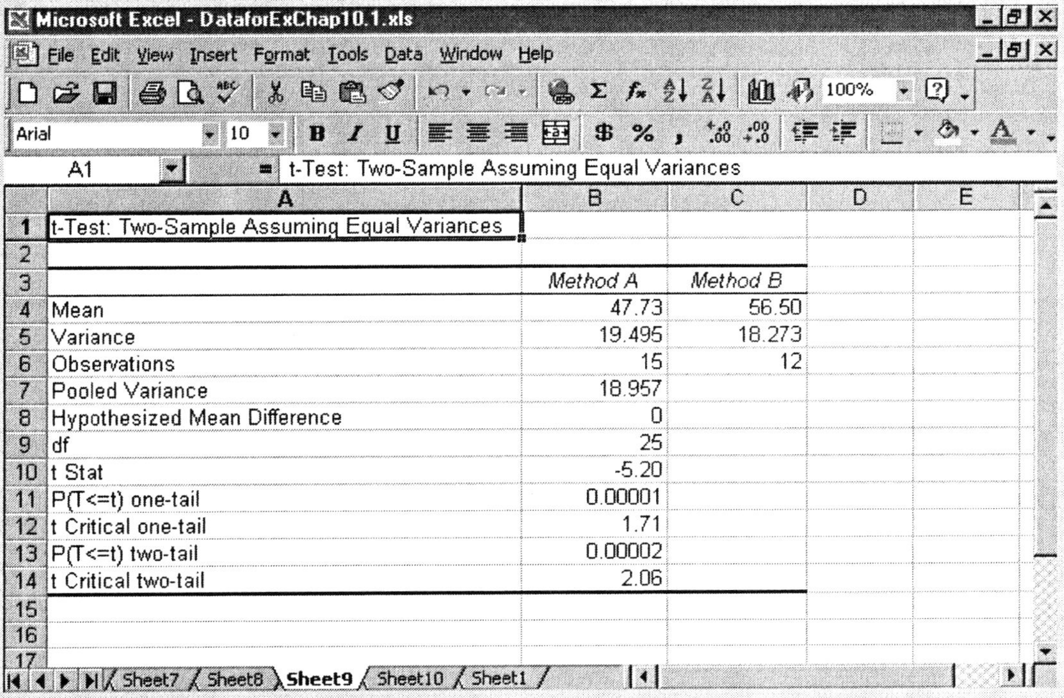

Microsoft Excel - DataforExChap10.1.xls

A1 = t-Test: Two-Sample Assuming Equal Variances

t-Test: Two-Sample Assuming Equal Variances		
	Method A	*Method B*
Mean	47.73	56.50
Variance	19.495	18.273
Observations	15	12
Pooled Variance	18.957	
Hypothesized Mean Difference	0	
df	25	
t Stat	-5.20	
P(T<=t) one-tail	0.00001	
t Critical one-tail	1.71	
P(T<=t) two-tail	0.00002	
t Critical two-tail	2.06	

the observed t value of -5.20 is less than the critical table value of -2.06, the decision is to reject the null hypothesis and conclude that the means for the populations are not equal. In addition, Excel reports the p-value for both a one-tail and a two-tail test. The two-tail p-value is .00002, which is less than $\alpha = .05$ and underscores the decision to reject the null hypothesis. This conclusion is consistent with the results obtained before using Formula 10.3. While not shown here, an analysis of this problem using the t-test for two-samples assuming unequal variances has been done. The only difference in the results is that the unequal variance-based t test yields an observed t value of -5.22 which is .02 different from that obtained using the equal variance-based test. Thus, for this problem, there is a negligible difference in the results.

DEMONSTRATION PROBLEM 10.2

Is there a difference in the way Chinese cultural values affect the purchasing strategies of industrial buyers in Taiwan and mainland China? A study by business analysts at the National Chiao-Tung University in Taiwan attempted to determine whether there is a significant difference in the purchasing strategies of industrial buyers in Taiwan and mainland China on the cultural dimension labeled "integration." Integration is being in harmony with one's self, family, and associates. For the study, 46 Taiwanese buyers and 26 mainland Chinese buyers were contacted and interviewed. Buyers were asked to respond to 35 items using a 9-point scale with possible answers ranging from no importance (1) to extreme importance (9). The resulting statistics for the two groups are shown in step 5. Using $\alpha = .01$, test to determine whether there is a significant difference between buyers of Taiwan and mainland China on integration.

SOLUTION

STEP **1.** If a two-tailed test is undertaken, the hypotheses and the table t value are as follows.

$$H_0: \mu_1 - \mu_2 = 0$$
$$H_a: \mu_1 - \mu_2 \neq 0$$

STEP **2.** The appropriate statistical test is Formula 10.4 since the variances appear to be unequal.

STEP **3.** The value of alpha is .01.

STEP **4.** The sample sizes are 46 and 26. The degrees of freedom computed by Formula 10.4 are 67. With this figure and $\alpha/2 = .005$, critical table t values can be determined.

$$t_{.005,67} = 2.70$$

STEP **5.** The sample data follow.

INTEGRATION

Taiwanese Buyers	*Mainland Chinese Buyers*
$n_1 = 46$	$n_2 = 26$
$X_1 = 5.47$	$X_2 = 5.03$
$S_1^2 = (.6958)^2 = .4842$	$S_2^2 = (.4838)^2 = .2341$

STEP **6.** The calculated t value is

$$t = \frac{(5.47 - 5.03) - (0)}{\sqrt{\frac{(.4842)}{46} + \frac{(.2341)}{26}}} = 3.15.$$

STEP **7.** Because the calculated value of $t = 3.15$ is greater than the critical table value of $t = 2.70$, the decision is to reject the null hypothesis.

STEP **8.** The Taiwan industrial buyers scored significantly higher than the mainland China industrial buyers on integration. Managers should keep in mind in dealing with Taiwanese buyers that they may be more likely to place worth on personal virtue and social hierarchy than do the mainland Chinese buyers.

The following graph shows the critical t values, the rejection regions, the observed t value, and the difference in the raw means.

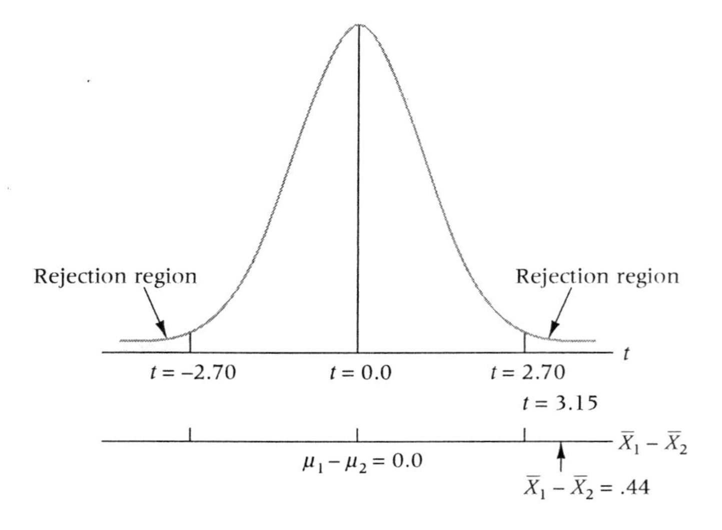

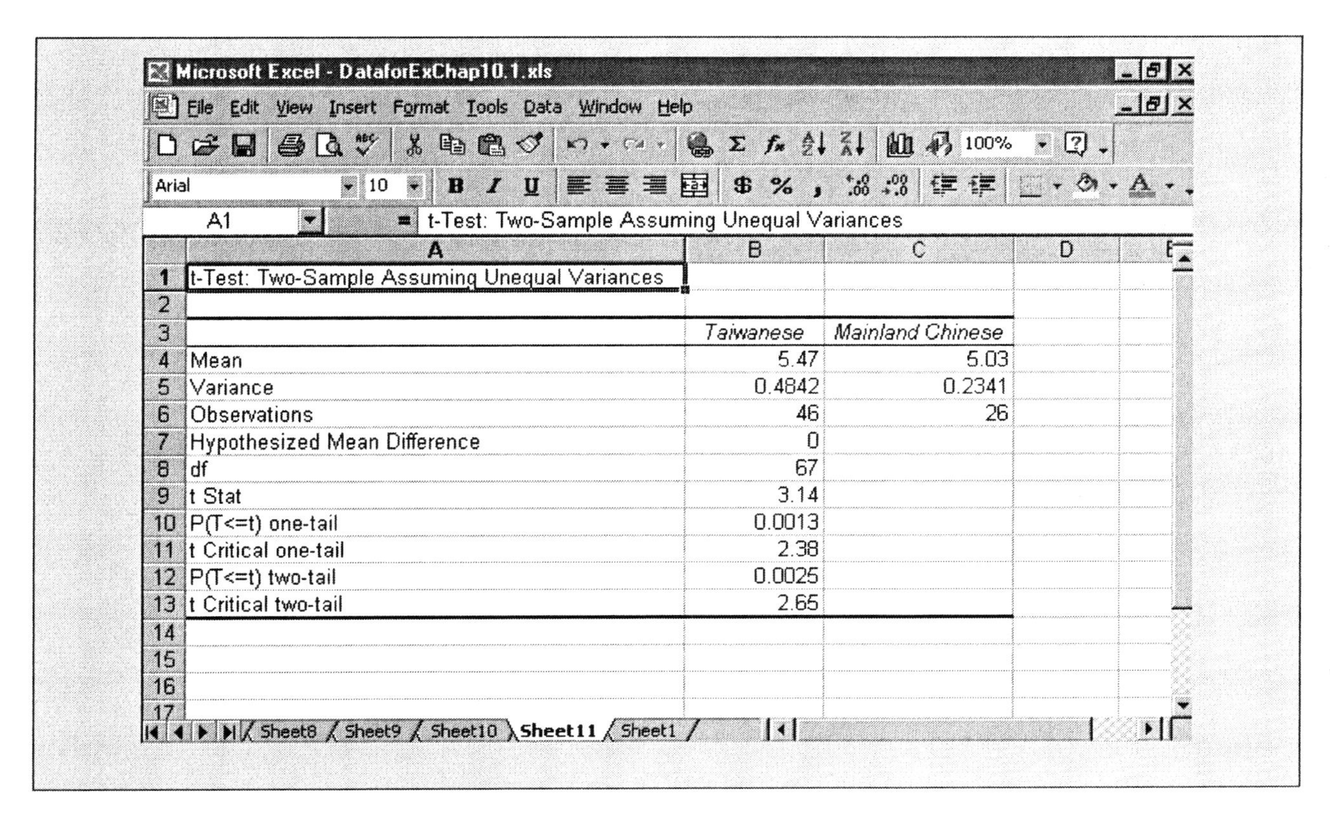

	A	B	C
1	t-Test: Two-Sample Assuming Unequal Variances		
2			
3		*Taiwanese*	*Mainland Chinese*
4	Mean	5.47	5.03
5	Variance	0.4842	0.2341
6	Observations	46	26
7	Hypothesized Mean Difference	0	
8	df	67	
9	t Stat	3.14	
10	P(T<=t) one-tail	0.0013	
11	t Critical one-tail	2.38	
12	P(T<=t) two-tail	0.0025	
13	t Critical two-tail	2.65	

Shown above is the Excel output for Demonstration Problem 10.2 using the ***t*-Test: Two-Sample Assuming Unequal Variances** analysis. Note that the observed t value is 3.14, which is essentially the same as the value obtained above using the formula. The p-value associated with this observed t is .0025, which is less than the value of α, which is .01, indicating that the decision should be to reject the null hypothesis. The Excel-reported critical table t value for a two-tail test with these degrees of freedom is 2.65.

10.2

Problems

10.7 Use the data given below to test the following hypotheses.

$$H_0: \mu_1 - \mu_2 = 0 \qquad H_a: \mu_1 - \mu_2 < 0$$

SAMPLE 1				SAMPLE 2			
24.43	23.79	23.19	28.91	27.76	33.28	26.08	28.17
21.39	20.90	23.87	24.63	30.18	28.19	29.76	21.54
				27.23	18.60	25.86	

10.8 Suppose that for years the mean of population 1 has been accepted to be the same as the mean of population 2, but that now population 1 is believed to have a greater mean than population 2. Letting $\alpha = .05$ and assuming the populations have equal variances and X is approximately normally distributed, use the following data to test this belief.

SAMPLE 1		SAMPLE 2	
43.6	45.7	40.1	36.4
44.0	49.1	42.2	42.3
45.2	45.6	43.1	38.8
40.8	46.5	37.5	43.3
48.3	45.0	41.0	40.2

10.9 Suppose you want to determine whether the average values for populations 1 and 2 are different, and you randomly gather the following data.

SAMPLE 1						SAMPLE 2					
2	10	7	8	2	5	10	12	8	7	9	11
9	1	8	0	2	8	9	8	9	10	11	10
11	2	4	5	3	9	11	10	7	8	10	10

Test your conjecture, using a probability of committing a Type I error of .01. Assume the population variances are the same and X is normally distributed in the populations.

10.10 Suppose a realtor is interested in comparing the asking prices of midrange homes in Peoria, Illinois and Evansville, Indiana. The realtor conducts a small telephone survey in the two cities, asking the prices of midrange homes. The resulting data from a random sample of 21 listings in Peoria and 26 listings in Evansville are shown below. Assuming that the prices of midrange homes are normally distributed, but that the variances of the prices in the two cities are different, test to determine whether there is any difference in the mean prices of midrange homes in the two cities. Let $\alpha = .05$.

PEORIA				EVANSVILLE			
87,743	84,144	85,545	89,022	87,741	85,959	80,911	86,724
85,579	87,251	86,486	84,721	85,742	83,099	88,744	83,797
83,101	84,527	91,343	87,658	84,517	84,392	84,477	83,091
85,550	82,480	87,159	87,706	85,428	84,534	84,769	82,046
84,213	88,841	87,598	85,908	85,403	84,214	79,190	82,311
91,012				83,566	81,600	84,742	82,336
				80,805	83,781		

10.11 There is some indication that mean daily car rental rates may be higher for Boston than for Dallas. Suppose a survey of eight car rental companies in Boston is taken, and the resulting data are those shown below. Further, suppose a survey of nine car rental companies in Dallas is taken, and the data are also shown below. Use a .01 level of significance to test to determine whether the average daily car rental rates in Boston are significantly higher than those in Dallas. Assume that car rental rates are normally distributed and the population variances are approximately equal.

BOSTON				DALLAS			
45.73	44.56	45.50	45.79	42.90	48.27	49.42	39.73
44.97	51.91	49.19	47.30	40.81	47.46	49.10	41.33
				45.47			

10.12 A study was made to compare the costs of supporting a family of four Americans for a year in different foreign cities. The lifestyle of living in the United States on an annual income of $75,000 was the standard against which living in foreign cities was compared. A comparable living standard in Toronto and Mexico City was attained for about $64,000. Suppose an executive wants to determine whether there is any difference in the average annual cost of supporting her family of four in the manner to which they are accustomed between Toronto and Mexico City. She uses the following data, randomly gathered from 11 families in each city, and an alpha of .01 to test this difference. She assumes the annual cost is normally distributed and the population variances are equal. What does the executive find?

TORONTO	MEXICO CITY
$69,000	$65,000
64,500	64,000
67,500	66,000
64,500	64,900
66,700	62,000
68,000	60,500
65,000	62,500
69,000	63,000
71,000	64,500
68,500	63,500
67,500	62,400

10.3 Hypothesis Testing about the Mean Difference in Two Related Populations

In the preceding section, hypotheses were tested about the difference in two population means when the samples are *independent*. In this section, a method is presented to analyze dependent samples or related samples. Some business analysts refer to this test as the **matched-pairs test.** Others call it the *t test for related measures* or the *correlated t test.*

Matched-pairs test
A t test to test the differences in two related or matched samples; sometimes called the t test for related measures or the correlated t test.

What are some types of situations in which the two samples being studied are related or dependent? Let's begin with the before-and-after study. Sometimes as an experimental control mechanism, the same person or object is measured both before and after a treatment. Certainly, the after measurement is *not* independent of the before measurement because the measurements are taken on the same person or object in both cases. Another example of dependent or related samples is when pairs of people such as twins, spouses, siblings, coworkers, or others are used as matched pairs from which the two measurements are taken (one from each member of the pair). Data gathered from research designs such as these from dependent samples are analyzed differently than data gathered from two independent samples. Table 10.3 gives data from a hypothetical study in which people were asked to rate a company before and after 1 week of viewing a 4-minute videocassette of the company twice a day. The before scores are one sample and the after scores are a second sample, but each pair of scores is related because the two measurements apply to the same person. The before scores and the after scores are not likely to vary from each other as much as scores gathered from independent samples because individuals bring their biases about businesses and the company to the study. These individual biases affect both the before scores and the after scores in the same way because each pair of scores is measured on the same person.

Other examples of related measures samples include studies in which twins, siblings, or spouses are matched and placed in two different groups. For example, a fashion merchandiser might be interested in comparing men's and women's perceptions of women's clothing. If the men and women selected for the study are spouses or siblings, a built-in

TABLE 10.3
Rating of a Company (on a Scale from 0 to 50)

INDIVIDUAL	BEFORE	AFTER
1	32	39
2	11	15
3	21	35
4	17	13
5	30	41
6	38	39
7	14	22

relatedness to the measurements of the two groups in the study is likely. Their scores are more apt to be alike or related than those of randomly chosen independent groups of men and women because of similar backgrounds or tastes.

Hypothesis Testing

To ensure the use of the proper hypothesis-testing techniques, the business analyst must determine whether the two samples being studied are dependent or independent. The approach to analyzing two *related* samples is different from the techniques used to analyze independent samples. Use of the techniques in Section 10.2 to analyze related group data can result in a loss of power and an increase in Type II errors.

The matched-pairs test for related samples requires that the two samples be the same size and that the individual related scores be matched. Formula 10.5 is used to test hypotheses about dependent populations.

t FORMULA TO TEST THE DIFFERENCE IN TWO DEPENDENT POPULATIONS

$$t = \frac{\bar{d} - D}{\frac{S_d}{\sqrt{n}}} \qquad (10.5)$$

$$\text{df} = n - 1$$

where:

n = number of pairs
d = sample difference in pairs
D = mean population difference
S_d = standard deviation of sample difference
$\bar{d}$ = mean sample difference

This t test for dependent measures uses the sample difference, d, between individual matched sample values as the basic measurement of analysis instead of individual sample values. Analysis of the d values effectively converts the problem from a two-sample problem to a single sample of differences, which is an adaptation of the single-sample means formula. This test utilizes the sample mean of differences, $\bar{d}$, and the standard deviation of differences, S_d, which can be computed by using Formulas (10.6) and (10.7).

FORMULAS FOR $\bar{d}$ AND S_d

$$\bar{d} = \frac{\Sigma d}{n} \qquad (10.6)$$

$$S_d = \sqrt{\frac{\Sigma(d - \bar{d})^2}{n - 1}} = \sqrt{\frac{\Sigma d^2 - \frac{(\Sigma d)^2}{n}}{n - 1}} \qquad (10.7)$$

An assumption for this test in the analysis of small samples is that the differences of the two populations are normally distributed.

Analyzing data by this method involves calculating a t value with Formula 10.5 and comparing it with a critical t value obtained from the table. The critical t value is obtained from the t distribution table in the usual way, with the exception that, in the degrees of freedom ($n - 1$), n is the number of matched pairs of scores.

TABLE 10.4
P/E Ratios for Nine Randomly Selected Companies

COMPANY	1998 P/E RATIO	1999 P/E RATIO
1	8.9	12.7
2	38.1	45.4
3	43.0	10.0
4	34.0	27.2
5	34.5	22.8
6	15.2	24.1
7	20.3	32.3
8	19.9	40.1
9	61.9	106.5

Suppose a stock market investor is interested in determining if there is a significant different in the P/E (price to earnings) ratio for companies from one year to the next. In an effort to study this, the investor randomly samples nine companies from the *Handbook of Common Stocks* and records the P/E ratios for each of these companies at the end of the 1998 year and at the end of the 1999 year. The data are shown in Table 10.4.

These data are related data because each P/E value for 1999 has a corresponding 1998 measurement on the same company. Since there is no prior indication as to whether or not it is believed that P/E ratios have gone up or down, the hypothesis tested is two-tailed. Assume $\alpha = .01$.

STEP **1.**

$$H_0\text{: } D = 0$$

$$H_a\text{: } D \neq 0$$

STEP **2.** The appropriate statistical test is

$$t = \frac{\bar{d} - D}{\frac{S_d}{\sqrt{n}}}$$

STEP **3.** $\alpha = .01$.

STEP **4.** Because $\alpha = .01$ and this test is two-tailed, $\alpha/2 = .005$ is used to obtain the table t value. With nine pairs of data, $n = 9$, df $= n - 1 = 8$. The table t value is $t_{.005,8} = \pm 3.355$. If the observed test statistic is greater than 3.355 or less than -3.355, the null hypothesis will be rejected.

STEP **5.** The sample data are given in Table 10.4.

STEP **6.** Table 10.5 shows the calculations to obtain the observed value of the test statistic, which is $t = -0.70$.

STEP **7.** Because the observed t value is greater than the critical table t value in the lower tail ($t = -0.70 > t = -3.355$), it is in the non rejection region.

STEP **8.** There is not enough evidence from the data to declare a significant difference in the average P/E ratio between 1998 and 1999. The graph in Figure 10.9 depicts the rejection regions, the critical values of t, and the computed (observed) value of t for this example.

Analysis Using Excel

Excel contains a ***t*-Test: Paired Two Sample for Means** data analysis tool that can be selected and used to test hypotheses about the difference in two related sample means. The

TABLE 10.5
Analysis of P/E Ratio Data

COMPANY	1998 P/E	1999 P/E	d
1	8.9	12.7	–3.8
2	38.1	45.4	–7.3
3	43.0	10.0	33.0
4	34.0	27.2	6.8
5	34.5	22.8	11.7
6	15.2	24.1	–8.9
7	20.3	32.3	–12.0
8	19.9	40.1	–20.2
9	61.9	106.5	–44.6

$\bar{d} = -5.033, \quad S_d = 21.599, \quad n = 9$

$$\text{Calculated (observed) } t = \frac{-5.033 - 0}{\frac{21.599}{\sqrt{9}}} = -0.70$$

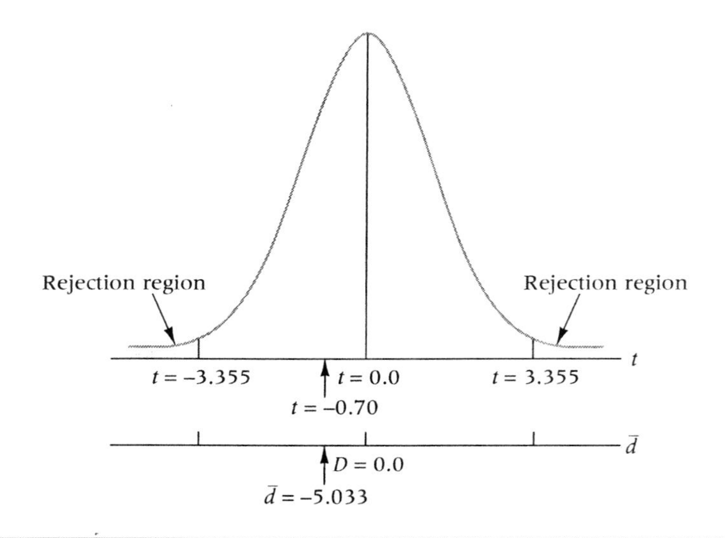

Figure 10.9

Graphical depiction of P/E ratio analysis

dialog box for this test, shown in Figure 10.10, requests the location of data for the first group (variable one), the location of data for the second group (variable two), the hypothesized mean difference (usually zero), and the value of alpha.

The P/E ratio data are analyzed using Excel, and the resulting output is shown in Figure 10.11. The output includes the mean, the variance, and the number of observations in each sample. In addition, the hypothesized mean difference is given along with the degrees of freedom, the observed t value, the p-value, and the critical table t values. The observed t value shown here is the same as the value computed earlier ($t = -0.70$). Since this is a two-tailed test, we use the critical table t values of ± 3.355 shown in Figure 10.11. A comparison of the observed value to the critical table value reveals that the observed value ($t = -0.70$) is in the non-rejection region, and the decision is to fail to reject the null hypothesis. In addition, the two-tailed p-value of this observed t statistic (p-value $= .5043$) is greater than $\alpha = .01$ underscoring the decision to fail to reject the null hypothesis. There appears to be no evidence of significant change in P/E ratios from 1998 to 1999.

Figure 10.10 Excel dialog box for the **Paired Two Sample *t*-Test for Means**

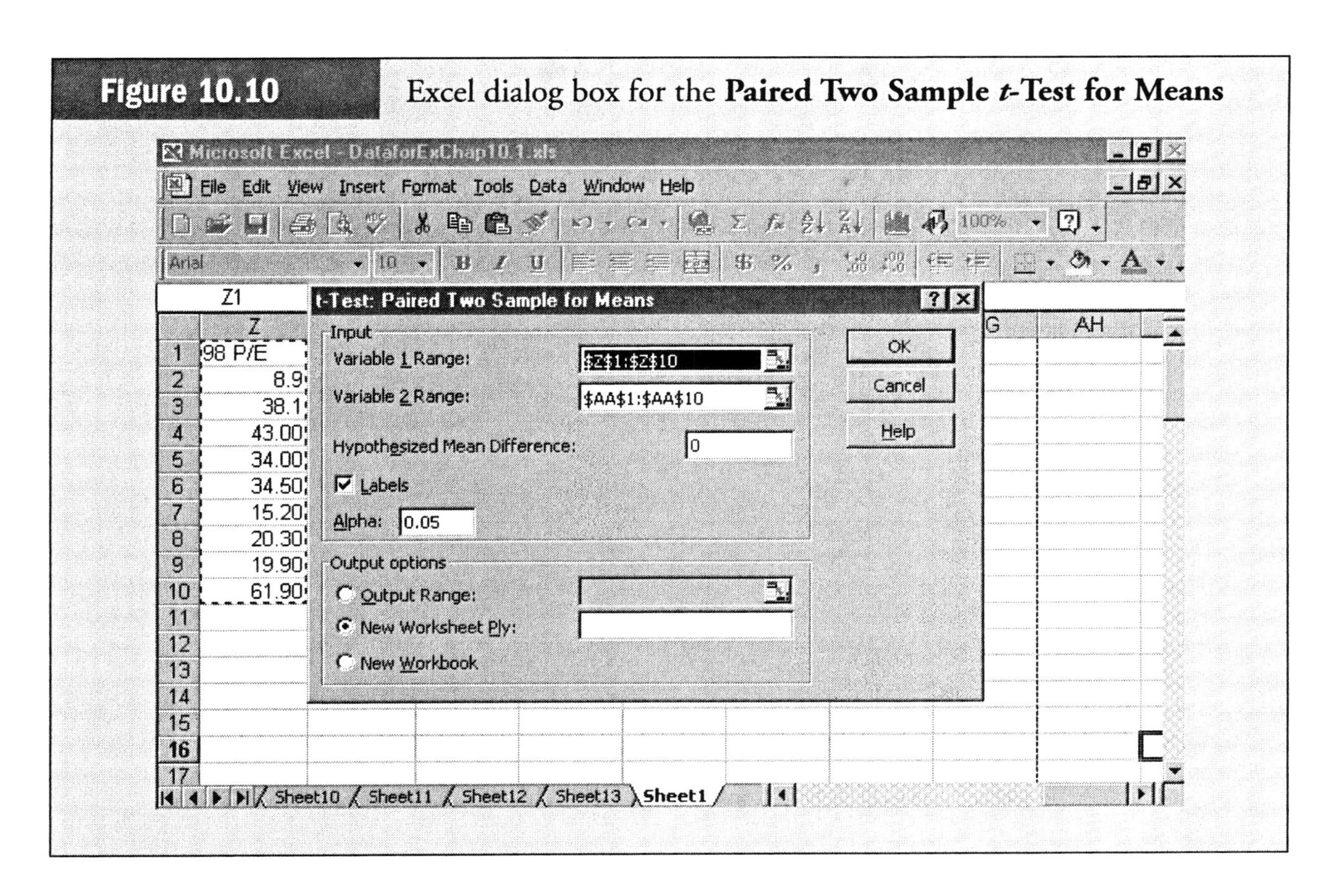

Figure 10.11 Excel output for the P/E ratio problem

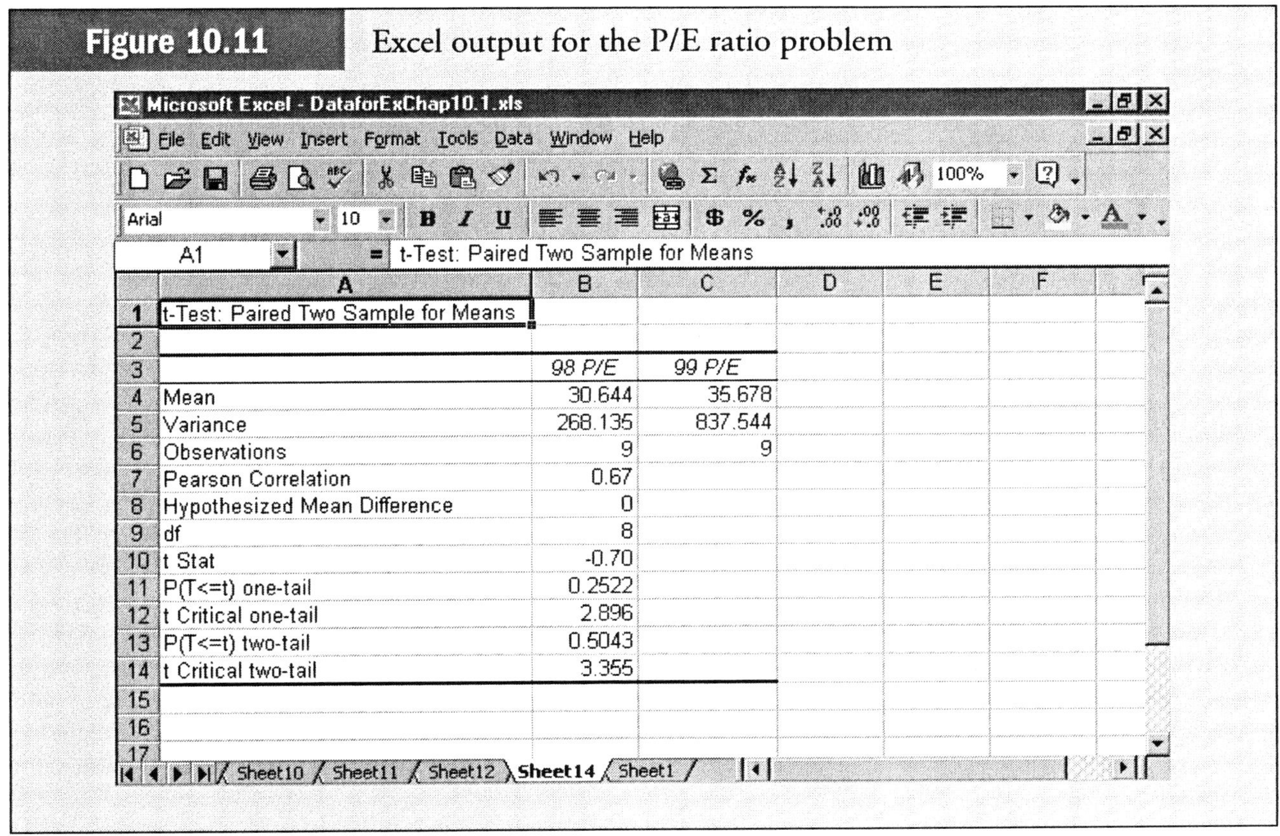

t-Test: Paired Two Sample for Means

	98 P/E	99 P/E
Mean	30.644	35.678
Variance	268.135	837.544
Observations	9	9
Pearson Correlation	0.67	
Hypothesized Mean Difference	0	
df	8	
t Stat	-0.70	
P(T<=t) one-tail	0.2522	
t Critical one-tail	2.896	
P(T<=t) two-tail	0.5043	
t Critical two-tail	3.355	

DEMONSTRATION PROBLEM 10.3

Let us revisit the hypothetical study discussed earlier in the section in which consumers are asked to rate a company both before and after of viewing a video on the company twice a day for a week. The data from Table 10.4 are displayed again here. Use an alpha of .05 to test to determine if there is a significant increase in the ratings of the company after the one-week video treatment.

INDIVIDUAL	BEFORE	AFTER
1	32	39
2	11	15
3	21	35
4	17	13
5	30	41
6	38	39
7	14	22

SOLUTION

Because the same individuals are being used in a before-and-after study, this is a related measures study. Since the desired effect is to increase ratings, the hypothesis test is one-tailed.

STEP **1.**

$$H_0: D = 0$$

$$H_a: D < 0$$

Because the business analysts want to "prove" that the ratings increase from 1998 to 1999 and since the difference is computed by subtracting 1999 ratings from 1998, the desired alternative hypothesis is $D < 0$.

STEP **2.** The appropriate test statistic is Formula 10.5.

STEP **3.** The Type I error rate is .05.

STEP **4.** The degrees of freedom are $n - 1 = 7 - 1 = 6$. For $\alpha = .05$, the table t value is $t_{.05,6} = -1.943$. The decision rule is to reject the null hypothesis if the observed value is less than -1.943.

STEP **5.** The sample data and some calculations follow.

INDIVIDUAL	BEFORE	AFTER	d
1	32	39	-7
2	11	15	-4
3	21	35	-14
4	17	13	4
5	30	41	-11
6	38	39	-1
7	14	22	-8

$$\bar{d} = -5.857 \qquad S_d = 6.0945$$

STEP **6.** The calculated (observed) t value is:

$$t = \frac{-5.857 - 0}{\frac{6.0945}{\sqrt{7}}} = -2.54$$

STEP **7.** Since the calculated (observed) value of -2.54 is less than the critical, table value of -1.943, the decision is to reject the null hypothesis.

STEP **8.** There is enough evidence to conclude that, on average, the ratings have increased significantly. This might be used by managers to support a decision to continue using the videos or to expand the use of such videos in an effort to increase public support for their company.

The following graph depicts the calculated value, the rejection region, and the critical t value for the problem.

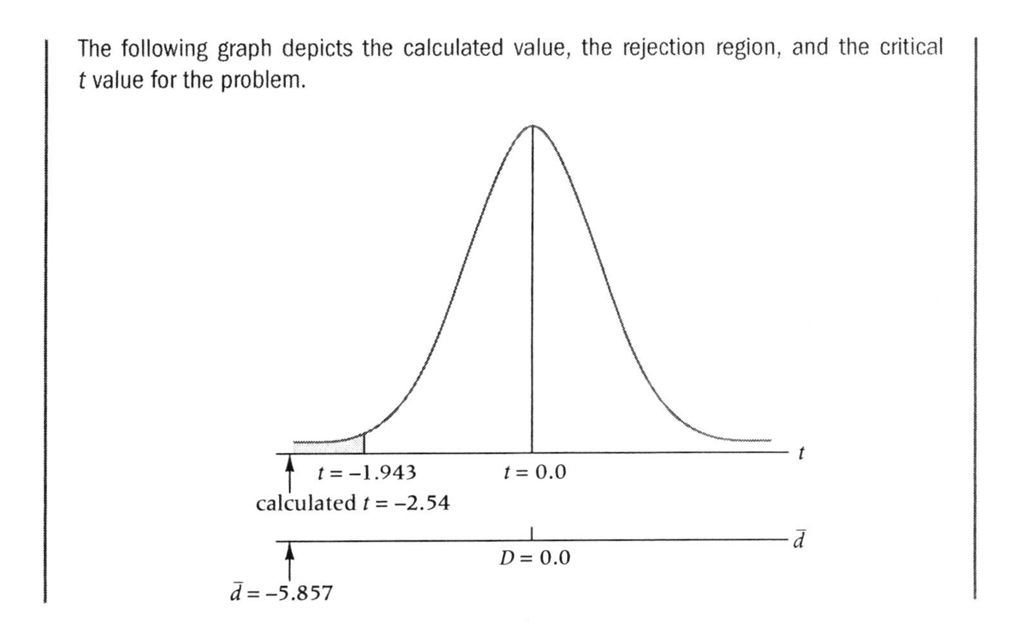

Shown below is Excel output for Demonstration Problem 10.3 using the **t-Test: Paired Two Sample for Means.** The observed value of −2.54 (same as computed above) is less than the one-tailed critical table value of −1.94, leading the business analyst to reject the null hypothesis. The one-tailed p-value of .0220, which is less than .05, also underscores the decision to reject the null hypothesis.

Microsoft Excel - DataforExChap10.1.xls

File Edit View Insert Format Tools Data Window Help

A1 = t-Test: Paired Two Sample for Means

	A	B	C	D	E	F
1	t-Test: Paired Two Sample for Means					
2						
3		*Before*	*After*			
4	Mean	23.286	29.143			
5	Variance	103.238	146.810			
6	Observations	7	7			
7	Pearson Correlation	0.86				
8	Hypothesized Mean Difference	0				
9	df	6				
10	t Stat	-2.54				
11	P(T<=t) one-tail	0.0220				
12	t Critical one-tail	1.94				
13	P(T<=t) two-tail	0.0439				
14	t Critical two-tail	2.45				
15						
16						
17						

Sheet11 Sheet12 Sheet14 Sheet15 Sheet1

10.3
Problems

10.13 Use the data given and a 1% level of significance to test the following hypotheses. Assume the differences are normally distributed in the population.

$$H_0: D = 0 \qquad H_a: D > 0$$

PAIR	SAMPLE 1	SAMPLE 2
1	38	22
2	27	28
3	30	21
4	41	38
5	36	38
6	38	26
7	33	19
8	35	31
9	44	35

10.14 Use the data given to test the following hypotheses ($\alpha = .05$). Assume the differences are normally distributed in the population.

$$H_0: D = 0 \qquad H_a: D \neq 0$$

INDIVIDUAL	BEFORE	AFTER
1	107	102
2	99	98
3	110	100
4	113	108
5	96	89
6	98	101
7	100	99
8	102	102
9	107	105
10	109	110
11	104	102
12	99	96
13	101	100

10.15 Because of uncertainty in real estate markets, many homeowners are considering remodeling and constructing additions rather than selling. Probably the most expensive room in the house to remodel is the kitchen, with an average cost of around $23,400. In terms of resale value, is remodeling the kitchen worth the cost? Below are cost and added resale figures published by *Remodeling* magazine for 11 cities. Use these data and $\alpha = .01$ to test to determine if the added resale value of a kitchen is significantly more than the cost. Assume the differences are normally distributed in the population.

CITY	COST	RESALE
Atlanta	$20,427	$25,163
Boston	27,255	24,625
Des Moines	22,115	12,600
Kansas City, MO	23,256	24,588
Louisville	21,887	19,267
Portland, OR	24,255	20,150
Raleigh-Durham	19,852	22,500
Reno	23,624	16,667
Ridgewood, NJ	25,885	26,875
San Francisco	28,999	35,333
Tulsa	20,836	16,292

10.16 The vice president of marketing brought to the attention of sales managers that most of the company's manufacturer representatives contacted clients and maintained client relationships in a disorganized, haphazard way. The sales managers brought the reps in for a 3-day seminar and training session on how to use an organizer to schedule visits and recall pertinent information about each client more effectively. Sales reps were taught how to schedule visits most efficiently to maximize their efforts. Sales managers were given data on the number of site visits by sales reps on a randomly selected day both before and after the seminar. Use the following data to test whether there were significantly more site visits after the seminar ($\alpha = .05$). Assume the differences in the number of site visits are normally distributed.

REP	BEFORE	AFTER
1	2	4
2	4	5
3	1	3
4	3	3
5	4	3
6	2	5
7	2	6
8	3	4
9	1	5

10.17 Eleven employees were put under the care of the company nurse because of high cholesterol readings. The nurse lectured them on the dangers of this condition and put them on a new diet. Shown are the cholesterol readings of the 11 employees both before the new diet and 1 month after use of the diet began. Using the data given below, test to determine if the cholesterol readings have been significantly lowered after the 1-month diet. Let $\alpha = .05$. Assume that differences in cholesterol readings are normally distributed in the population.

EMPLOYEE	BEFORE	AFTER
1	255	197
2	230	225
3	290	215
4	242	215
5	300	240
6	250	235
7	215	190
8	230	240
9	225	200
10	219	203
11	236	223

10.18 Lawrence and Glover published the results of a study in the *Journal of Managerial Issues* in which they examined the effects of accounting firm mergers on auditing delay. Auditing delay is the time between a company's fiscal year-end and the date of the auditor's report. The hypothesis is that with the efficiencies gained through mergers, the length of the audit delay would decrease. Suppose to test their hypothesis they examined the audit delays on 27 clients of Big Six firms from both before and after the Big Six firm merger (a span of 5 years), and the resulting data are those given on the next page. Use these data and $\alpha = .01$ to test to determine whether the audit delays after the merger were significantly lower than before the merger. Assume that the differences in before and after delays are normally distributed in the population.

COMPANY	BEFORE	AFTER	COMPANY	BEFORE	AFTER
1	21	16	15	26	22
2	30	27	16	20	17
3	22	14	17	22	23
4	15	16	18	29	21
5	29	23	19	16	15
6	27	26	20	21	17
7	19	19	21	26	28
8	25	20	22	19	17
9	37	26	23	15	14
10	31	24	24	26	19
11	24	25	25	33	28
12	19	16	26	25	25
13	23	17	27	21	20
14	21	20			

10.4

Hypothesis Testing about the Difference in Two Population Proportions

Sometimes a business analyst wishes to make inferences about the difference in two population proportions. This type of analysis has many applications in business, such as comparing the market share of a product for two different markets, studying the difference in the proportion of female customers in two different geographic regions, or comparing the proportion of defective products from one period to another. In making inferences about the difference in two population proportions, the statistic normally used is the difference in the sample proportions: $\hat{p}_1 - \hat{p}_2$. This statistic is computed by taking random samples and determining $\hat{p}$ for each sample for a given characteristic, then calculating the difference in these sample proportions.

The central limit theorem states that for large samples (each of $n_1 \cdot \hat{p}_1$, $n_1 \cdot \hat{q}_1$, $n_2 \cdot \hat{p}_2$, and $n_2 \cdot \hat{q}_2 > 5$, where $\hat{q} = 1 - \hat{p}$), the difference in sample proportions is normally distributed with a mean difference of

$$\mu_{\hat{p}_1 - \hat{p}_2} = P_1 - P_2$$

and a standard deviation of the difference of sample proportions of

$$\sigma_{\hat{p}_1 - \hat{p}_2} = \sqrt{\frac{P_1 \cdot Q_1}{n_1} + \frac{P_2 \cdot Q_2}{n_2}}.$$

From this information, a Z formula for the difference in sample proportions can be developed.

Z FORMULA FOR THE DIFFERENCE IN TWO POPULATION PROPORTIONS

$$Z = \frac{(\hat{p}_1 - \hat{p}_2) - (P_1 - P_2)}{\sqrt{\frac{P_1 \cdot Q_1}{n_1} + \frac{P_2 \cdot Q_2}{n_2}}} \quad (10.8)$$

where:

$\hat{p}_1$ = proportion from sample 1
$\hat{p}_2$ = proportion from sample 2
n_1 = size of sample 1
n_2 = size of sample 2
P_1 = proportion from population 1
P_2 = proportion from population 2
$Q_1 = 1 - P_1$
$Q_2 = 1 - P_2$

Hypothesis Testing

Formula 10.8 is the formula that can be used to determine the probability of getting a particular difference in two sample proportions when given the values of the population proportions. In testing hypotheses about the difference in two population proportions, particular values of the population proportions are not usually known or assumed. Rather, the hypotheses are about the difference in the two population proportions ($P_1 - P_2$). Note that Formula 10.8 requires knowledge of the values of P_1 and P_2. Hence, a modified version of Formula 10.8 is used when testing hypotheses about $P_1 - P_2$. This formula utilizes a pooled value obtained from the sample proportions to replace the population proportions in the denominator of Formula 10.8.

The denominator of Formula 10.8 is the standard deviation of the difference in two sample proportions and uses the population proportions in its calculations. However, the population proportions are unknown, so an estimate of the standard deviation of the difference in two sample proportions is made by using sample proportions as point estimates of the population proportions. The sample proportions are combined by using a weighted average to produce $\overline{P}$, which in conjunction with $\overline{Q}$ and the sample sizes produces a point estimate of the standard deviation of the difference in sample proportions. The result is Formula 10.9 which we shall use to test hypotheses about the difference in two population proportions.

Z FORMULA TO TEST THE DIFFERENCE IN POPULATION PROPORTIONS

(10.9)

$$Z = \frac{(\hat{p}_1 - \hat{p}_2) - (P_1 - P_2)}{\sqrt{(\overline{P} \cdot \overline{Q})\left(\frac{1}{n_1} + \frac{1}{n_2}\right)}}$$

where:

$$\overline{P} = \frac{X_1 + X_2}{n_1 + n_2} = \frac{n_1\hat{p}_1 + n_2\hat{p}_2}{n_1 + n_2}$$

$$\overline{Q} = 1 - \overline{P}$$

Testing the difference in two population proportions is useful whenever the business analyst is interested in comparing the proportion of one population that has a certain characteristic with the proportion of a second population that has the same characteristic. For example, a business analyst might be interested in determining whether the proportion of people driving new cars (less than 1 year old) in Houston is different from the proportion in Denver. A study could be conducted with a random sample of Houston drivers and a random sample of Denver drivers to test this idea. The results could be used to compare the new-car potential of the two markets and the propensity of drivers in these areas to buy new cars.

Do consumers and CEOs have different perceptions of ethics in business? A group of business analysts attempted to determine whether there was a difference in the proportion of consumers and the proportion of CEOs who believe that fear of getting caught or losing one's job is a strong influence of ethical behavior. In their study, they found that 57% of consumers said that fear of getting caught or losing one's job was a strong influence on ethical behavior but only 50% of CEOs felt the same way.

Suppose these data were determined from a sample of 755 consumers and 616 CEOs. Is this enough evidence to declare that a significantly higher proportion of consumers than of CEOs believe fear of getting caught or losing one's job is a strong influence on ethical behavior?

STEP **1.** Suppose sample 1 is the consumer sample and sample 2 is the CEO sample. Because we are trying to prove that a higher proportion of consumers than of CEOs believe this, the alternative hypothesis should be $P_1 - P_2 > 0$. The following hypotheses are being tested.

$$H_0: P_1 - P_2 = 0$$
$$H_a: P_1 - P_2 > 0$$

where:

P_1 is the proportion of consumers who select the factor
P_2 is the proportion of CEOs who select the factor

STEP **2.** The appropriate statistical test is Formula 10.9.

STEP **3.** Let $\alpha = .10$.

STEP **4.** As this is a one-tailed test, the critical table Z value is $Z_c = 1.28$. If an observed value of Z of more than 1.28 is obtained, the null hypothesis will be rejected. Figure 10.12 shows the rejection region and the critical value for this problem.

STEP **5.** The sample information follows.

CONSUMERS	CEOs
$n_1 = 755$	$n_2 = 616$
$\hat{p}_1 = .57$	$\hat{p}_2 = .50$

STEP **6.**

$$\overline{P} = \frac{n_1\hat{p}_1 + n_2\hat{p}_2}{n_1 + n_2} = \frac{(755)(.57) + (616)(.50)}{755 + 616} = .539$$

If the statistics had been given as raw data instead of sample proportions, we would have used the following formula.

$$\overline{P} = \frac{X_1 + X_2}{n_1 + n_2}$$

Figure 10.12

Rejection region for the ethics example

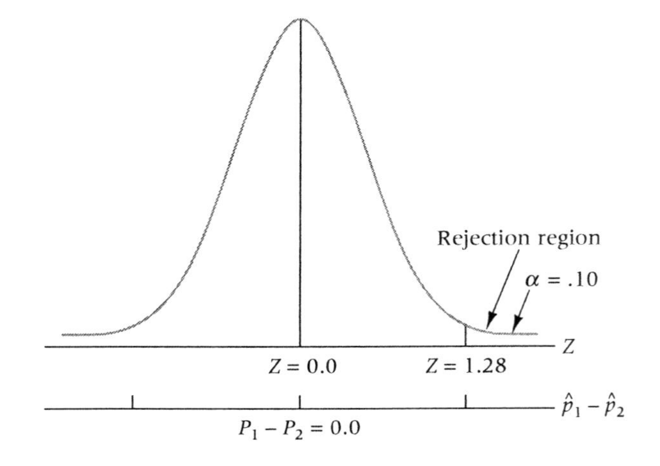

The calculated Z value is

$$Z = \frac{(.57 - .50) - (0)}{\sqrt{(.539)(.461)\left(\frac{1}{755} + \frac{1}{616}\right)}} = 2.59.$$

STEP 7. Because $Z = 2.59$ is greater than the critical table Z value of 1.28 and is in the rejection region, the null hypothesis is rejected.

STEP 8. A significantly higher proportion of consumers than of CEOs believe fear of getting caught or losing one's job is a strong influence on ethical behavior. CEOs might want to take another look at ways to influence ethical behavior. If employees are more like consumers than CEOs, CEOs might be able to use fear of getting caught or losing one's job as a means of ensuring ethical behavior on the job. By transferring the idea of ethical behavior to the consumer, retailers might use fear of being caught and prosecuted to retard shoplifting in the retail trade.

Analysis Using Excel

Excel does not have the built-in capability of testing hypotheses about the difference in two proportions. However, **FAST\STAT**, can perform such tests. The two proportion hypothesis test is **2 Proportions Hyp. Test** selected from the FAST\STAT pull-down menu. The dialog box for this test is shown in Figure 10.13. Along with the sample sizes and the value of alpha, this dialog box requires the raw number of "successes" from each sample and the hypothesized difference in population proportions (usually zero).

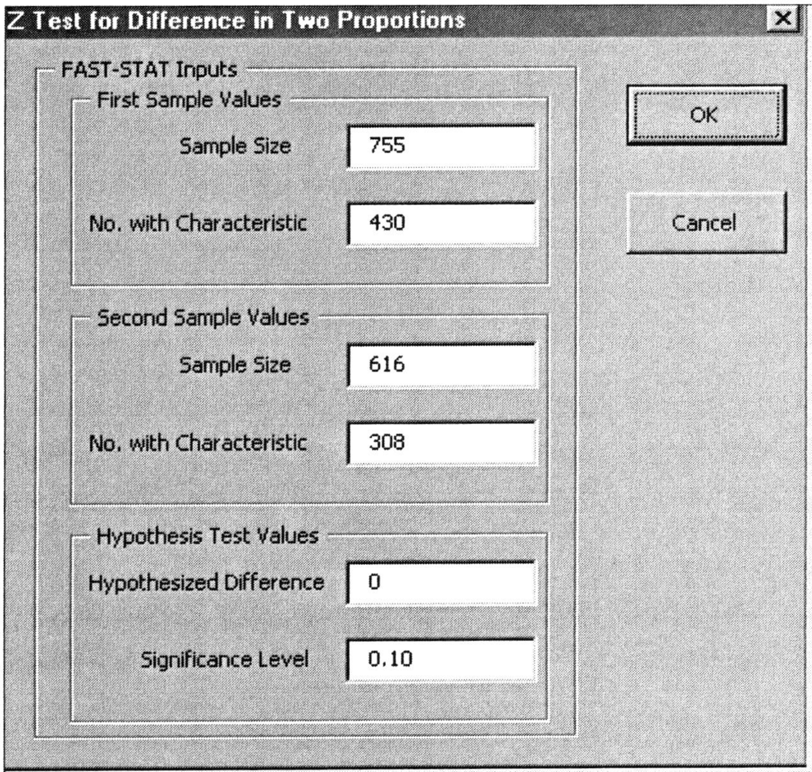

Z Test for Difference in Two Proportions
FAST-STAT Inputs
First Sample Values
Sample Size 755
No. with Characteristic 430
Second Sample Values
Sample Size 616
No. with Characteristic 308
Hypothesis Test Values
Hypothesized Difference 0
Significance Level 0.10
OK
Cancel

Figure 10.13

FAST\STAT dialog box for the **2 Proportions Hyp. Test**

Figure 10.14 FAST\STAT output for the consumer/CEO ethics problem

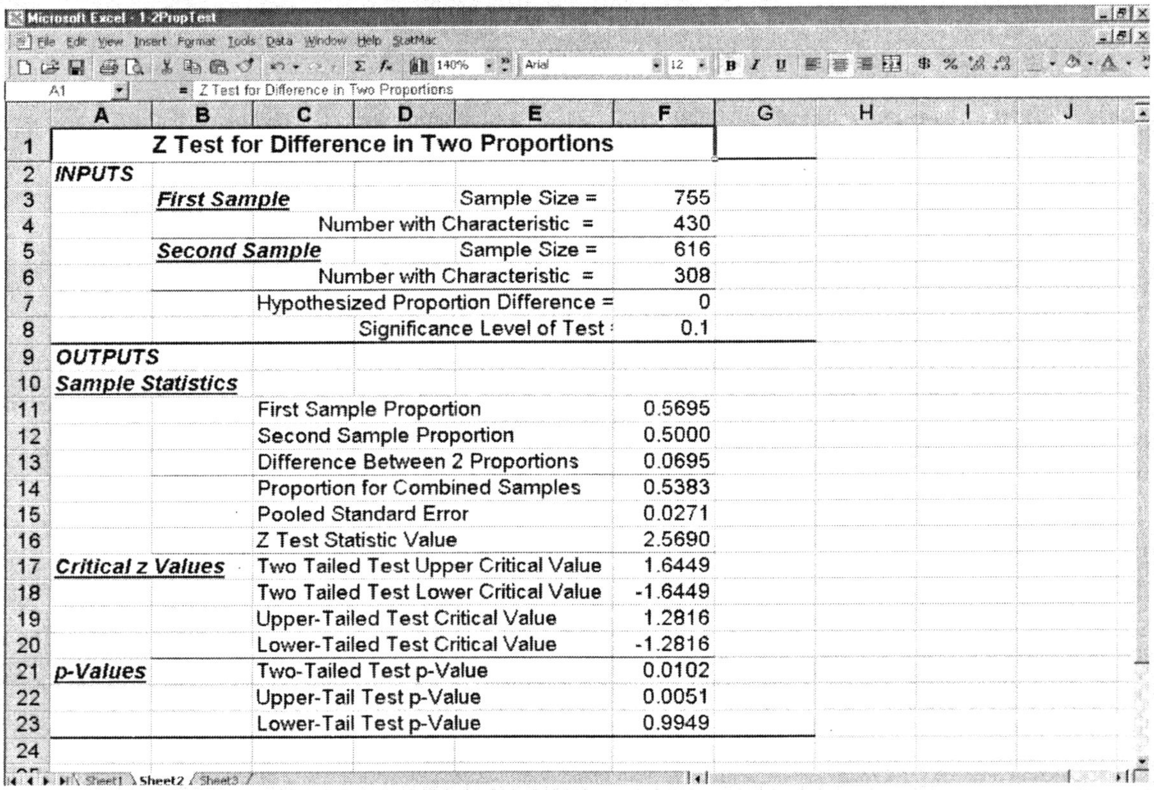

Z Test for Difference in Two Proportions		
INPUTS		
First Sample	Sample Size =	755
	Number with Characteristic =	430
Second Sample	Sample Size =	616
	Number with Characteristic =	308
	Hypothesized Proportion Difference =	0
	Significance Level of Test =	0.1
OUTPUTS		
Sample Statistics		
	First Sample Proportion	0.5695
	Second Sample Proportion	0.5000
	Difference Between 2 Proportions	0.0695
	Proportion for Combined Samples	0.5383
	Pooled Standard Error	0.0271
	Z Test Statistic Value	2.5690
Critical z Values	Two Tailed Test Upper Critical Value	1.6449
	Two Tailed Test Lower Critical Value	-1.6449
	Upper-Tailed Test Critical Value	1.2816
	Lower-Tailed Test Critical Value	-1.2816
p-Values	Two-Tailed Test p-Value	0.0102
	Upper-Tail Test p-Value	0.0051
	Lower-Tail Test p-Value	0.9949

The **FAST\STAT** results are displayed in Figure 10.14. Note that the results include a summary of the input data including the sample sizes, number of successes in each sample, the hypothesized value of the difference in the population proportions, and alpha. In addition, the outputs include the observed Z value (Z Test Statistic Value) along with its associated p-value. Note that the observed (calculated) value of Z shown in Figure 10.14 is 2.57, similar to the observed Z previously calculated in Step 6 (with slight rounding difference). Since the displayed p-value of .0051 (Upper-Tail Test-p-Value) is less than $\alpha = .10$, the decision is to reject the null hypothesis and conclude that a higher proportion of consumers believe fear of getting caught or losing one's job is a strong influence on ethical behavior.

DEMONSTRATION PROBLEM 10.4

A study of female entrepreneurs was conducted to determine their definition of success. The women were offered optional choices such as happiness/self-fulfillment, sales/profit, and achievement/challenge. The women were divided into groups according to the gross sales of their businesses. A significantly higher proportion of female entrepreneurs in the \$100,000 to \$500,000 category than in the less than \$100,000 category seemed to rate sales/profit as a definition of success.

Suppose you decide to test this result by taking a survey of your own and identify female entrepreneurs by gross sales. You interview 100 female entrepreneurs with gross sales of less than \$100,000, and 24 of them define sales/profit as success. You then interview 95 female entrepreneurs with gross sales of \$100,000 to \$500,000, and 39 cite sales/profit as a definition of success. Use this information to test to determine whether there is a significant difference in the proportions of the two groups that define success as sales/profit. Use $\alpha = .01$.

SOLUTION

STEP **1.** You are testing to determine whether there is a difference between two groups of entrepreneurs, so a two-tailed test is required. The hypotheses follow.

$$H_0: P_1 - P_2 = 0$$
$$H_a: P_1 - P_2 \neq 0$$

STEP **2.** The appropriate statistical test is Formula 10.9.

STEP **3.** Alpha has been specified as .01.

STEP **4.** With $\alpha = .01$, you obtain a critical Z value from Table A.5 for $\alpha/2 = .005$, $Z_{.005} = \pm 2.575$. If the observed Z value is more than 2.575 or less than −2.575, the null hypothesis is rejected.

STEP **5.** The sample information follows.

LESS THAN \$100,000	\$100,000 TO \$500,000
$n_1 = 100$	$n_2 = 95$
$X_1 = 24$	$X_2 = 39$
$\hat{p}_1 = \frac{24}{100} = .24$	$\hat{p} = \frac{39}{95} = .41$

where:

$$\bar{P} = \frac{X_1 + X_2}{n_1 + n_2} = \frac{24 + 39}{100 + 95} = \frac{63}{195} = .323$$

X = the number of entrepreneurs who define sales/profits as success

STEP **6.** The calculated Z value is

$$Z = \frac{(\hat{p}_1 - \hat{p}_2) - (P_1 - P_2)}{\sqrt{(\bar{P} \cdot \bar{Q})\left(\frac{1}{n_1} + \frac{1}{n_2}\right)}} = \frac{(.24 - .41) - 0}{\sqrt{(.323)(.677)\left(\frac{1}{100} + \frac{1}{95}\right)}}$$

$$= \frac{-.17}{.067} = -2.54.$$

STEP **7.** Although this calculated value is near the rejection region, it is in the nonrejection region. The null hypothesis is not rejected. That is, there is not enough evidence here to reject the null hypothesis and declare that the responses to the question by the two groups are different statistically. Note that alpha was small and that a two-tailed test was conducted. If a one-tailed test had been used, Z_c would have been $Z_{.01} = 2.33$, and the null hypothesis would have been rejected. If alpha had been .05, Z_c would have been $Z_{.025} = 1.96$, and the null hypothesis would have been rejected. This result underscores the crucial importance of selecting alpha and determining whether to use a one-tailed or two-tailed test in hypothesis testing.

The following diagram shows the critical values, the rejection regions, and the observed value for this problem.

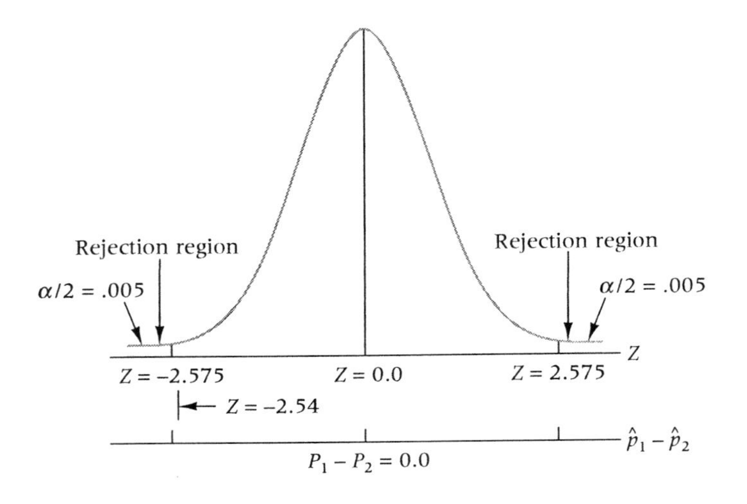

STEP **8.** We cannot statistically conclude that a greater proportion of female entrepreneurs in the higher gross sales category define success as sales/profit. One of the payoffs of such a determination is to find out what motivates the people with whom we do business. If sales/profits motivate people, offers or premises of greater sales and profits can be a means of attracting their services, their interest, or their business. If sales/profits do not motivate people, such offers would not generate the kind of response wanted and we would need to look for other ways to motivate them.

Displayed below are the FAST⧹STAT results for Demonstration Problem 10.4 using the Two Proportion Test. The observed value of 2.5451 has a p-value of 0.0109 for the two-tailed test being done here. Since the p-value is greater than alpha = 0.01, the decision is to fail to reject the null hypothesis.

	A	B	C–E	F
1		**Z Test for Difference in Two Proportions**		
2	***INPUTS***			
3		***First Sample***	Sample Size =	100
4			Number with Characteristic =	24
5		***Second Sample***	Sample Size =	95
6			Number with Characteristic =	39
7			Hypothesized Proportion Difference =	0
8			Significance Level of Test	0.01
9	***OUTPUTS***			
10	***Sample Statistics***			
11			First Sample Proportion	0.2400
12			Second Sample Proportion	0.4105
13			Difference Between 2 Proportions	-0.1705
14			Proportion for Combined Samples	0.3231
15			Pooled Standard Error	0.0670
16			Z Test Statistic Value	-2.5451
17	***Critical z Values***		Two Tailed Test Upper Critical Value	2.5758
18			Two Tailed Test Lower Critical Value	-2.5758
19			Upper-Tailed Test Critical Value	2.3263
20			Lower-Tailed Test Critical Value	-2.3263
21	***p-Values***		Two-Tailed Test p-Value	0.0109
22			Upper-Tail Test p-Value	0.9945
23			Lower-Tail Test p-Value	0.0055
24				

10.4
Problems

10.19 Using the given sample information, test the following hypotheses.

a. H_0: $P_1 - P_2 = 0$ H_a: $P_1 - P_2 \neq 0$

SAMPLE 1	SAMPLE 2	
$n_1 = 368$	$n_2 = 405$	
$X_1 = 175$	$X_2 = 182$	Let $\alpha = .05$.

Note that X is the number in the sample having the characteristic of interest.

b. H_0: $P_1 - P_2 = 0$ H_a: $P_1 - P_2 > 0$

SAMPLE 1	SAMPLE 2	
$n_1 = 649$	$n_2 = 558$	
$\hat{p}_1 = .38$	$\hat{p}_2 = .25$	Let $\alpha = .10$.

10.20 According to a study conducted for Gateway Computers, 59% of men and 70% of women say that weight is an extremely/very important factor in purchasing a laptop computer. Suppose this survey was conducted using 374 men and 481 women. Is there enough evidence in these data to declare that a significantly higher proportion of women than men believe that weight is an extremely/very important factor in purchasing a laptop computer? Use a 5% level of significance.

10.21 Does age make a difference in the amount of savings a worker feels is needed to be secure at retirement? A study by CommSciences for Transamerica Asset Management found that .24 of workers in the 25–33 age category feel that $250,000 to $500,000 is enough to be secure at retirement. However, .35 of the workers in the 34–52 age category feel that this is enough. Suppose 210 workers in the 25–33 age category and 176 workers in the 34–52 age category were involved in this study. Use these data to determine if there is a significant difference in population proportions by age. Let $\alpha = .01$.

10.22 Companies that had recently developed new products were asked to rate which activities are most difficult to accomplish with new products. Options included such activities as assessing market potential, market testing, finalizing the design, developing a business plan, and the like. A business analyst wants to conduct a similar study to compare the results between two industries: the computer hardware industry and the banking industry. He takes a random sample of 56 computer firms and 89 banks. The business analyst asks whether market testing is the most difficult activity to accomplish in developing a new product. Some 48% of the sampled computer companies and 56% of the sampled banks respond that it is the most difficult activity. Use a level of significance of .20 to test whether there is a significant difference in the responses to the question from these two industries.

10.23 A large production facility uses two machines to produce a key part for its main product. Inspectors have expressed concern about the quality of the finished product. Quality control investigation has revealed that the key part made by the two machines is defective at times. The inspectors randomly sampled 35 units of the key part from each machine. Of those produced by machine A, five were defective. Seven of the 35 sampled parts from machine B were defective. The production manager is interested in estimating the difference in proportions of the populations of parts that are defective between machine A and machine B. Test to determine if there is a significant difference in the proportions of defective parts between machine A and machine B. Assume $\alpha = .10$.

10.24 According to a CCH Unscheduled Absence survey, 9% of small businesses use telecommuting of workers in an effort to reduce unscheduled absenteeism. This compares to 6% for all businesses. Is there really a significant difference between small businesses and all businesses on this issue? Use these data and an alpha of .05 to test this question. Assume that there were 780 small businesses and 915 other businesses in this survey.

10.5

Hypotheses Testing about the Difference in Two Population Variances

Sometimes we are interested in the variability of a population of data rather than a measure of central tendency such as the mean or proportion. Recall from Chapter 3 that a variance is a measure of dispersion or variability. There are occasions when business analysts are interested in testing hypotheses about two population variances. This section discusses how to do such tests. When would a business analyst be interested in the variances from two populations?

In quality control, statisticians often examine both a measure of central tendency (mean or proportion) and a measure of variability. Suppose a manufacturing plant has made two batches of an item, produced items on two different machines, or produced items on two different shifts. It might be of interest to compare the variances from the two batches or groups in an effort to determine whether there is more variability in one than another. For example, if one machine or shift has more variability than another, managers might want to investigate why that machine or shift is not as consistent as the other.

Variance is sometimes used as a measure of the risk of a stock in the stock market. The greater the variance, the greater the risk. By using techniques discussed here, a financial business analyst could determine whether the variances (or risk) of two stocks are the same.

In testing hypotheses about two population variances, the sample variances are used. It makes sense that if two samples come from the same population (or populations with equal variances), the ratio of the sample variances, S_1^2/S_2^2, should be about 1. However, because of sampling error, sample variances even from the same population (or from two populations with equal variances) will vary. This *ratio of two sample variances* formulates what is called an ***F* value.**

***F* value**
The ratio of two sample variances, used to reach statistical conclusions regarding the null hypothesis; in ANOVA, the ratio of the treatment variance to the error variance.

$$F = \frac{S_1^2}{S_2^2}$$

These ratios, if computed repeatedly for pairs of sample variances taken from a population, are distributed as an ***F* distribution.** The F distribution will vary by the sizes of the samples, which are converted to degrees of freedom.

***F* distribution**
A distribution based on the ratio of two random variances; used in testing two variances and in analysis of variance.

With the F distribution, there are degrees of freedom associated with the numerator (of the ratio) and the denominator. An assumption underlying the F distribution is that the populations from which the samples are drawn are normally distributed for X. The F test of two population variances is extremely sensitive to violations of the assumption that the populations are normally distributed. The business analyst should carefully investigate the shape of the distributions of the populations from which the samples are drawn to be certain the populations are normally distributed. The formula used to test hypotheses comparing two population variances follows.

F TEST FOR TWO POPULATION VARIANCES

$$F = \frac{S_1^2}{S_2^2} \qquad (10.10)$$

$$df_{numerator} = \nu_1 = n_1 - 1$$
$$df_{denominator} = \nu_2 = n_2 - 1$$

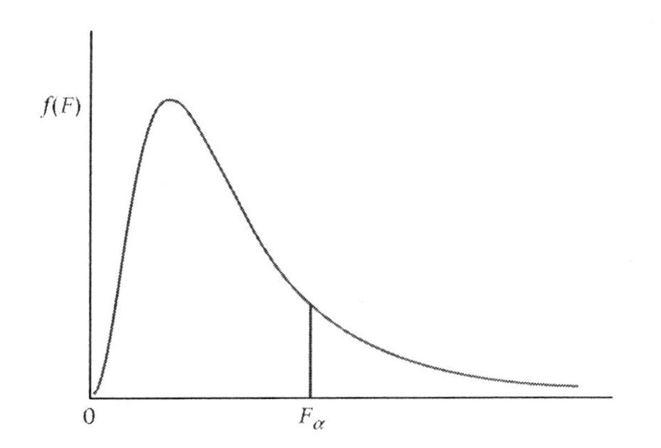

Figure 10.15

An F distribution for $v_1 = 6$, $v_2 = 30$

Table A.7 contains F distribution table values for $\alpha = .10, .05, .025, .01$, and $.005$. Figure 10.15 shows an F distribution for $v_1 = 6$ and $v_2 = 30$. Notice that the distribution is nonsymmetric. This can be a problem when we are conducting a two-tailed test and want to determine the critical value for the lower tail. Table A.7 contains only F values for the upper tail. However, the F distribution is not symmetric nor does it have a mean of zero as do the Z and t distributions; therefore, we cannot merely place a minus sign on the upper-tail critical value and obtain the lower-tail critical value (in addition, the F ratio is always positive—it is the ratio of two variances). This dilemma can be solved by using Formula 10.11, which essentially states that the critical F value for the lower tail $(1 - \alpha)$ can be solved for by taking the inverse of the F value for the upper tail (α). The degrees of freedom numerator for the upper-tail critical value is the degrees of freedom denominator for the lower-tail critical value, and the degrees of freedom denominator for the upper-tail critical value is the degrees of freedom numerator for the lower-tail critical value.

(10.11)

$$F_{1-\alpha, v_2, v_1} = \frac{1}{F_{\alpha, v_1, v_2}}$$

FORMULA FOR DETERMINING THE CRITICAL VALUE FOR THE LOWER-TAIL F

A hypothesis test can be done by using two sample variances and Formula 10.10. The following example illustrates this process.

Suppose a machine produces metal sheets that are specified to be 22 mm thick. Because of the machine, the operator, the raw material, the manufacturing environment, and other factors, there is variability in the thickness. Two machines produce these sheets. Operators are concerned about the consistency of the two machines. To test consistency, they randomly sample 10 sheets produced by machine 1 and 12 sheets produced by machine 2. The thickness measurements of sheets from each machine are given in the accompanying table. Assume sheet thickness is normally distributed in the population. How can we test to determine whether the variance from each sample comes from the same population variance (population variances are equal) or from different population variances (population variances are not equal)?

STEP **1.** Determine the null and alternative hypotheses. In this case, we are conducting a two-tailed test (variances are the same or not), and the following hypotheses are used.

$$H_0: \sigma_1^2 = \sigma_2^2$$
$$H_a: \sigma_1^2 \neq \sigma_2^2$$

STEP **2.** The appropriate statistical test is

$$F = \frac{S_1^2}{S_2^2}.$$

STEP **3.** Let $\alpha = .05$.

STEP **4.** As we are conducting a two-tailed test, $\alpha/2 = .025$. Because $n_1 = 10$ and $n_2 = 12$, the degrees of freedom numerator for the upper-tail critical value is $v_1 = n_1 - 1 = 10 - 1 = 9$ and the degrees of freedom denominator for the upper-tail critical value is $v_2 = n_2 - 1 = 12 - 1 = 11$. The critical F value for the upper tail obtained from Table A.7 is

$$F_{.025,9,11} = 3.59.$$

Table 10.6 is a copy of the F distribution for a one-tailed $\alpha = .025$ (which yields equivalent values for two-tailed $\alpha = .05$ where the upper tail contains .025 of the area). Locate $F_{.025,9,11} = 3.59$ in the table by finding the numerator degrees of freedom (9) across the top of the table, the denominator degrees of freedom (11) down the left side of the table, and determining where the two degrees of freedom meet in the table as shown in Table 10.6. The lower-tail critical value can be calculated from the upper-tail value by using Formula 10.11.

$$F_{.975,11,9} = \frac{1}{F_{.025,9,11}} = \frac{1}{3.59} = .28$$

The decision rule is to reject the null hypothesis if the observed F value is greater than 3.59 or less than .28.

STEP **5.** Next we computed the sample variances. The data are shown here.

MACHINE 1		MACHINE 2	
22.3	21.9	22.0	21.7
21.8	22.4	22.1	21.9
22.3	22.5	21.8	22.0
21.6	22.2	21.9	22.1
21.8	21.6	22.2	21.9
		22.0	22.1
$S_1^2 = .1138$		$S_2^2 = .0202$	
$n_1 = 10$		$n_2 = 12$	

TABLE 10.6 A Portion of the *F* Distribution Table

PERCENTAGE POINTS OF THE *F* DISTRIBUTION

$f(F)$ 0 F_α

$\alpha = 0.025$

Numerator Degrees of Freedom

v_2 \ v_1	1	2	3	4	5	6	7	8	9
1	647.80	799.5	864.2	899.6	921.8	937.1	948.2	956.7	963.3
2	38.51	39.00	39.17	39.25	39.30	39.33	39.36	39.37	39.39
3	17.44	16.04	15.44	15.10	14.88	14.73	14.62	14.54	14.47
4	12.22	10.65	9.98	9.60	9.36	9.20	9.07	8.98	8.90
5	10.01	8.43	7.76	7.39	7.15	6.98	6.85	6.76	6.68
6	8.81	7.26	6.60	6.23	5.99	5.82	5.70	5.60	5.52
7	8.07	6.54	5.89	5.52	5.29	5.12	4.99	4.90	4.82
8	7.57	6.06	5.42	5.05	4.82	4.65	4.53	4.43	4.36
9	7.21	5.71	5.08	4.72	4.48	4.32	4.20	4.10	4.03
10	6.94	5.46	4.83	4.47	4.24	4.07	3.95	3.85	3.78
11	6.72	5.26	4.63	4.28	4.04	3.88	3.76	3.66	3.59
12	6.55	5.10	4.47	4.12	3.89	3.73	3.61	3.51	3.44
13	6.41	4.97	4.35	4.00	3.77	3.60	3.48	3.39	3.31
14	6.30	4.86	4.24	3.89	3.66	3.50	3.38	3.29	3.21
15	6.20	4.77	4.15	3.80	3.58	3.41	3.29	3.20	3.12
16	6.12	4.69	4.08	3.73	3.50	3.34	3.22	3.12	3.05
17	6.04	4.62	4.01	3.66	3.44	3.28	3.16	3.06	2.98
18	5.98	4.56	3.95	3.61	3.38	3.22	3.10	3.01	2.93
19	5.92	4.51	3.90	3.56	3.33	3.17	3.05	2.96	2.88
20	5.87	4.46	3.86	3.51	3.29	3.13	3.01	2.91	2.84
21	5.83	4.42	3.82	3.48	3.25	3.09	2.97	2.87	2.80
22	5.79	4.38	3.78	3.44	3.22	3.05	2.93	2.84	2.76
23	5.75	4.35	3.75	3.41	3.18	3.02	2.90	2.81	2.73
24	5.72	4.32	3.72	3.38	3.15	2.99	2.87	2.78	2.70
25	5.69	4.29	3.69	3.35	3.13	2.97	2.85	2.75	2.68
26	5.66	4.27	3.67	3.33	3.10	2.94	2.82	2.73	2.65
27	5.63	4.24	3.65	3.31	3.08	2.92	2.80	2.71	2.63
28	5.61	4.22	3.63	3.29	3.06	2.90	2.78	2.69	2.61
29	5.59	4.20	3.61	3.27	3.04	2.88	2.76	2.67	2.59
30	5.57	4.18	3.59	3.25	3.03	2.87	2.75	2.65	2.57
40	5.42	4.05	3.46	3.13	2.90	2.74	2.62	2.53	2.45
60	5.29	3.93	3.34	3.01	2.79	2.63	2.51	2.41	2.33
120	5.15	3.80	3.23	2.89	2.67	2.52	2.39	2.30	2.22
∞	5.02	3.69	3.12	2.79	2.57	2.41	2.29	2.19	2.11

Denominator Degrees of Freedom

$F_{.025,9,11}$

Figure 10.16

Graph of F values and rejection region for the sheet metal example

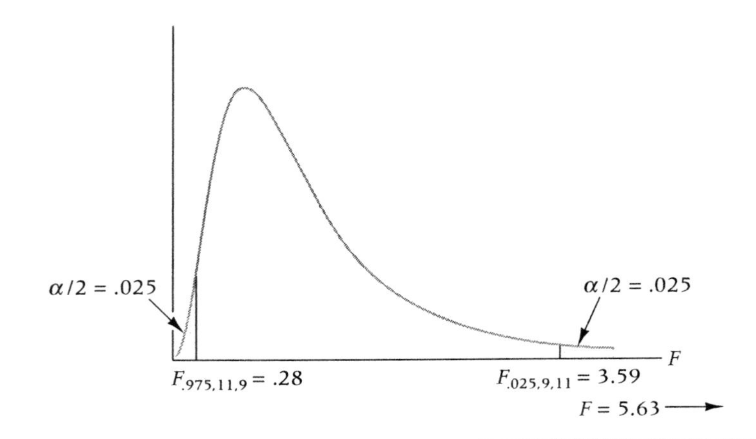

STEP **6.**

$$F = \frac{S_1^2}{S_2^2} = \frac{.1138}{.0202} = 5.63$$

The ratio of sample variances is 5.63.

STEP **7.** The calculated F value is 5.63, which is greater than the upper-tail critical value of 3.59. As Figure 10.16 shows, this F value is in the rejection region. Thus, the decision is to reject the null hypotheses. The population variances are not equal.

STEP **8.** An examination of the sample variances reveals that the variance from machine 1 measurements is greater than that from machine 2 measurements. The operators and process managers might want to examine machine 1 further: an adjustment may be needed or there may be some other reason for the seemingly greater variations on that machine.

Analysis Using Excel

Excel can test hypotheses about two population variances using the **F-Test Two-Sample for Variances** selection under **Data Analysis** from the **Tools** menu. The dialog box for this feature is presented in Figure 10.17. Note that the dialog box requires the location of the data for each of the two variables, along with the value of alpha. Excel always does a one-tailed test for two-sample variances. If the business analyst is only interested in the lower tail, place the location of the variable with the smaller variance in box 1. If the analysis is for the upper tail, then place the location of the variable with the larger variance in box 1. For a two-tailed test, place the location of the variable with the larger variance in box 1 and place the value of $\alpha/2$ in the box for alpha. Note that in Figure 10.17 the value of α entered is .025, which is one-half the value of alpha for the machine problem since it is a two-tailed test.

The Excel output shown in Figure 10.18 for the machine variance problem includes the means, the variances, the number of observations, and the degrees of freedom for each sample. In addition, the output includes the observed value of F (5.63), which is the same as the value computed in Step 6. The Excel output also includes the critical table F value of 3.59 and the p-value associated with the observed F. Since the observed F of 5.63 is greater than the critical table F of 3.59, the decision is to reject the null hypothesis. This decision is underscored using a p-value criterion since the p-value of .0047 is less than $\alpha/2 = .025$.

Figure 10.17 Excel dialog box for the **F-Test Two-Sample for Variances**

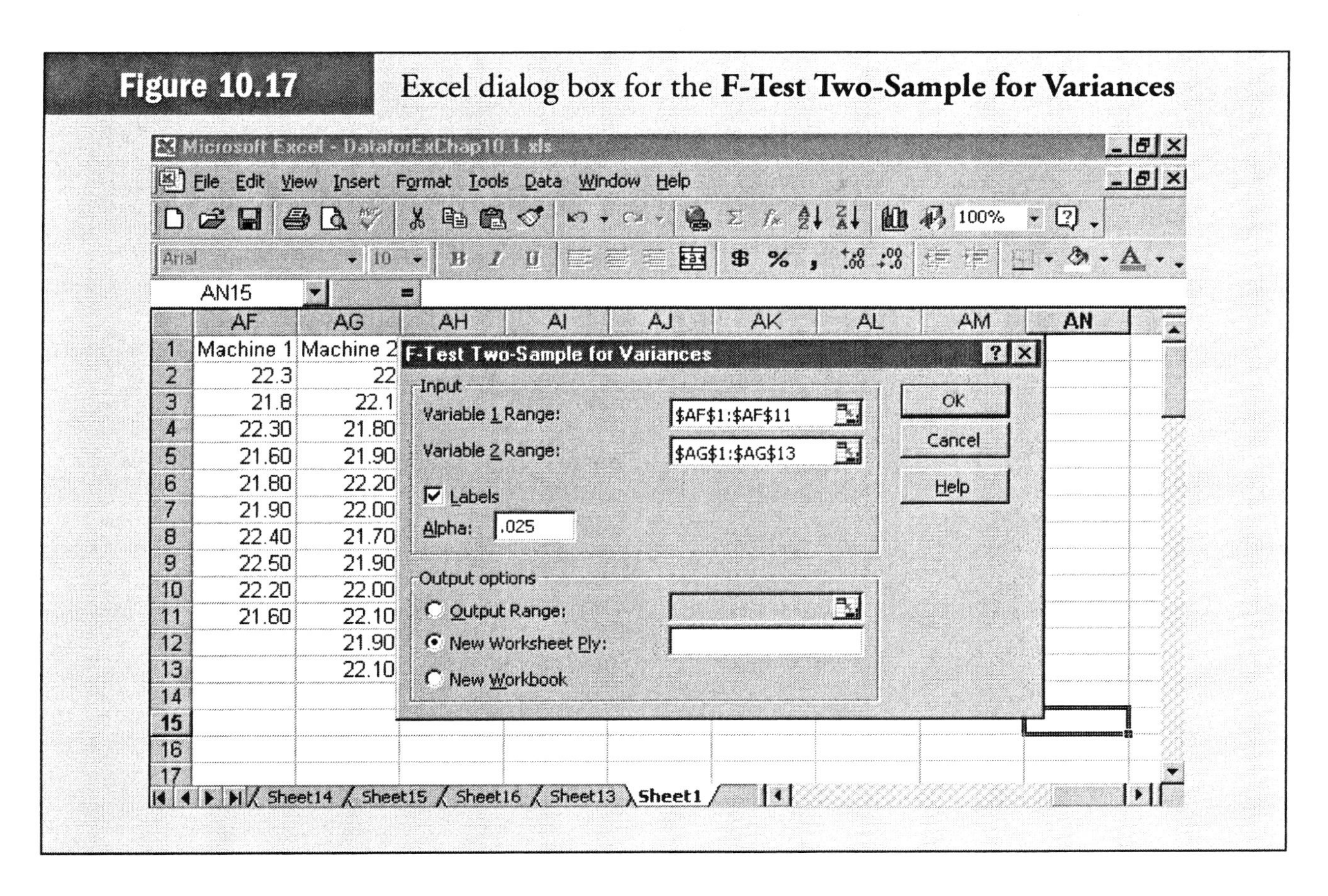

Figure 10.18 Excel output for the **F-Test Two-Sample for Variances**

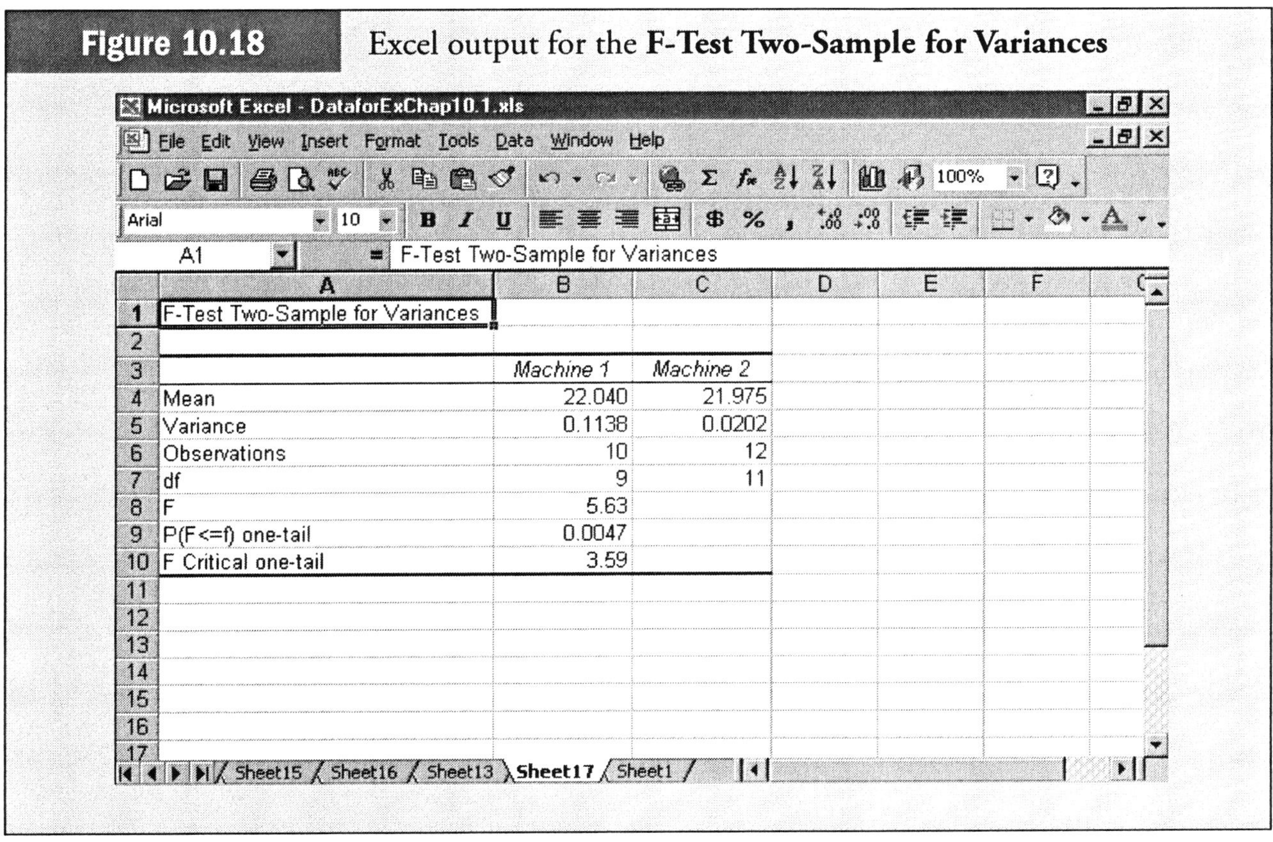

DEMONSTRATION PROBLEM 10.5

According to Runzheimer International, a family of four in Manhattan with \$60,000 annual income spends more than \$22,000 a year on basic goods and services. In contrast, a family of four in San Antonio with the same annual income spends only \$15,460 on the same items. Suppose we want to test to determine whether the variance of money spent per year on the basics by families across the United States is greater than the variance of money spent on the basics by families in Manhattan—that is, whether the amounts spent by families of four in Manhattan are more homogeneous than the amounts spent by such families nationally. Suppose a random sample of eight Manhattan families produces the accompanying figures, which are given along with those reported from a random sample of seven families across the United States. Complete a hypothesis-testing procedure to determine whether the variance of values taken from across the United States can be shown to be greater than the variance of values obtained from families in Manhattan. Let $\alpha = .01$. Let population 1 be "Across United States" and population 2 be "Manhattan." Assume the amount spent on the basics is normally distributed in the population.

AMOUNT SPENT ON BASICS BY FAMILY OF FOUR WITH \$60,000 ANNUAL INCOME

Across United States	*Manhattan*
\$18,500	\$23,000
19,250	21,900
16,400	22,500
20,750	21,200
17,600	21,000
21,800	22,800
14,750	23,100
	21,300

SOLUTION

STEP **1.** This is a one-tailed test with the following hypotheses.

$$H_0: \sigma_1^2 = \sigma_2^2$$
$$H_a: \sigma_1^2 > \sigma_2^2$$

Note that what we are trying to prove—that the variance for the U.S. population is greater than the variance for families in Manhattan—is in the alternative hypothesis.

STEP **2.** The appropriate statistical test is

$$F = \frac{s_1^2}{s_2^2}.$$

STEP **3.** The Type I error rate is .01.

STEP **4.** This is a one-tailed test, so we will use the F distribution table in Appendix A.7 with $\alpha = .01$. The degrees of freedom for $n_1 = 7$ and $n_2 = 8$ are $v_1 = 6$ and $v_2 = 7$. The critical F value for the upper tail of the distribution is

$$F_{.01,6,7} = 7.19.$$

The decision rule is to reject the null hypothesis if the observed value of F is greater than 7.19.

STEP **5.** The following sample variances are computed from the data.

$$S_1^2 = 5{,}961{,}428.6$$
$$n_1 = 7$$
$$S_2^2 = 737{,}142.9$$
$$n_2 = 8$$

STEP **6.** The calculated F value can be determined by

$$F = \frac{S_1^2}{S_2^2} = \frac{5{,}961{,}428.6}{737{,}142.9} = 8.09.$$

STEP **7.** Because the calculated value of $F = 8.09$ is greater than the table critical F value of 7.19, the decision is to reject the null hypothesis.

STEP **8.** The variance for families in the United States is greater than the variance of families in Manhattan. Families in Manhattan are more homogeneous in amount spent on basics than families across the United States. Marketing managers need to understand this as they attempt to find niches in the Manhattan population. There may not be as many different subgroups in Manhattan as there are across the United States. The task of locating market niches may be easier in Manhattan than in the rest of the country because there are likely to be fewer possibilities. The following graph shows the rejection region as well as the critical and calculated values of F.

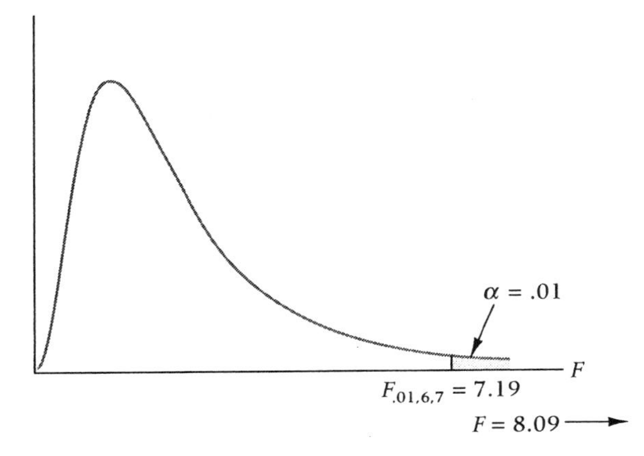

Note: Some authors recommend the use of this F test to determine whether the data being analyzed by a t test for two population means are meeting the assumption of equal population variances. However, some statistical analysts suggest that for equal sample sizes, the t test is insensitive to the equal variance assumption, and therefore the F test is not needed in that situation. For unequal sample sizes, the F test of variances is "not generally capable of detecting assumption violations that lead to poor performance" with the t test.* This text does not present the application of the F test to determine whether variance assumptions for the t test have been met.

*Carol A. Markowski and Edward P. Markowski, "Conditions for the Effectiveness of a Preliminary Test of Variance," *The American Statistician*, 44, November 1990, 322–326.

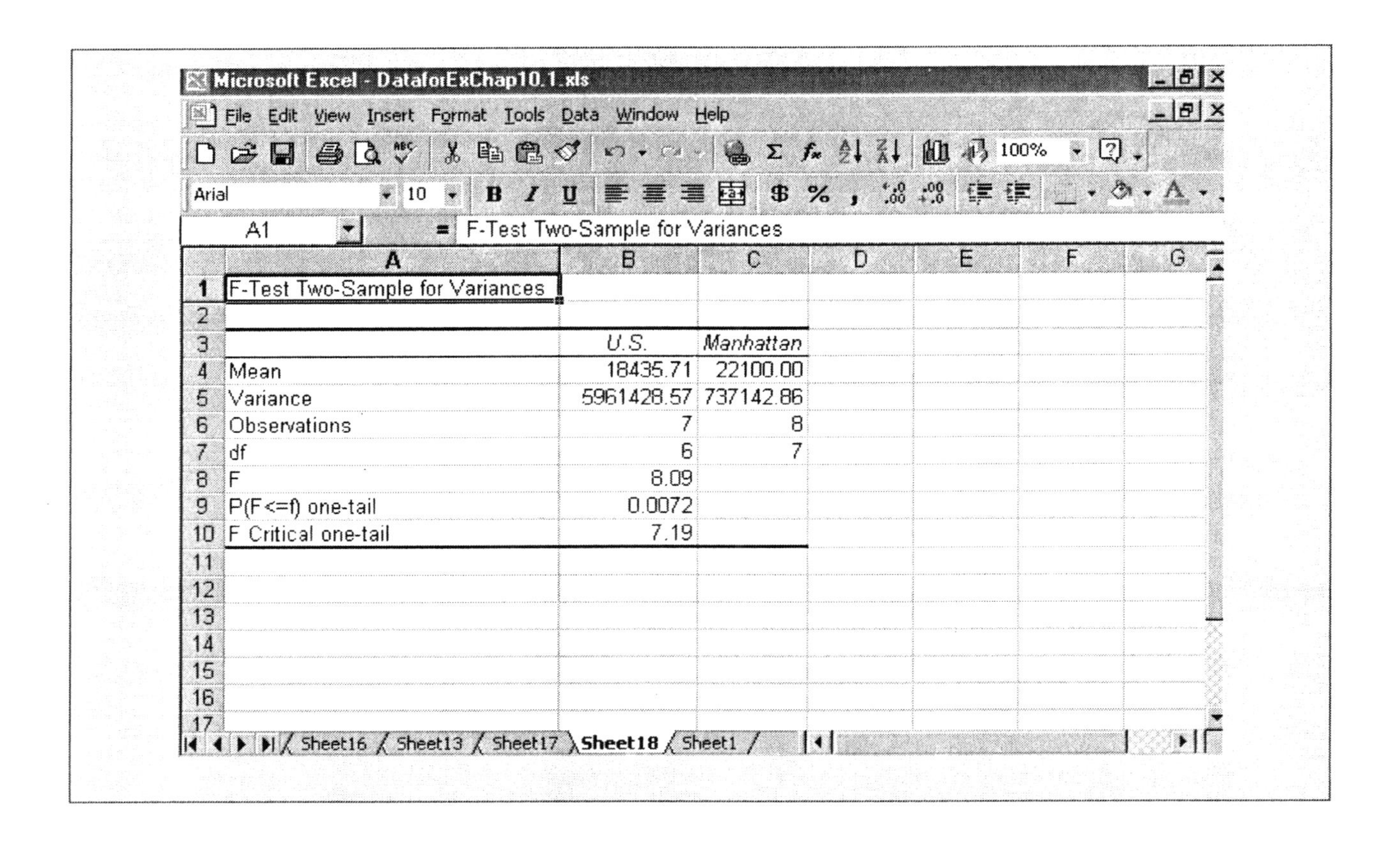

Microsoft Excel - DataforExChap10.1.xls

A1 = F-Test Two-Sample for Variances

F-Test Two-Sample for Variances

	U.S.	Manhattan
Mean	18435.71	22100.00
Variance	5961428.57	737142.86
Observations	7	8
df	6	7
F	8.09	
P(F<=f) one-tail	0.0072	
F Critical one-tail	7.19	

Shown above is Excel output for Demonstration Problem 10.5. Note that the observed value of $F = 8.09$ is greater than the critical table F value of 7.19 underscoring the decision to reject the null hypothesis. In addition, the p-value of .0072 is less than $\alpha = .01$.

10.5
Problems

10.25 Test the following hypotheses by using the given sample information and $\alpha = .01$. Assume the populations are normally distributed.

$$H_0: \sigma_1^2 = \sigma_2^2 \qquad H_a: \sigma_1^2 < \sigma_2^2$$

SAMPLE 1	SAMPLE 2
130	160
146	92
124	164
152	166
147	176
102	197
173	104
177	149
122	162
130	136
	157
	110

10.26 Test the following hypotheses by using the given sample information and $\alpha = .05$. Assume the populations are normally distributed.

$$H_0: \sigma_1^2 = \sigma_2^2 \qquad H_a: \sigma_1^2 \neq \sigma_2^2$$

SAMPLE 1		SAMPLE 2		
19	20	22	19	20
23	21	20	23	24
27	20	25	20	22
19	19	21	20	19
15	23	22	18	

10.27 Suppose the data shown here are the results of a survey to investigate gasoline prices. Ten service stations were selected randomly in each of two cities and the figures represent the prices of a gallon of unleaded regular gasoline on a given day. Use the *F* test to determine whether there is a significant difference in the variances of the prices of unleaded regular gasoline between these two cities. Let $\alpha = .10$. Assume gasoline prices are normally distributed.

CITY 1					CITY 2				
1.58	1.47	1.53	1.55	1.54	1.48	1.45	1.59	1.57	1.61
1.53	1.54	1.53	1.43	1.49	1.52	1.54	1.54	1.53	1.51

10.28 How long are resale houses on the market? One survey by the Houston Association of Realtors reported that in Houston, resale houses are on the market an average of 112 days. Of course, the length of time will vary by market. Suppose random samples of 13 houses in Houston and 11 houses in Chicago that are for resale are traced. The data shown here represent the number of days each house was on the market before being sold. Use the given data and a 1% level of significance to determine whether the population variances for the number of days until resale are different in Houston than in Chicago. Assume the numbers of days resale houses are on the market are normally distributed.

HOUSTON	CHICAGO
132	118
138	85
131	113
127	81
99	94
126	93
134	56
126	69
94	67
161	54
133	137
119	
88	

10.29 One recent study showed that the average annual amount spent by an East Coast household on frankfurters was \$23.84 compared with an average of \$19.83 for West Coast households. Suppose a random sample of 12 East Coast households showed that the standard deviation of these purchases (frankfurters) was \$7.52, whereas a random sample of 15 West Coast households resulted in a standard deviation of \$6.08. Is there enough evidence from these samples to conclude that the variance of annual frankfurter purchases for East Coast households is greater than the variance of annual frankfurter purchases for West Coast households? Let alpha be .05. Assume amounts spent per year on frankfurters are normally distributed. Suppose the data did show that the variance among East Coast households is greater than that among West Coast households. What might this mean to decision makers in the frankfurter industry?

EAST COAST				WEST COAST			
28.18	22.83	23.52	20.91	18.08	20.62	17.58	19.33
25.02	21.64	19.54	20.02	19.40	21.43	21.12	18.76
25.98	23.64	21.83	22.97	20.70	21.19	21.36	20.50
				19.07	20.55	20.06	

10.30 According to the General Accounting Office of the U.S. government, the average age of a male federal worker is 43.6 and that of a male worker in the nonfederal sector is 37.3 years. Is there any difference in the variation of ages of men in the federal sector and men in the nonfederal sector? Suppose a random sample of 15 male federal workers is taken and a random sample of 15 male nonfederal workers is taken, each is asked their age, and the data below are the results. Use these data and $\alpha = .01$ to answer the question. Assume ages of workers in each of the populations are normally distributed.

FEDERAL SECTOR					NONFEDERAL SECTOR				
46	53	45	27	54	26	27	40	31	44
27	41	59	45	42	27	47	36	30	31
40	32	53	46	58	40	42	40	30	30

Summary

Business analysts sometimes want to study the differences in two populations. This chapter examines the differences in two populations using three different parameters (means, proportions, and variances) through the use of hypothesis testing.

The population means are analyzed by comparing two sample means. When sample sizes are large ($n \geq 30$), a Z test is used. When sample sizes are small, the population variances are known, and the populations are normally distributed, the Z test is used to analyze the population means. If sample size is small, the population variances are unknown, and the populations are normally distributed, the t test of means for independent samples is used. For populations that are related on some measure, such as twins or before-and-after, a t test for dependent measures (matched pairs) is used.

The difference in population proportions can be tested by using the difference in two sample proportions, one from each population, as the sample statistic. The Z distribution is used to test this difference in sample proportions.

The population variances are analyzed by an F test when the assumption that the populations are normally distributed is met. The F value is a ratio of the two variances. The F distribution is a distribution of possible ratios of two sample variances taken from one population or from two populations containing the same variance.

Key Terms

dependent samples
F distribution
F value
independent samples
matched-pairs data
matched-pairs test
paired data
related measures
related samples

SUPPLEMENTARY PROBLEMS

10.31 Test the following hypotheses with the data given. Let $\alpha = .10$.

H_0: $\mu_1 - \mu_2 = 0$ H_a: $\mu_1 - \mu_2 \neq 0$

SAMPLE 1

150	140	138	132	131	143	134
140	138	143	139	149	133	136
139	141	135	140	149	156	136
129	137	152	120	144	144	139
130	136	135	140	156	137	145
142	148	132	147	141	144	146
138	122	144	143	142	137	

SAMPLE 2

138	143	136	149	144	146	147
151	141	134	144	135	151	143
125	129	127	144	127	155	141
148	136	123	146	131	145	138
121	137	147	140	142	138	144
131	134	144	148			

10.32 The following data come from independent samples drawn from normally distributed populations. Use these data to test the following hypotheses. Let the Type I error rate by .05. Assume the population variances are unequal.

H_0: $\mu_1 - \mu_2 = 0$ H_0: $\mu_1 - \mu_2 > 0$

SAMPLE 1

1.82	1.85	1.91	2.01	2.53
2.18	1.68	2.00	1.86	1.86
2.08	2.33			

SAMPLE 2

1.83	1.93	1.89	1.86	1.86	2.11
1.80	1.84	2.03	2.00	1.89	1.90
1.87	1.89	1.78			

10.33 The following data have been gathered from two related samples. The differences are assumed to be normally distributed in the population. Use these data and alpha of .01 to test the following hypotheses.

H_0: $D = 0$

H_a: $D \neq 0$

RESPONDENT	BEFORE	AFTER
1	47	63
2	33	35
3	38	36
4	50	56
5	39	44
6	27	29
7	35	32
8	46	54
9	41	47

10.34 Test the following hypotheses by using the given data and alpha equal to .05.

H_0: $P_1 - P_2 = 0$ H_a: $P_1 - P_2 \neq 0$

SAMPLE 1	SAMPLE 2
$n_1 = 783$	$n_2 = 896$
$X_1 = 345$	$X_2 = 421$

10.35 Test the following hypotheses by using the given data. Let alpha = .05.

H_0: $\sigma_1^2 = \sigma_2^2$ H_a: $\sigma_1^2 \neq \sigma_2^2$

SAMPLE 1				SAMPLE 2			
75.3	82.6	70.4	82.5	82.5	75.4	77.7	83.8
84.8	79.6	77.3	64.8	72.9	77.8	87.6	83.7
				89.7	80.1		

10.36 A study is conducted to estimate the average difference in bus ridership for a large city during the morning and afternoon rush hours. The transit authority's business analyst randomly selects nine buses because of the variety of routes they represent. On a given day the number of riders on each bus is counted at 7:45 A.M. and at 4:45 P.M., with the following results.

BUS	MORNING	AFTERNOON
1	43	41
2	51	49
3	37	44
4	24	32
5	47	46
6	44	42
7	50	47
8	55	51
9	46	49

Use these data and a 5% level of significance to test to determine if there is a significant difference between the average morning ridership and the average afternoon ridership.

10.37 A study was conducted to compare the salaries of accounting clerks and data entry operators. One of the hypotheses to be tested is that the variability of salaries among accounting clerks is the same as the variability of salaries of data entry operators. To test this, a random sample of 11 accounting clerks was taken and a random sample of 12 data entry operators was taken. The salary data are shown below. Use these data and $\alpha = .05$ to test to determine whether the population variance of salaries is the same for accounting clerks as it is for data operators. Assume the salaries are normally distributed in the population.

ACCOUNTING CLERKS			DATA ENTRY OPERATORS		
28,431	23,536	26,765	24,183	25,467	25,120
23,703	28,833	28,163	24,756	25,047	26,978
25,307	26,895	23,051	25,141	24,136	26,252
26,772	26,323		26,105	26,504	25,769

10.38 A national grocery store chain wants to estimate the difference in the average weight of turkeys sold in Detroit and the average weight of turkeys sold in Charlotte. The chain's business analyst has a random sample of 20 turkeys selected in Detroit and 24 turkeys selected in Charlotte. The weights of the turkeys are recorded and displayed below. Use a 1% level of significance to determine whether there is a difference in the mean weight of turkeys sold in these two cities. Assume the population variances are approximately the same and that the weights of turkeys sold in the stores are normally distributed.

DETROIT				
11.9	21.0	14.6	17.1	18.8
16.5	18.9	17.5	15.4	19.6
9.7	16.5	13.7	21.2	18.9
18.9	14.7	17.1	17.5	18.1

CHARLOTTE				
16.7	13.8	12.0	12.9	12.2
12.9	15.7	15.4	21.2	14.5
18.4	11.3	13.4	14.6	10.1
14.5	20.4	10.3	15.3	11.6
19.0	12.7	12.0	14.9	

10.39 A tree nursery has been experimenting with fertilizer to increase the growth of seedlings. A sample of 35 two-year-old pine trees is grown for three more years with a cake of fertilizer buried in the soil near the trees' roots. A second sample of 35 two-year-old pine trees is grown for three more years under identical conditions (soil, temperature, water) as the first group, but not fertilized. Tree growth is measured over the 3-year period with the following results.

TREES WITH FERTILIZER				
31.2	46.9	33.3	26.3	35.8
28.4	34.0	21.2	54.6	34.6
35.9	25.1	32.3	31.0	43.9
25.3	26.0	28.4	42.9	45.3
48.1	20.5	39.8	51.8	28.2
45.6	42.8	59.2	40.5	48.9
31.7	41.3	51.8	33.0	35.4

TREES WITHOUT FERTILIZER				
21.9	26.1	19.7	23.0	22.2
26.1	27.8	14.6	21.4	28.0
14.5	22.8	22.9	12.2	20.6
20.0	22.5	24.7	19.7	22.6
23.3	27.0	23.0	26.5	31.0
21.3	19.3	13.4	20.5	28.3
15.6	14.8	21.7	18.0	14.7

Do the data support the theory that the population of trees with the fertilizer grew significantly larger during the period in which they were fertilized than the nonfertilized trees? Use $\alpha = .01$.

10.40 One of the most important aspects of a store's image is the perceived quality of its merchandise. Other factors include merchandise pricing, assortment of products, convenience of location, and service. Suppose image perceptions of shoppers of specialty stores and shoppers of discount stores are being compared. A random sample of shoppers is taken at each type of store, and the shoppers are asked whether the quality of merchandise is a determining factor in their perception of the store's image. Some 75% of the 350 shoppers at the specialty stores say yes, but only 52% of the 500 shoppers at the discount store say yes.

Use these data and test to determine if there is a significant difference between specialty stores and discount stores in the proportion of shoppers who say that the quality of merchandise is a determining factor in their perceptions of the store's image. Use an alpha of .05.

10.41 Is the average price of a name-brand soup greater than the average price of a store-brand soup? To test this, a business analyst randomly samples eight stores. Each store sells its own brand and a national name brand. The prices of a can of name-brand tomato soup and a can of store-brand tomato soup follow. Use these data and $\alpha = .10$ to test this theory. Assume that prices are normally distributed in the population.

STORE	NAME BRAND	STORE BRAND
1	54¢	49¢
2	55	50
3	59	52
4	53	51
5	54	50
6	61	56
7	51	47
8	53	49

10.42 As the prices of heating oil and natural gas increase, consumers become more careful about heating their homes. Business analysts want to know how warm homeowners keep their houses in January and how the results from Wisconsin and Tennessee compare. The business analysts randomly call 23 Wisconsin households between 7 P.M. and 9 P.M. on January 15 and ask the respondent how warm the house is according to the thermostat. The business analysts then call 19 households in Tennessee the same night and ask the same question. The results follow.

WISCONSIN				TENNESSEE			
71	71	65	68	73	75	74	71
70	61	67	69	74	73	74	70
75	68	71	73	72	71	69	72
74	68	67	69	74	73	70	72
69	72	67	72	69	70	67	
70	73	72					

For $\alpha = .01$, is the average temperature of a house in Tennessee significantly higher than that of a house in Wisconsin on the evening of January 15? Assume the population variances are equal and the house temperatures are normally distributed in each population.

10.43 A manufacturer has two machines that drill holes in pieces of sheet metal used in engine construction. The workers who attach the sheet metal to the engine become inspectors in that they reject sheets that have been so poorly drilled that they cannot be attached. The production manager is interested in knowing whether one machine produces more defective drillings than the other machine. As an experiment, employees mark the sheets so that the manager can determine which machine was used to drill the holes. A random sample of 191 sheets of metal drilled by machine 1 is taken, and 38 of the sheets are defective. A random sample of 202 sheets of metal drilled by machine 2 is taken, and 21 of the sheets are defective. Use $\alpha = .05$ to determine whether there is a significant difference in the proportion of sheets drilled with defective holes between machine 1 and machine 2.

10.44 Executives often spend so many hours in meetings that they have relatively little time to manage their individual areas of operation. What is the difference in mean time spent in meetings by executives of the aerospace industry and executives of the automobile industry? Suppose random samples of 33 aerospace executives and 35 automobile executives are monitored for a week to determine how much time they spend in meetings. The results follow.

AEROSPACE						
15	9	6	11	11	12	15
16	14	12	11	10	17	9
11	10	13	14	13	14	9
12	16	13	12	12	10	12
12	15	10	13	13		

AUTOMOBILE						
7	4	6	4	4	8	7
3	6	8	5	8	2	6
2	1	4	2	2	10	7
4	6	2	4	6	7	3
5	4	8	5	3	6	4

Use these data to test to determine if there is a significant difference between aerospace executives and automobile executives in the average number of hours spent per week in meetings. Let alpha be .01.

10.45 Is there more variation in output of one shift in a manufacturing plant than in another shift? In an effort to study this question, plant managers gathered productivity reports from the 8 A.M. to 4 P.M. shift for 8 days. The reports indicated that the following numbers of units were produced on each day for this shift.

5528 4779 5112 5380 4918 4763 5055 5106

Productivity information was also gathered from 7 days for the 4 P.M. to midnight shift, resulting in the following data.

4325 4016 4872 4559 3982 4754 4116

Use these data and $\alpha = .01$ to test to determine whether the variances of productivity for the two shifts are the same. Assume productivity is normally distributed in the population.

10.46 Various types of retail outlets sell toys during the holiday season. Among them are specialty toy stores, the large discount toy stores, and other retailers that carry toys as only one part of their stock of goods. Is there any difference in the dollar amount of a customer purchase between a large discount toy store and a specialty toy store if they carry relatively comparable types of toys? Suppose in December a random sample of 40 sales slips is selected from a large discount toy outlet and a random sample of 36 sales slips is selected from a specialty toy store. The data gathered from these samples follow.

DISCOUNT

34.60	31.52	32.89	52.47	33.63
38.85	43.65	57.90	57.94	42.20
54.19	42.13	53.41	31.27	47.41
61.41	26.51	13.76	45.74	47.68
47.88	67.62	55.61	41.38	47.89
36.73	56.09	45.34	42.36	35.79
43.06	37.12	49.96	62.36	57.56
56.58	58.40	21.04	36.86	46.14

SPECIALTY

22.00	24.30	46.89	49.47	39.41
34.52	33.35	28.94	40.91	33.34
37.53	35.64	28.53	24.57	27.52
13.54	27.68	25.63	27.48	39.66
14.34	20.63	26.77	25.68	51.17
25.66	6.45	21.19	39.21	21.44
36.83	12.69	40.15	25.25	24.66
34.05				

Use $\alpha = .01$ and the data to determine whether there is a significant difference in the average size of purchases at these stores.

10.47 One of the new thrusts of quality control management is to examine the process by which a product is produced. This approach also applies to paperwork. In industries where large long-term projects are undertaken, days and even weeks may elapse as a change order makes its way through a maze of approvals before receiving final approval. This process can result in long delays and stretch schedules to the breaking point. Suppose a quality control consulting group claims that it can significantly reduce the number of days required for such paperwork to receive approval. In an attempt to "prove" its case, the group selects five jobs for which it revises the paperwork system. The following data show the number of days required for a change order to be approved before the group intervened and the number of days required for a change order to be approved after the group instituted a new paperwork system.

BEFORE	AFTER
12	8
7	3
10	8
16	9
8	5

Use $\alpha = .01$ to determine whether there was a significant drop in the number of days required to process paperwork to approve change orders. Assume that in each case the number of days of paperwork is normally distributed.

10.48 There are two large newspapers in your city. You are interested in knowing whether there is a significant difference in the average number of pages in each newspaper dedicated solely to advertising. You randomly select 10 editions of newspaper A and six editions of newspaper B (excluding weekend editions). The data follow. Use $\alpha = .01$ to test whether there is a significant difference in averages. Assume the number of pages of advertising per edition is normally distributed and the population variances are approximately equal.

A		B	
17	17	8	14
21	15	11	10
11	19	9	6
19	22		
26	16		

10.49 Is there a difference in the proportion of construction workers who are under 35 years of age and the proportion of telephone repair people who are under 35 years of age? Suppose a study is conducted in Calgary, Alberta, using random samples of 338 construction workers and 281 telephone repair people. The sample of construction workers includes 297 people under 35 years of age and the sample of telephone repair people includes 192 people under that age. Use these data to test to determine if there is a significant difference in the proportions of workers who are under 35 years of age in construction and in telephone repair. Let alpha be .10.

10.50 Suppose a large insurance company wants to test to determine if the average amount of term life insurance purchased per family is greater than the average amount of whole life insurance purchased per family. To test this hypothesis, one of the company's actuaries randomly selects 27 families who have term life insurance only and 29 families who have whole life insurance only. Each sample is taken from families in which the leading provider is younger than 45 years of age. Suppose the data from this study are those given below. Use these data to test the hypothesis. Use a 5% level of significance, assume that the amount of insurance is normally distributed, and assume that the variances are unequal.

TERM LIFE ($1,000)						
80	65	65	70	60	100	75
115	120	60	75	60	45	75
95	30	35	25	60	45	95
75	60	100	80	110	115	

WHOLE LIFE ($1,000)						
35	60	40	55	30	45	20
15	60	60	55	60	65	35
65	40	40	35	30	45	35
25	50	30	15	45	70	50
55						

ANALYZING THE DATABASES

1. Test to determine whether there is a significant difference between mean value added by the manufacturer and the cost of materials in manufacturing. Use the manufacturing database as the sample data and let alpha be .01.
2. Use the manufacturing database to test to determine whether there is a significantly greater variance among the values of end-of-year inventories than among cost of materials. Let $\alpha = .05$.
3. Is there a difference between the average number of admissions at a general medical hospital and a psychiatric hospital? Use the hospital database to test this hypothesis with $\alpha = .10$. The variable Service in the hospital database differentiates general medical hospitals (coded 1) and psychiatric hospitals (coded 2). Now test to determine whether there is a difference between these two types of hospitals on the variables Beds and Total Expenses.
4. Use the financial database to test to determine whether there is a significant difference in the proportion of companies whose earnings per share are more than $2.00 and the proportion of companies whose dividends per share are more than $1.00. Let $\alpha = .05$.

CASE

SEITZ CORPORATION: PRODUCING QUALITY GEAR-DRIVEN AND LINEAR-MOTION PRODUCTS

The Seitz Corporation is a QS 9000 certified company that designs and manufactures thermoplastic mechanical drives, such as gears and pulleys, and pin-feed tractors for printers. They specialize in complete gear train design and converting drive systems from metals to plastics for cost reductions and higher performance. Founded in 1949 by the late Karl F. Seitz, this family-owned company based in Torrington, Connecticut has plants in Connecticut and Illinois and is in the process of opening a plant in Loveland, Colorado. Currently, Seitz's plants employ around 300 people; the new Loveland facility is expected to add around 200 employees to that number in the next two years.

Seitz began as a small toolmaking business and grew slowly. In the late 1960s, the company expanded its services to include custom injection molding. As their customer base grew to include leading printer manufacturers, Seitz developed and patented a proprietary line of perforated-form-handling tractors. Utilizing its injection-molding technology, the company engineered an all-plastic tractor called Data Motion, which replaced the costly metal version. By the late 1970s, business was booming, and Data Motion had become the worldwide industry leader.

In the 1980s, foreign competition entered the business-equipment market, and many of Seitz's customers relocated or closed shop. The ripple effect hit Seitz as sales declined and profits eroded. Employment at the company dropped from a high of 313 in 1985 to only 125 in 1987. Drastic changes had to be made at Seitz.

To meet the challenge in 1987, Seitz made a crucial decision to change the way it did business. The company implemented a formal 5-year plan with measurable goals called "World-Class Excellence Through Total Quality." Many hours were devoted by senior managers to improving employee training and involvement. New concepts were explored and integrated into the business plan. Teams and programs were put into place to immediately correct deficiencies in Seitz's systems that were revealed in customer-satisfaction surveys. All employees from machine operators to accountants were taught that quality means understanding customers' needs and fulfilling them correctly the first time.

Once the program started, thousands of dollars in cost savings and two new products generating almost $1 million in sales resulted. Annual sales grew from $10.8 million in 1987 to $19 million in 1990. Seitz's customer base expanded from 312 in 1987 to 550 at the end of 1990.

In the decade of the 1990s, Seitz continued its steady growth. By 1999, Seitz was shipping products to 28 countries, and customers included Xerox, Hewlett Packard, Canon, U.S. Tsubaki, and many more worldwide. By 1998, sales had topped the $30 million mark and were expected to reach $45 million by the year 2000. CEO and President Alan F. Seitz stated that the "Seitz Corporation is dedicated to providing products and services that consistently meet or exceed our customers' requirements."

DISCUSSION

1. Seitz has a growing list of several hundred business-to-business customers. Managers would like to know whether the average dollar amount of sales per transaction per customer has changed from last year to this year. Suppose company accountants sampled 20 customers randomly from last year's records and 25 customers randomly from this year's files and the resulting dollar amount of each sales transaction is shown below. Analyze these data and summarize your findings for managers. Explain how this information can be used by decision makers. Assume that sales per customer are normally distributed and that the variances are likely to be unequal.

SALES LAST YEAR					SALES THIS YEAR				
1739	2482	2163	2938	2710	2199	1766	2425	1374	2188
2047	2096	2324	2462	2192	2227	1866	3100	2281	2768
1733	1380	2816	2045	1964	2736	2913	2613	2530	2977
2929	2618	2575	2067	2114	2420	2236	2046	1360	1866
					2206	2462	1895	3121	2337

2. One common approach to measuring a company's quality is through the use of customer-satisfaction surveys. Suppose a random sample of Seitz's customers are asked whether the plastic tractor produced by Seitz has outstanding quality (yes or no). Assume Seitz produces these tractors at two different plant locations and that the tractor customers can be divided according to where their tractors were manufactured. Suppose a random sample of 45 customers who bought tractors made at plant 1 results in 18 saying the tractors have excellent quality and a random sample of 51 customers who bought tractors made at plant 2 results in 12 saying the tractors have excellent quality. Test the difference in population proportions of excellent ratings between the two groups of customers using $\alpha = .05$. Does it seem to matter which plant produces the tractors in terms of the quality rating received from customers? What would you report from these data?

3. Suppose the customer-satisfaction survey included a question on the overall quality of Seitz measured on a 5-point scale, with 1 indicating low quality and 5 indicating high quality. Company managers monitor the figures from year to year to help determine whether Seitz is improving customers' perception of its quality. Suppose random samples of the responses from 2000 and 2001 customers are taken and analyzed on this question, and the following Excel analysis of the data results. Help managers interpret this analysis so that comparisons can be made between 2000 and 2001. Discuss the samples, the statistics, and the conclusions.

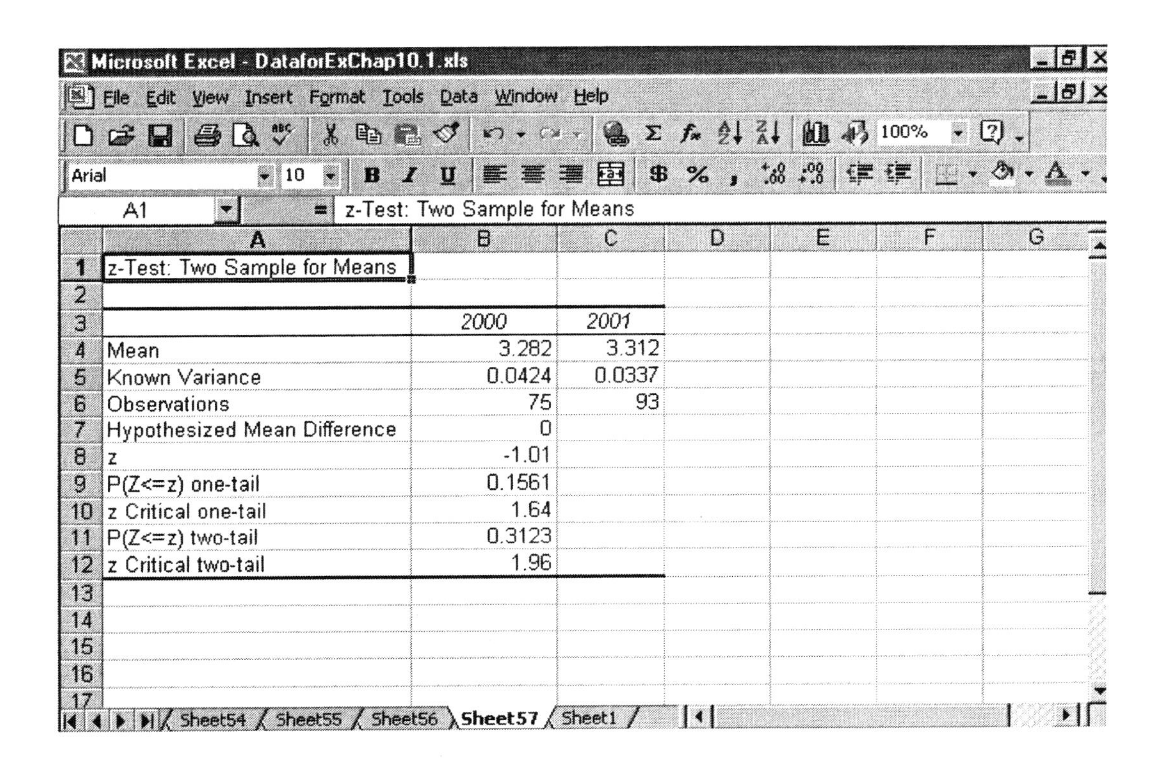
Microsoft Excel - DataforExChap10.1.xls

z-Test: Two Sample for Means		
	2000	*2001*
Mean	3.282	3.312
Known Variance	0.0424	0.0337
Observations	75	93
Hypothesized Mean Difference	0	
z	-1.01	
P(Z<=z) one-tail	0.1561	
z Critical one-tail	1.64	
P(Z<=z) two-tail	0.3123	
z Critical two-tail	1.96	

4. Suppose Seitz produces pulleys that are specified to be 50 mm in diameter. A large batch of pulleys is made in week 1 and another is made in week 5. Quality control people want to determine whether there is a difference in the variance of the diameters of the two batches. Assume that a sample of six pulleys from the week-1 batch results in the following diameter measurements (in mm): 51, 50, 48, 50, 49, 51. Assume that a sample of seven pulleys from the week-5 batch results in the following diameter measurements (in mm): 50, 48, 48, 51, 52, 50, 52. Conduct a test to determine whether the variance in diameters differs between these two populations. Why would the quality control people be interested in such a test? What results of this test would you relate to them? What about the means of these two batches? Analyze these data in terms of the means and report on the results.

ADAPTED FROM: "Seitz Corporation," *Strengthening America's Competitiveness: Resource Management Insights for Small Business Success.* Published by Warner Books on behalf of Connecticut Mutual Life Insurance Company and the U.S. Chamber of Commerce in association with the Blue Chip Enterprise Initiative, 1991. See also the Seitz Corporation's website located at http://www.seitzcorp.com.

11

Analysis of Variance and Chi-Square Applications

Learning Objectives

The focus of this chapter is the analysis of variance and applications of the chi-square statistic, thereby enabling you to:

1. Understand the differences between various experimental designs and when to use them.
2. Compute and interpret the results of a one-way ANOVA.
3. Compute and interpret the results of a random block design.
4. Compute and interpret the results of a two-way ANOVA.
5. Understand and interpret interaction.
6. Understand the chi-square goodness-of-fit test and how to use it.
7. Analyze data by using the chi-square test of independence.

Chapter 11 explores two very important and widely used types of statistical tests: analysis of variance (ANOVA) and chi-square. Analysis of variance tests are used to extend the hypothesis tests of means from two independent populations presented in Chapter 10 to include more than two populations and can be used to statistically test hypotheses from more complex research designs. The chi-square techniques presented in this chapter are appropriate for testing hypotheses using categorical data. The first part of the chapter includes three analysis of variance techniques presented in a design of experiments setting. The last two sections of the chapter present two of the more widely used chi-square techniques.

11.1

Introduction to Design of Experiments

Sometimes business research entails more complicated hypothesis-testing scenarios than those presented to this point in the text. Instead of comparing the wear of tire tread for two brands of tires to determine whether there is a significant difference between the brands, as we could have done by using Chapter 10 techniques, a tire researcher may choose to compare three, four, or even more brands of tires at the same time. In addition, the researcher may want to include different levels of quality of tires in the experiment, such as low-quality, medium-quality, and high-quality tires. Tests may be conducted under varying conditions of temperature, precipitation, or road surface.

How does a business analyst set up designs for such experiments as these? How can the data be analyzed? These questions can be answered, in part, through the use of analysis of variance and the design of experiments.

An **experimental design** is *a plan and a structure to test hypotheses in which the researcher either controls or manipulates one or more variables.* It contains *independent* and *dependent* variables. In an experimental design, an **independent variable** may be either a treatment viable or a classification variable. A **treatment variable** is one *the experimenter controls or modifies in the experiment.* A **classification variable** is some characteristic of the experimental subjects that was *present prior to the experiment and is not a result of the experimenter's manipulations or control.* Independent variables are sometimes also referred to as **factors.** Wal-Mart executives might sanction an in-house study to compare daily sales volumes for a given size store in four different demographic settings: (1) Inner-city stores (large city), (2) Suburban stores (large city), (3) Stores in a medium-size city, and (4) Stores in a small town. Managers might also decide to compare sales on the five different weekdays (Monday through Friday). In this study, the independent variables are store demographics and day of the week. A finance researcher might conduct a study to determine whether there is a significant difference in application fees for home loans in five geographic regions of the United States and might include three different types of lending organizations. In this study, the independent variables are geographic region and types of lending organizations. Or suppose a manufacturing organization produces a valve that is specified to have an opening of 6.37 cm. Quality controllers within the company might decide to test to determine how the openings for produced valves vary among four different machines on three different shifts. This experiment includes the independent variables of type of machine and work shift.

Whether an independent variable can be manipulated by the business analyst depends on the concept being studied. Independent variables such as work shift, gender of employee, geographic region, type of machine, and quality of tire are classification variables with conditions that existed prior to the study. The business analyst cannot change the characteristic of the variable, so he or she studies the phenomenon being explored under several conditions of the various aspects of the variable. As an example, the valve experiment is conducted under the conditions of all three work shifts.

Experimental design
A plan and a structure to test hypotheses in which the researcher either controls or manipulates one or more variables.

Independent variable
In an analysis of variance, the treatment or factor being analyzed. In regression analysis, the predictor variable.

Treatment variable
The independent variable of an experimental design that the researcher either controls or modifies.

Classification variable
The independent variable of an experimental design that was present prior to the experiment and is not the result of the researcher's manipulations or control.

Factors
Another name for the independent variables of an experimental design.

However, some independent variables can be manipulated by the researcher. For example, in the well-known Hawthorne studies of the Western Electric Company in the 1920s in Illinois, the amount of light in production areas was varied to determine the effect of light on productivity. In theory, this independent variable could be manipulated by the researcher to allow any level of lighting. Other examples of independent variables that can be manipulated include the amount of bonuses offered workers, level of humidity, and temperature.

Each independent variable has two or more levels, or classifications. **Levels,** or **classifications,** of independent variables are *the subcategories of the independent variable used by the researcher in the experimental design.* For example, the different demographic settings listed for the Wal-Mart study are four levels, or classifications, of the independent variable store demographics: (1) inner-city store, (2) suburban store, (3) store in a medium-size city, and (4) store in small town. In the valve experiment, there are four levels, or classifications of machines within the independent variable machine type: machine 1, machine 2, machine 3, and machine 4.

Levels, or Classifications
The subcategories of the independent variable used by the researcher in the experimental design.

The other type of variable in an experimental design is a dependent variable. A **dependent variable** is *the response to the different levels of the independent variables.* It is the measurement taken under the conditions of the experimental design that reflect the effects of the independent variable(s). In the Wal-Mart study, the dependent variable is probably the dollar amount of daily total sales. For the study on loan application fees, the fee charged for a loan application is probably the dependent variable. In the valve experiment, the dependent variable is the size of the opening of the valve.

Dependent variable
In analysis of variance, the measurement that is being analyzed; the response to the different levels of the independent variables. In regression analysis, the variable that is being predicted.

Experimental designs in this chapter are analyzed statistically by a group of techniques referred to as **analysis of variance** or **ANOVA.** The analysis of variance concept begins with the notion that individual items being studied, such as employees, machine-produced products, district offices, hospitals, and so on, are not all the same. Note the measurements for the openings of 24 valves randomly selected from an assembly line that are given in Table 11.1. The mean opening is 6.34 cm. Only one of the 24 valve openings is actually the mean. Why do the valve openings vary? Notice that the total sum of squares of deviation of these valve openings around the mean is .3915 cm^2. Why is this value not zero? Using various types of experimental designs, we can explore some possible reasons for this variance with analysis of variance techniques. As we explore each of the experimental designs and their associated analysis, note that the statistical technique is attempting to "break down" the total variance among the objects being studied into possible causes. In the case of the valve openings, this variance of measurements might be due to such variables as machine, operator, shift, supplier, and production conditions, among others.

Analysis of variance (ANOVA)
A technique for statistically analyzing the data from a completely randomized design; uses the F test to determine whether there is a significant difference in two or more independent groups.

Many different types of experimental designs are available to business analysts. In this chapter, we will present and discuss three specific types of experimental designs: completely randomized design, randomized block design, and factorial experiments.

TABLE 11.1
Valve Opening Measurements (in cm) for 24 Valves Produced on an Assembly Line

6.26	6.19	6.33	6.26	6.50
6.19	6.44	6.22	6.54	6.23
6.29	6.40	6.23	6.29	6.58
6.27	6.38	6.58	6.31	6.34
6.21	6.19	6.36	6.56	

$\bar{X} = 6.34$

Total Sum of Squares Deviation = SST = $\Sigma(X_i - \bar{X})^2 = .3915$

11.2
The Completely Randomized Design (One-Way ANOVA)

Completely randomized design
An experimental design wherein there is one treatment or independent variable with two or more treatment levels and one dependent variable. This design is analyzed by analysis of variance.

One of the simplest experimental designs is the completely randomized design. In the **completely randomized design,** subjects are assigned randomly to treatments. The completely randomized design contains only one independent variable, with two or more treatment levels, or classifications. If there are only two treatment levels, or classifications, of the independent variable, the design is the same one used to test the difference in means of two independent populations presented in Chapter 10, which used the t test to analyze the data.

In this section, we will focus on completely randomized designs with three or more classification levels. Analysis of variance, or ANOVA, will be used to analyze the data that result from the treatments. Completely randomized design experiments contain only one dependent variable.

A completely randomized design could be structured for a tire-quality study in which tire quality is the independent variable and the treatment levels are low, medium, and high quality. The dependent variable might be the number of miles driven before the tread fails state inspection. A study of daily sales volumes for Wal-Mart stores could be undertaken by using a completely randomized design with demographic setting as the independent variable. The treatment levels, or classifications, would be inner-city stores, suburban stores, stores in medium-size cities and stores in small towns. The dependent variable would be sales dollars.

Suppose a business analyst decides to analyze the effects of the machine operator on the valve opening measurements of valves produced in a manufacturing plant, like those shown in Table 11.1. The independent variable in this design is machine operator. Suppose further that there are three different operators (one for each shift). These three machine operators are the levels of treatment, or classification, of the independent variable. The dependent variable is the opening measurement of the valve. Figure 11.1 shows the structure of this completely randomized design. Is there a significant difference in the mean valve openings between the three machine operators? The data from Table 11.1 have been organized by machine operator as shown in Figure 11.1 and are displayed in Table 11.2.

Figure 11.1
Completely randomized design

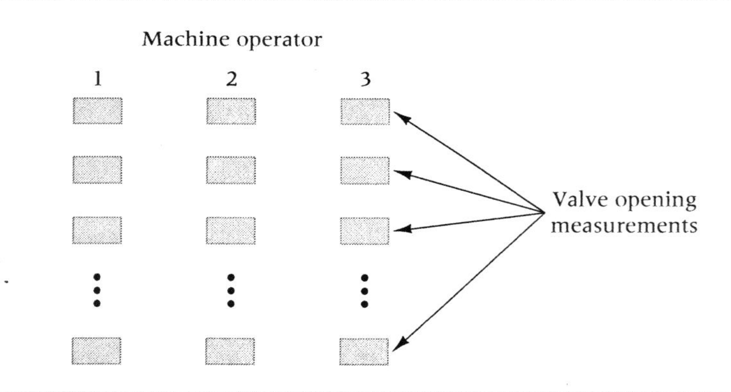

TABLE 11.2
Valve Openings by Machine Operator

OPERATOR 1	OPERATOR 2	OPERATOR 3
6.56	6.38	6.39
6.40	6.19	6.33
6.54	6.26	6.29
6.34	6.23	6.43
6.58	6.22	6.36
6.44	6.27	6.41
6.36	6.29	6.31
6.50	6.19	6.50

One-Way Analysis of Variance

In the machine operator example, is it possible to analyze the three samples by using a t test for the difference in two sample means? These three samples would require ${}_3C_2 = 3$ individual t tests to accomplish the analysis of two groups at a time. Recall that if $\alpha = .05$ for a particular test, there is a 5% chance of rejecting a null hypothesis that is true (i.e., committing a Type I error). If enough tests are done, eventually one or more null hypotheses will be falsely rejected by chance. Hence, $\alpha = .05$ is valid only for one t test. In this problem, with three t tests, the error rate compounds, so when the analyst is finished with the problem there is a much greater than .05 chance of committing a Type I error. Fortunately, a technique has been developed that analyzes all the sample means at one time and thus precludes the buildup of error rate: analysis of variance (ANOVA). A completely randomized design is analyzed by a **one-way analysis of variance.**

One-way analysis of variance
The process used to analyze a completely randomized experimental design. This process involves computing a ratio of the variance between treatment levels of the independent variable to the error variance. This ratio is an F value, which is then used to determine whether there are any significant differences between the means of the treatment levels.

In general, if k samples are being analyzed, the following hypotheses are being tested in a one-way ANOVA.

$$H_0: \mu_1 = \mu_2 = \mu_3 = \cdots = \mu_k$$

H_a: At least one of the means is different from the others.

The null hypothesis states that the population means for all treatment levels are equal. Because of the way the alternative hypothesis is stated, if even one of the population means is different from the others, the null hypothesis is rejected.

Testing these hypotheses by using one-way ANOVA is accomplished by partitioning the total variance of the data into the following two variances.

1. The variance resulting from the treatment (columns)
2. The error variance, or that portion of the total variance unexplained by the treatment

As part of this process, the total sum of squares of deviation of values around the mean can be divided into two additive and independent parts.

$$\text{SST} = \text{SSC} + \text{SSE}$$

$$\sum_{i=1}^{n_j}\sum_{j=1}^{C}(X_{ij} - \overline{X})^2 = \sum_{j=1}^{C} n_j(\overline{X}_j - \overline{X})^2 + \sum_{i=1}^{n_j}\sum_{j=1}^{C}(X_{ij} - \overline{X}_j)^2$$

where:
i = particular member of a treatment level
j = a treatment level
C = number of treatment levels
n_j = number of observations in a given treatment level
$\overline{X}$ = grand mean
$\overline{X}_j$ = mean of a treatment group or level
X_{ij} = individual value

This relationship is shown in Figure 11.2. Observe that the total sum of squares of variation is partitioned into the sum of squares of treatment (columns) and the sum of squares of error.

The formulas used to accomplish one-way analysis of variance are developed from this relationship. The double summation sign indicates that the values are summed within a treatment level and across treatment levels. Basically, ANOVA compares the relative sizes of the treatment variation and the *error* variation (within-group variation). The error variation is unaccounted-for variation and can be viewed at this point as variation due to individual differences within treatment groups. If there is a significant difference in treatments, the treatment variation should be large relative to the error variation.

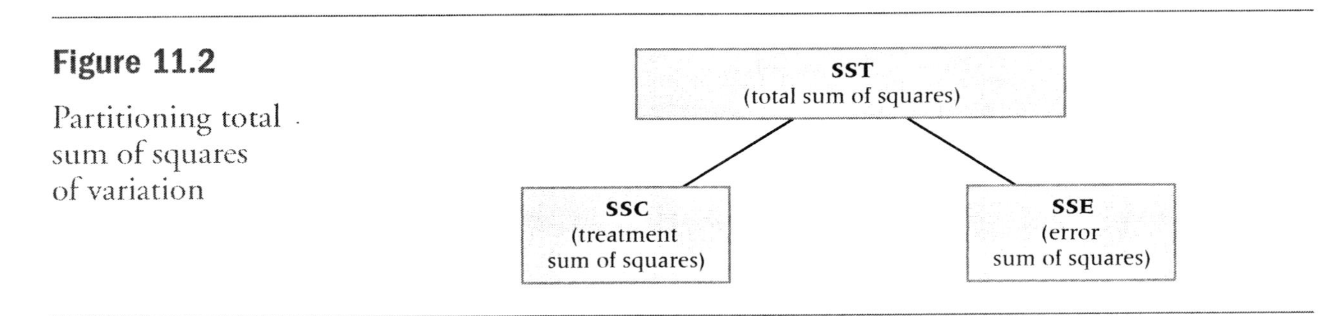

Figure 11.2

Partitioning total sum of squares of variation

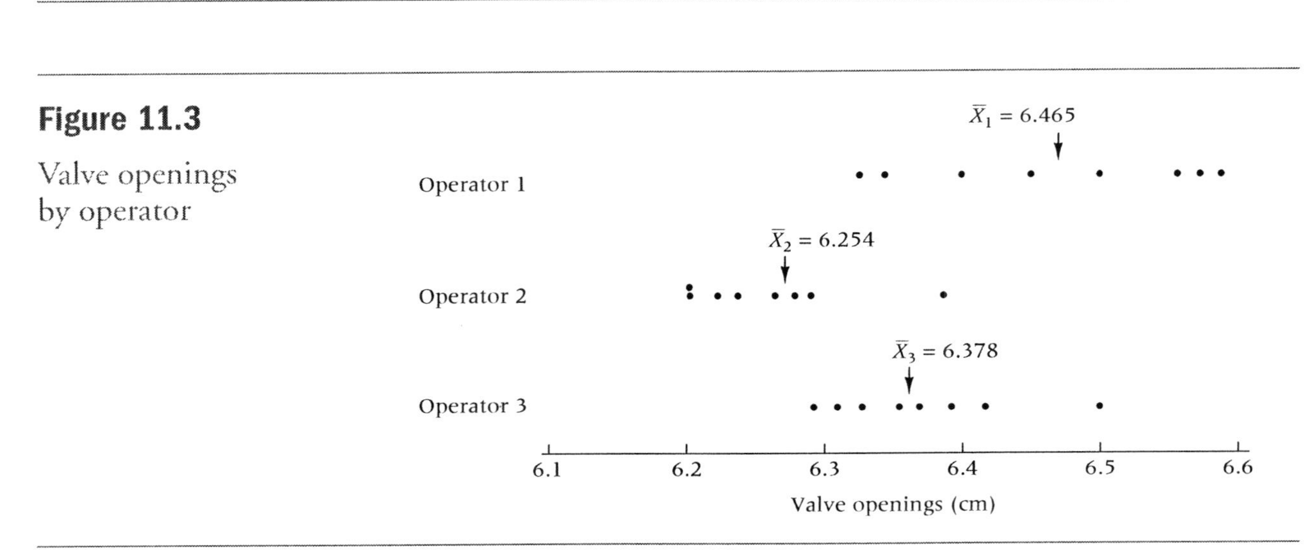

Figure 11.3

Valve openings by operator

Figure 11.3 displays the data from the machine operator example in terms of treatment level. Note the variation of values (X) *within* each treatment level. Now examine the variation *between* levels 1 through 3 (the difference in the machine operator groupings). Note that the means are located somewhat apart from each other. This difference also is underscored by the mean values for each treatment level:

$$\bar{X}_1 = 6.465 \quad \bar{X}_2 = 6.254 \quad \bar{X}_3 = 6.378.$$

Analysis of variance is used to determine statistically whether the variance between the treatment level means is greater than the variances within levels (error variance). There are several important assumptions underlying analysis of variance:

1. Observations are drawn from normally distributed populations.
2. Observations represent random samples from the populations.
3. Variances of the populations are equal.

These assumptions are similar to those for using the t test for small independent samples in Chapter 10. It is assumed that the populations are normally distributed and that the population variances are equal. These techniques should be used only with random samples.

An ANOVA is computed with the three sums of squares: total, treatment (columns), and error. Shown here are the formulas to compute a one-way analysis of variance. The term SS represents sum of squares, and the term MS represents mean square. SSC is the sum of squares columns, which yields the sum of squares between treatments. This measures the variation between columns or between treatments since the independent variable treatment levels are presented as columns. SSE is the sum of squares of error, which yields the variation within treatments (or columns). Some say that this is a measure of the individual differences unaccounted for by the treatments. SST is the total sum of squares and is a measure of all variation in the dependent variable. As shown previously, SST contains both SSC and SSE and can be partitioned into SSC and SSE. MSC, MSE, and MST are the mean squares of column, error, and total, respectively. Mean square is an average and is computed by dividing the sum of squares by the degrees of freedom. Finally, the ***F* value** is determined by dividing the treatment variance (MSC) by the error variance (MSE). As discussed in Chapter 10, the *F* is a ratio of two variances. In the ANOVA situation, the *F* is *a ratio of the treatment variance to the error variance.*

***F* value**
The ratio of two variances, used to reach statistical conclusions regarding the null hypothesis; in ANOVA, the ratio of the treatment variance to the error variance.

FORMULAS FOR COMPUTING A ONE-WAY ANOVA

$$\text{SSC} = \sum_{j=1}^{C} n_j(\bar{X}_j - \bar{X})^2 \qquad df_C = C - 1 \qquad \text{MSC} = \frac{\text{SSC}}{df_C}$$

$$\text{SSE} = \sum_{i=1}^{n_j}\sum_{j=1}^{C} (X_{ij} - \bar{X}_j)^2 \qquad df_E = N - C \qquad \text{MSE} = \frac{\text{SSE}}{df_E}$$

$$\text{SST} = \sum_{i=1}^{n_j}\sum_{j=1}^{C} (X_{ij} - \bar{X})^2 \qquad df_T = N - 1 \qquad F = \frac{\text{MSC}}{\text{MSE}}$$

where:
i = a particular member of a treatment level
j = a treatment level
C = number of treatment levels
n_j = number of observations in a given treatment level
$\bar{X}$ = grand mean
$\bar{X}_j$ = column mean
X_{ij} = individual value

Performing these calculations for the machine operator example yields the following.

Valve Openings by Machine Operator

OPERATOR 1	OPERATOR 2	OPERATOR 3
6.56	6.38	6.39
6.40	6.19	6.33
6.54	6.26	6.29
6.34	6.23	6.43
6.58	6.22	6.36
6.44	6.27	6.41
6.36	6.29	6.31
6.50	6.19	6.50

T_j:	$T_1 = 51.72$	$T_2 = 50.03$	$T_3 = 51.02$	$T = 152.77$
n_j:	$n_1 = 8$	$n_2 = 8$	$n_3 = 8$	$n = 24$
$\bar{X}_j$:	$\bar{X}_1 = 6.465$	$\bar{X}_2 = 6.25375$	$\bar{X}_3 = 6.3775$	$\bar{X} = 6.36542$

$$\text{SSC} = \sum_{j=1}^{C} n_j(\bar{X}_j - \bar{X})^2$$
$$= [8(6.465 - 6.36542)^2 + 8(6.25375 - 6.36542)^2 + 8(6.3775 - 6.36542)^2]$$
$$= 0.07933 + 0.09976 + 0.00117$$
$$= 0.18026$$

$$\text{SSE} = \sum_{i=1}^{n_j}\sum_{j=1}^{C} (X_{ij} - \bar{X}_j)^2$$
$$= [(6.56 - 6.465)^2 + (6.40 - 6.465)^2 + (6.54 - 6.465)^2 + (6.34 - 6.465)^2$$
$$+ (6.58 - 6.465)^2 + (6.44 - 6.465)^2 + (6.36 - 6.465)^2 + (6.50 - 6.465)^2$$
$$+ (6.38 - 6.25375)^2 + (6.19 - 6.25375)^2 + \cdots + (6.31 - 6.3775)^2$$
$$+ (6.50 - 6.3775)^2]$$
$$= 0.121738$$

$$\text{SST} = \sum_{i=1}^{n_j}\sum_{j=1}^{C} (X_{ij} - \bar{X})^2$$
$$= [(6.56 - 6.36542)^2 + (6.40 - 6.36542)^2 + (6.54 - 6.36542)^2$$
$$+ \cdots + (6.31 - 6.36542)^2 + (6.50 - 6.36542)^2]$$
$$= 0.301997$$

$$\text{df}_C = C - 1 = 3 - 1 = 2$$
$$\text{df}_E = N - C = 24 - 3 = 21$$
$$\text{df}_T = N - 1 = 24 - 1 = 23$$
$$\text{MSC} = \frac{\text{SSC}}{\text{df}_C} = \frac{0.18026}{2} = 0.090130$$
$$\text{MSE} = \frac{\text{SSE}}{\text{df}_E} = \frac{0.121738}{21} = 0.005797$$
$$F = \frac{\text{MSC}}{\text{MSE}} = \frac{0.090130}{0.005797} = 15.55$$

From these computations, an analysis of variance chart can be constructed, as shown in Table 11.3. The observed F value is 15.55. It is compared to a critical value from the F table to determine whether there is a significant difference in treatment or classification.

***F* distribution**
A distribution based on the ratio of two random variances; used in testing two variances and in analysis of variance.

Reading the F Distribution Table

The ***F* distribution** table is in Table A.7. Associated with every F value in the table are two unique df values: degrees of freedom in the numerator (df_C) and degrees of freedom in the denominator (df_E). To look up a value in the F distribution table, the researcher must know both degrees of freedom. Because each F distribution is determined by a

TABLE 11.3
Analysis of Variance Table for the Machine Operator Example

SOURCE OF VARIANCE	*df*	SS	MS	*F*
Between (columns)	2	0.180259	0.090130	15.55
Error	21	0.121738	0.005797	
Total	23	0.301997		

unique pair of degrees of freedom, there are many F distributions. Space constraints limit Table A.7 to F values for only $\alpha = .005, .01, .025, .05$, and $.10$. However, statistical computer software packages for computing ANOVAs usually give a probability for the F value, which allows a hypothesis-testing decision for any alpha based on the p-value method.

In the one-way ANOVA, the df_C values are the treatment (column) degrees of freedom, $C - 1$. The df_E values are the error degrees of freedom, $N - C$. Table 11.4 contains an abbreviated F distribution table for $\alpha = .05$. For the machine operator example, $df_C = 2$ and $df_E = 21$. $F_{.05,2,21}$ from Table 11.4 is 3.47. This value is the critical value of the F test. Analysis of variance tests are *always* one-tailed tests with the rejection region in the upper tail. The decision rule is to reject the null hypothesis if the observed F value is greater than the critical F value ($F_{.05,2,21} = 3.47$). In this case, the observed F value of 15.55 is larger than the table F value of 3.47, so the null hypothesis is rejected. Not all means are equal, so there is a significant difference in the mean number of valve openings by machine operator. Figure 11.4 is a graph of an F distribution showing the critical F value for this example and the rejection region. Note that the F distribution begins at zero and contains no negative values. The reason is that an F value is the ratio of two variances, and variances are always positive.

Multiple Comparisons

Analysis of variance techniques are particularly useful in testing hypotheses about the differences of means in multiple groups because ANOVA utilizes only one single overall test. The advantage of this is that the probability of committing a Type I error, α, is controlled. As noted in Section 11.2, if three groups are tested two at a time, it takes three tests (${}_3C_2$) to analyze hypotheses between all possible pairs. In general, if k groups are tested two at a time, there are ${}_kC_2 = k(k - 1)/2$ possible paired comparisons.

TABLE 11.4
An Abbreviated F Table for $\alpha = .05$

DENOMINATOR DEGREES OF FREEDOM	NUMERATOR DEGREES OF FREEDOM								
	1	2	3	4	5	6	7	8	9
•									
•									
•									
20	4.35	3.49	3.10	2.87	2.71	2.60	2.51	2.45	2.39
21	4.32	3.47	3.07	2.84	2.68	2.57	2.49	2.42	2.37
22	4.30	3.44	3.05	2.82	2.66	2.55	2.46	2.40	2.34

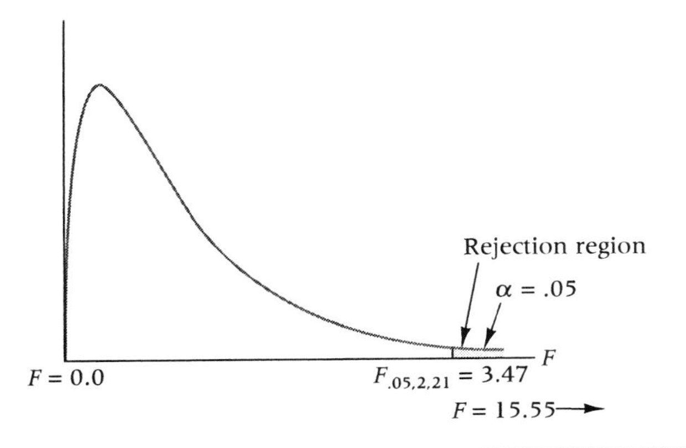

Figure 11.4
Graph of F values for the machine operator example

Suppose alpha for an experiment is to be .05. If two different pairs of comparisons are made in the experiment using alpha of .05 in each, there is a .95 probability of not making a Type I error in each comparison. This results in a .9025 probability of not making a Type I error in either comparison (.95 × .95), and a .0975 probability of committing a Type I error in at least one comparison (1 – .9025). Thus, the probability of committing a Type I error for this experiment is not .05 but .0975. In an experiment where the means of three groups are being tested two at a time (like the machine operator problem), three different tests would need to be conducted. If each is analyzed using $\alpha = .05$, the probability that no Type I error would be committed in any of the three tests is .95 × .95 × .95 = .857 and the probability of committing at least one Type I error in the three tests is 1 – .857 = .143. However, computing one ANOVA on all three groups simultaneously using $\alpha = .05$ maintains the value of alpha for the experiment.

Sometimes the researcher is satisfied with conducting an overall test of differences in groups such as the one ANOVA provides. However, when it is determined that there is an overall difference in population means, it is often desirable to go back to the groups and determine from the data which pairs of means are significantly different, if any. Such pairwise analyses can lead to the buildup of the Type I experimental error rate, as mentioned. Fortunately, several techniques, referred to as **multiple comparisons,** have been developed to handle this problem.

Multiple comparisons Statistical techniques used to compare pairs of treatment means when the analysis of variance yields an overall significant difference in the treatment means.

Multiple comparisons are to be used only when an overall significant difference between groups has been obtained by using the F value of the analysis of variance. Some of these techniques protect more for Type I errors and others protect more for Type II errors. Some multiple comparison techniques require equal sample sizes. There seems to be some difference of opinion in the literature about which techniques are more appropriate. The variety of multiple comparison tests available include the following:* Dunn's multiple comparison procedure, Fisher's LSD test, Tukey's HSD test, Scheffe's S method, Newman-Keuls test, and Duncan's new multiple range test. These tests differ in the way they analyze the means and the manner in which they control error. The use of these techniques is beyond the scope of this text, and they will not be presented in detail here.

Analysis Using Excel

It is relatively easy to compute a one-way ANOVA in Excel. From **Tools** and then **Data Analysis,** select **ANOVA: Single Factor.** The dialog box for **ANOVA: Single Factor** is displayed in Figure 11.5. For the ***Input* Range,** insert the location of all the data. Check whether the data are arranged in columns or rows. The default is columns. Check whether or not there are labels in the first row, and insert the value of alpha for the test.

The Excel output for the machine operator problem is shown in Figure 11.6. This output contains a summary table and an ANOVA table. The summary table displays descriptive data for the samples including size, sum, mean, and variance. The ANOVA table is a standard ANOVA table, which contains the sum of squares (SS) for the between groups, the sum of squares for the within groups (error), and the total sum of squares along with degrees of freedom, the mean squares, and the observed F value. Note that these computed values are essentially the same as those computed by hand in this section (with slight rounding error). The p-value, reported for this problem in scientific notation as 7.19E-05 (7.19×10^{-5}), is .0000719. Since this is less than the assumed alpha (.05), the decision is to reject the null hypothesis and declare that there is a significant difference between machine operators. In addition, the Excel output contains the table value, which for this problem is $F = 3.47$. This Excel feature is a convenience for those business analysts who prefer using a critical value rather than a p-value for decision making.

*Kirk, Roger, *Experimental Design: Procedures for the Behavioral Sciences.* (Belmont, CA: Brooks/Cole, 1968).

Figure 11.5 Excel dialog box for **ANOVA: Single Factor**

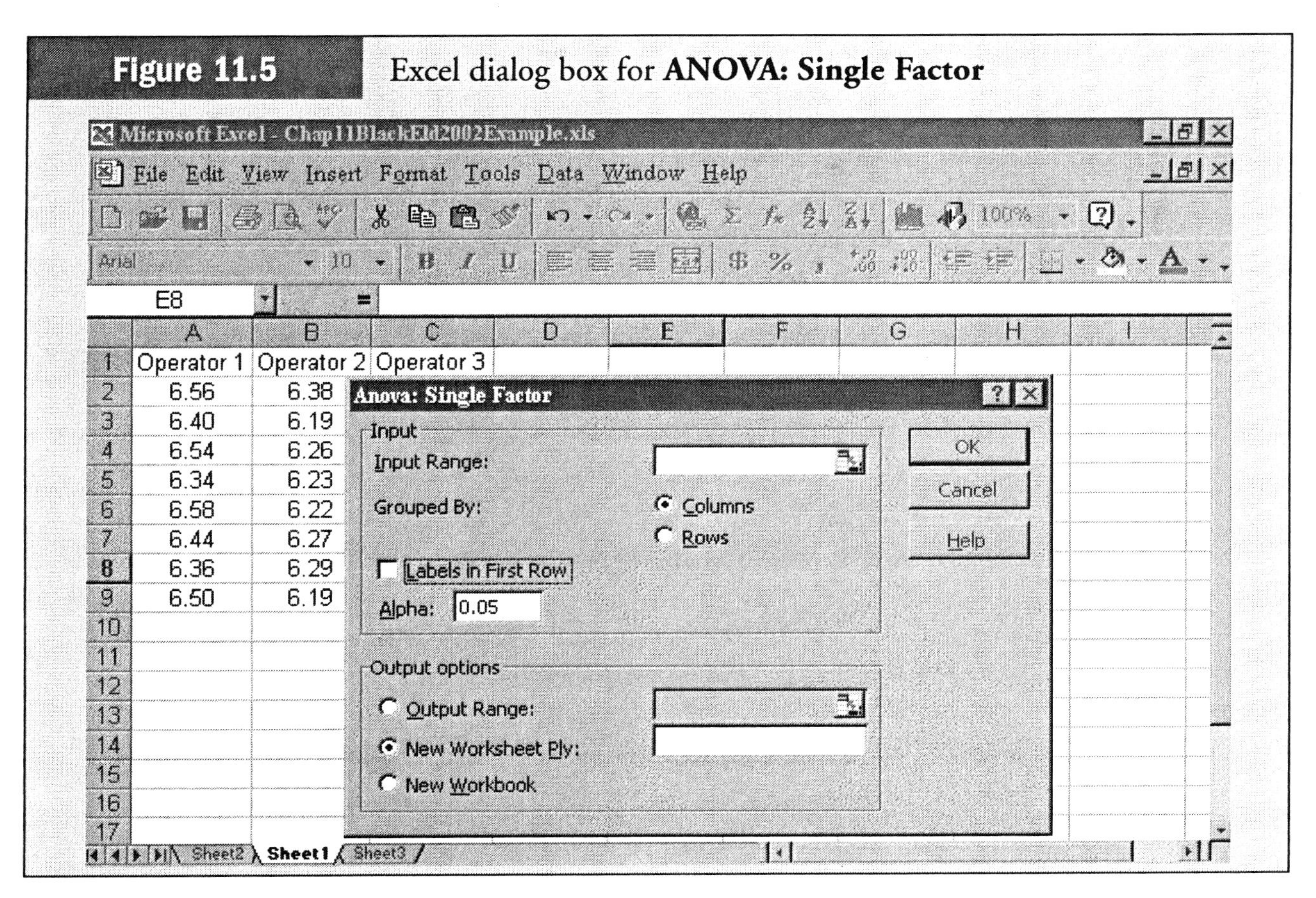

Figure 11.6 Excel output for the machine operator problem

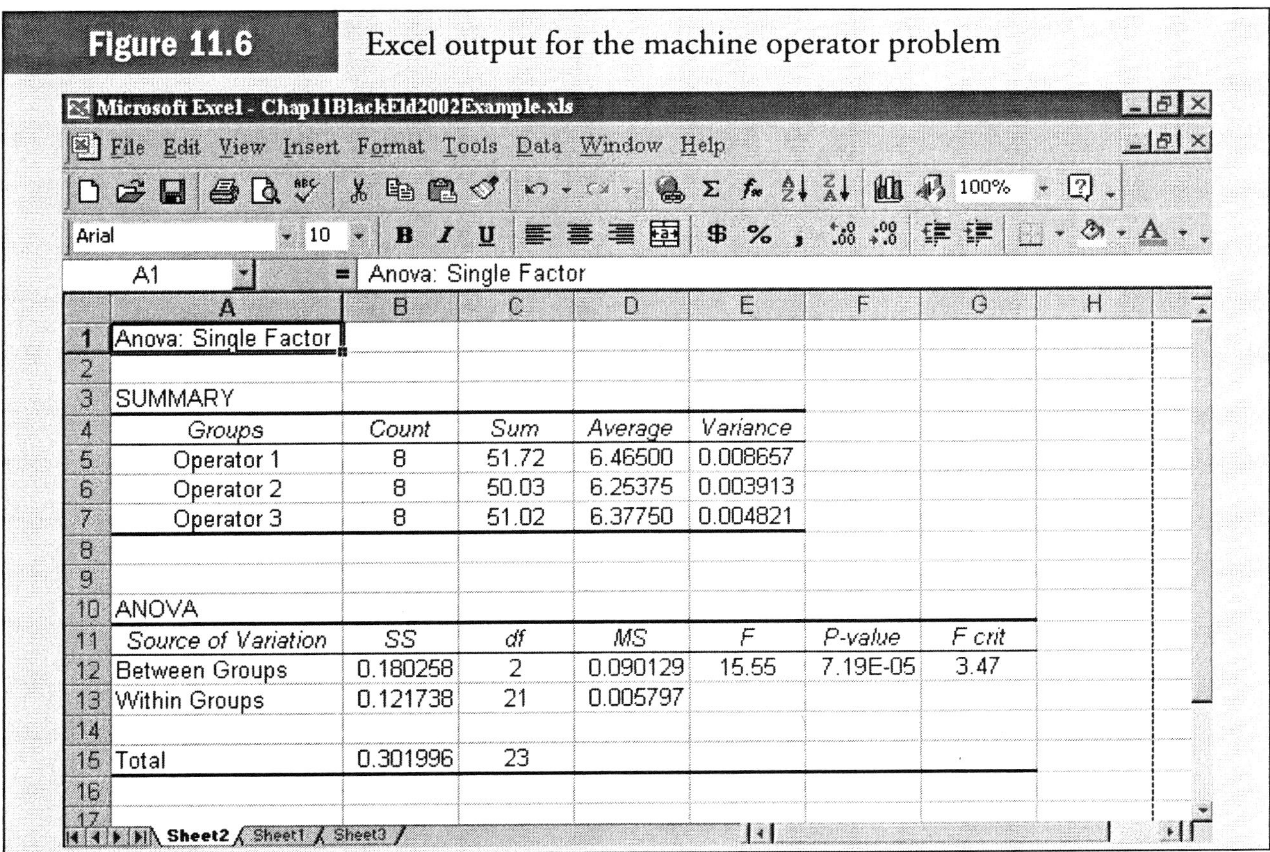

Anova: Single Factor

SUMMARY

Groups	Count	Sum	Average	Variance
Operator 1	8	51.72	6.46500	0.008657
Operator 2	8	50.03	6.25375	0.003913
Operator 3	8	51.02	6.37750	0.004821

ANOVA

Source of Variation	SS	df	MS	F	P-value	F crit
Between Groups	0.180258	2	0.090129	15.55	7.19E-05	3.47
Within Groups	0.121738	21	0.005797			
Total	0.301996	23				

DEMONSTRATION PROBLEM 11.1

A company has four manufacturing plants, and company officials want to determine whether there is a difference in the average age of workers at the four locations. The following data are the ages of randomly selected workers at each plant. Perform a one-way ANOVA to determine whether there is a significant difference in the mean ages of the workers at the four plants. Use $\alpha = .01$.

SOLUTION

STEP **1.** The hypotheses follow.

H_0: $\mu_1 = \mu_2 = \mu_3 = \mu_4$

H_a: At least one of the means is different from the others.

STEP **2.** The appropriate test statistic is the F test calculated from ANOVA.

STEP **3.** The value of α is .01.

STEP **4.** The degrees of freedom for this problem are $4 - 1 = 3$ for the numerator (treatments – columns) and $18 - 4 = 14$ for the denominator (error). The critical F value is $F_{.01,3,14} = 5.56$. Because ANOVAs are always one-tailed with the rejection region in the upper tail, the decision rule is to reject the null hypothesis if the observed value of F is greater than 5.56.

STEP **5.**

PLANT (EMPLOYEE AGES)

1	2	3	4
29	32	25	27
27	33	24	24
30	31	24	26
27	34	25	
	30	26	
	28		

STEP **6.**

T_j:	$T_1 = 113$	$T_2 = 188$	$T_3 = 124$	$T_4 = 77$	$T = 502$
n_j:	$n_1 = 4$	$n_2 = 6$	$n_3 = 5$	$n_4 = 3$	$N = 18$
$\bar{X}_j$:	$\bar{X}_1 = 28.25$	$\bar{X}_2 = 31.33$	$\bar{X}_3 = 24.8$	$\bar{X}_4 = 25.67$	$\bar{X} = 27.89$

$$SSC = 4(28.25 - 27.89)^2 + 6(31.33 - 27.89)^2 + 5(24.8 - 27.89)^2 + 3(25.67 - 27.89)^2$$
$$= 134.23$$

$$SSE = (29 - 28.25)^2 + (27 - 28.25)^2 + \cdots + (24 - 25.67)^2 + (26 - 25.67)^2$$
$$= 37.55$$

$$SST = (29 - 27.89)^2 + (27 - 27.89)^2 + \cdots + (24 - 27.89)^2 + (26 - 27.89)^2$$
$$= 171.78$$

$$df_C = 4 - 1 = 3$$

$$df_E = 18 - 4 = 14$$

$$df_T = 18 - 1 = 17$$

SOURCE OF VARIANCE	SS	df	MS	F
Between	134.23	3	44.74	16.7
Error	37.55	14	2.68	
Total	171.78	17		

STEP **7.** The decision is to reject the null hypothesis because the observed F value of 16.7 is greater than the critical table F value of 5.56.

STEP **8.** There is a significant difference in the mean ages of workers at the three plants.

Following is the Excel output for Demonstration Problem 11.1.

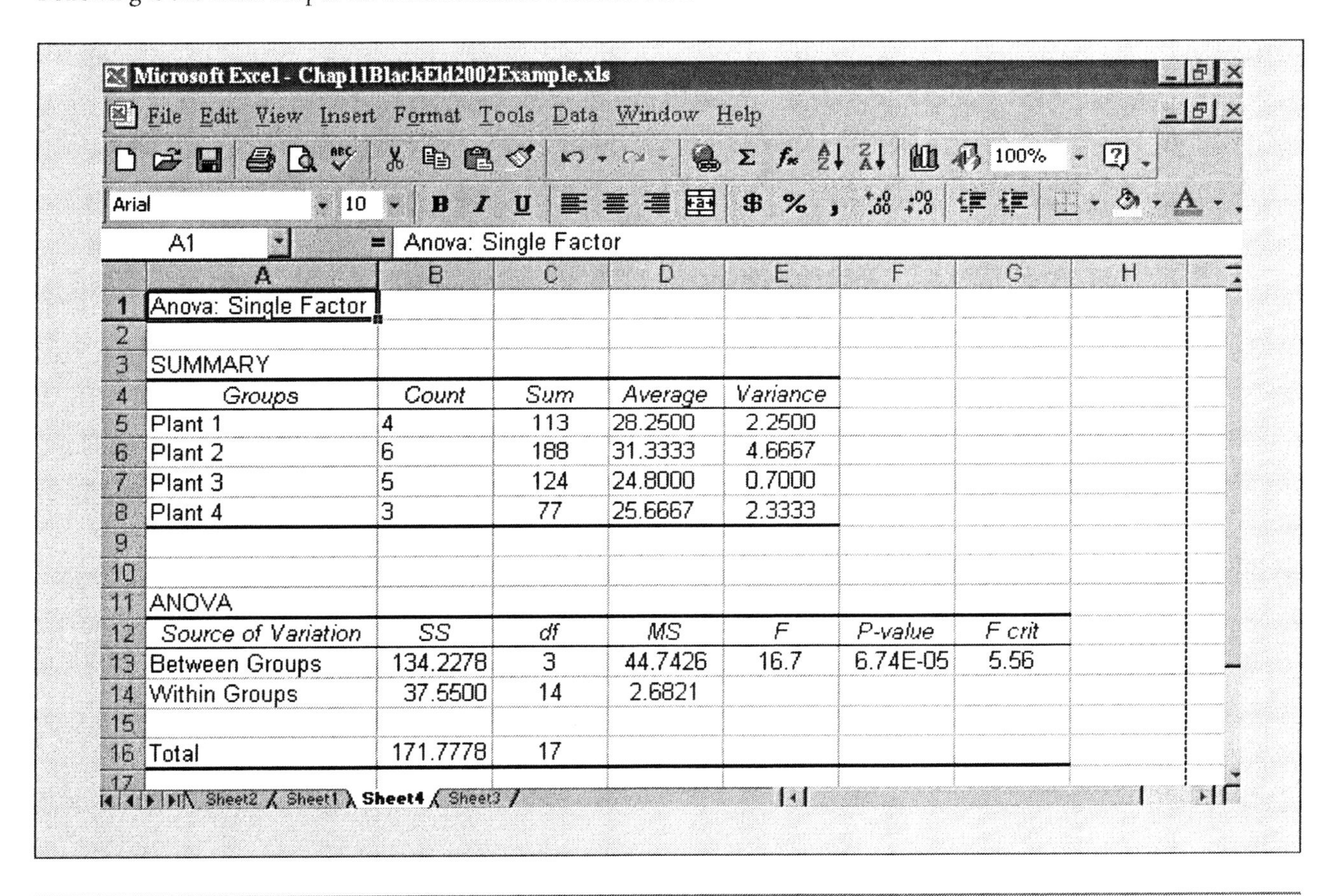
Microsoft Excel - Chap11BlackEld2002Example.xls

A1 = Anova: Single Factor

Anova: Single Factor

SUMMARY

Groups	Count	Sum	Average	Variance
Plant 1	4	113	28.2500	2.2500
Plant 2	6	188	31.3333	4.6667
Plant 3	5	124	24.8000	0.7000
Plant 4	3	77	25.6667	2.3333

ANOVA

Source of Variation	SS	df	MS	F	P-value	F crit
Between Groups	134.2278	3	44.7426	16.7	6.74E-05	5.56
Within Groups	37.5500	14	2.6821			
Total	171.7778	17				

Sheet2 / Sheet1 / Sheet4 / Sheet3

11.2
Problems

11.1 Compute a one-way ANOVA on the following data.

1	2	3
2	5	3
1	3	4
3	6	5
3	4	5
2	5	3
1		5

Determine the computed F value. Compare the F value with the critical table F value and decide whether to reject the null hypothesis. Use $\alpha = .05$.

11.2 Compute a one-way ANOVA on the following data.

1	2	3	4	5
14	10	11	16	14
13	9	12	17	12
10	12	13	14	13
	9	12	16	13
	10		17	12
				14

Determine the computed F value. Compare the F value with the critical table F value and decide whether to reject the null hypothesis. Use $\alpha = .01$.

11.3 Develop a one-way ANOVA on the following data.

1	2	3	4
113	120	132	122
121	127	130	118
117	125	129	125
110	129	135	125

Determine the computed F value. Compare it to the critical F value and decide whether to reject the null hypothesis. Use a 1% level of significance.

11.4 A milk company has four machines that fill gallon jugs with milk. The quality control manager is interested in determining whether the average fill for these machines is the same. The following data represent random samples of fill measures (in quarts) for 19 jugs of milk filled by the different machines. Use $\alpha = .01$ to test the hypotheses.

MACHINE 1	MACHINE 2	MACHINE 3	MACHINE 4
4.05	3.99	3.97	4.00
4.01	4.02	3.98	4.02
4.02	4.01	3.97	3.99
4.04	3.99	3.95	4.01
	4.00	4.00	
	4.00		

11.5 That the starting salaries of new accounting graduates would differ according to geographic regions of the United States seems logical. A random selection of accounting firms is taken from three geographic regions, and each is asked to state the starting salary for a new accounting graduate who is going to work in auditing. The data obtained follow. Use a one-way ANOVA to analyze these data. Note that the data can be restated to make the computations more reasonable (example: \$32,500 = 3.25). Use a 1% level of significance.

SOUTH	NORTHEAST	WEST
\$30,500	\$41,000	\$35,500
31,500	39,500	33,500
30,000	39,000	35,000
31,000	38,000	36,500
31,500	39,500	36,000

11.6 A management consulting company presents a 3-day seminar on project management to various clients. The seminar is basically the same each time it is given. However, sometimes it is presented to high-level managers, sometimes to midlevel managers, and sometimes to low-level managers. The seminar facilitators believe evaluations of the seminar may vary with the audience. Suppose the following data are some randomly selected evaluation scores from different levels of managers after they have attended the seminar. The ratings are on a scale from 1 to 10, with 10 being the highest. Use a one-way ANOVA to determine whether there is a significant difference in the evaluations according to manager level. Assume $\alpha = .05$.

HIGH LEVEL	MIDLEVEL	LOW LEVEL
7	8	5
7	9	6
8	8	5
7	10	7
9	9	4
	10	8
	8	

11.7 Family transportation costs are usually higher than most people believe because those costs include car payments, insurance, fuel costs, repairs, parking, and public transportation. Twenty randomly selected families in four major cities are asked to use their records to estimate a monthly figure for transportation cost. Use the data obtained and ANOVA to test whether there is a significant difference in monthly transportation costs for families living in these cities. Assume that $\alpha = .05$.

ATLANTA	NEW YORK	LOS ANGELES	CHICAGO
$650	$250	$850	$540
480	525	700	450
550	300	950	675
600	175	780	550
675	500	600	600

11.3 The Randomized Block Design

A second research design is the **randomized block design.** The randomized block design is similar to the completely randomized design in that there is one independent variable (treatment variable) of interest. However, the randomized block design also includes a second variable, referred to as a blocking variable, that can be used to control for confounding or concomitant variables.

Confounding or **concomitant** variables are *variables that are not being controlled by the researcher in the experiment but can have an effect on the outcome of the treatment being studied.* For example, suppose a completely randomized design is used to analyze the effects of temperature on the tensile strengths of metal. Other variables not being controlled by the business analyst in this experiment may affect the tensile strength of metal, such as humidity, raw materials, machine, and shift. One way to control for these variables is to include them in the experimental design. The randomized block design has the capability of adding one of these variables into the analysis as a blocking variable. A **blocking variable** is *a variable that the researcher wants to control but is not the treatment variable of interest.*

One of the first people to use the randomized block design was Sir Ronald A. Fisher. He applied the design to the field of agriculture, where he was interested in studying the growth patterns of various varieties of seeds for a given type of plant. The seed variety was his independent variable. However, he realized that as he experimented on different plots of ground, the "block" of ground might make some difference in the experiment. Fisher designated several different plots of ground as blocks, which he controlled as a second variable. Each of the seed varieties was planted on each of the blocks. The main thrust of his study was to compare the seed varieties (independent variable). He merely wanted to control for the difference in plots of ground (blocking variable).

In the example of the problem of analyzing the effects of temperature on the tensile strengths of metal, blocking variables might be machine number (if several machines are used to make the metal), worker, shift, or day of the week. The business analyst probably

Randomized block design
An experimental design in which there is one independent variable of interest and a second variable, known as a blocking variable, that is used to control for confounding or concomitant variables.

Confounding variables, or Concomitant variables
Variables that are not being controlled by the researcher in the experiment but can have an effect on the outcome of the treatment being studied.

Blocking variable
A variable that the researcher wants to control but is not the treatment variable of interest.

Repeated measures design
A randomized block design in which each block level is an individual item or person, and that person or item is measured across all treatments.

already knows that different workers or different machines will produce at least slightly different metal tensile strengths because of individual differences. However, designating the variable (machine or worker) as the blocking variable and computing a randomized block design affords the potential for a more powerful analysis. In other experiments, some other possible variables that might be used as blocking variables include gender of subject, age of subject, intelligence of subject, economic level of subject, brand, supplier, or vehicle.

A special case of the randomized block design is the repeated measures design. The **repeated measures design** is *a randomized block design in which each block level is an individual item or person, and that person or item is measured across all treatments.* Thus, where a block level in a randomized block design is night shift and items produced under different treatment levels on the night shift are measured, in a repeated measures design, a block level might be an individual machine or person; items produced by that person or machine are then randomly chosen across all treatments. Thus, there is a *repeated measure* of the person or machine across all treatments. This repeated measures design is an extension of the t test for dependent samples presented in Section 10.3.

The sum of squares in a completely randomized design is

$$\text{SST} = \text{SSC} + \text{SSE}.$$

In a randomized block design, the sum of squares is

$$\text{SST} = \text{SSC} + \text{SSR} + \text{SSE}$$

where:
SST = sum of squares total,
SSC = sum of squares columns (treatment),
SSR = sum of squares rows (blocking), and
SSE = sum of squares error.

SST and SSC are the same for a given analysis whether a completely randomized design or a randomized block design is used. Because of this, the SSR (blocking effects) must come out of the SSE. That is, some of the error variation in the completely randomized design is accounted for in the blocking effects of the randomized block design, as shown in Figure 11.7. By reducing the error term, it is possible that the value of F for treatment will increase (the denominator of the F value is decreased). However, if there is not sufficient difference between levels of the blocking variable, the use of a randomized block design can lead to a less powerful result than would a completely randomized design computed on the same problem. Thus, the researcher should seek out blocking variables that he or she believes are significant contributors to variation among measurements of the dependent variable. Figure 11.8 shows the layout of a randomized block design.

In each of the intersections of independent variable and blocking variable in Figure 11.8, one measurement is taken. In the randomized block design, there is one measurement for each treatment level under each blocking level.

The null and alternate hypotheses for the treatment effects in the randomized block design are

$$H_0: \mu_{.1} = \mu_{.2} = \mu_{.3} = \cdots = \mu_{.C}$$

H_a: At least one of the treatment means is different from the others.

For the blocking effects, they are

$$H_0: \mu_{1.} = \mu_{2.} = \mu_{3.} = \cdots = \mu_{R.}$$

H_a: At least one of the blocking means is different from the others.

Figure 11.7

Partitioning the total sum of squares in a randomized block design

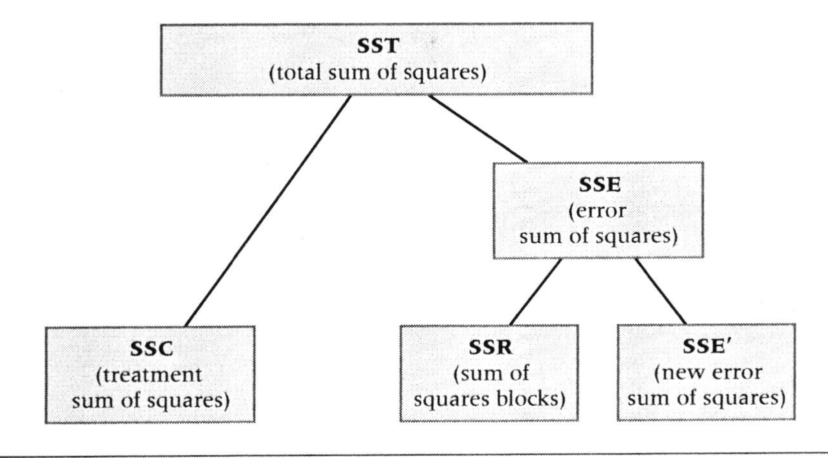

Figure 11.8

A randomized block design

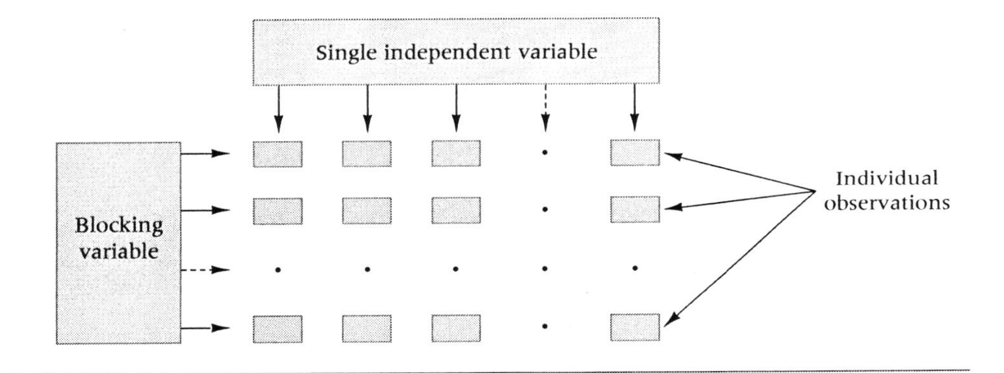

Essentially, we are testing the null hypothesis that the population means of the treatment groups are equal. If the null hypothesis is rejected, at least one of the population means does not equal the others.

The formulas for computing a randomized block design are on the following page.

The F value for treatments shown with the randomized block design design formulas is compared to a table F value, which is ascertained from Appendix A.7 by using α, df_C (treatment), and df_E (error). If the observed F value is greater than the table value, the null hypothesis is rejected for that alpha value. In addition, Excel output provides a p-value for the observed F. As usual, if the p-value is less than α, the decision is to reject the null hypothesis. Such a result would indicate that not all population treatment means are equal. At this point, the business analyst has the option of computing multiple comparisons if the null hypothesis has been rejected.

Some business analysts also compute an F value for blocks even though the main emphasis in the experiment is on the treatments. This value is compared to a critical table F value determined from Appendix A.7 by using α, df_R (blocks), and df_E (error). If the F value for blocks is greater than the critical F value, the null hypothesis that all block population means are equal is rejected. This tells the researcher that including the blocking in the design was probably worthwhile and that a significant amount of variance was drawn off from the error term, thus increasing the power of the treatment test. In this text, we have omitted F_{blocks} from the normal presentation and problem solving. We leave the use of this F value to the discretion of the reader.

FORMULAS FOR COMPUTING A RANDOMIZED BLOCK DESIGN

$$SSC = n\sum_{j=1}^{C}(\bar{X}_j - \bar{X})^2$$

$$SSR = C\sum_{i=1}^{n}(\bar{X}_i - \bar{X})^2$$

$$SSE = \sum_{i=1}^{n}\sum_{j=1}^{C}(X_{ij} - \bar{X}_j - \bar{X}_i + \bar{X})^2$$

$$SST = \sum_{i=1}^{n}\sum_{j=1}^{C}(X_{ij} - \bar{X})^2$$

where:

i = block group (row)
j = treatment level (column)
C = number of treatment levels (columns)
n = number of observations in each treatment level (number of blocks or rows)
X_{ij} = individual observation
$\bar{X}_j$ = treatment (column) mean
$\bar{X}_i$ = block (row) mean
$\bar{X}$ = grand mean
N = total number of observations

$$df_C = C - 1$$

$$df_R = n - 1$$

$$df_E = (C - 1)(n - 1) = N - n - C + 1$$

$$MSC = \frac{SSC}{C - 1}$$

$$MSR = \frac{SSR}{n - 1}$$

$$MSE = \frac{SSE}{N - n - C + 1}$$

$$F_{\text{treatments}} = \frac{MSC}{MSE}$$

$$F_{\text{blocks}} = \frac{MSR}{MSE}$$

As an example of the application of the randomized block design, consider a tire company that has developed a new tire. The company has conducted tread-wear tests on the tire to determine whether there is a significant difference in tread wear if the average speed with which the automobile is driven varies. The company set up an experiment in which the independent variable was speed of automobile. There were three treatment levels: slow speed (car is driven 20 mph), medium speed (car is driven 40 mph), and high speed (car is driven 60 mph). The company researchers realized that several possible variables could confound the study. One of these variables was supplier. The company uses five suppliers to provide a major component of the rubber from which the tires are made. To control for this variable experimentally, the researchers used supplier as a blocking variable. Fifteen tires were randomly selected for the study, three from each supplier. Each of the three was assigned to be tested under a different speed condition. The data are given here, along with treatment and block totals. These figures represent tire wear in units of 10,000 miles.

	SPEED			BLOCK MEANS
SUPPLIER	*Slow*	*Medium*	*Fast*	$\bar{X}_i$
1	3.7	4.5	3.1	3.77
2	3.4	3.9	2.8	3.37
3	3.5	4.1	3.0	3.53
4	3.2	3.5	2.6	3.10
5	3.9	4.8	3.4	4.03
Treatment Means ($\bar{X}_j$)	3.54	4.16	2.98	$\bar{X} = 3.56$

To analyze this randomized block design using $\alpha = .01$, the computations are as follows.

$$C = 3$$
$$n = 5$$
$$N = 15$$

$$\begin{aligned}\text{SSC} &= n\sum_{j=1}^{C}(\bar{X}_j - \bar{X})^2 \\ &= 5[(3.54 - 3.56)^2 + (4.16 - 3.56)^2 + (2.98 - 3.56)^2] \\ &= 3.484\end{aligned}$$

$$\begin{aligned}\text{SSR} &= C\sum_{i=1}^{n}(\bar{X}_i - \bar{X})^2 \\ &= 3[(3.77 - 3.56)^2 + (3.37 - 3.56)^2 + (3.53 - 3.56)^2 + (3.10 - 3.56)^2 \\ &\quad + (4.03 - 3.56)^2] \\ &= 1.549\end{aligned}$$

$$\begin{aligned}\text{SSE} &= \sum_{i=1}^{n}\sum_{j=1}^{C}(X_{ij} - \bar{X}_j - \bar{X}_i + \bar{X})^2 \\ &= (3.7 - 3.54 - 3.77 + 3.56)^2 + (3.4 - 3.54 - 3.37 + 3.56)^2 + \cdots \\ &\quad + (2.6 - 2.98 - 3.10 + 3.56)^2 + (3.4 - 2.98 - 4.03 + 3.56)^2 \\ &= .143\end{aligned}$$

$$\begin{aligned}\text{SST} &= \sum_{i=1}^{n}\sum_{j=1}^{C}(X_{ij} - \bar{X})^2 \\ &= (3.7 - 3.56)^2 + (3.4 - 3.56)^2 + \cdots + (2.6 - 3.56)^2 + (3.4 - 3.56)^2 \\ &= 5.176\end{aligned}$$

$$\text{MSC} = \frac{\text{SSC}}{C - 1} = \frac{3.484}{2} = 1.742$$

$$\text{MSR} = \frac{\text{SSR}}{n - 1} = \frac{1.549}{4} = .387$$

$$\text{MSE} = \frac{\text{SSE}}{N - n - C + 1} = \frac{.143}{8} = .018$$

$$F = \frac{\text{MSC}}{\text{MSE}} = \frac{1.742}{0.018} = 96.78$$

SOURCE OF VARIANCE	SS	df	MS	F
Treatment	3.484	2	1.742	96.78
Block	1.549	4	.387	
Error	.143	8	.018	
Total	5.176	14		

For alpha of .01, the critical F value is

$$F_{.01,2,8} = 8.65.$$

Because the observed value of F for treatment (96.78) is greater than this critical F value, the null hypothesis is rejected. At least one of the population means of the treatment levels is not the same as the others. That is, there is a significant difference in tread wear for cars driven at different speeds. If this problem had been set up as a completely randomized design, the SSR would have been a part of the SSE. The degrees of freedom for the blocking effects would have been combined with degrees of freedom of error. Thus, the value of SSE would have been 1.549 + .143 = 1.692, and df_E would have been 4 + 8 = 12. These would then have been used to recompute MSE = 1.692/12 = .141. The value of F for treatments would have been

$$F = \frac{\text{MSC}}{\text{MSE}} = \frac{1.742}{0.141} = 12.35.$$

Thus, the F value for treatment *with* the blocking was 96.78 and *without* the blocking was 12.35. By using the random block design, a much larger observed F value was determined.

Analysis Using Excel

Excel can analyze a randomized block design using its **Anova: Two-Factor Without Replication** feature. This feature is located in the ***Data Analysis*** drop-down menu. ***Data Analysis*** is selected from the drop-down menu provided by ***Tools*** on the menu bar. The dialog box for **Anova: Two-Factor Without Replication** is displayed in Figure 11.9.

After loading the data in the worksheet, you have the option of placing labels on the rows and the columns. Give the location of the data under ***Input* Range** including all labels. If you have labels, then check the ***Labels*** box. If you place labels on rows, then you must place labels on columns. Do not place an overall label for rows or columns in addition to the individual row and column labels. As an example, in the tire tread problem, you may place the numbers 1, 2, 3, 4, 5 beside each row to designate the supplier. However, do not place the label "supplier" in another column beside these numbers because Excel will only accept one column of labels and one row of labels. Insert the value of alpha in the box, ***Alpha.***

The Excel output for the tire tread wear problem is shown in Figure 11.10. The summary table shows the number in each row and each column, the sum total for each row and column, the row and column means, and the row and column variances. The ANOVA table contains the sum of squares (SS) and the degrees of freedom (df) for the rows (blocks), the columns (treatments), error, and total. In addition, the mean squares (MS) are given for rows (blocks), columns (treatments), and error. An observed F value is given for rows (blocks) and columns (treatments) along with its associated p-value and critical table F value.

Note the observed F value of 97.68 for columns (treatments). The difference between this value and the hand calculated value is due to rounding error. The p-value for this observed F is .00000, which is less than α = .01 indicating that the decision is to reject the

Figure 11.9 Dialog box for **Anova: Two-Factor Without Replication**

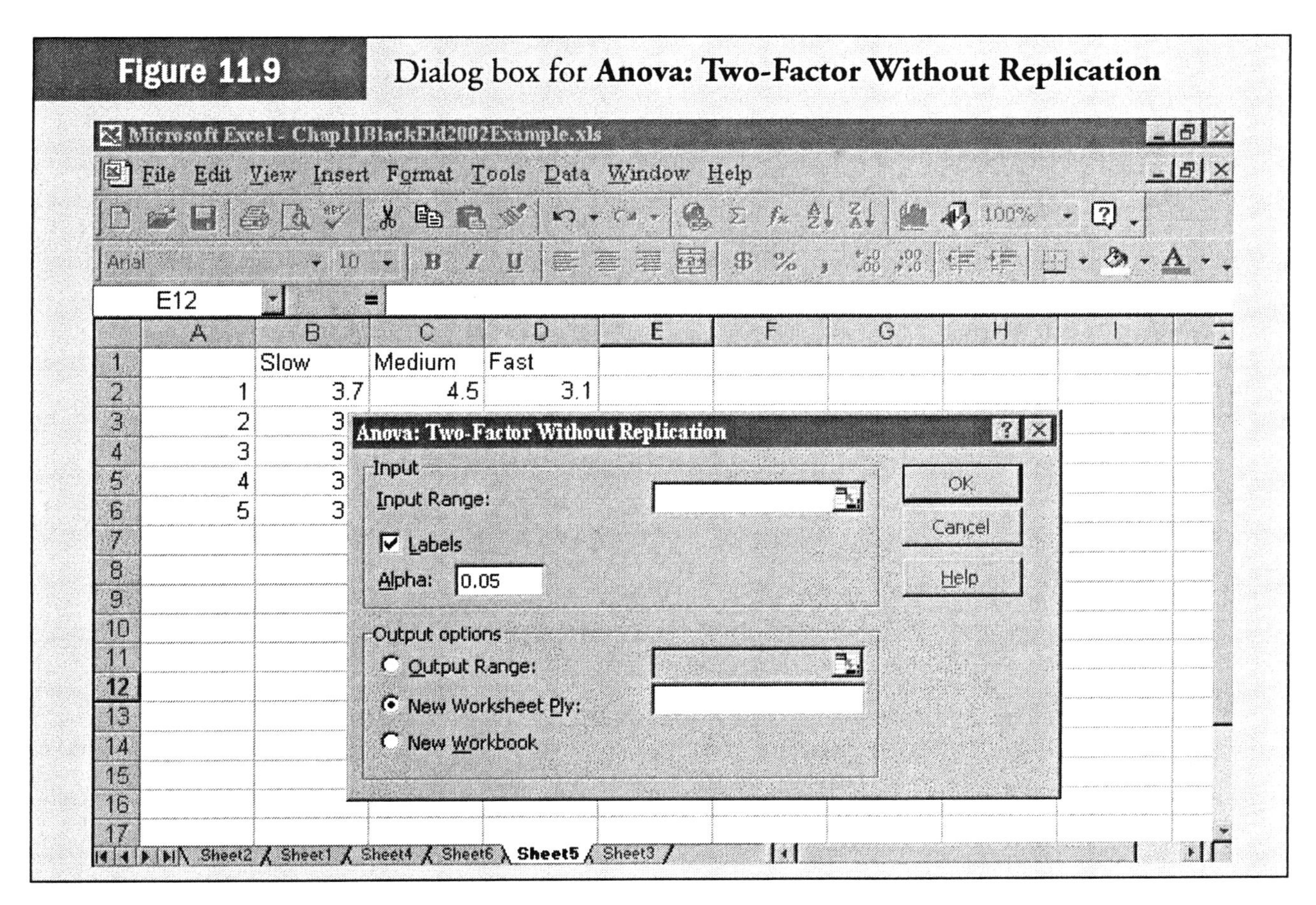

Figure 11.10 Output for the tire tread wear problem

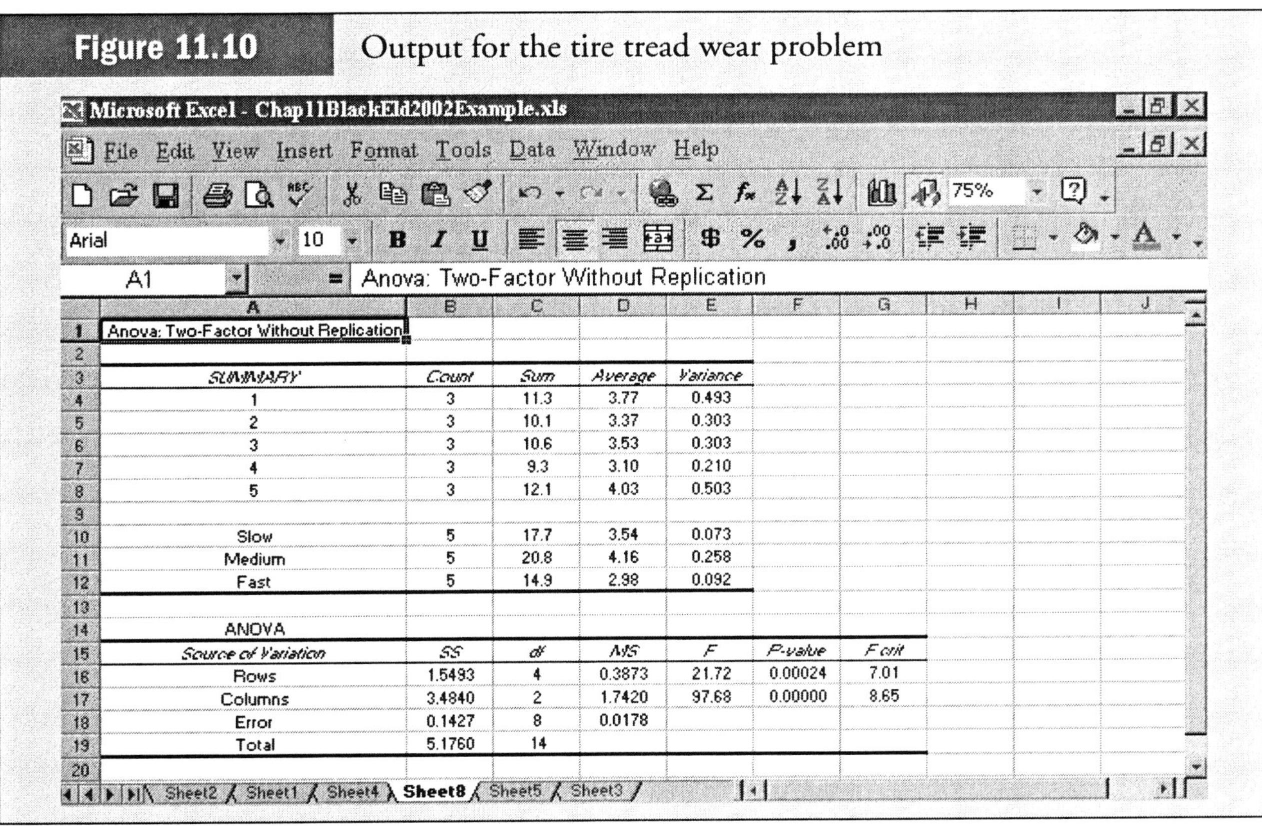

Anova: Two-Factor Without Replication

SUMMARY	Count	Sum	Average	Variance
1	3	11.3	3.77	0.493
2	3	10.1	3.37	0.303
3	3	10.6	3.53	0.303
4	3	9.3	3.10	0.210
5	3	12.1	4.03	0.503
Slow	5	17.7	3.54	0.073
Medium	5	20.8	4.16	0.258
Fast	5	14.9	2.98	0.092

ANOVA

Source of Variation	SS	df	MS	F	P-value	F crit
Rows	1.5493	4	0.3873	21.72	0.00024	7.01
Columns	3.4840	2	1.7420	97.68	0.00000	8.65
Error	0.1427	8	0.0178			
Total	5.1760	14				

null hypothesis. The Excel-produced critical F of 8.65 for columns (treatments) is identical to the table value obtained earlier during hand calculations. Since the observed F = 97.68 is greater than this critical F = 8.65, the decision is to reject the null hypothesis consistent with the results obtained using the p-value method. While the main emphasis in these problems is not on the F value for blocking effects, the Excel output shows that the observed F for blocking (21.72) is significant at $\alpha = .01$ with a p-value of .00024 and a critical F of 7.01.

DEMONSTRATION PROBLEM 11.2

Suppose a national travel association studied the cost of premium unleaded gasoline in the United States during the summer of 2001. From experience, association directors believed there was a significant difference in the average cost of a gallon of premium gasoline among urban areas in different parts of the country. To test this belief, they placed random calls to gasoline stations in five different cities. In addition, the researchers realized that the brand of gasoline might make a difference. They were mostly interested in the differences between cities, so they made city their treatment variable. To control for the fact that pricing varies with brand, the researchers included brand as a blocking variable and selected six different brands to participate. The researchers randomly telephoned one gasoline station for each brand in each city, resulting in 30 measurements (five cities and six brands). Each station operator was asked to report the current cost of a gallon of premium unleaded gasoline at that station. The data are shown here. Test these data by using a randomized block design analysis to determine whether there is a significant difference in the average cost of premium unleaded gasoline by city. Let $\alpha = .01$.

	GEOGRAPHIC REGION					
BRAND	*Miami*	*Philadelphia*	*Minneapolis*	*San Antonio*	*Oakland*	$\bar{X}_i$
A	1.47	1.40	1.38	1.32	1.50	1.414
B	1.43	1.41	1.42	1.35	1.44	1.410
C	1.44	1.41	1.43	1.36	1.45	1.418
D	1.46	1.45	1.40	1.30	1.45	1.412
E	1.46	1.40	1.39	1.39	1.48	1.424
F	1.44	1.43	1.42	1.39	1.49	1.434
$\bar{X}_j$	1.450	1.417	1.407	1.352	1.468	$\bar{X} = 1.419$

SOLUTION

STEP **1.** The hypotheses follow.

For treatments,

$$H_0: \mu_{\cdot 1} = \mu_{\cdot 2} = \mu_{\cdot 3} = \mu_{\cdot 4} = \mu_{\cdot 5}$$

H_a: At least one of the treatment means is different from the others.

For blocks,

$$H_0: \mu_{1\cdot} = \mu_{2\cdot} = \mu_{3\cdot} = \mu_{4\cdot} = \mu_{5\cdot} = \mu_{6\cdot}$$

H_a: At least one of the blocking means is different from the others.

STEP **2.** The appropriate statistical test is the F test in the ANOVA for randomized block designs.

STEP **3.** Let $\alpha = .01$.

STEP **4.** There are four degrees of freedom for the treatment ($C - 1 = 5 - 1 = 4$), five degrees of freedom for the blocks ($n - 1 = 6 - 1 = 5$), and 20 degrees of freedom for error [$(C - 1)(n - 1) = (4)(5) = 20$]. Using these, $\alpha = .01$, and Table A.7, we find the critical F values.

$$F_{.01,4,20} = 4.43 \text{ for treatments}$$

$$F_{.01,5,20} = 4.10 \text{ for blocks}$$

The decision rule is to reject the null hypothesis for treatments if the observed F value for treatments is greater than 4.43 and to reject the null hypothesis for blocking effects if the observed F value for blocks is greater than 4.10.

STEP **5.** The sample data including row and column means and the grand mean are given in the preceding table.

STEP **6.**

$$\begin{aligned} SSC &= n\sum_{j=1}^{C}(\overline{X}_j - \overline{X})^2 \\ &= 6[(1.450 - 1.419)^2 + (1.417 - 1.419)^2 + (1.407 - 1.419)^2 \\ &\quad + (1.352 - 1.419)^2 + (1.468 - 1.419)^2] \\ &= .04851 \end{aligned}$$

$$\begin{aligned} SSR &= C\sum_{i=1}^{n}(\overline{X}_i - \overline{X})^2 \\ &= 5[(1.414 - 1.419)^2 + (1.410 - 1.419)^2 + (1.418 - 1.419)^2 \\ &\quad + (1.412 - 1.419)^2 + (1.424 - 1.419)^2 + (1.434 - 1.419)^2] \\ &= .00203 \end{aligned}$$

$$\begin{aligned} SSE &= \sum_{i=1}^{n}\sum_{j=1}^{C}(X_{ij} - \overline{X}_j - \overline{X}_i + \overline{X})^2 \\ &= (1.47 - 1.450 - 1.414 + 1.419)^2 + (1.43 - 1.450 - 1.410 + 1.419)^2 \\ &\quad + \cdots + (1.48 - 1.468 - 1.424 + 1.419)^2 + (1.49 - 1.468 - 1.434 + 1.419)^2 \\ &= .01281 \end{aligned}$$

$$\begin{aligned} SST &= \sum_{i=1}^{n}\sum_{j=1}^{C}(X_{ij} - \overline{X})^2 \\ &= (1.47 - 1.419)^2 + (1.43 - 1.419)^2 + \cdots + (1.48 - 1.419)^2 + (1.49 - 1.419)^2 \\ &= .06335 \end{aligned}$$

$$MSC = \frac{SSC}{C-1} = \frac{.04851}{4} = .01213$$

$$MSR = \frac{SSR}{n-1} = \frac{0.00203}{5} = .00041$$

$$MSE = \frac{SSE}{(C-1)(n-1)} = \frac{.01281}{20} = .00064$$

$$F = \frac{MSC}{MSE} = \frac{.01213}{.00064} = 18.95$$

SOURCE OF VARIANCE	SS	df	MS	F
Treatment	.04851	4	.01213	18.95
Block	.00203	5	.00041	
Error	.01281	20	.00064	
Total	.06335	29		

STEP **7.** Because $F_{treat} = 18.95 > F_{.01,4,20} = 4.43$, the null hypothesis is rejected for the treatment effects. There is a significant difference in the average price of a gallon of premium unleaded gasoline in various cities.

A glance at the MSR reveals that there appears to be relatively little blocking variance. The result of determining an F value for the blocking effects is

$$F = \frac{\text{MSR}}{\text{MSE}} = \frac{.00041}{.00064} = 0.64.$$

The value of F for blocks is *not* significant at $\alpha = .01$ ($F_{.01,5,20} = 4.10$). This indicates that the blocking portion of the experimental design did not contribute significantly to the analysis. If the blocking effects (SSR) are added back into SSE and the df_R are included with df_E, the MSE becomes .00059 instead of .00064. Using the value .00059 in the denominator for the treatment F increases the observed treatment F value to 20.56. Thus, including nonsignificant blocking effects in the original analysis caused a loss of power.

Shown below is the Excel output for this problem.

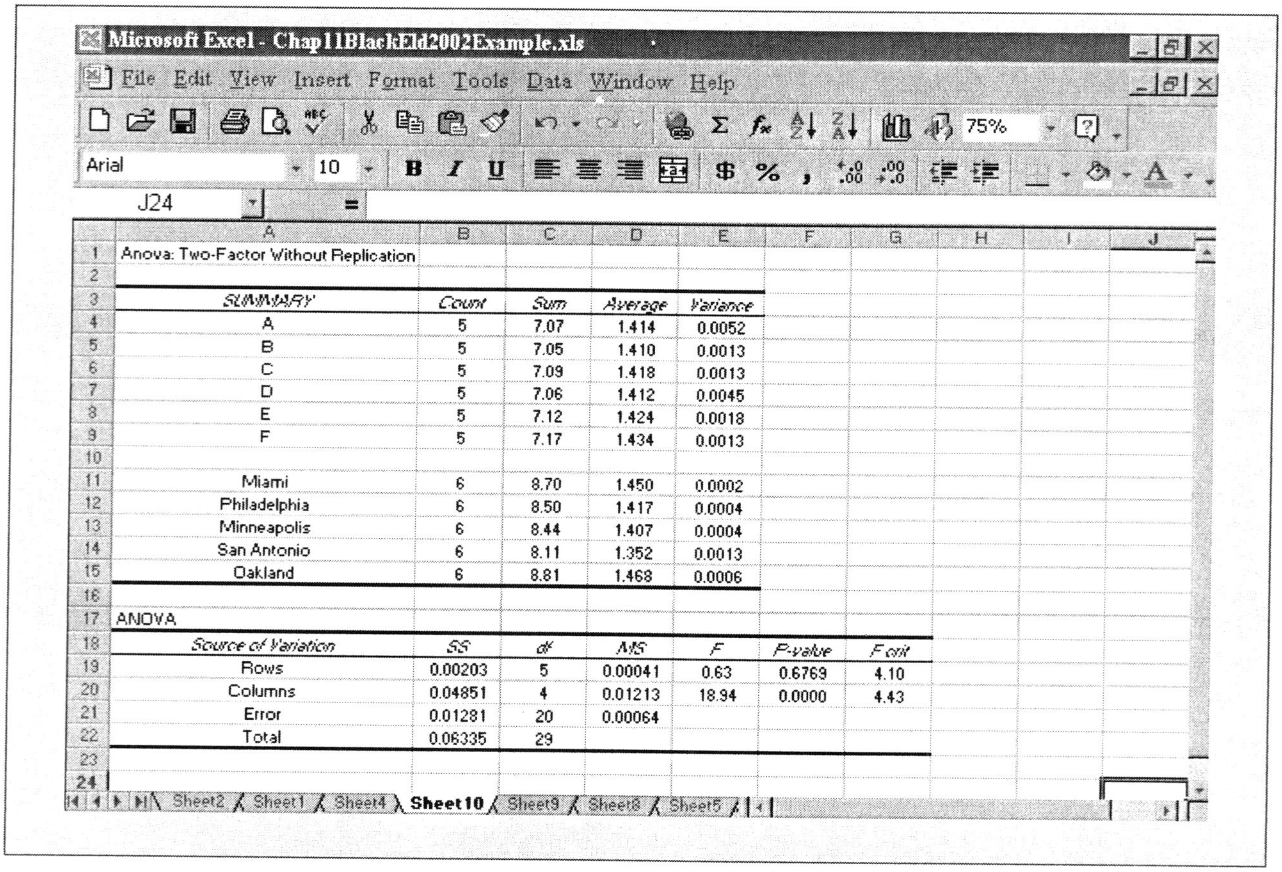
Microsoft Excel - Chap11BlackEld2002Example.xls
File Edit View Insert Format Tools Data Window Help
75%
Arial
10
J24
Sheet2 Sheet1 Sheet4 Sheet10 Sheet9 Sheet8 Sheet5

Anova: Two-Factor Without Replication

SUMMARY	Count	Sum	Average	Variance
A	5	7.07	1.414	0.0052
B	5	7.05	1.410	0.0013
C	5	7.09	1.418	0.0013
D	5	7.06	1.412	0.0045
E	5	7.12	1.424	0.0018
F	5	7.17	1.434	0.0013
Miami	6	8.70	1.450	0.0002
Philadelphia	6	8.50	1.417	0.0004
Minneapolis	6	8.44	1.407	0.0004
San Antonio	6	8.11	1.352	0.0013
Oakland	6	8.81	1.468	0.0006

ANOVA

Source of Variation	SS	df	MS	F	P-value	F crit
Rows	0.00203	5	0.00041	0.63	0.6769	4.10
Columns	0.04851	4	0.01213	18.94	0.0000	4.43
Error	0.01281	20	0.00064			
Total	0.06335	29				

The ANOVA table in the Excel output summarizes the results of this problem. The F value for treatments shown as Columns yields a p value of .0000, which indicates that the treatment F is significant at an alpha of .0001. The F value for blocks shown as Rows is less than 1. The p value is .6769, which means that this F would not be significant even at $\alpha = .10$. The critical table F values are given for $\alpha = .01$.

STEP **8.** The fact that there is a significant difference in the price of gasoline in different parts of the country can be useful information to decision makers. For example, companies in the ground transportation business are impacted greatly by increases in the cost of fuel. Knowledge of price differences in fuel can help these companies plan strategies and routes. Fuel price differences can sometimes be indications of cost-of-living differences and/or distribution problems, which can impact a company's relocation decision or cost-of-living increases given to employees who transfer to the higher-priced locations. Knowing that the price of gasoline varies around the country can generate interest among market researchers who might want to study why the differences are there and what drives them. This can sometimes result in a better understanding of the marketplace.

11.3 Problems

11.8 Use ANOVA to analyze the data from the randomized block design given here. Let $\alpha = .05$. State the null and alternative hypotheses and determine whether the null hypothesis is rejected.

		TREATMENT LEVEL			
		1	2	3	4
BLOCK	*1*	23	26	24	24
	2	31	35	32	33
	3	27	29	26	27
	4	21	28	27	22
	5	18	25	27	20

11.9 The following data have been gathered from a randomized block design. Use $\alpha = .01$ to test for a significant difference in the treatment levels. Establish the hypotheses and reach a conclusion about the null hypothesis.

		TREATMENT LEVEL		
		1	2	3
BLOCK	*1*	1.28	1.29	1.29
	2	1.40	1.36	1.35
	3	1.15	1.13	1.19
	4	1.22	1.18	1.24

11.10 Safety in motels and hotels is a growing concern among travelers. Suppose a survey was conducted by the National Motel and Hotel Association to determine the U.S. travelers' perception of safety in various motel chains. The association chose four different national chains from the economy lodging sector and randomly selected 10 people who had stayed overnight in a motel in each of the four chains in the past 2 years. Each selected traveler was asked to rate each motel chain on a scale from 0 to 100 to indicate how safe he or she felt at that motel. A score of 0 indicates completely unsafe and a score of 100 indicates perfectly safe. The scores follow. Test this randomized block design to determine whether there is a significant difference in the safety ratings of the four motels. Use $\alpha = .05$.

TRAVELER	MOTEL 1	MOTEL 2	MOTEL 3	MOTEL 4
1	40	30	55	45
2	65	50	80	70
3	60	55	60	60
4	20	40	55	50
5	50	35	65	60
6	30	30	50	50
7	55	30	60	55
8	70	70	70	70
9	65	60	80	75
10	45	25	45	50

11.11 In recent years, there has been constant debate over the U.S. economy. The electorate seems somewhat divided as to whether the economy is in a recovery or not. Suppose a survey was undertaken to ascertain whether the perception of economic recovery differs according to political affiliation. People were selected for the survey from the Democratic party, the Republican party, and those classifying themselves as independents. A 25-point scale was developed in which respondents gave a score of 25 if they felt the economy was definitely in complete recovery, a 0 if the economy was definitely not in a recovery, and some value in between for more uncertain responses. To control for differences in socioeconomic class, a blocking variable was maintained using five different socioeconomic categories. The data are given here in the form of a randomized block design. Use $\alpha = .01$ to determine whether there is a significant difference in mean responses according to political affiliation.

SOCIOECONOMIC CLASS	POLITICAL AFFILIATION *Democrat*	*Republican*	*Independent*
Upper	11	5	8
Upper middle	15	9	8
Middle	19	14	15
Lower middle	16	12	10
Lower	9	8	7

11.12 As part of a manufacturing process, a plastic container is supposed to be filled with 46 ounces of saltwater solution. The plant has three machines that fill the containers. Managers are concerned that the machines might not be filling the containers with the same amount of saltwater solution, so they set up a randomized block design to test this concern. There is a pool of five machine operators who at different times operate each of the three machines. Company technicians randomly select five containers filled by each machine (one container for each of the five operators). The measurements are shown below. Use $\alpha = .05$ to analyze the design.

		MACHINE 1	2	3
OPERATOR	1	46.05	45.99	46.02
	2	45.97	46.08	45.98
	3	45.91	46.05	45.95
	4	46.01	46.03	46.12
	5	45.96	46.04	45.99

11.4
A Factorial Design (Two-Way ANOVA)

There are times when an experiment is designed so that *two or more treatments* (independent variables) *are explored simultaneously.* Such experimental designs are referred to as **factorial designs.** In factorial designs, *every level of each treatment is studied under the conditions of every level of all other treatments.* Factorial designs can be arranged such that three, four, or *n* treatments or independent variables are studied simultaneously in the same experiment. As an example, consider the valve opening data in Table 11.1. The mean valve opening for the 24 measurements is 6.34 cm. However, every valve but one in the sample measures something other than the mean. Why? Company workers realize that valves at this firm are made on different machines, by different operators, on different shifts, on different days, with raw materials from different suppliers. Business analysts who are interested in finding the sources of variation might decide to set up a factorial design that incorporates all five of these independent variables in one study. In this text, we explore the factorial designs with two treatments only.

Factorial design
An experimental design in which two or more independent variables are studied simultaneously and every level of each treatment is studied under the conditions of every level of all other treatments. Also called a factorial experiment.

Advantages of the Factorial Design

If two variables are analyzed by using a completely randomized design, the effects of each variable are explored separately (one per design). Thus, it takes two completely randomized designs to analyze the effects of the two variables. By using a factorial design, the researcher can analyze both variables at the same time in one design, saving the time and effort of doing two different analyses and minimizing the experimentwise error rate.

Some researchers use the factorial design as a way to control confounding or concomitant variables in a study. By building variables into the design, the researcher is attempting to control for the effects of multiple variables *in* the experiment. With the completely randomized design, the variables are studied in isolation. With the factorial design, there is potential for increased power over the completely randomized design because the additional effects of the second variable are removed from the error sum of squares.

The business analyst can explore the possibility of interaction between the two treatment variables in a two-factor factorial design if multiple measurements are taken under every combination of levels of the two treatments. Interaction will be discussed later.

Factorial designs with two treatments are similar to randomized block designs. However, whereas randomized block designs focus on one treatment variable and *control* for a blocking effect, a two-treatment factorial design focuses on the effects of both variables. Because the randomized block design contains only one measure for each (treatment–block) combination, interaction cannot be analyzed in randomized block designs.

Factorial Designs with Two Treatments

The structure of a two-treatment factorial design is featured in Figure 11.11. Note that there are two independent variables (two treatments) and that there is an intersection of each level of each treatment. These intersections are referred to as *cells.* One treatment is arbitrarily designated as *row* treatment (forming the rows of the design) and the other treatment is designated as *column* treatment (forming the columns of the design). Although it is possible to analyze factorial designs with unequal numbers of items in the cells, the analysis of unequal cell designs is beyond the scope of this text. All factorial designs discussed here have cells of equal size.

Treatments (independent variables) of factorial designs must have at least two levels each. The simplest factorial design is a 2×2 factorial design, where each treatment has two levels. If such a factorial design were diagrammed in the manner of Figure 11.11, there would be two rows and two columns, forming four cells.

Figure 11.11

Two-way factorial design

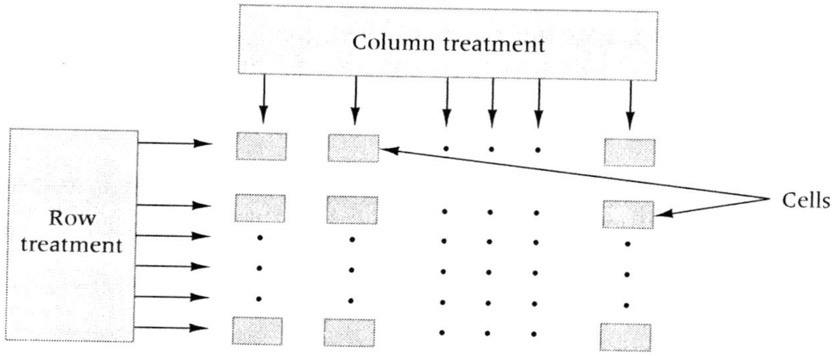

In this section, we study only factorial designs with $n > 1$ measurements for each combination of treatment levels (cells). This allows us to attempt to measure the interaction of the treatment variables. As with the completely randomized design and the randomized block design, there is only *one* dependent variable in a factorial design.

Applications

There are many possible applications of the factorial design in business research. For example, the natural gas industry can design an experiment to study usage rates and how they are affected by temperature and precipitation. Theorizing that the outside temperature and type of precipitation make a difference in natural gas usage, industry researchers can gather usage measurements for a given community over a variety of temperature and precipitation conditions. At the same time, they can make an effort to determine whether certain types of precipitation combined with certain temperature levels affect usage rates differently than other combinations of temperature and precipitation (interaction effects).

Stock market analysts can select a company from an industry such as the construction industry and observe the behavior of its stock under different conditions. A factorial design can be set up by using volume of the market and prime interest as two independent variables. For volume of the market, researchers can select some days when the volume is up from the day before, some days when the volume is down from the day before, and some other days when the volume is essentially the same as on the preceding day. These groups of days would constitute three levels of the independent variable, volume. The business analysts can do the same thing with prime rate. Levels can be selected such that the prime rate is (1) up, (2) down, and (3) essentially the same. For the dependent variable, the researchers would measure how much the company's stock rises or falls on those randomly selected days. Using the factorial design, the researcher can determine whether stock rates are different under various levels of volume, whether stock rates are different under various levels of the prime interest rate, and whether stock rates react differently under various combinations of volume and prime rate (interaction effects).

Two-way analysis of variance (two-way ANOVA)
The process used to statistically test the effects of variables in factorial designs with two independent variables.

Statistically Testing the Factorial Design

Analysis of variance is used to analyze data gathered from factorial designs. For factorial designs with two factors (independent variables), a **two-way analysis of variance (two-way ANOVA)** is used to test hypotheses statistically. The following hypotheses are tested by a two-way ANOVA.

Row effects: H_0: Row means all are equal.
H_a: At least one row mean is different from the others.

Column effects: H_0: Column means are all equal.
H_a: At least one column mean is different from the others.

Interaction effects: H_0: The interaction effects are zero.
H_a: There is an interaction effect.

Formulas for computing a two-way ANOVA are given in the following box. These formulas are computed in a manner similar to computations for the completely randomized design and the randomized block design. *F* values are determined for three effects:

1. row effects,
2. column effects, and
3. interaction effects.

The row effects and the column effects are sometimes referred to as the *main* effects. Although *F* values are determined for these main effects, an *F* value is also computed for interaction effects. Using these *F* values, the researcher can make a decision about the null hypotheses for each effect.

Each of these observed *F* values is compared to a table *F* value. The table *F* value is determined by α, df_{num}, and df_{denom}. The degrees of freedom for the numerator (df_{num}) are determined by the effect being studied. If the observed *F* value is for columns, the degrees of freedom for the numerator are $C - 1$. If the observed *F* value is for rows, the degrees of freedom for the numerator are $R - 1$. If the observed *F* value is for interaction, the degrees of freedom for the numerator are $(R - 1)(C - 1)$. The number of degrees of freedom for the denominator of the table value for each of the three effects is the same, the error degrees of freedom, $RC(n - 1)$. The table *F* values (critical *F*) for a two-way ANOVA follow.

Table F Values for a Two-Way ANOVA

Row effects: $F_{\alpha,R-1,RC(n-1)}$
Column effects: $F_{\alpha,C-1,RC(n-1)}$
Interaction effects: $F_{\alpha,(R-1)(C-1),RC(n-1)}$

Formulas for Computing a Two-Way ANOVA

$$SSR = nC\sum_{i=1}^{R}(\bar{X}_i - \bar{X})^2$$

$$SSC = nR\sum_{j=1}^{C}(\bar{X}_j - \bar{X})^2$$

$$SSI = n\sum_{i=1}^{R}\sum_{j=1}^{C}(\bar{X}_{ij} - \bar{X}_i - \bar{X}_j + \bar{X})^2$$

$$SSE = \sum_{i=1}^{R}\sum_{j=1}^{C}\sum_{k=1}^{n}(X_{ijk} - \bar{X}_{ij})^2$$

$$SST = \sum_{i=1}^{R}\sum_{j=1}^{C}\sum_{k=1}^{n}(X_{ijk} - \bar{X})^2$$

continued

FORMULAS FOR COMPUTING A TWO-WAY ANOVA (continued)

where:

n = number of observations per cell
C = number of column treatments
R = number of row treatments
i = row treatment level
j = column treatment level
k = cell member
X_{ijk} = individual observation
$\bar{X}_{ij}$ = cell mean
$\bar{X}_i$ = row mean
$\bar{X}_j$ = column mean
$\bar{X}$ = grand mean

$$\text{df}_R = R - 1$$
$$\text{df}_C = C - 1$$
$$\text{df}_I = (R-1)(C-1)$$
$$\text{df}_E = RC(n-1)$$
$$\text{df}_T = N - 1$$

$$\text{MSR} = \frac{\text{SSR}}{R-1}$$
$$\text{MSC} = \frac{\text{SSC}}{C-1}$$
$$\text{MSI} = \frac{\text{SSI}}{(R-1)(C-1)}$$
$$\text{MSE} = \frac{\text{SSE}}{RC(n-1)}$$

$$F_R = \frac{\text{MSR}}{\text{MSE}}$$
$$F_C = \frac{\text{MSC}}{\text{MSE}}$$
$$F_I = \frac{\text{MSI}}{\text{MSE}}$$

Interaction

Interaction
When the effects of one treatment in an experimental design vary according to the levels of treatment of the other effect(s).

As noted before, along with testing the effects of the two treatments in a factorial design, it is possible to test for the interaction effects of the two treatments whenever multiple measures are taken in each cell of the design. **Interaction** occurs *when the effects of one treatment vary according to the levels of treatment of the other effect.* For example, in a study examining the impact of temperature and humidity on a manufacturing process, it is possible that temperature and humidity will interact in such a way that the effect of temperature on the process varies with the humidity. Low temperatures might not be a significant manufacturing factor when humidity is low but might be a factor when humidity is high. Similarly, high temperatures might be a factor with low humidity but not with high humidity.

As another example, suppose a business analyst is studying the amount of red meat consumed by families per month and is examining economic class and religion as two independent variables. Class and religion might interact in such a way that with certain religions, economic class does not matter in the consumption of red meat, but with other religions, class does make a difference.

In terms of the factorial design, interaction occurs when the pattern of cell means in one row (going across columns) varies from the pattern of cell means in other rows. This indicates that the differences in column effects depend on which row is being examined. Hence, there is an interaction of the rows and columns. The same thing can happen when the pattern of cell means within a column is different from the pattern of cell means in other columns.

Interaction can be depicted graphically by plotting the cell means within each row (and can also be done by plotting the cell means within each column). The means within each row (or column) are then connected by a line. If the broken lines for each row (or column) are parallel, there is no interaction.

Figure 11.12 is a graph of the means for each cell in each row in a 2 × 3 (2 rows, 3 columns) factorial design with interaction. Note that the lines connecting the means in

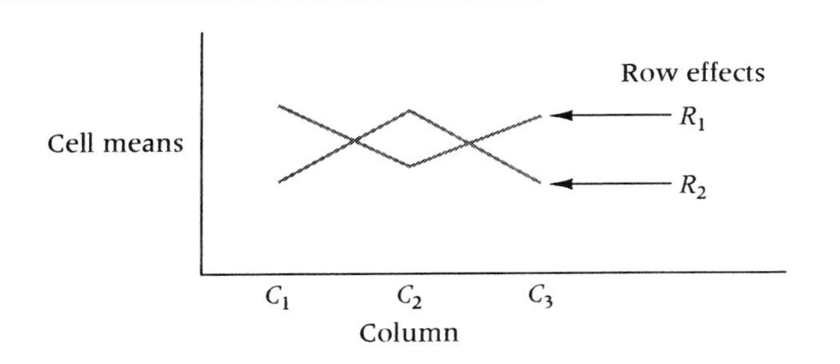

Figure 11.12

A 2 × 3 factorial design with interaction

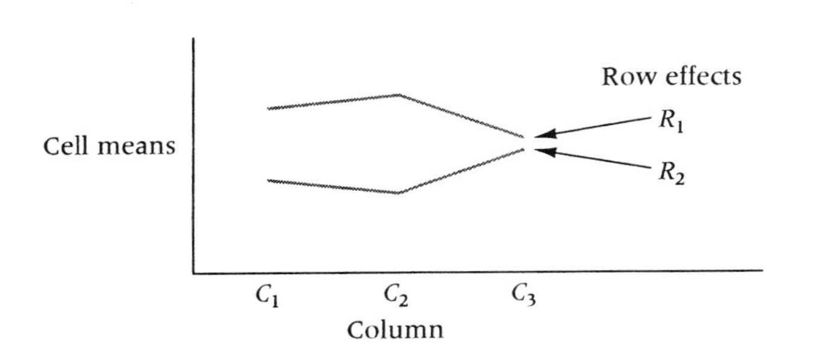

Figure 11.13

A 2 × 3 factorial design with some interaction

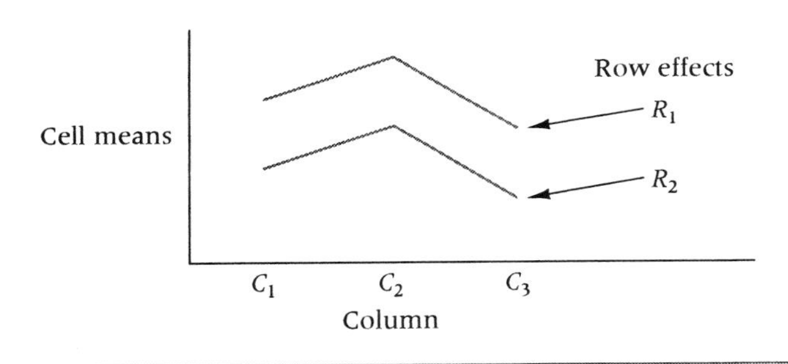

Figure 11.14

A 2 × 3 factorial design with no interaction

each row cross each other. In Figure 11.13 the lines converge, indicating the likely presence of some interaction. Figure 11.14 depicts a 2 × 3 factorial design with no interaction.

When the interaction effects are significant, the main effects (row and column) are confounded and should not be analyzed in the usual manner. In this case, it is not possible to state unequivocally that the row effects or the column effects are significantly different because the difference in means of one main effect varies according to the level of the other main effect (interaction is present). There are some recommended ways of examining main effects when significant interaction is present. However, these techniques are beyond the scope of material presented here. Hence, in this text, whenever interaction effects are present (F_{inter} is significant), the business analyst should *not* attempt to interpret the main effects (F_{row} and F_{col}).

As an example of a factorial design, consider the fact that at the end of a financially successful fiscal year, CEOs often must decide whether to award a dividend to stockholders or to make a company investment. One factor in this decision would seem to be whether attractive investment opportunities are available.* To determine whether this factor is important, business analysts randomly select 24 CEOs and ask them to rate how important "availability of profitable investment opportunities" is in deciding whether to pay dividends or invest. The CEOs are requested to respond to this item on a scale from 0 to 4, where

0 = no importance,
1 = slight importance,
2 = moderate importance,
3 = great importance, and
4 = maximum importance.

The 0–4 response is the dependent variable in the experimental design.

The business analysts are concerned that where the company's stock is traded (New York Stock Exchange, American Stock Exchange, and over the counter) might make a difference in the CEOs' response to the question. In addition, the business analysts believe that how stockholders are informed of dividends (annual reports vs. presentations) might affect the outcome of the experiment. Thus, a two-way ANOVA is set up with "where the company's stock is traded" and "how stockholders are informed of dividends" as the two independent variables. The variable "how stockholders are informed of dividends" has two treatment levels, or classifications.

1. Annual/quarterly reports
2. Presentations to analysts

The variable "where company stock is traded" has three treatment levels, or classifications.

1. New York Stock Exchange
2. American Stock Exchange
3. Over the counter

This factorial design is a 2 × 3 design (2 rows, 3 columns) with four measurements (ratings) per cell, as shown in the following table.

		Where Company Stock Is Traded			
		New York Stock Exchange	*American Stock Exchange*	*Over the Counter*	$\overline{X}_i$
How Stockholders Are Informed of Dividends	*Annual/Quarterly Reports*	2 1 2 1 $\overline{X}_{11} = 1.5$	2 3 3 2 $\overline{X}_{12} = 2.5$	4 3 4 3 $\overline{X}_{13} = 3.5$	2.5
	Presentations to Analysts	2 3 1 2 $\overline{X}_{21} = 2.0$	3 3 2 4 $\overline{X}_{22} = 3.0$	4 4 3 4 $\overline{X}_{23} = 3.75$	2.9167
	$\overline{X}_j =$	1.75	2.75	3.625	
			$\overline{X} = 2.7083$		

*ADAPTED FROM: H. Kent Baker, "Why Companies Pay No Dividends," *Akron Business and Economic Review*, 20, Summer 1989, 48–61.

These data are analyzed by using a two-way analysis of variance and $\alpha = .05$.

$$\begin{aligned}
\text{SSR} &= nC\sum_{i=1}^{R}(\overline{X}_i - \overline{X})^2 \\
&= 4(3)[(2.5 - 2.7083)^2 + (2.9167 - 2.7083)^2] \\
&= 1.0418
\end{aligned}$$

$$\begin{aligned}
\text{SSC} &= nR\sum_{j=1}^{C}(\overline{X}_j - \overline{X})^2 \\
&= 4(2)[(1.75 - 2.7083)^2 + (2.75 - 2.7083)^2 + (3.625 - 2.7083)^2] \\
&= 14.0833
\end{aligned}$$

$$\begin{aligned}
\text{SSI} &= n\sum_{i=1}^{R}\sum_{j=1}^{C}(\overline{X}_{ij} - \overline{X}_i - \overline{X}_j + \overline{X})^2 \\
&= 4[(1.5 - 2.5 - 1.75 + 2.7083)^2 + (2.5 - 2.5 - 2.75 + 2.7083)^2 \\
&\quad + (3.5 - 2.5 - 3.625 + 2.7083)^2 + (2.0 - 2.9167 - 1.75 + 2.7083)^2 \\
&\quad + (3.0 - 2.9167 - 2.75 + 2.7083)^2 + (3.75 - 2.9167 - 3.625 + 2.7083)^2] \\
&= .0833
\end{aligned}$$

$$\begin{aligned}
\text{SSE} &= \sum_{i=1}^{R}\sum_{j=1}^{C}\sum_{k=1}^{n}(X_{ijk} - \overline{X}_{ij})^2 \\
&= (2 - 1.5)^2 + (1 - 1.5)^2 + \cdots + (3 - 3.75)^2 + (4 - 3.75)^2 \\
&= 7.7500
\end{aligned}$$

$$\begin{aligned}
\text{SST} &= \sum_{i=1}^{R}\sum_{j=1}^{C}\sum_{k=1}^{n}(X_{ijk} - \overline{X})^2 \\
&= (2 - 2.7083)^2 + (1 - 2.7083)^2 + \cdots + (3 - 2.7083)^2 + (4 - 2.7083)^2 \\
&= 22.9583
\end{aligned}$$

$$\text{MSR} = \frac{\text{SSR}}{R-1} = \frac{1.0418}{1} = 1.0418$$

$$\text{MSC} = \frac{\text{SSC}}{C-1} = \frac{14.0833}{2} = 7.0417$$

$$\text{MSI} = \frac{\text{SSI}}{(R-1)(C-1)} = \frac{.0833}{2} = .0417$$

$$\text{MSE} = \frac{\text{SSE}}{RC(n-1)} = \frac{7.7500}{18} = .4306$$

$$F_R = \frac{\text{MSR}}{\text{MSE}} = \frac{1.0418}{.4306} = 2.42$$

$$F_C = \frac{\text{MSC}}{\text{MSE}} = \frac{7.0417}{.4306} = 16.35$$

$$F_I = \frac{\text{MSI}}{\text{MSE}} = \frac{.0417}{.4306} = 0.10$$

SOURCE OF VARIANCE	SS	df	MS	F
Row	1.0418	1	1.0418	2.42
Column	14.0833	2	7.0417	16.35*
Interaction	.0833	2	.0417	0.10
Error	7.7500	18	.4306	
Total	22.9583	23		

*Denotes significance at $\alpha = .01$.

The critical F value for the interaction effects at $\alpha = .05$ is

$$F_{.05,2,18} = 3.55.$$

The observed F value for interaction effects is .10. As this value is less than the critical table value (3.55), there are no significant interaction effects. Because there are no significant interaction effects, it is possible to examine the main effects.

The critical F value of the row effects at $\alpha = .05$ is

$$F_{.05,1,18} = 4.41.$$

The calculated F value of 2.42 is less than the table value. Hence, there are no significant row effects. The critical F value of the column effects at $\alpha = .05$ is

$$F_{.05,2,18} = 3.55.$$

This value is coincidently the same as the critical table value for interaction because in this problem the degrees of freedom are the same for interaction and column effects. The observed F value for columns (16.35) is greater than this critical value. Hence, there is a significant difference in row effects at $\alpha = .05$.

There is a significant difference in the CEOs' mean ratings of the item "availability of profitable investment opportunities" according to where the company's stock is traded. A cursory examination of the means for the three levels of the column effects (where stock is traded) reveals that the lowest mean was from CEOs whose company traded stock on the New York Stock Exchange. The highest mean rating was from CEOs whose company traded stock over the counter. Using multiple comparison techniques, the business analysts could statistically test for differences in the means of these three groups.

Analysis Using Excel

A two-way ANOVA with more than one observation per cell can be computed using Excel. Begin by selecting ***Tools*** from the menu bar. From the ***Tools***' pull-down menu, select ***Data Analysis.*** From the ***Data Analysis***' list box, select **Anova: Two-Factor With Replication.** This feature will compute a two-way ANOVA with interaction. For two-way ANOVA designs with only one observation per cell, select **Anova: Two-Factor Without Replication.** The dialog box for **Anova: Two-Factor With Replication** is shown is Figure 11.15.

Load the data into a worksheet. The worksheet entries for the CEO/Stock problem are displayed in Figure 11.16. Excel assumes there will be labels and will not execute without a label for each "treatment level" row and column. Place the number of observations per sample in the ***Rows*** per sample box. Because Excel is told how many row lines there are per sample (number of observations per sample), there need not be a label for each row line (each row of the worksheet). As an example, note that in Figure 11.16 each column

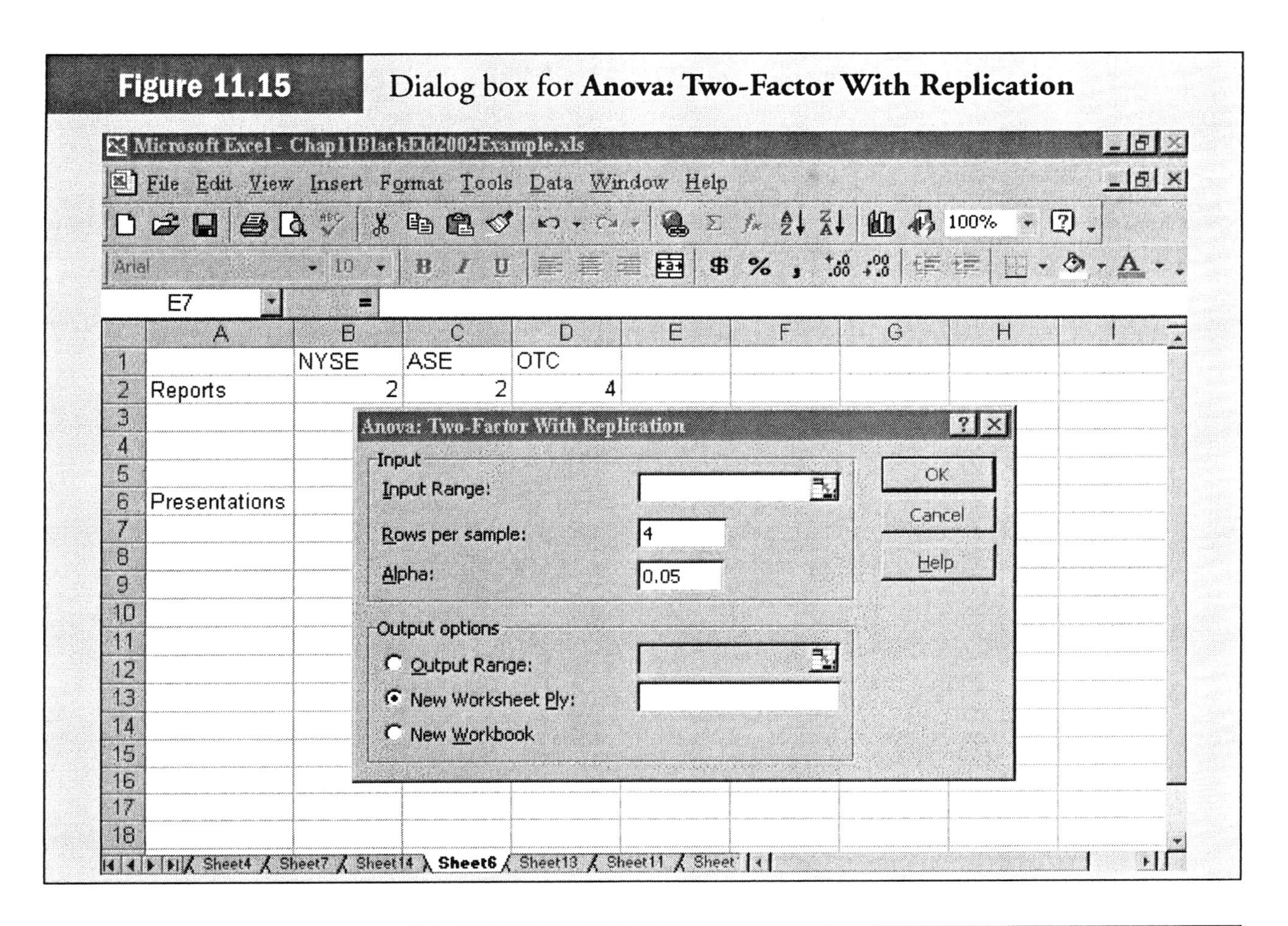

Figure 11.15 Dialog box for **Anova: Two-Factor With Replication**

Figure 11.16 Spreadsheet entries for CEO/stock problem

	A	B	C	D
1		NYSE	ASE	OTC
2	Reports	2	2	4
3		1	3	3
4		2	3	4
5		1	2	3
6	Presentations	2	3	4
7		3	3	4
8		1	2	3
9		2	4	4

Figure 11.17 Excel output for CEO/stock problem

Microsoft Excel - Chap11BlackEld2002Example.xls

File Edit View Insert Format Tools Data Window Help

Arial 10 63%

M28

	A	B	C	D	E	F	G
1	Anova: Two-Factor With Replication						
2							
3	SUMMARY	NYSE	ASE	OTC	Total		
4	*Reports*						
5	Count	4	4	4	12		
6	Sum	6	10	14	30		
7	Average	1.5	2.5	3.5	2.5		
8	Variance	0.3333	0.3333	0.3333	1		
9	*Presentations*						
10	Count	4	4	4	12		
11	Sum	8	12	15	35		
12	Average	2	3	3.75	2.917		
13	Variance	0.6667	0.6667	0.2500	0.9924		
14	*Total*						
15	Count	8	8	8			
16	Sum	14	22	29			
17	Average	1.75	2.75	3.625			
18	Variance	0.5	0.5	0.2679			
19							
20	ANOVA						
21	*Source of Variation*	*SS*	*df*	*MS*	*F*	*P-value*	*F crit*
22	Sample	1.042	1	1.042	2.42	0.1373	4.41
23	Columns	14.083	2	7.042	16.35	0.0001	3.55
24	Interaction	0.083	2	0.042	0.10	0.9082	3.55
25	Within	7.750	18	0.431			
26	Total	22.958	23				

Sheet4 Sheet7 Sheet6 Sheet13 Sheet11 Sheet10 Sheet

has a label and each row treatment level has a label but not each row line because there are four row lines (observations) per sample (row treatment level). Each sample constitutes a row treatment level; and there are two row treatment levels: **Reports** and **Presentations.** Enter the value of alpha in ***Alpha.***

The Excel output for the CEO/stock problem is shown in Figure 11.17. Note that the output contains a Summary table with counts, sums, averages, and variances of each sample and of each treatment level. In addition, there is an ANOVA table containing the sum of squares (SS) and degrees of freedom (df) for rows (denoted in the table as Sample), columns, interaction, error (denoted in the table as Within), and total. There are mean squares (MS) for rows, columns, interaction, and error. There are observed F values with associated p-values and critical (table) F values for rows (Sample), columns, and interaction. Note that the F values obtained here are the same as those values calculated by hand in the chapter. In addition, the provided p-values show that the observed F value for columns is significant at $\alpha = .05$ because the p-value is .0001 while the p-values for rows (Sample) and interaction are not (.1373 and .9062 respectively). For those business analysts who are more comfortable using the F tables, critical F values are provided. These values are the same as those displayed earlier in the chapter when the problem was worked by hand.

DEMONSTRATION PROBLEM 11.3

Some theorists believe that training warehouse workers can reduce absenteeism.* Suppose an experimental design is structured to test this belief. Warehouses in which training sessions have been held for workers are selected for the study. The four types of warehouses are (1) general merchandise, (2) commodity, (3) bulk storage, and (4) cold storage. The training sessions are differentiated by length. Researchers identify three levels of training sessions according to the length of sessions: (1) 1–20 days, (2) 21–50 days, and (3) more than 50 days. Three warehouse workers are selected randomly for each particular combination of type of warehouse and session length. The workers are monitored for the next year to determine how many days they are absent. The resulting data are in the following 4 × 3 design (4 rows, 3 columns) structure. Using this information, calculate a two-way ANOVA to determine whether there are any significant differences in effects. Use $\alpha = .05$.

SOLUTION

STEP **1.** The following hypotheses are being tested.

For row effects:

H_0: $\mu_{1\cdot} = \mu_{2\cdot} = \mu_{3\cdot} = \mu_{4\cdot}$

H_a: At least one of the row means is different from the others.

For column effects:

H_0: $\mu_{\cdot 1} = \mu_{\cdot 2} = \mu_{\cdot 3}$

H_a: At least one of the column means is different from the others.

For interaction effects:

H_0: The interaction effects are zero.

H_a: There is an interaction effect.

STEP **2.** The two-way ANOVA with the *F* test is the appropriate statistical test.

STEP **3.** $\alpha = .05$

STEP **4.**

$$df_{rows} = 4 - 1 = 3$$
$$df_{columns} = 3 - 1 = 2$$
$$df_{interaction} = (3)(2) = 6$$
$$df_{error} = (4)(3)(2) = 24$$

For row effects, $F_{.05,3,24} = 3.01$; for column effects, $F_{.05,2,24} = 3.40$; and for interaction effects, $F_{.05,6,24} = 2.51$. For each of these effects, if any observed *F* value is greater than its associated critical *F* value, the respective null hypothesis will be rejected.

*ADAPTED FROM: Paul R. Murphy and Richard F. Poist, "Managing the Human Side of Public Warehousing: An Overview of Modern Practices," *Transportation Journal*, 31, Spring 1992, 54–63.

STEP **5.**

Types of Warehouses	Length of Training Session (Days): 1–20	21–50	More than 50	$\bar{X}_r$
General Merchandise	3 4.5 4	2 2.5 2	2.5 1 1.5	2.5556
Commodity	5 4.5 4	1 3 2.5	0 1.5 2	2.6111
Bulk Storage	2.5 3 3.5	1 3 1.5	3.5 3.5 4	2.8333
Cold Storage	2 2 3	5 4.5 2.5	4 4.5 5	3.6111
$\bar{X}_c$	3.4167	2.5417	2.75	

$\bar{X} = 2.9028$

STEP **6.** The Excel output for this problem follows.

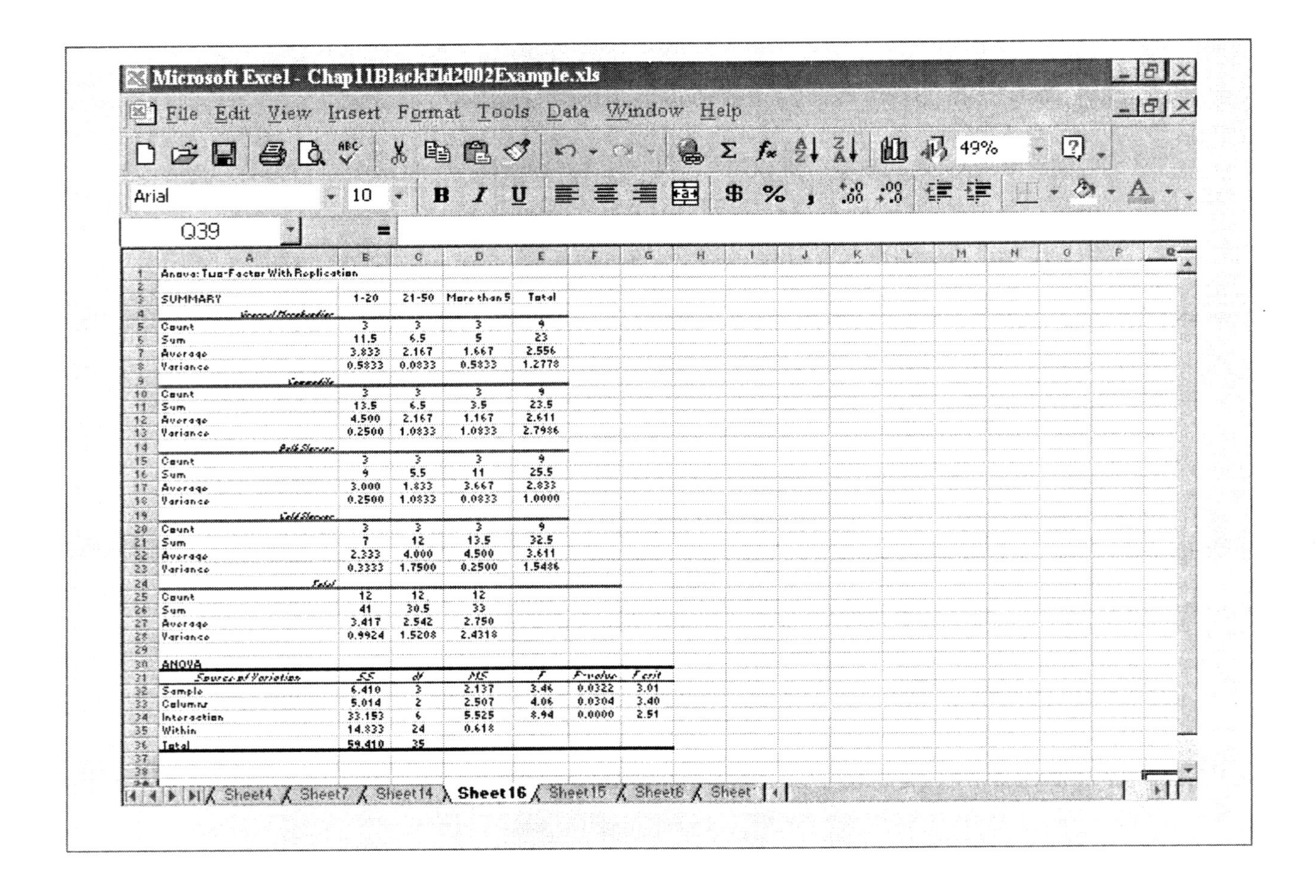

Microsoft Excel - Chap11BlackEld2002Example.xls

Anova: Two-Factor With Replication

SUMMARY	1-20	21-50	More than 5	Total
General Merchandise				
Count	3	3	3	9
Sum	11.5	6.5	5	23
Average	3.833	2.167	1.667	2.556
Variance	0.5833	0.0833	0.5833	1.2778
Commodity				
Count	3	3	3	9
Sum	13.5	6.5	3.5	23.5
Average	4.500	2.167	1.167	2.611
Variance	0.2500	1.0833	1.0833	2.7986
Bulk Storage				
Count	3	3	3	9
Sum	9	5.5	11	25.5
Average	3.000	1.833	3.667	2.833
Variance	0.2500	1.0833	0.0833	1.0000
Cold Storage				
Count	3	3	3	9
Sum	7	12	13.5	32.5
Average	2.333	4.000	4.500	3.611
Variance	0.3333	1.7500	0.2500	1.5486
Total				
Count	12	12	12	
Sum	41	30.5	33	
Average	3.417	2.542	2.750	
Variance	0.9924	1.5208	2.4318	

ANOVA

Source of Variation	SS	df	MS	F	P-value	F crit
Sample	6.410	3	2.137	3.46	0.0322	3.01
Columns	5.014	2	2.507	4.06	0.0304	3.40
Interaction	33.153	6	5.525	8.94	0.0000	2.51
Within	14.833	24	0.618			
Total	59.410	35				

STEP **7.** Looking at the source of variation table, we must first examine the interaction effects. The observed F value for interaction is 8.94. The observed F value for interaction is greater than the critical F value. The interaction effects are statistically significant at $\alpha = .05$. The p value for interaction is .0000. The interaction effects are significant at $\alpha = .0001$. The researcher should not bother to examine the main effects because the significant interaction confounds the main effects.

STEP **8.** The significant interaction effects indicate that certain warehouse types in combination with certain lengths of training session result in different absenteeism rates than do other combinations of levels for these two variables. Using the cell means shown here and Excel, we can depict the interactions graphically.

		Length of Training Session (Days)		
		1–20	*21–50*	*More than 50*
Types of Warehouses	*General Merchandise*	3.8	2.2	1.7
	Commodity	4.5	2.2	1.2
	Bulk Storage	3.0	1.8	3.7
	Cold Storage	2.3	4.0	4.5

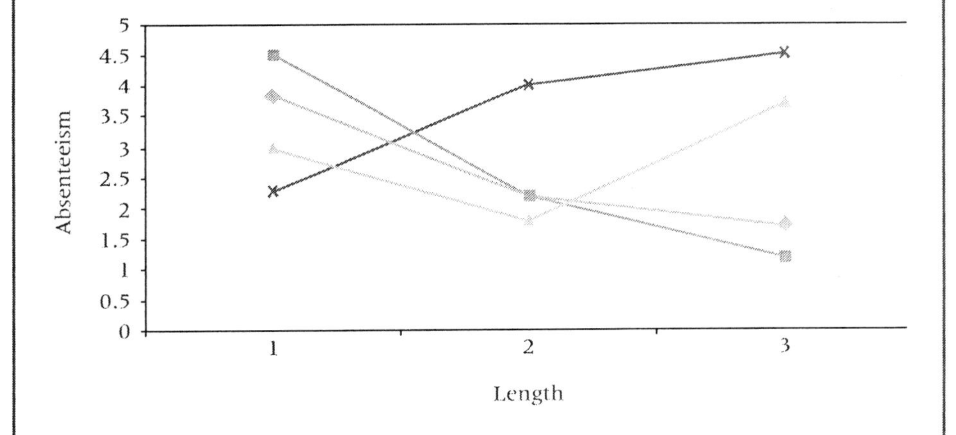

Note the intersecting and crossing lines, which indicate interaction. Under the short-length training sessions, 1, cold-storage workers had the lowest rate of absenteeism and workers at commodity warehouses had the highest. However, for medium-length sessions, 2, cold-storage workers had the highest rate of absenteeism and bulk-storage had the lowest. For the longest training sessions, 3, commodity warehouse workers had the lowest rate of absenteeism, even though these workers had the highest rate of absenteeism for short-length sessions. Thus, the rate of absenteeism for workers at a particular type of warehouse depended on length of session. There was an interaction between type of warehouse and length of session. This graph could be constructed with the row levels along the bottom axis instead of column levels.

11.4 Problems

11.13 The data gathered from a two-way factorial design follow. Use the two-way ANOVA to analyze these data. Let $\alpha = .01$.

		TREATMENT 1		
		A	*B*	*C*
TREATMENT 2	*A*	23	21	20
		25	21	22
	B	27	24	26
		28	27	27

11.14 Suppose the following data have been gathered from a study with a two-way factorial design. Use $\alpha = .05$ and a two-way ANOVA to analyze the data. State your conclusions.

		TREATMENT 1			TREATMENT 1	
		A	*B*		*A*	*B*
TREATMENT 2	*A*	1.2	1.9	*C*	1.7	1.9
		1.3	1.6		1.8	2.2
		1.3	1.7		1.7	1.9
		1.5	2.0		1.6	2.0
	B	2.2	2.7	*D*	2.4	2.8
		2.1	2.5		2.3	2.6
		2.0	2.8		2.5	2.4
		2.3	2.8		2.4	2.8

11.15 Children are generally believed to have considerable influence over their parents in the purchase of certain items, particularly food and beverage items. To study this notion further, a study is conducted in which parents are asked to report how many food and beverage items purchased by the family per week are purchased mainly because of the influence of their children. Because the age of the child may have an effect on the study, parents are asked to focus on one particular child in the family for the week, and to report the age of the child. Four age categories are selected for the children: 4–5 years, 6–7 years, 8–9 years, and 10–12 years. Also, because the number of children in the family might make a difference, three different sizes of families are chosen for the study: families with one child, families with two children, and families with three or more children. Suppose the following data represent the reported number of child-influenced buying incidents per week. Use the data to compute a two-way ANOVA. Let $\alpha = .05$.

		NUMBER OF CHILDREN IN FAMILY		
		1	*2*	*3 or more*
AGE OF CHILD (YEARS)	*4–5*	2	1	1
		4	2	1
	6–7	5	3	2
		4	1	1
	8–9	8	4	2
		6	5	3
	10–12	7	3	4
		8	5	3

11.16 A shoe retailer has conducted a study to determine whether there is a difference in the number of pairs of shoes sold per day by stores according to the number of competitors within a 1-mile radius and the location of the store. The company researchers have selected three types of stores for consideration in the study: stand-alone suburban stores, mall stores, and downtown stores. These stores have varied numbers of competing stores within a 1-mile radius, which have been reduced to four categories: 0 competitors, 1 competitor, 2 competitors, and 3 or more competitors. Suppose the following data represent the number of pairs of shoes sold per day for each of these types of stores with the given number of competitors. Use $\alpha = .05$ and a two-way ANOVA to analyze the data.

		NUMBER OF COMPETITORS			
		0	*1*	*2*	*3 or more*
STORE LOCATION	*Stand-Alone*	41	38	59	47
		30	31	48	40
		45	39	51	39
	Mall	25	29	44	43
		31	35	48	42
		22	30	50	53
	Downtown	18	22	29	24
		29	17	28	27
		33	25	26	32

11.17 In Section 11.2, we tested to determine if there were any significant differences in the mean valve openings among three different operators. Suppose four different machines are used to make the valves by the three operators and that the quality controllers want to know whether there is any difference in the mean measurements of valve openings by operator or by machine. The data are given below, organized by machine and operator. Analyze these data using a two-way ANOVA and $\alpha = .01$.

		VALVE OPENINGS (cm)		
		Operator 1	*Operator 2*	*Operator 3*
MACHINE	1	6.56	6.38	6.29
		6.40	6.19	6.23
	2	6.54	6.26	6.19
		6.34	6.23	6.33
	3	6.58	6.22	6.26
		6.44	6.27	6.31
	4	6.36	6.29	6.21
		6.50	6.19	6.58

11.5 Chi-Square Goodness-of-Fit Test

In Chapter 5, we studied the binomial distribution in which only two possible outcomes can occur on a single trial in an experiment. An extension of the binomial distribution is a multinomial distribution in which more than two possible outcomes can occur in a single trial. The **chi-square goodness-of-fit test** is *used to analyze probabilities of multinomial distribution trials along a single dimension.* For example, if the variable being studied is type of industry with the three possible outcomes of 1) information technology, 2) financial, and 3) transportation, the single dimension is industry and the three possible outcomes are information technology, financial, and transportation. On each trial, one and only one of the outcomes can occur; that is, the company or respondent must be in one and only one of these three industries. The chi-square goodness-of-fit test uses the chi-square distribution in the analysis of data as does many other statistical techniques including the chi-square test of independence, which is introduced in Section 11.6.

Chi-square goodness-of-fit test
A statistical test that compares expected or theoretical frequencies of categories from a population distribution to the actual or observed frequencies from a distribution.

The chi-square goodness-of-fit test compares the *expected,* or theoretical, *frequencies* of categories from a population distribution to the *observed,* or actual, *frequencies* from a distribution to determine whether there is a difference between what was expected and what was observed. For example, airline industry officials might theorize that the ages of airline ticket purchasers are distributed in a particular way. To validate or reject this expected distribution, an actual sample of ticket purchaser ages can be gathered randomly, and the observed results can be compared to the expected results with the chi-square goodness-of-fit test. This test also can be used to determine whether the observed arrivals at teller windows at a bank are Poisson distributed, as might be expected. In the paper industry, manufacturers can use the chi-square goodness-of-fit test to determine whether the demand for paper follows a uniform distribution throughout the year.

Formula 11.1 is used to compute a chi-square goodness-of-fit test.

CHI-SQUARE GOODNESS-OF-FIT TEST

$$\chi^2 = \sum \frac{(f_o - f_e)^2}{f_e} \quad (11.1)$$

$$df = k - 1 - c$$

where:
f_o = frequency of observed values
f_e = frequency of expected values
k = number of categories
c = number of parameters being estimated from the sample data

This formula compares the frequency of observed values to the frequency of the expected values across the distribution. The test loses one degree of freedom because the total number of expected frequencies must equal the number of observed frequencies. That is, the observed total taken from the sample is used as the total for the expected frequencies. In addition, in some instances a population parameter, such as λ, μ, or σ, is estimated from the sample data to determine the frequency distribution of expected values. Each time this estimation occurs, an additional degree of freedom is lost. As a rule, if a uniform distribution is being used as the expected distribution or if an expected distribution of values is *given,* $k - 1$ degrees of freedom are used in the test. In testing to determine whether an observed distribution is Poisson, the degrees of freedom are $k - 2$ because an additional degree of freedom is lost in estimating λ. In testing to determine whether an observed distribution is normal, the degrees of freedom are $k - 3$ because two additional degrees of freedom are lost in estimating μ and σ from the observed sample data.

Chi-square distribution
A continuous distribution determined by the sum of the squares of k independent random variables.

Karl Pearson introduced the chi-square test in 1900. The **chi-square distribution** is *the sum of the squares of k independent random variables* and therefore can never be less than zero; it extends indefinitely in the positive direction. Actually the chi-square distributions constitute a family, with each distribution defined by the degrees of freedom (df) associated with it. For small df values the chi-square distribution is skewed considerably to the right (positive values). As the df increase, the chi-square distribution begins to approach the normal curve. Table values for the chi-square distribution are given in Appendix A. Because of space limitations, chi-square values are listed only for certain probabilities.

How can the chi-square goodness-of-fit test be applied to business situations? One survey of U.S. consumers conducted by *The Wall Street Journal* and NBC News asked the question: "In general, how would you rate the level of service that American businesses provide?" The distribution of responses to this question was as follows:

Excellent	8%
Pretty good	47%
Only fair	34%
Poor	11%

Suppose a store manager wants to find out whether the results of this consumer survey apply to customers of supermarkets in her city. To do so, she interviews 207 randomly selected consumers as they leave supermarkets in various parts of the city. She asks the customers how they would rate the level of service at the supermarket from which they had just exited. The response categories are excellent, pretty good, only fair, and poor. The observed responses from this study are given in Table 11.5. Now the manager can use a chi-square goodness-of-fit test to determine whether the observed frequencies of responses from this survey are the same as the frequencies that would be expected on the basis of the national survey.

STEP **1.** The hypotheses for this example follow.

H_0: The observed distribution is the same as the expected distribution.
H_a: The observed distribution is not the same as the expected distribution.

STEP **2.** The statistical test being used is

$$\chi^2 = \sum \frac{(f_o - f_e)^2}{f_e}$$

STEP **3.** Let $\alpha = .05$.

STEP **4.** Chi-square goodness-of-fit tests are one-tailed because a chi-square of zero indicates perfect agreement between distributions. Any deviation from zero difference occurs in the positive direction only because chi-square is determined by a sum of squared values and can never be negative. With four categories in this example (excellent, pretty good, only fair, and poor), $k = 4$. The degrees of freedom are $k - 1$ because the expected distribution is given: $k - 1 = 4 - 1 = 3$. For $\alpha = .05$ and df $= 3$, the critical chi-square value is

$$\chi^2_{.05,3} = 7.815.$$

After the data have been analyzed, an observed chi-square greater than 7.815 must be computed in order to reject the null hypothesis.

STEP **5.** The observed values gathered in the sample data from Table 11.5 sum to 207. Thus $n = 207$. The expected *proportions* are given, but the expected *frequencies* must be calculated by multiplying the expected proportions by the sample total of the observed frequencies, as shown in Table 11.6.

STEP **6.** The chi-square goodness-of-fit can then be calculated, as shown in Table 11.7.

STEP **7.** The observed value of chi-square is 6.25 versus a critical table value of 7.815. Because the observed chi-square is not greater than the critical chi-square, the store manager will not reject the null hypothesis.

TABLE 11.5
Results of a Local Survey of Consumer Satisfaction

RESPONSE	FREQUENCY (f_o)
Excellent	21
Pretty good	109
Only fair	62
Poor	15

TABLE 11.6
Construction of Expected Values for Service Satisfaction Study

RESPONSE	EXPECTED PROPORTION	EXPECTED FREQUENCY (f_e) (PROPORTION × SAMPLE TOTAL)
Excellent	.08	(.08)(207) = 16.56
Pretty good	.47	(.47)(207) = 97.29
Only fair	.34	(.34)(207) = 70.38
Poor	.11	(.11)(207) = 22.77
		207.00

TABLE 11.7
Calculation of Chi-Square for Service Satisfaction Example

RESPONSE	f_o	f_e	$\frac{(f_o - f_e)^2}{f_e}$
Excellent	21	16.56	1.19
Pretty good	109	97.29	1.41
Only fair	62	70.38	1.00
Poor	15	22.77	2.65
	207	207.00	6.25

$$\chi^2 = \sum \frac{(f_o - f_e)^2}{f_e} = 6.25$$

Figure 11.18

Graph of chi-square distribution for service satisfaction example

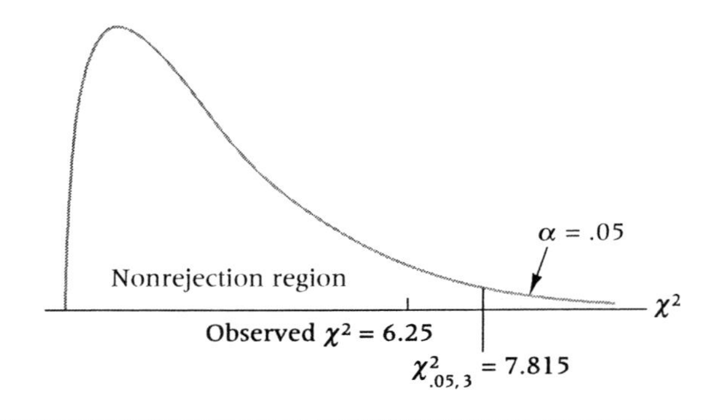

STEP **8.** Thus the data gathered in the sample of 207 supermarket shoppers indicates that the distribution of responses of supermarket shoppers in the manager's city is not significantly different from the distribution of responses to the national survey.

The store manager may conclude that her customers do not appear to have attitudes different than those people who took the survey. Figure 11.18 depicts the chi-square distribution for this example, along with the observed and critical values.

Analysis Using Excel

By using two different Excel statistical functions, Excel has the capability of computing an observed χ^2 along with its associated p-value and a critical value of χ^2 when conducting a chi-square goodness-of-fit test. Start with the **CHITEST** from the paste function. The dialog box for this is shown in Figure 11.19. The dialog box requires only the location of the actual values and the location of the expected values. The output for **CHITEST** is limited to the p-value of the observed chi-square only.

Using the p-value obtained from **CHITEST,** it is possible to determine the observed χ^2 by using the **CHIINV** feature of the paste function. The dialog box for **CHIINV** is displayed in Figure 11.20. Also, by using **CHIINV,** it is possible to determine the critical

Figure 11.19 Excel dialog box for **CHITEST**

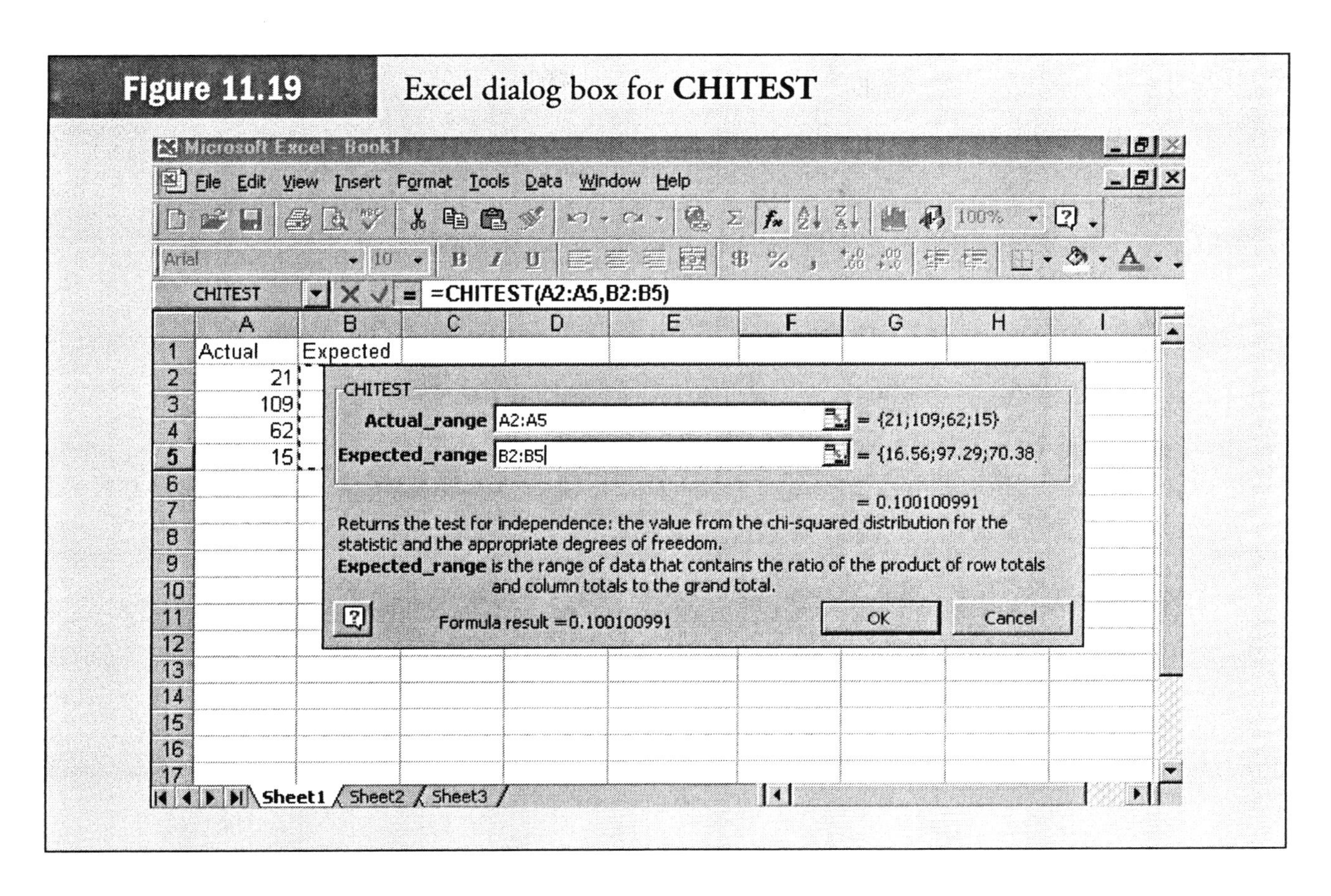

Figure 11.20 Excel dialog box for **CHIINV**

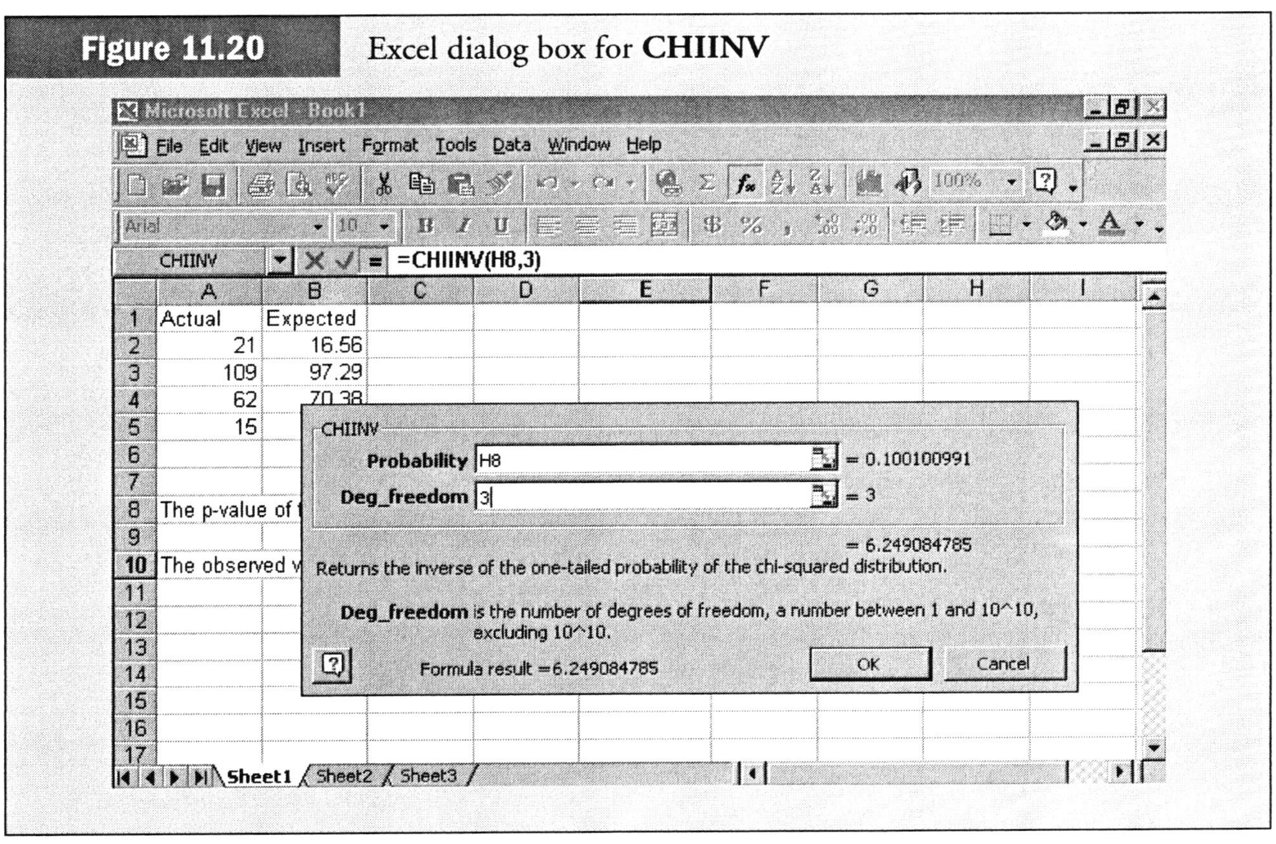

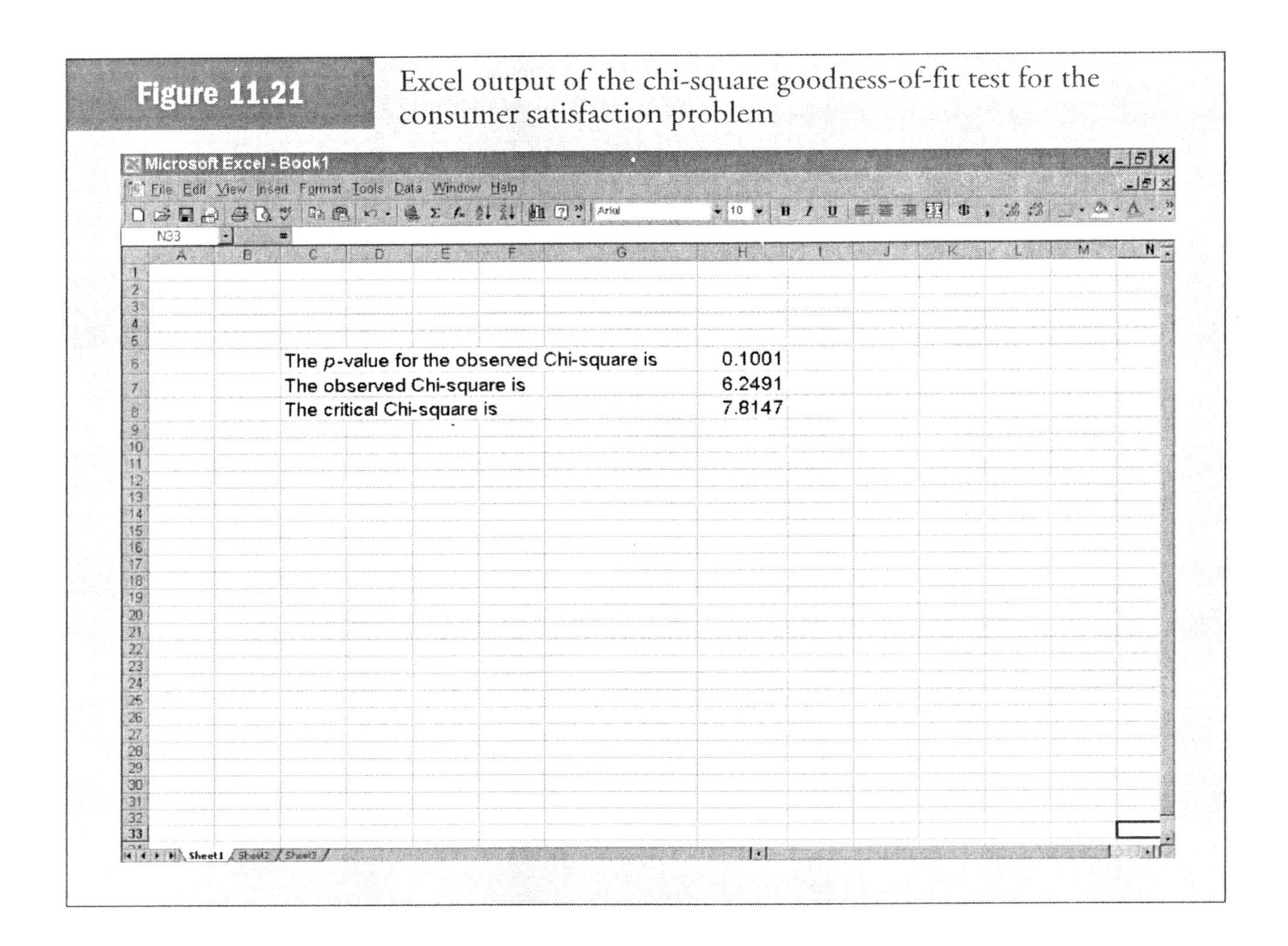

Figure 11.21 Excel output of the chi-square goodness-of-fit test for the consumer satisfaction problem

table value. In both cases, **CHIINV** requires the probability which for the observed value is the p-value and for the critical value is the value of alpha. In addition, **CHIINV** requires the degrees of freedom for the test.

The output for **CHITEST** is the p-value for the observed chi-square. The output for **CHIINV** is the value of the chi-square. Figure 11.21 displays the output for the consumer satisfaction problem including the p-value, the observed value of chi-square, and the critical value of chi-square. Note that the p-value is .1001, which is greater than $\alpha = .05$ and that the observed chi-square is less than the critical chi-square underscoring the decision to fail to reject the null hypothesis.

DEMONSTRATION PROBLEM 11.4

Dairies would like to know whether the sales of milk are distributed uniformly over a year so they can plan for milk production and storage. A uniform distribution means that the frequencies are the same in all categories. In this situation, the producers are attempting to determine whether the amounts of milk sold are the same for each month of the year. They ascertain the number of gallons of milk sold by sampling one large supermarket each month during a year, obtaining the following data. Use $\alpha = .01$ to test whether the data fit a uniform distribution.

MONTH	GALLONS	MONTH	GALLONS
January	1,553	August	1,450
February	1,585	September	1,495
March	1,649	October	1,564
April	1,590	November	1,602
May	1,497	December	1,609
June	1,443	Total	18,447
July	1,410		

SOLUTION

STEP **1.** The hypotheses follow.

H_0: The monthly figures for milk sales are uniformly distributed.

H_a: The monthly figures for milk sales are not uniformly distributed.

STEP **2.** The statistical test used is

$$\chi^2 = \sum \frac{(f_o - f_e)^2}{f_e}.$$

STEP **3.** Alpha is .01.

STEP **4.** There are 12 categories and a uniform distribution is the expected distribution, so the degrees of freedom are $k - 1 = 12 - 1 = 11$. For $\alpha = .01$, the critical value is $\chi^2_{.01,11} = 24.725$. An observed chi-square value of more than 24.725 must be obtained to reject the null hypothesis.

STEP **5.** The data are given above.

STEP **6.** The first step in calculating the test statistic is to determine the expected frequencies. The total for the expected frequencies must equal the total for the observed frequencies (18,447). If the frequencies are uniformly distributed, the same number of gallons of milk are expected to be sold each month. The expected monthly figure is

$$\frac{18,447}{12} = 1537.25 \text{ gallons.}$$

The following table shows the observed frequencies, the expected frequencies, and the chi-square calculations for this problem.

MONTH	f_o	f_e	$\frac{(f_o - f_e)^2}{f_e}$
January	1,553	1,537.25	0.16
February	1,585	1,537.25	1.48
March	1,649	1,537.25	8.12
April	1,590	1,537.25	1.81
May	1,497	1,537.25	1.05
June	1,443	1,537.25	5.78
July	1,410	1,537.25	10.53
August	1,450	1,537.25	4.95
September	1,495	1,537.25	1.16
October	1,564	1,537.25	.47
November	1,602	1,537.25	2.73
December	1,609	1,537.25	3.35
Total	18,447	18,447.00	$\chi^2 = 41.59$

STEP **7.** The observed χ^2 value of 41.59 is greater than the critical table value of $\chi^2_{.01,11} = 24.725$, so the decision is to reject the null hypothesis. There is enough evidence in this problem to indicate that the distribution of milk sales is not uniform.

STEP **8.** As retail milk demand is not uniformly distributed, sales and production managers need to generate a production plan to cope with uneven demand. In times of heavy demand, more milk will need to be processed or on reserve; in times of less demand, provision for milk storage or for a reduction in the purchase of milk from dairy farmers will be necessary.

The following graph depicts the chi-square distribution, critical chi-square value, and observed chi-square value.

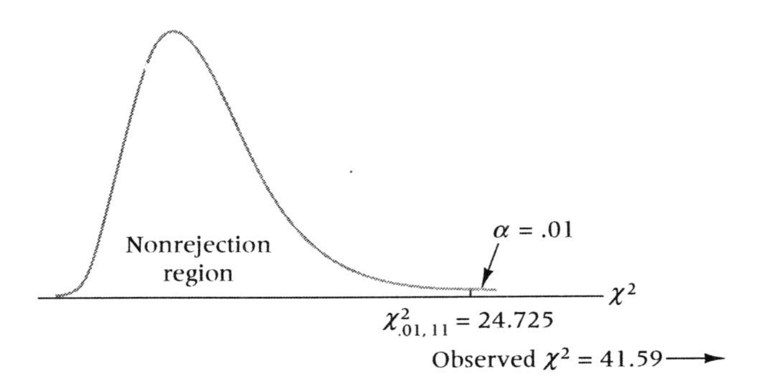

Shown below is the Excel output for Demonstration Problem 11.4.

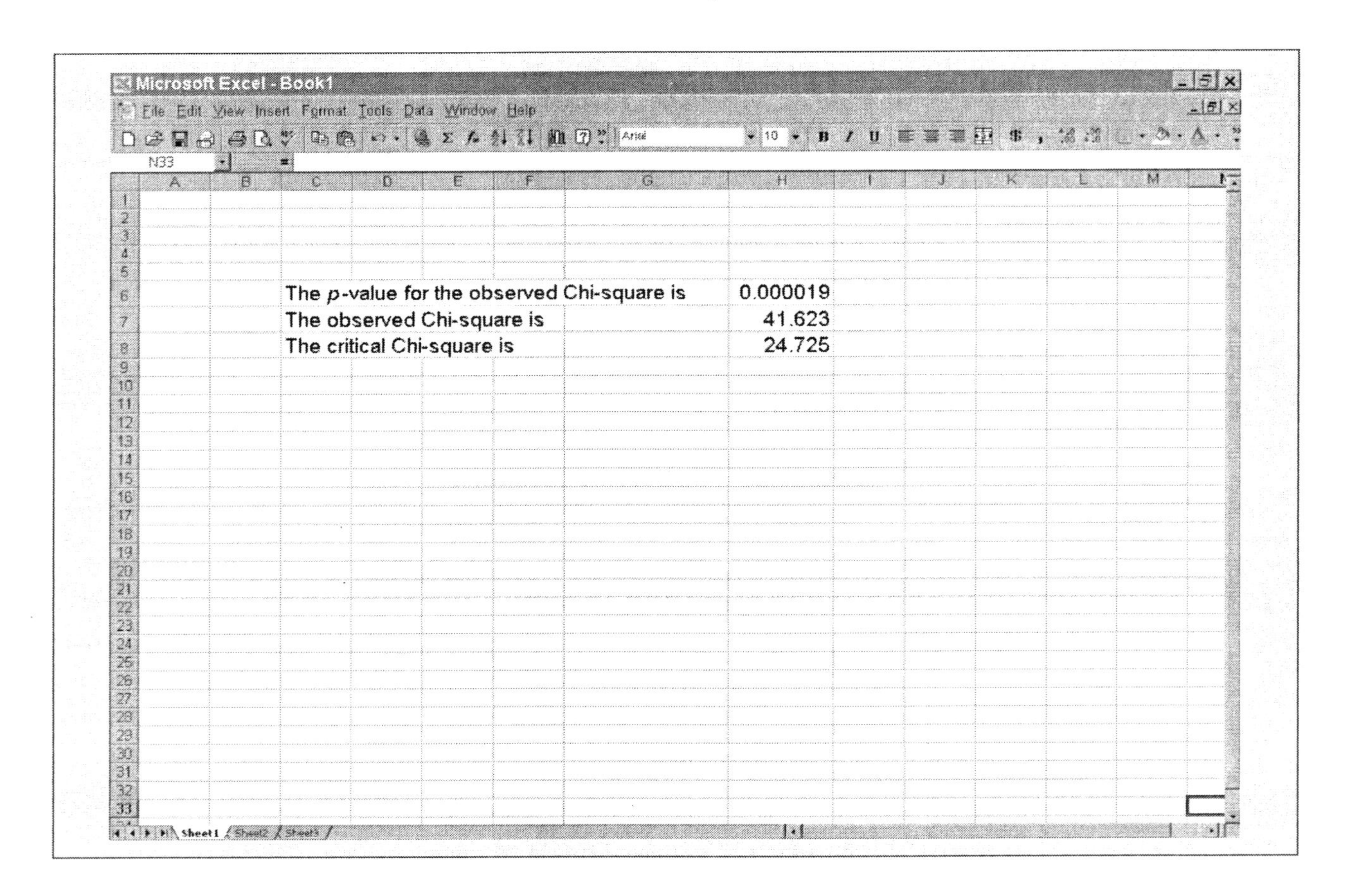

Testing a Population Proportion by Using the Chi-Square Goodness-of-Fit Test as an Alternative Technique to the Z Test

In Chapter 9 we discussed a technique for testing the value of a population proportion. When sample size is large enough ($n \cdot P \geq 5$ and $n \cdot Q \geq 5$), sample proportions are normally distributed and the following formula can be used to test hypotheses about P.

$$Z = \frac{\hat{p} - P}{\sqrt{\frac{P \cdot Q}{n}}}$$

The chi-square goodness-of-fit test can also be used to conduct tests about P; this situation can be viewed as a special case of the chi-square goodness-of-fit test where the number of classifications equals two (binomial distribution situation). The observed chi-square is computed in the same way as in any other chi-square goodness-of-fit test but, as there are only two classifications (success/failure), $k = 2$ and the degrees of freedom are $k - 1 = 2 - 1 = 1$.

As an example, we will work two problems from Section 9.4 by using chi-square methodology. The first example in Section 9.4 tests the hypothesis that exactly 8% of a manufacturer's products are defective. The following hypotheses are being tested.

$$H_0: P = .08$$
$$H_a: P \neq .08$$

The value of alpha was given to be .10. To test this claim, a researcher randomly selected a sample of 200 items and determined that 33 of the items had at least one flaw.

Working this problem by the chi-square goodness-of-fit test, we view this as a two-category expected distribution in which we expect .08 defects and .92 nondefects. The observed categories are 33 defects and 200 – 33 = 167 nondefects. Using the total observed items (200), we can determine an expected distribution as .08(200) = 16 and .92(200) = 184. Shown here are the observed and expected frequencies.

	f_o	f_e
Defects	33	16
Nondefects	167	184

Alpha is .10 and this is a two-tailed test, so $\alpha/2 = .05$. The degrees of freedom are 1. The critical table chi-square value is

$$\chi^2_{.05,1} = 3.841.$$

An observed chi-square value greater than this value must be obtained to reject the null hypothesis. The chi-square for this problem is calculated as follows.

$$\chi^2 = \sum \frac{(f_o - f_e)^2}{f_e} = \frac{(33 - 16)^2}{16} + \frac{(167 - 184)^2}{184} = 18.06 + 1.57 = 19.63$$

Notice that this observed value of chi-square, 19.63, is greater than the critical table value, 3.841. The decision is to reject the null hypotheses. The manufacturer does not produce 8% defects according to this analysis. Observing the actual sample result, in which .165 of the sample was defective, indicates that the proportion of the population that is defective might be greater than 8%.

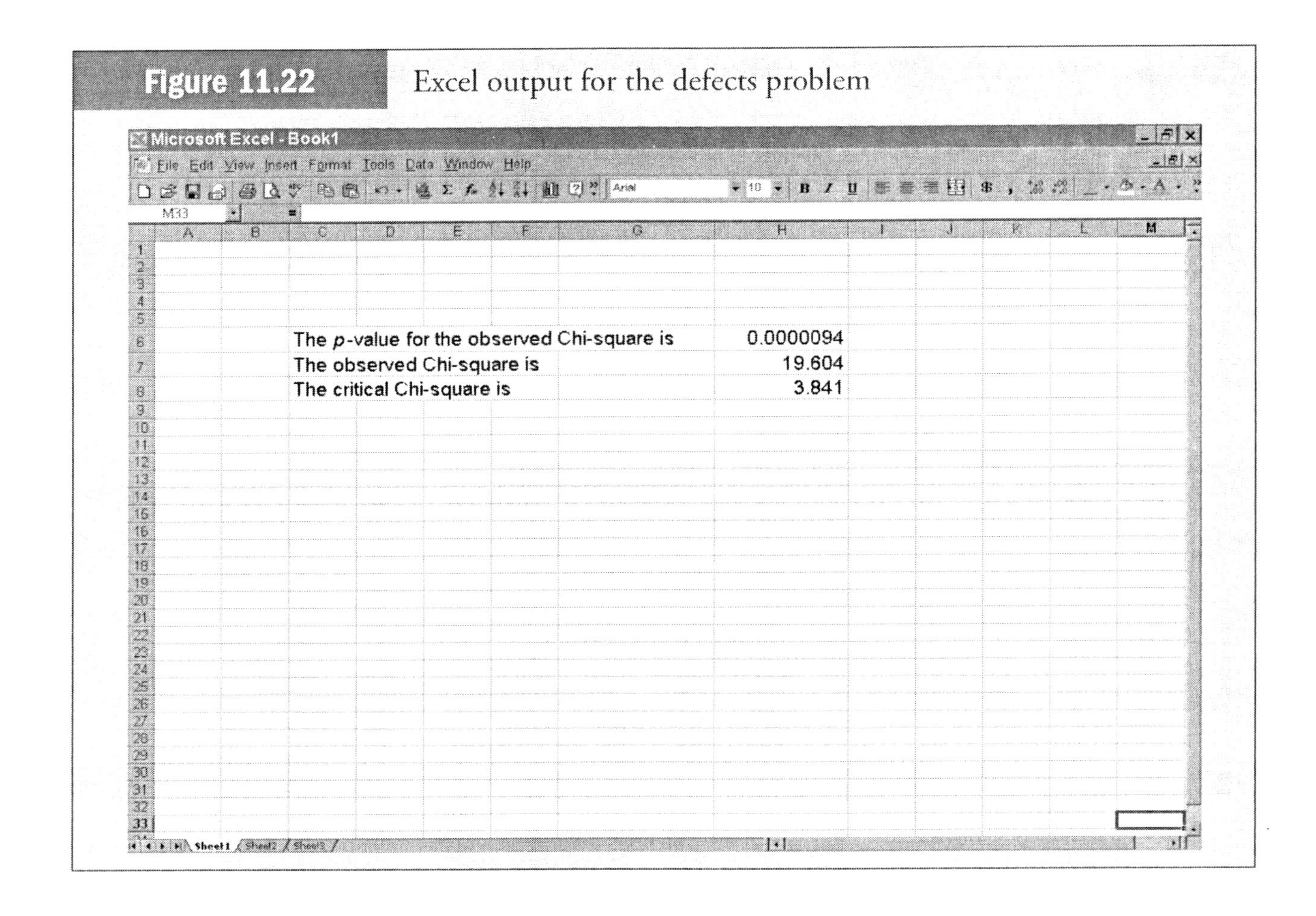

Figure 11.22 Excel output for the defects problem

The results obtained are approximately the same as those computed in Chapter 9, in which an observed Z value of 4.43 was determined and compared to a critical Z value of 1.645, causing us to reject the null hypothesis. This is not surprising to business analysts, who understand that when the degrees of freedom equal 1, the value of χ^2 equals Z^2.

Figure 11.22 shows the Excel output for this problem. Note the observed value of chi-square and its associated p-value. Since the p-value of .0000094 is smaller than .05, the decision based on a p-value analysis is to reject the null hypothesis, which is consistent with the findings previously computed by hand.

11.5 Problems

11.18 Use the following data and $\alpha = .01$ to determine whether the observed frequencies represent a uniform distribution.

CATEGORY	f_o
1	19
2	17
3	14
4	18
5	19
6	21
7	18
8	18

11.19 In one survey, successful female entrepreneurs were asked to state their personal definition of success in terms of several categories from which they could select. Thirty-nine percent responded that happiness was their definition of success, 12% said that sales/profit was their definition, 18% responded that helping others was their definition, and 31% responded that achievements/challenge was their definition. Suppose you wanted to determine whether male entrepreneurs felt the same way and took a random sample of men, resulting in the data shown. Use the chi-square goodness-of-fit test to determine whether the observed frequency distribution of data for men is the same as the distribution for women. Let $\alpha = .05$.

DEFINITION	f_o
Happiness	42
Sales/profit	95
Helping others	27
Achievements/challenge	63

11.20 The following percentages are from a national survey of the ages of prerecorded-music shoppers. A local survey produced the observed values. Is there evidence in the observed data to reject the national survey distribution for local prerecorded-music shoppers? Use $\alpha = .01$.

AGE	PERCENT FROM SURVEY	f_o
10–14	9	22
15–19	23	50
20–24	22	43
25–29	14	29
30–34	10	19
≥35	22	49

11.21 The Springfield Emergency Medical Service keeps records of emergency telephone calls. A study of 150 five-minute time intervals resulted in the distribution of number of calls shown. For example, there were 18 five-minute intervals in which there were no calls. Use the chi-square goodness-of-fit test and $\alpha = .01$ to determine whether this distribution is Poisson.

NUMBER OF CALLS (PER 5-MIN INTERVAL)	FREQUENCY
0	18
1	28
2	47
3	21
4	16
5	11
6 or more	9

11.22 According to an extensive survey conducted for *Business Marketing* by Leo J. Shapiro & Associates, 66% of all computer companies are going to spend more on marketing this year than in previous years. Only 33% of other information technology companies and 28% of non-information technology companies are going to spend more. Suppose a researcher wanted to conduct a survey of her own to test the claim that 28% of all non-information technology companies are spending more on marketing next year than this year. She randomly selects 270 companies and determines that 62 of the companies do plan to spend more on marketing next year. Use $\alpha = .05$, the chi-square goodness-of-fit test, and the sample data to test to determine whether the 28% figure holds for all non-information technology companies.

11.23 Cross-cultural training is rapidly becoming a popular way to prepare executives for foreign management positions within their company. This training includes such things as foreign language, previsit orientations, meetings with former expatriates, and cultural background information on the country. According to Runzheimer International, 30% of all major companies provide formal cross-cultural programs to their executives being relocated in foreign countries. Suppose a researcher wants to test this figure for companies in the communications industry to determine whether the figure is too high for that industry. A random sample of 180 communications firms are contacted; 42 provide such a program. Let $\alpha = .05$ and use the chi-square goodness-of-fit test to determine whether the .30 proportion for all major companies is too high for this industry.

11.6

Contingency Analysis: Chi-Square Test of Independence

Chi-square test of independence
A statistical test used to analyze the frequencies of two variables with multiple categories to determine whether the two variables are independent.

The chi-square goodness-of-fit test is used to analyze the distribution of frequencies for categories of *one* variable, such as age or number of bank arrivals, to determine whether the distribution of these frequencies is the same as some hypothesized or expected distribution. However, the goodness-of-fit test cannot be used to analyze *two* variables simultaneously. A different chi-square test, the **chi-square test of independence,** can be *used to analyze the frequencies of two variables with multiple categories to determine whether the two variables are independent.* Many times this type of analysis is desirable. For example, a market researcher might want to determine whether the type of soft drink preferred by a consumer is independent of the consumer's age. An organizational behaviorist might want to know whether absenteeism is independent of job classification. Financial investors might want to determine whether type of preferred stock investment is independent of the region where the investor resides.

The chi-square test of independence can be used to analyze any level of data measurement, but it is particularly useful in analyzing nominal data. Suppose a researcher is interested in determining whether geographic region is independent of type of financial investment. On a questionnaire, the following two questions might be used to measure geographic region and type of financial investment.

In which region of the country do you reside?

A. Northeast **B.** Midwest **C.** South **D.** West

Which type of financial investment are you most likely to make today?

E. Stocks **F.** Bonds **G.** Treasury Bills

Contingency table
A two-way table that contains the frequencies of responses to two questions; also called a raw values matrix.

Contingency analysis
A chi-square test of independence.

The researcher would tally the frequencies of responses to these two questions into a two-way table called a **contingency table.** Because the chi-square test of independence uses a contingency table, this test is sometimes referred to as **contingency analysis.**

Depicted in Table 11.8 is a contingency table for these two variables. Variable 1, geographic region, has four categories: A, B, C, and D. Variable 2, type of financial investment, has three categories: E, F, and G. The observed frequency for each cell is denoted as o_{ij}, where i is the row and j is the column. Thus, o_{13} is the observed frequency for the cell in the first row and third column. The expected frequencies are denoted in a similar manner.

If the two variables are independent, they are not related. In a sense, the chi-square test of independence is a test of whether the variables are related. The null hypothesis for a chi-square test of independence is that the two variables are independent. If the null hypothesis is rejected, the conclusion is that the two variables are not independent and are related.

Assume at the beginning that variable 1 and variable 2 are independent. The probability of the intersection of two of their respective categories, A and F, can be found by using the multiplicative law for independent events presented in Chapter 4:

$$P(A \cap F) = P(A) \cdot P(F),$$

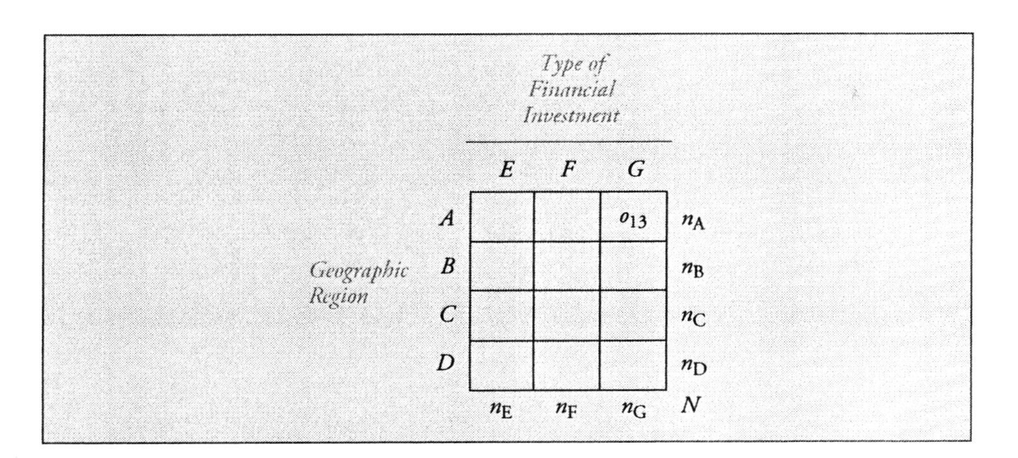

TABLE 11.8
Contingency Table for the Investment Example

if A and F are independent. Then

$$P(\text{A}) = \frac{n_\text{A}}{N}, \quad P(\text{F}) = \frac{n_\text{F}}{N}, \quad \text{and} \quad P(\text{A} \cap \text{F}) = \frac{n_\text{A}}{N} \cdot \frac{n_\text{F}}{N}.$$

If $P(\text{A} \cap \text{F})$ is multiplied by the total number of frequencies, N, the expected frequency for the cell of A and F can be determined.

$$e_\text{AF} = \frac{n_\text{A}}{N} \cdot \frac{n_\text{F}}{N}(N) = \frac{n_\text{A} \cdot n_\text{F}}{N}$$

In general, if the two variables are independent, the expected frequency values of each cell can be determined by

$$e_{ij} = \frac{(n_i)(n_j)}{N},$$

where:
i = the row,
j = the column,
n_i = the total of row i,
n_j = the total of column j, and
N = the total of all frequencies.

Using these expected frequency values and the observed frequency values, we can compute a chi-square test of independence to determine whether the variables are independent. Formula 11.2 is the formula for accomplishing this.

CHI-SQUARE TEST OF INDEPENDENCE

(11.2)

$$\chi^2 = \sum\sum\frac{(f_o - f_e)^2}{f_e}$$

where:
df = $(r - 1)(c - 1)$
r = number of rows
c = number of columns

The null hypothesis for a chi-square test of independence is that the two variables are independent. The alternative hypothesis is that the variables are not independent. This test is one-tailed. The degrees of freedom are $(r - 1)(c - 1)$. Note that Equation 11.2 is similar to Equation 11.1, with the exception that the values are summed across both rows and columns and the degrees of freedom are different.

Suppose a business analyst wants to determine whether type of gasoline preferred is independent of a person's income. He takes a random survey of gasoline purchasers, asking them one question about gasoline preference and a second question about income. The respondent is to check whether he or she prefers (1) regular gasoline, (2) premium gasoline, or (3) extra premium gasoline. The respondent also is to check his or her income brackets as being (1) less than $30,000, (2) $30,000 to $49,999, (3) $50,000 to $99,999, or (4) more than $100,000. The business analyst tallies the responses and obtains the results in Table 11.9. Using $\alpha = .01$, he can use the chi-square test of independence to determine whether type of gasoline preferred is independent of income level.

STEP **1.** The hypotheses follow.

H_0: Type of gasoline is independent of income.

H_a: Type of gasoline is not independent of income.

STEP **2.** The appropriate statistical test is

$$\chi^2 = \sum\sum\frac{(f_o - f_e)^2}{f_e}$$

STEP **3.** Alpha is .01.

STEP **4.** Here, there are four rows ($r = 4$) and three columns ($c = 3$). The degrees of freedom are $(4 - 1)(3 - 1) = 6$. The critical value of chi-square for $\alpha = .01$ is $\chi^2_{.01,6} = 16.812$. The decision rule is to reject the null hypothesis if the observed chi-square is greater than 16.812.

STEP **5.** The observed data are in Table 11.9.

STEP **6.** To determine the observed value of chi-square, the business analyst must compute the expected frequencies. The expected values for this example are calculated as follows, with the first term in the subscript (and numerator) representing the row and the second term in the subscript (and numerator) representing the column.

TABLE 11.9
Contingency Table for the Gasoline Consumer Example

		Type of Gasoline			
		Regular	*Premium*	*Extra Premium*	
Income	*Less than $30,000*	41	16	6	63
	$30,000 to $49,999	70	27	13	110
	$50,000 to $99,999	52	18	15	85
	More than $100,000	19	17	25	61
		182	78	59	319

$$e_{11} = \frac{(n_1.)(n._1)}{N} = \frac{(63)(182)}{319} = 35.94$$

$$e_{12} = \frac{(n_1.)(n._2)}{N} = \frac{(63)(78)}{319} = 15.40$$

$$e_{13} = \frac{(n_1.)(n._3)}{N} = \frac{(63)(59)}{319} = 11.65$$

$$e_{21} = \frac{(n_2.)(n._1)}{N} = \frac{(110)(182)}{319} = 62.76$$

$$e_{22} = \frac{(n_2.)(n._2)}{N} = \frac{(110)(78)}{319} = 26.90$$

$$e_{23} = \frac{(n_2.)(n._3)}{N} = \frac{(110)(59)}{319} = 20.34$$

$$e_{31} = \frac{(n_3.)(n._1)}{N} = \frac{(85)(182)}{319} = 48.50$$

$$e_{32} = \frac{(n_3.)(n._2)}{N} = \frac{(85)(78)}{319} = 20.78$$

$$e_{33} = \frac{(n_3.)(n._3)}{N} = \frac{(85)(59)}{319} = 15.72$$

$$e_{41} = \frac{(n_4.)(n._1)}{N} = \frac{(61)(182)}{319} = 34.80$$

$$e_{42} = \frac{(n_4.)(n._2)}{N} = \frac{(61)(78)}{319} = 14.92$$

$$e_{43} = \frac{(n_4.)(n._3)}{N} = \frac{(61)(59)}{319} = 11.28$$

The business analyst then lists the expected frequencies in the cells of the contingency tables along with observed frequencies. In this text, expected frequencies are enclosed in parentheses. Table 11.10 is the contingency table for this example.

TABLE 11.10 Contingency Table of Observed and Expected Frequencies for Gasoline Consumer Example

Income	*Type of Gasoline*: *Regular*	*Premium*	*Extra Premium*	
Less than $30,000	(35.94) 41	(15.40) 16	(11.65) 6	63
$30,000 to $49,999	(62.76) 70	(26.90) 27	(20.34) 13	110
$50,000 to $99,999	(48.50) 52	(20.78) 18	(15.72) 15	85
More than $100,000	(34.80) 19	(14.92) 17	(11.28) 25	61
	182	78	59	319

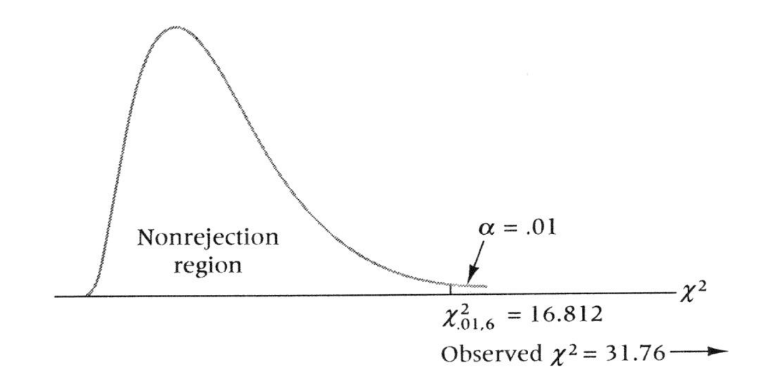

Figure 11.23

Graph of chi-square distribution for gasoline consumer example

Next, the business analyst computes the chi-square value by summing $(f_o - f_e)^2/f_e$ for all cells.

$$\chi^2 = \frac{(41-35.94)^2}{35.94} + \frac{(16-15.40)^2}{15.40} + \frac{(6-11.65)^2}{11.65} + \frac{(70-62.76)^2}{62.76}$$
$$+ \frac{(27-26.90)^2}{26.90} + \frac{(13-20.34)^2}{20.34} + \frac{(52-48.50)^2}{48.50} + \frac{(18-20.78)^2}{20.78}$$
$$+ \frac{(15-15.72)^2}{15.72} + \frac{(19-34.80)^2}{34.80} + \frac{(17-14.92)^2}{14.92} + \frac{(25-11.28)^2}{11.28}$$
$$= 0.71 + 0.02 + 2.74 + 0.84 + 0.00 + 2.65 + 0.25 + 0.37 + 0.03 + 7.17$$
$$+ 0.29 + 16.69$$
$$= 31.76$$

STEP **7.** The observed value of chi-square, 31.76, is greater than the critical value of chi-square, 16.812, obtained from Table A.8. The business analyst's decision is to reject the null hypothesis. That is, type of gasoline preferred is not independent of income.

STEP **8.** Having established that conclusion, the business analyst can then examine the outcome to determine which people, by income brackets, tend to purchase which type of gasoline and use this information in market decisions.

Figure 11.23 is the chi-square graph with the critical value, the rejection region, and the observed χ^2.

Analysis Using Excel

While Excel can compare observed values to expected values and compute p-values for the resulting chi-square, it does not have the capability of computing chi-square values for tests of independence. For this then, we turn to **FAST⧹STAT,** which can analyze contingency tables testing for independence with the chi-square statistic. From the pull-down menu provided by **FAST⧹STAT**, select **Chi-Square Indep. Test.** Observe the dialog box for this test in Figure 11.24. Note that this dialog box requires the location of the observed frequencies and the value of alpha (significance level).

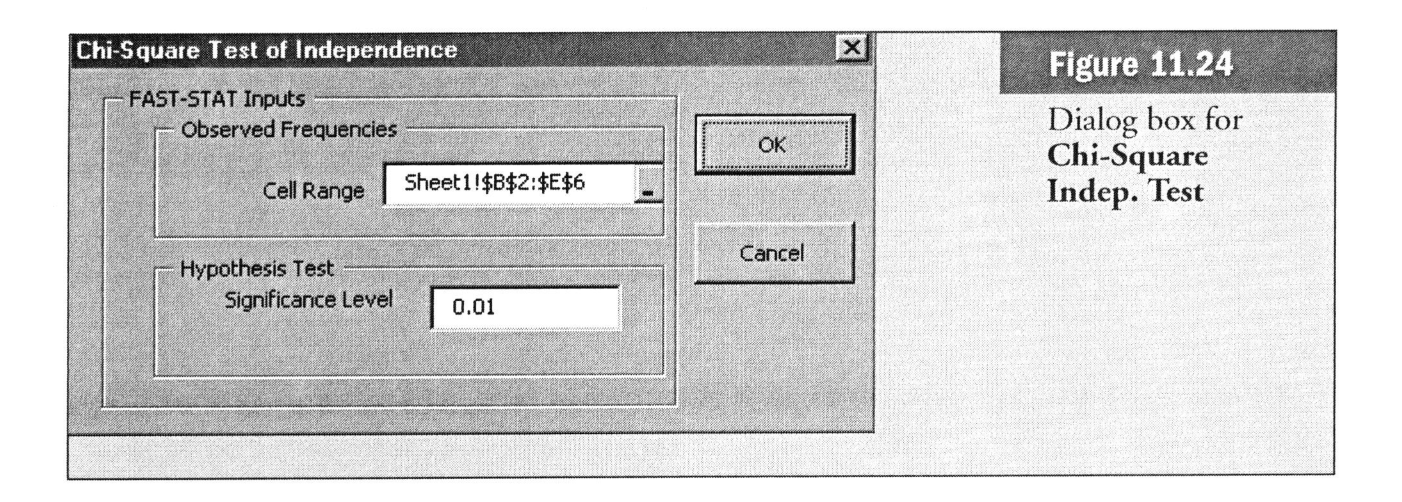

Figure 11.24

Dialog box for **Chi-Square Indep. Test**

Figure 11.25 FAST⧹STAT output for the gasoline problem

Microsoft Excel - 010-Chi.Sq.Indep.Test Macro

A1 = Chi-Square Test of Independence

	A	B	C	D	E
1	Chi-Square Test of Independence				
2	*INPUTS*				
3		Significance Level of the Test			0.01
4					
5		***Observed Frequencies***			
6	First Variable		Second Variable		
7		Regular	Premium	Extra Prem.	
8	<$30,000	41	16	6	
9	$30-49,999	70	27	13	
10	$50-99,999	52	18	15	
11	>=$100,00	19	17	25	
12–17					
18	*OUTPUTS*				
19		***Sample Statistics***			
20		Total of All Observed Frequencies			319
21					
22		No. of Categories-First Variable			4
23		No. of Categories-Second Variab			3
24		Degrees of Freedom			6
25					
26		Chi-Square Test Statistic			31.7689
27		Chi-Square Critical Value			16.8119
28		p-Value for Test			0.0000
29					
30		***Expected Frequencies***			
31	First Variable		Second Variable		
32		Regular	Premium	Extra Pren	
33	<$30,000	35.94357	15.40439	11.65204	
34	$30-49,999	62.75862	26.89655	20.34483	
35	$50-99,999	48.4953	20.7837	15.721	
36	>=$100,00	34.80251	14.91536	11.28213	

Sheet1 | Chi Square | Sheet3

Shown in Figure 11.25 are the results for **FAST⧹STAT's Chi-Square Indep. Test** analysis on the gasoline problem. Note the calculated value of chi-square, its associated p-value, and the critical value of chi-square. Since the p-value of .00002 is less than $\alpha = .01$, the decision is to reject the null hypothesis. This conclusion is consistent with that previously computed by hand.

DEMONSTRATION PROBLEM 11.5

Is the type of beverage ordered with lunch at a restaurant independent of the age of the consumer? A random poll of 259 lunch customers is taken, resulting in the following contingency table of observed values. Use $\alpha = .01$ to determine whether the two variables are independent.

Preferred Beverage

Age	*Coffee/Tea*	*Soft Drink*	*Other (Milk, etc.)*	
21-34	26	45	18	89
35-55	41	40	20	101
>55	24	13	32	69
	91	98	70	259

SOLUTION

STEP **1.** The hypotheses follow.

H_0: Type of beverage preferred is independent of age.

H_a: Type of beverage preferred is not independent of age.

STEP **2.** The appropriate statistical test is

$$\chi^2 = \sum\sum \frac{(f_o - f_e)^2}{f_e}$$

STEP **3.** Alpha is .01.

STEP **4.** The degrees of freedom are $(3 - 1)(3 - 1) = 4$, and the critical value is $\chi^2_{.01,4} = 13.277$. The decision rule is to reject the null hypothesis if the observed value of chi-square is greater than 13.277.

STEP **5.** The sample data are shown above.

STEP **6.** The expected frequencies are the product of the row and column totals divided by the grand total. The contingency table, with expected frequencies, follows.

Preferred Beverage

Age	*Coffee/Tea*	*Soft Drink*	*Other (Milk, etc.)*	
21-34	(31.27) 26	(33.68) 45	(24.05) 18	89
35-55	(35.49) 41	(38.22) 40	(27.30) 20	101
>55	(24.24) 24	(26.11) 13	(18.65) 32	69
	91	98	70	259

For these values, the observed χ^2 is

$$\chi^2 = \frac{(26-31.27)^2}{31.27} + \frac{(45-33.68)^2}{33.68} + \frac{(18-24.05)^2}{24.05} + \frac{(41-35.49)^2}{35.49}$$
$$+ \frac{(40-38.22)^2}{38.22} + \frac{(20-27.30)^2}{27.30} + \frac{(24-24.24)^2}{24.24} + \frac{(13-26.11)^2}{26.11}$$
$$+ \frac{(32-18.65)^2}{18.65}$$
$$= 0.89 + 3.80 + 1.52 + 0.86 + 0.08 + 1.95 + 0.00 + 6.58 + 9.56$$
$$= 25.24$$

STEP **7.** The observed value of chi-square, 25.24, is greater than the critical value, 13.277, so the null hypothesis is rejected.

STEP **8.** The two variables—preferred beverage and age—are not independent. The type of beverage that a customer orders with lunch is related to or dependent on age. Examination of the categories reveals that younger people tend to prefer soft drinks and older people prefer other types of beverages. Managers of eating establishments and marketers of beverage products can utilize such information in targeting their market and in providing appropriate products.

Shown below is FAST⋱STAT output for Demonstration Problem 11.5. Note the p-value of .000045, which is less than $\alpha = .01$, indicating a decision to reject the null hypothesis.

Microsoft Excel - Book2

File Edit View Insert Format Tools Data Window FAST-STAT Help

A1 = Chi-Square Test of Independence

Chi-Square Test of Independence

INPUTS

Significance Level of the Test 0.01

Observed Frequencies

First Variable	Second Variable		
	Coffee/Tea	Soft Drink	Other
21-34	26	45	18
35-55	41	40	20
>55	24	13	32

OUTPUTS

Sample Statistics

Total of All Observed Frequencie:	259
No. of Categories-First Variable	3
No. of Categories-Second Variab	3
Degrees of Freedom	4
Chi-Square Test Statistic	25.2531
Chi-Square Critical Value	13.2767
p-Value for Test	0.0000

Expected Frequencies

First Variable	Second Variable		
	Coffee/Tea	Soft Drink	Other
21-34	31.27027	33.67568	24.05405
35-55	35.48649	38.21622	27.2973
>55	24.24324	26.10811	18.64865

Chi Square / Sheet1 / Sheet2 / Sheet3

Caution: As with the chi-square goodness-of-fit test, small expected frequencies can lead to inordinately large chi-square values with the chi-square test of independence. Hence contingency tables should not be used with expected cell values of less than 5. One way to avoid small expected values is to collapse (combine) columns or rows whenever possible and whenever doing so makes sense.

11.6
Problems

11.24 Use the following contingency table to test whether variable 1 is independent of variable 2. Let $\alpha = .01$.

	Variable 2			
Variable 1	24	13	47	58
	93	59	187	244

11.25 Use the following contingency table and the chi-square test of independence to determine whether social class is independent of number of children in a family. Let $\alpha = .05$.

Number of Children	Social Class: Lower	Middle	Upper
0	7	18	6
1	9	38	23
2 or 3	34	97	58
More than 3	47	31	30

11.26 A group of 30-year-olds is interviewed to determine whether the type of music most listened to by people in their age category is independent of the geographic location of their residence. Use the chi-square test of independence, $\alpha = .01$, and the following contingency table to determine whether music preference is independent of geographic location.

Geographic Region	Type of Music Preferred: Rock	R & B	Country	Classical
Northeast	140	32	5	18
South	134	41	52	8
West	154	27	8	13

11.27 Is the transportation mode used to ship goods independent of type of industry? Suppose the following contingency table represents frequency counts of types of transportation used by the publishing and the computer hardware industries. Analyze the data by using the chi-square test of independence to determine whether type of industry is independent of transportation mode. Let $\alpha = .05$.

		Transportation Mode		
		Air	*Train*	*Truck*
Industry	*Publishing*	32	12	41
	Computer Hardware	5	6	24

11.28 According to data released by the U.S. Department of Housing and Urban Development about new homes built in the United States, there is an almost 50–50 split between one-story and two-story homes. In addition, over half of all new homes have three bedrooms. Suppose a study is done to determine whether the number of bedrooms in a new home is independent of the number of stories. Use $\alpha = .10$ and the following contingency table to conduct a chi-square test of independence to determine whether, in fact, the number of bedrooms is independent of the number of stories.

		Number of Bedrooms		
		≤ 2	3	≥ 4
Number of Stories	*1*	116	101	57
	2	90	325	160

11.29 A study was conducted to determine the impact of a major Mexican peso devaluation on U.S. border retailers. As a part of the study, data were gathered on the magnitude of business that U.S. border retailers were doing with Mexican citizens. Forty-one shoppers of border city department stores were interviewed; 24 were Mexican citizens, and the rest were U.S. citizens. Thirty-five discount store shoppers were interviewed, as were 30 hardware store and 60 shoe store customers. In these three groups, 20, 11, and 32 were Mexican citizens, and the remaining shoppers were U.S. citizens. Use a chi-square contingency analysis to determine whether the shoppers' citizenship (Mexican versus U.S.) is independent of type of border city retailer (department, discount, hardware, shoe) for these data. Let $\alpha = .05$.

Summary

In this chapter, two types of statistical tests are presented: analysis of variance (ANOVA) and chi-square. Analysis of variance tests are used to test the differences in the means of two or more populations and are often used to test statistically hypotheses from complex experimental designs. The chi-square techniques presented in this chapter are used for testing hypotheses using categorical data.

Sound business research requires that the business analyst plan and establish a design for the experiment before a study is undertaken. The design of experiment should encompass the treatment variables to be studied, manipulated, and controlled. These variables are often referred to as the independent variables. It is possible to study several independent variables and several levels, or classifications, of each of those variables in one design. In addition, the business analyst selects one measurement to be taken from sample items under the conditions of the experiment. This measurement is referred to as the dependent variable because if the treatment effect is significant, the measurement of the dependent variable will "depend" on the independent variable(s) selected. This chapter explored three types of experimental designs: completely randomized design, randomized block design, and the factorial experimental designs.

The completely randomized design is the simplest of the experimental designs presented in this chapter. It has only one independent, or treatment, variable. With the completely randomized design, subjects are assigned randomly to treatments. If the treatment variable has only two levels, the design becomes identical to the one used to test the difference in means of independent populations presented in Chapter 10. The data from a completely randomized design are analyzed by a one-way analysis of variance (ANOVA). A one-way ANOVA produces an F value that can be compared to table F values in Appendix A.7 to determine whether the ANOVA F value is statistically significant. If it is, the null hypothesis that all population means are equal is rejected and at least one of the means is different from the others. Analysis of variance does not tell the business analyst which means, if any, are significantly different from others. Although the business analyst can visually examine means to determine which ones are greater and lesser, statistical techniques called multiple comparisons must be used to determine statistically whether pairs of means are significantly different.

A second experimental design is the randomized block design. This design contains a treatment variable (independent variable) and a blocking variable. The independent variable is the main variable of interest in this design. The blocking variable is a variable the business analyst is interested in controlling rather than studying. A special case of randomized block design is the repeated measures design, in which the blocking variable represents subjects or items for which repeated measures are taken across the full range of treatment levels.

In randomized block designs, the variation of the blocking variable is removed from the error variance. This can potentially make the test of treatment effects more powerful. If the blocking variable contains no significant differences, the blocking can make the treatment effects test less powerful. Usually an F is computed only for the treatment effects in a randomized block design. Sometimes an F value is computed for blocking effects to determine whether the blocking was useful in the experiment.

A third experimental design is the factorial design. A factorial design enables the business analyst to test the effects of two or more independent variables simultaneously, In complete factorial designs, every treatment level of each independent variable is studied under the conditions of every other treatment level for all independent variables. This chapter focused only on factorial designs with two independent variables. Each independent variable can have two or more treatment levels. These two-way factorial designs are analyzed by two-way analysis of variance (ANOVA). This analysis produces an F value for each of the two treatment effects and for interaction. Interaction is present when the results of one treatment vary significantly according to the levels of the other treatment. There must be at least two measurements per cell in order to compute interaction. If the F value for interaction is statistically significant, the main effects of the experiment are confounded and should not be examined in the usual manner.

The chi-square goodness-of-fit test is used to compare a theoretical or expected distribution of measurements for several categories of variable with the actual or observed distribution of measurements. It can be used to determine whether a distribution of values fits a given distribution, such as the Poisson or normal distribution. If there are only two categories, the test can be used as the equivalent of a Z test for a single proportion.

The chi-square test of independence is used to analyze frequencies for categories of two variables to determine whether the two variables are independent. The data used in analysis by a chi-square test of independence are arranged in a two-dimensional table called a contingency table. For this reason, the test is sometimes referred to as contingency analysis. A chi-square test of independence is computed in a manner similar to that used with the chi-square goodness-of-fit test. Expected values are computed for each cell of the contingency table and then compared to observed values with the chi-square statistic. Both the chi-square test of independence and the chi-square goodness-of-fit test require that expected values be greater than or equal to 5.

Key Terms

analysis of variance (ANOVA)
blocking variable
chi-square distribution
chi-square goodness-of-fit test
chi-square test of independence
classification variable
classifications
completely randomized design
concomitant variables
confounding variables
contingency analysis
contingency table
dependent variable
experimental design
F distribution
F value
factorial design
factors
independent variable
interaction
levels
multiple comparisons
one-way analysis of variance
randomized block design
repeated measures design
treatment variable
two-way analysis of variance

SUPPLEMENTARY PROBLEMS

11.30 Compute a one-way ANOVA on the following data. Use $\alpha = .05$.

TREATMENT			
1	*2*	*3*	*4*
10	9	12	10
12	7	13	10
15	9	14	13
11	6	14	12

11.31 Compute a one-way ANOVA on the following data. Let $\alpha = .01$.

TREATMENT		
1	*2*	*3*
7	11	8
12	17	6
9	16	10
11	13	9
8	10	11
9	15	7
11	14	10
10	18	
7		
8		

11.32 Analyze the following data, gathered from a randomized block design using $\alpha = .05$.

		TREATMENT			
		A	*B*	*C*	*D*
BLOCKING VARIABLE	*1*	17	10	9	21
	2	13	9	8	16
	3	20	17	18	22
	4	11	6	5	10
	5	16	13	14	22
	6	23	19	20	28

11.33 Compute a two-way ANOVA on the following data ($\alpha = .01$).

		TREATMENT 1		
		A	*B*	*C*
TREATMENT 2	*A*	5	2	2
		3	4	3
		6	4	5
	B	11	9	13
		8	10	12
		12	8	10
	C	6	7	4
		4	6	6
		5	7	8
	D	9	8	8
		11	12	9
		9	9	11

11.34 Use a chi-square goodness-of-fit test to determine whether the following observed frequencies are distributed the same as the expected frequencies. Let $\alpha = .01$.

CATEGORY	f_o	f_e
1	214	206
2	235	232
3	279	268
4	281	284
5	264	268
6	254	232
7	211	206

11.35 Use the chi-square contingency analysis to test to determine whether variable 1 is independent of variable 2. Use a 5% level of significance.

	VARIABLE 2		
VARIABLE 1	12	23	21
	8	17	20
	7	11	18

11.36 A company has conducted a consumer research project to ascertain customer service ratings from its customers. The customers were asked to rate the company on a scale from 1 to 7 on various quality characteristics. One question was the promptness of company response to a repair problem. The following data represent customer responses to this question. The customers were divided by geographic region and by age. Use analysis of variance to analyze the responses. Let $\alpha = .05$. Graph the cell means and observe any interaction.

		GEOGRAPHIC REGION			
		Southeast	*West*	*Midwest*	*Northeast*
AGE	*21–35*	3	2	3	2
		2	4	3	3
		3	3	2	2
	36–50	5	4	5	6
		5	4	6	4
		4	6	5	5
	Over 50	3	2	3	3
		1	2	2	2
		2	3	3	1

11.37 A major automobile manufacturer wants to know whether there is any difference in the average mileage of four different brands of tires (A, B, C, and D) because the manufacturer is trying to select the best supplier in terms of tire durability. The manufacturer selects comparable levels of tires from each company and tests some on comparable cars. The mileage results follow.

A	*B*	*C*	*D*
31,000	24,000	30,500	24,500
25,000	25,500	28,000	27,000
28,500	27,000	32,500	26,000
29,000	26,500	28,000	21,000
32,000	25,000	31,000	25,500
27,500	28,000		26,000
	27,500		

Use $\alpha = .05$ to test whether there is a significant difference in the mean mileage of these four brands. Assume tire mileage is normally distributed.

11.38 Is a manufacturer's geographic location independent of type of customer? Use the following data for companies with primarily industrial customers and companies with primarily retail customers to test this question. Let $\alpha = .10$.

		Geographic Location		
		Northeast	*West*	*South*
Customer Type	*Industrial Customer*	230	115	68
	Retail Customer	185	143	89

11.39 Agricultural researchers are studying three different ways of planting peanuts to determine whether significantly different levels of production yield will result. The researchers have access to a very large peanut farm on which to conduct their tests. They identify six blocks of land. In each block of land, peanuts are planted in each of the three different ways. At the end of the growing season, the peanuts are harvested and the average number of pounds per acre is determined for peanuts planted under each method in each block. Using the following data and $\alpha = .01$, test to determine whether there is a significant difference in yields among the planting methods.

BLOCK	METHOD 1	METHOD 2	METHOD 3
1	1310	1080	850
2	1275	1100	1020
3	1280	1050	780
4	1225	1020	870
5	1190	990	805
6	1300	1030	910

11.40 According to *Beverage Digest/Maxwell Report*, the distribution of market share for the top six soft drinks in the United States was Coca-Cola Classic 20.6%, Pepsi 14.5%, Diet Coke 8.5%, Mountain

Dew 6.3%, Sprite 6.2%, Dr. Pepper 5.9%, and others 38%. Suppose a marketing analyst wants to determine whether this distribution fits that of her geographic region. She randomly surveys 1726 local people and asks them to name their favorite soft drink. The responses are: Classic Coke 361, Pepsi 272, Diet Coke 192, Mountain Dew 121, Sprite 102, Dr. Pepper 94, and others 584. She then tests to determine whether the local distribution of soft-drink preferences is the same or different from the national figures, using $\alpha = .05$. What does she find?

11.41 The Construction Labor Research Council lists a number of construction labor jobs that seem to pay approximately the same wages per hour. Some of these are bricklaying, iron working, and crane operation. Suppose a labor researcher takes a random sample of workers from each of these types of construction jobs and from across the country and asks what their hourly wages are. If this survey yields the following data, is there a significant difference in mean hourly wages for these three jobs? Let $\alpha = .05$.

JOB TYPE		
Bricklaying	*Iron Working*	*Crane Operation*
19.25	26.45	16.20
17.80	21.10	23.30
20.50	16.40	22.90
24.33	22.86	19.50
19.81	25.55	27.00
22.29	18.50	22.95
21.20		25.52
		21.20

11.42 Are the types of professional jobs held in the computing industry independent of the number of years a person has worked in the industry? Suppose 246 workers are interviewed. Use the results obtained to determine whether type of professional job held in the computer industry is independent of years worked in the industry. Let $\alpha = .01$.

		Professional Position			
		Manager	*Programmer*	*Operator*	*Systems Analyst*
Years	*0-3*	6	37	11	13
	4-8	28	16	23	24
	More than 8	47	10	12	19

11.43 A study by Market Facts/TeleNation for Personnel Decisions International (PDI) found that the average workweek is getting longer for U.S. full-time workers. Forty-three percent of the responding workers in the survey cited "more work, more business" as the number one reason for this increase in workweek. Suppose you want to test this figure in California to determine whether California workers feel the same way. A random sample of 315 California full-time workers whose workweek has been getting longer is chosen. They are offered a selection of possible reasons for this increase and 120 pick "more work, more business." Use techniques presented in this chapter and an alpha of .05 to test to determine whether the 43% U.S. figure for this reason holds true in California.

11.44 Why are mergers attractive to CEOs? One of the reasons might be a potential increase in market share that can come with the pooling of company markets. Suppose a random survey of CEOs is taken, and they are asked to respond on a scale from 1 to 5 (5 representing strongly agree) whether increase in market share is a good reason for considering a merger of their company with another. Suppose also that the data are as given here and that CEOs have been categorized by size of company and years they have been with their company. Use a two-way ANOVA to determine whether there are any significant differences in the responses to this question. Let $\alpha = .05$.

		COMPANY SIZE ($ MILLION PER YEAR IN SALES)			
		0–5	*6–20*	*21–100*	*>100*
YEARS WITH THE COMPANY	*0–2*	2	2	3	3
		3	1	4	4
		2	2	4	4
		2	3	5	3
	3–5	2	2	3	3
		1	3	2	3
		2	2	4	3
		3	3	4	4
	Over 5	2	2	3	2
		1	3	2	3
		1	1	3	2
		2	2	3	3

11.45 Are some unskilled office jobs viewed as having more status than others? Suppose a study is conducted in which eight unskilled, unemployed people are interviewed. The people are asked to rate each of five positions on a scale from 1 to 10 to indicate the status of the position, with 10 denoting most status and 1 denoting least status. The resulting data are given here. Use $\alpha = .05$ to analyze these repeated measures randomized block design data.

		JOB				
		Mail Clerk	*Typist*	*Receptionist*	*Secretary*	*Telephone Operator*
	1	4	5	3	7	6
	2	2	4	4	5	4
	3	3	3	2	6	7
RESPONDENT	*4*	4	4	4	5	4
	5	3	5	1	3	5
	6	3	4	2	7	7
	7	2	2	2	4	4
	8	3	4	3	6	6

11.46 Following is Excel output for an ANOVA problem. Describe the experimental design. The given value of alpha was .05. Discuss the output in terms of significant findings.

ANOVA: Two-Factor Without Replication

SUMMARY	Count	Sum	Average	Variance
1	3	72	24	1
2	3	80	26.67	0.333
3	3	80	26.67	4.333
4	3	87	29	9
5	3	86	28.67	4.333
6	3	82	27.33	1.333
1	6	165	27.5	5.9
2	6	166	27.67	6.667
3	6	156	26	3.2

ANOVA

Source of Variation	SS	df	MS	F	P-value	F crit
Rows	48.278	5	9.656	3.16	0.057	3.33
Columns	10.111	2	5.056	1.65	0.239	4.10
Error	30.556	10	3.056			
Total	88.944	17				

11.47 Interpret the following Excel output. Discuss the structure of the experimental design and any significant effects. Alpha is .01.

ANOVA: Two-Factor With Replication

SUMMARY	Column 1	Column 2	Column 3	Total
Row 1				
Count	3	3	3	9
Sum	611	645	559	1815
Average	203.67	215	186.33	201.67
Variance	6.333	1	2640.333	818.25
Row 2				
Count	3	3	3	9
Sum	657	681	698	2036
Average	219	227	232.67	226.22
Variance	13	13	9.333	44.194
Row 3				
Count	3	3	3	9
Sum	618	626	635	1879
Average	206	208.67	211.67	208.78
Variance	9	6.333	2.333	10.444
Row 4				
Count	3	3	3	9
Sum	628	631	629	1888
Average	209.33	210.33	209.67	209.78
Variance	2.333	2.333	4.333	2.444
Total				
Count	12	12	12	
Sum	2514	2583	2521	
Average	209.5	215.25	210.08	
Variance	42.818	60.205	776.627	

ANOVA

Source of Variation	SS	df	MS	F	P-value	F crit
Sample	2913.889	3	971.296	4.30	0.0146	3.01
Columns	240.389	2	120.194	0.53	0.5940	3.40
Interaction	1342.944	6	223.824	0.99	0.4533	2.51
Within	5419.333	24	225.806			
Total	9916.556	35				

ANALYZING THE DATABASES

1. Do various financial indicators differ significantly according to type of company? Use a one-way ANOVA and the financial database to answer this question. Let Type of Company be the independent variable with seven levels (Apparel, Chemical, Electric Power, Grocery, Healthcare Products, Insurance, and Petroleum). Compute three one-way ANOVAs, one for each of the following dependent variables: Earnings Per Share, Dividend, and Average P/E Ratio.
2. Use the stock market database to determine whether there is any difference in stock market statistics for different parts of the month. Use a one-way ANOVA with Composite Index as the dependent variable and Part of the Month (1 = 10th, 2 = 20th, and 3 = 30th) as the independent variable with three levels. Compute a second ANOVA with Stock Volume as the dependent variable and Part of the Month as the independent variable. Is there a significant difference in Part of the Month on either of these variables?
3. In the manufacturing database, the Value of Industrial Shipments has been precoded into four classifications (1–4) according to magnitude of value. Let this be the independent variable with four levels of classifications. Compute a one-way ANOVA to determine whether there is any significant difference in classification of the Value of Industrial Shipments on the Number of Production Workers (dependent variable). Perform the same analysis using End-of-Year Inventory as the dependent variable. Now change the independent variable to Industry Group, of which there are 20, and perform first a one-way ANOVA using Number of Production Workers as the dependent variable and then a one-way ANOVA using End-of-Year Inventory as the dependent variable.
4. The hospital database contains data on hospitals from seven different geographic regions. Let this variable be the independent variable. Determine whether there is a significant difference in Admissions for these geographic regions using a one-way ANOVA. Perform the same analysis using Births as the dependent variable. Control is a variable with four levels of classification denoting the type of control the hospital is under (such as federal government or for-profit). Use this variable as the independent variable and test to determine whether there is a significant difference in the Admissions of a hospital by Control. Perform the same test using Births as the dependent variable.
5. Use a chi-square test of independence to determine whether Control is independent of Service in the hospital database.

CASE

PROLIGHT: A BUMPY PATH TO A BRIGHT FUTURE

In 1983, Boyd Berends started the Progressive Technology Lighting Company (ProLight) in Holland, Michigan. Berends' goal was to develop and market compact fluorescent lights, which he felt had a big future as energy-savers to replace incandescent bulbs. The road to success was a bumpy one.

Berends designed the specifications of the bulb that he wanted to sell. However, a manufacturer that Berends thought would produce a ballast for his bulb declined. The manufacturer did offer to sell Berends the ballast design and do some of the work if Berends would pay for tooling. Berends accepted this challenge, and he and his wife took out a second mortgage on their home as financing.

ProLight began manufacturing with several other companies and produced 10,000 units for sale. However, because of an oversight, all 10,000 proved to be defective. The second-mortgage money was gone, and there was still no product to sell. Berends was able to get a line of credit and new bulbs were produced. During this time, however, Berends was involved in a legal dispute with one manufacturer, which ended in an out-of-court settlement.

At this point, a manufacturer that was assembling the light bulbs refused to continue. ProLight ended up having to buy equipment, half-finished product, and the raw-material inventory from the manufacturer. The total cost was around $70,000. ProLight's financial base was seriously eroded. Nevertheless, a lender was persuaded to supply additional funds to the company.

ProLight was now a manufacturer and a marketer. Product and raw-material inventory continued to grow. More product and inventory existed than could be sold. There was a cash-flow crisis. Suppliers were persuaded to wait for payment. At this point, Berends bought out a manager who had been given stock as an enticement to join the company.

Two years after start-up, just when things appeared to be going well for the company, a competitor emerged with a similar product. The rival firm was well financed and marketed aggressively. ProLight's sales went flat.

ProLight reacted by designing new fluorescent products that sold well. The company worked to cut costs and improved assembly techniques so much that ProLight believes it is cheaper to assemble the bulbs in Michigan than it would be in a low-wage country. The company imports only parts it does not make itself.

ProLight's sales doubled annually for 6 years. Profits have been on the rise, and the competitor that arose a few years back filed for bankruptcy. Currently, ProLight's product line includes the widest variety of compact fluorescent products available in the industry as well as LED (light emitting diode) energy-saving lighting products.

DISCUSSION

In producing a fluorescent bulb, both mercury vapor and argon gas are used. A fluorescent powder coating on the inner surface of the tube allows for the chemical reaction to produce visible light. This coating consists of several compounds, including zinc silicate, cadmium borate, and barium silicate, which convert ultraviolet radiation into visible light. The fluorescent bulb has pins on the end, through which a source of electricity flows. Because the color of light depends on the makeup of the phosphor, more than two dozen different colors of white can be produced.

1. Suppose you work for ProLight in research and design. You want to study the effects of certain variables on the power, life, or cost of the bulbs. Use the discussion given here to describe a completely randomized design that could be developed to study these bulbs. What are some possible independent variables? Select one independent variable and name some possible levels of treatment for this variable. Name one dependent variable.
2. Suppose ProLight fluorescent bulbs are sold in packages of four bulbs per package. Suppose further that ProLight's managers believe wholesalers in different regions of the country charge different prices to businesses for their bulbs. ProLight researchers set up an experimental design to determine whether the average price at which a package of ProLight bulbs is sold to businesses by wholesalers differs by region. A random sample of wholesalers taken from three regions (Northeast, West, and South) yielded the following data on the price per package of four bulbs. Analyze these data and write a brief report on what you find. Discuss the implications of the results for ProLight in terms of management and marketing decisions.

NORTHEAST	WEST	SOUTH
$5.62	$5.93	$5.78
5.71	5.98	5.83
5.57	6.03	5.80
5.62	5.84	5.83
5.56	5.91	5.87
	5.96	5.84
		5.86

3. ProLight produces light bulbs in many shades of white. Is there any difference in cost to produce bulbs in various shades of white? Cost of bulb production may depend on which of three major suppliers of components is used. To test these ideas, suppose a two-way ANOVA is set up in which there are two independent variables, shade of white and major supplier. Four shades of white and three major suppliers are used in the study. The costs of producing each of three light bulbs under each shade of white and each major supplier are analyzed. The Excel output follows. Your job is to analyze the output and write a brief report of your findings.

ANOVA: Two-Factor With Replication

SUMMARY	Supplier A	Supplier B	Supplier C	Total
Color A				
Count	3	3	3	9
Sum	3.37	3.18	3.34	9.89
Average	1.123333	1.06	1.113333	1.098889
Variance	0.000633	0.0007	0.000233	0.001261
Color B				
Count	3	3	3	9
Sum	3.19	3	3.23	9.42
Average	1.063333	1	1.076667	1.046667
Variance	0.000233	0.0004	0.000433	0.001525
Color C				
Count	3	3	3	9
Sum	3.36	3.2	3.31	9.87
Average	1.12	1.066667	1.103333	1.096667
Variance	1E-04	0.000133	0.000233	0.000675
Color D				
Count	3	3	3	9
Sum	3.5	3.33	3.46	10.29
Average	1.166667	1.11	1.153333	1.143333
Variance	0.000233	1E-04	0.000233	0.0008
Total				
Count	12	12	12	
Sum	13.42	12.71	13.34	
Average	1.118333	1.059167	1.111667	
variance	0.001688	0.001917	0.001033	

ANOVA

Source of Variation	SS	df	MS	F	P-value	F crit
Color	0.042142	3	0.014047	45.97273	4.21E-10	3.008786
Supplier	0.025206	2	0.012603	41.24545	1.72E-08	3.402832
Interaction	0.00155	6	0.000258	0.845455	0.547739	2.508187
Within	0.007333	24	0.000306			
Total	0.076231	35				

4. Suppose ProLight strongly encourages its employees to make formal suggestions to improve the process, the product, and the working environment. Suppose a quality auditor keeps records of the suggestions and persons who have submitted them. A

possible breakdown of the number of suggestions over a 3-year period by employee gender and function follows. Is there any relationship between the function of the employee and gender in terms of number of suggestions?

		GENDER	
		Male	*Female*
FUNCTION	Engineering	209	32
	Manufacturing	483	508
	Shipping	386	185

ADAPTED FROM: "ProLight: A Bumpy Path to a Bright Future," *Real-World Lessons for America's Small Businesses: Insights from the Blue Chip Enterprise Initiative.* Published by *Nation's Business Magazine* on behalf of Connecticut Mutual Life Insurance Company and the U.S. Chamber of Commerce in association with the Blue Chip Enterprise Initiative, 1992. Also from *Encyclopedia Americana,* vol. 11 (Danbury, CT: Grolier International, 1988), 466. See also ProLight's website at http://www.prolight.com/.

12

Simple Regression and Correlation Analysis

Learning Objectives

The overall objective of this chapter is to give you an understanding of bivariate linear regression analysis and correlation, thereby enabling you to:

1. Compute the equation of a simple regression line from a sample of data and interpret the slope and intercept of the equation.
2. Understand the usefulness of residual analysis in testing the assumptions underlying regression analysis and in examining the fit of the regression line to the data.
3. Compute a standard error of the estimate and interpret its meaning.
4. Compute a coefficient of determination and interpret it.
5. Test hypotheses about the slope of the regression model and interpret the results.
6. Estimate values of Y by using the regression model.
7. Compute a coefficient of correlation and interpret it.

In many business research situations, the key to decision making lies in understanding the relationships between two or more variables. For example, in an effort to predict the value of airline stock from day to day, an analyst might find it helpful to determine whether the price of an airline stock is related to the price of West Texas intermediate (WTI) crude oil. In studying the behavior of the bond market, a broker might find it useful to know whether the interest rate of bonds is related to the prime interest rate. In studying the effect of advertising on sales, an account executive might find it useful to know whether there is a strong relationship between advertising dollars and sales dollars for a company.

What variables are related to unemployment rates? Are minimum hourly wage rates, the inflation rate, or the wholesale price index usable for predicting an unemployment rate? This chapter presents techniques that can be used to determine the strength of a relationship between variables and to construct mathematical models for predicting one variable from another.

Correlation
A measure of the degree of relatedness of two or more variables.

Regression
The process of constructing a mathematical model or function that can be used to predict or determine one variable by any other variable.

Two main types of techniques are presented: correlation techniques and regression techniques. **Correlation** is *a measure of the degree of relatedness of two variables.* Correlation is widely used in exploratory research when the objective is to locate variables that might be related in some way to the variable of interest. **Regression** analysis is *the process of constructing a mathematical model or function that can be used to predict or determine one variable by another variable* (multiple variables in multiple regression). Whereas correlation attempts to determine the strength of a relationship between variables, regression attempts to determine the functional relationship between the variables. The first part of this chapter focuses on regression analysis and its ramifications.

12.1 Introduction to Simple Regression Analysis

Simple regression
Bivariate, linear regression.

Dependent variable
In regression analysis, the variable that is being predicted.

Independent variable
In regression analysis, the predictor variable.

The most elementary regression model is called **simple regression,** which is *bivariate linear regression.* That is, simple regression involves only two variables; one variable is predicted by another variable. *The variable to be predicted* is called the **dependent variable** and is designated as *Y. The predictor* is called the **independent variable,** or *explanatory variable,* and is designated as *X.* In simple regression analysis, only a straight-line relationship between two variables is examined. Nonlinear relationships and/or regression models with more than one independent variable can be explored by using multiple regression models, which are presented in Chapter 13.

Can the cost of flying a commercial airliner be predicted using regression analysis? If so, what variables are related to such cost? A few of the many variables that can potentially contribute are type of plane, distance, number of passengers, amount of luggage/freight, weather conditions, direction of destination, and perhaps even pilot skill. Suppose a study is conducted using only Boeing 737s traveling 500 miles on comparable routes during the same season of the year in an effort to reduce the number of possible predictor variables. Can the number of passengers predict the cost of flying such routes? It seems logical that more passengers result in more weight and more baggage, which could in turn result in increased fuel consumption and other costs. Suppose the data displayed in Table 12.1 are the costs and associated number of passengers for 12 five-hundred-mile commercial airline flights using Boeing 737s during the same season of the year. We will use these data to develop a regression model to predict cost by number of passengers.

Scatter Plots

Scatter plot
A plot or graph of the pairs of data from a simple regression analysis.

Usually, the first step in simple regression analysis is to construct a **scatter plot** (or *scatter diagram*). The independent (predictor) variable is scaled along the *X* axis and the dependent variable (variable being predicted or determined) is scaled along the *Y* axis. Graphing the data in this way yields preliminary information about the shape and spread of the data. Beware that one of the ways to "cheat" or mislead with statistics is to plot variables on axes having different scales. However, many real-life regression problems contain data stated on different scales, and caution should be exercised in interpreting scatter plots.

Figure 12.1 is an Excel scatter plot of the data in Table 12.1. Figure 12.2 is a more closeup view of the scatter plot produced by Excel. Try to imagine a line passing through

TABLE 12.1
Airline Cost Data

NUMBER OF PASSENGERS	COST ($1000)
61	4.280
63	4.080
67	4.420
69	4.170
70	4.480
74	4.300
76	4.820
81	4.700
86	5.110
91	5.130
95	5.640
97	5.560

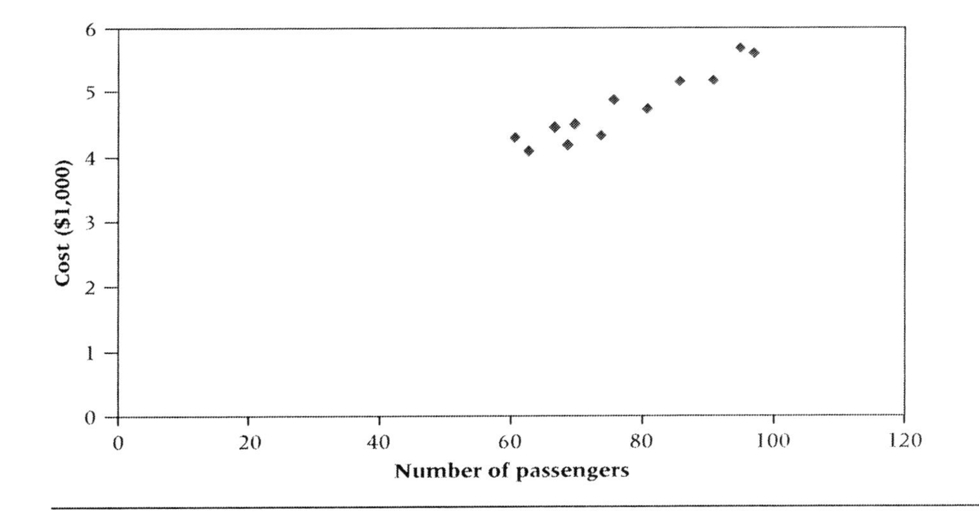

Figure 12.1
Excel scatter plot of airline cost data

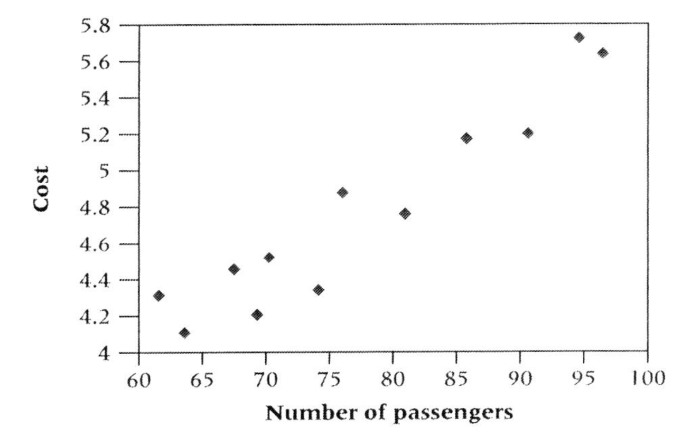

Figure 12.2
Close-up Excel scatter plot of airline cost data

the points. Is there a linear fit? Would a curve fit the data better? The scatter plot gives some idea of how well a regression line fits the data. Later in the chapter, statistical techniques are presented that can be used to determine more precisely how well a regression line fits the data.

12.2

Determining the Equation of the Regression Line

The first step in determining the equation of the regression line that passes through the sample data is to establish the equation's form. Several different types of equations of lines are discussed in algebra, finite math, or analytic geometry courses. Recall that among these equations of a line are the two-point form, the point-slope form, and the slope-intercept form. In regression analysis, business analysts use the slope-intercept equation of a line. In math courses, the slope-intercept form of the equation of a line often takes the form

$$Y = mX + b$$

where:

m = slope of the line, and
b = Y intercept of the line.

In statistics, the slope-intercept form of the equation of the regression line through the population points is

$$\hat{Y} = \beta_0 + \beta_1 X$$

where:

$\hat{Y}$ = the predicted value of Y,
β_0 = the population Y intercept, and
β_1 = the population slope.

For any specific dependent variable value, Y_i,

$$Y_i = \beta_0 + \beta_1 X_i + \epsilon_i$$

where:

X_i = the value of the independent variable for the ith value
Y_i = the value of the dependent variable for the ith value,
β_0 = the population Y intercept,
β_1 = the population slope, and
ϵ_i = the error of prediction for the ith value.

Unless the points being fitted by the regression equation are in perfect alignment, the regression line will miss at least some of the points. In the preceding equation, ϵ_i represents the error of the regression line in fitting these points, that is, the distances the data values are from their projected values on the regression line. If a point is on the regression line, $\epsilon_i = 0$.

These mathematical models can be either deterministic models or probabilistic models. **Deterministic models** are *mathematical models that produce an "exact" output for a given input.* For example, suppose the equation of a regression line is

Deterministic model
Mathematical models that produce an "exact" output for a given input.

$$Y = 1.68 + 2.40X.$$

For a value of $X = 5$, the exact predicted value of Y is

$$Y = 1.68 + 2.40(5) = 13.68.$$

We recognize, however, that most of the time the values of Y will not equal exactly the values yielded by the equation. Random error will occur in the prediction of the Y values for values of X because it is likely that the variable X does not explain all the variability of the variable Y. For example, suppose we are trying to predict the volume of sales (Y) for a company through regression analysis by using the annual dollar amount of advertising (X) as the predictor. Although sales are often related to advertising, there are other factors related to sales that are not accounted for by amount of advertising. Hence, a regression model to predict sales volume by amount of advertising probably involves some error. For this reason, in regression, we present the general model as a probabilistic model. A **probabilistic model** is *one that includes an error term that allows for the Y values to vary for any given value of X.*

Probabilistic model
A model that includes an error term that allows for various values of output to occur for a given value of input.

A deterministic regression model is

$$Y = \beta_0 + \beta_1 X.$$

The probabilistic regression model is

$$Y = \beta_0 + \beta_1 X + \epsilon.$$

$\beta_0 + \beta_1 X$ is the deterministic portion of the probabilistic model, $\beta_0 + \beta_1 X + \epsilon$. In a deterministic model, all points are assumed to be on the line and in all cases ϵ is zero.

Virtually all regression analyses of business data involve sample data, not population data. As a result, β_0 and β_1 are unattainable and must be estimated by using the sample statistics, b_0 and b_1. Hence the equation of the regression line contains the sample Y intercept, b_0, and the sample slope, b_1.

EQUATION OF THE SIMPLE REGRESSION LINE

$$\hat{Y} = b_0 + b_1 X$$

where:
b_0 = the sample intercept
b_1 = the sample slope

To determine the equation of the regression line for a sample of data, the business analyst must determine the values for b_0 and b_1. This process is sometimes referred to as least squares analysis. **Least squares analysis** is *a process whereby a regression model is developed by producing the minimum sum of the squared error values.* On the basis of this premise and calculus, a particular set of equations has been developed to produce components of the regression model.

Least squares analysis
The process by which a regression model is developed based on calculus techniques that attempt to produce a minimum sum of the squared error values.

Examine the regression line fit through the points in Figure 12.3 using Excel. The points (X, Y) contain the actual values of Y for given values of X. Observe that the line does not actually pass through any of these points. The vertical distance from each point to the line is the error of the prediction. In theory, an infinite number of lines could be constructed to pass through these points in some manner. The least squares regression line is the regression line that results in the smallest sum of errors squared.

Fitting a Line Using Excel

Excel has the ability to fit lines and curves through data. To accomplish this, first construct a scatter chart of the regression data using the Chart Wizard (see Chapter 2), producing a scatter plot like the one displayed in Figure 12.2. To fit a line or curve through the scatter plot while in Excel, touch one of the points on the graph with the mouse

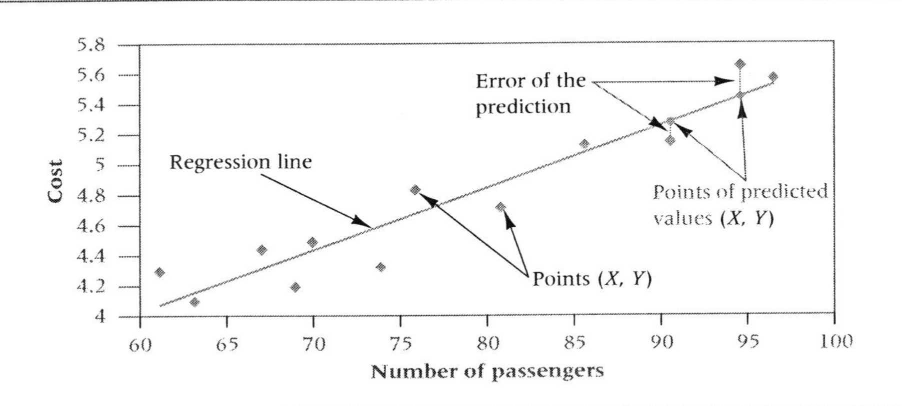

Figure 12.3

Excel plot of a regression line through the airline cost data

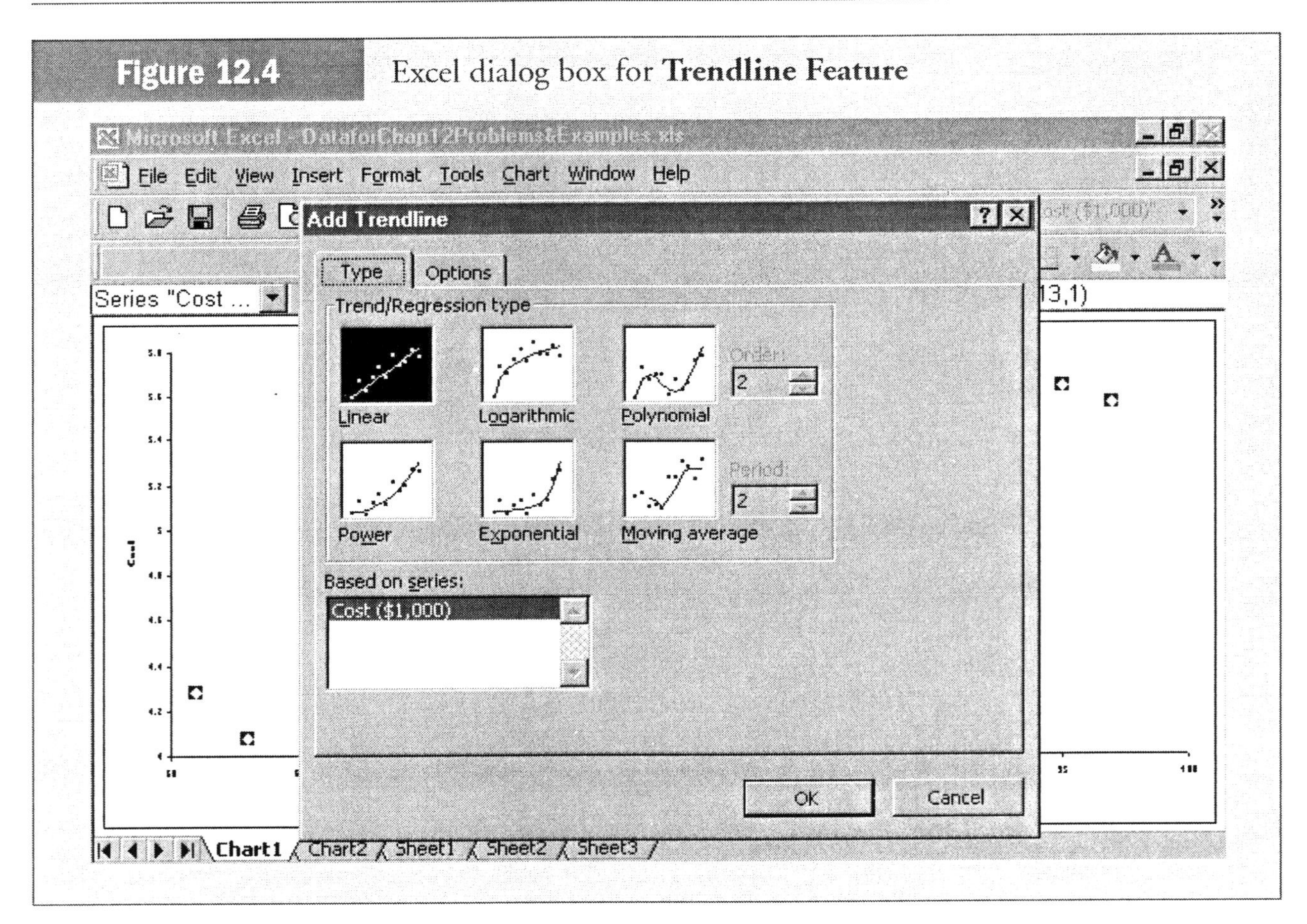

Figure 12.4 Excel dialog box for **Trendline Feature**

pointer and "right-click" on the mouse. A shortcut menu will appear and one of the items on it is **Add *Trendline*.** Clicking on this item will produce the dialog box shown in Figure 12.4. Note that there are six types of trend line/curves that can be fit through the data of the scatter plot. Since this chapter deals only with the linear trend (simple regression analysis), click on **Linear** and the result is the graph displayed in Figure 12.3. Curvilinear fits will be explored in Chapter 13 (Multiple Regression Analysis) and Chapter 14 (Time Series Forecasting).

Equation 12.1 is a formula for computing the value of the sample slope. Three versions of the equation are given to afford latitude in doing the computations.

$$b_1 = \frac{\Sigma(X - \bar{X})(Y - \bar{Y})}{\Sigma(X - \bar{X})^2} = \frac{\Sigma XY - n\bar{X}\bar{Y}}{\Sigma X^2 - n\bar{X}^2} = \frac{\Sigma XY - \frac{(\Sigma X)(\Sigma Y)}{n}}{\Sigma X^2 - \frac{(\Sigma X)^2}{n}} \tag{12.1}$$

SLOPE OF THE REGRESSION LINE

The expression in the numerator of the slope formula (12.1) appears frequently in this chapter and is denoted as SS_{XY}.

$$SS_{XY} = \Sigma(X - \bar{X})(Y - \bar{Y}) = \Sigma XY - \frac{(\Sigma X)(\Sigma Y)}{n}$$

The expression in the denominator of the slope formula (12.1) also appears frequently in this chapter and is denoted as SS_{XX}.

$$SS_{XX} = \Sigma(X - \bar{X})^2 = \Sigma X^2 - \frac{(\Sigma X)^2}{n}$$

With these abbreviations, the formula for the slope can be expressed as in Equation 12.2.

$$b_1 = \frac{SS_{XY}}{SS_{XX}} \tag{12.2}$$

ALTERNATIVE FORMULA FOR SLOPE

Equation 12.3 is used to compute the sample Y intercept. The slope must be computed before the Y intercept.

$$120.17 \pm (2.228)(15.65)\sqrt{\frac{1}{12} + \frac{(40 - 4}{}} \tag{12.3}$$

Y INTERCEPT OF THE REGRESSION LINE

Equations 12.1, 12.2, and 12.3 show that the following data are needed from sample information to compute the slope and intercept: ΣX, ΣY, ΣX^2, and ΣXY, unless sample means are used. Table 12.2 contains the results of solving for the slope and intercept and determining the equation of the regression line for the data in Table 12.1.

The least squares equation of the regression line for this problem is

$$\hat{Y} = 1.570 + .0407X.$$

The slope of this regression line is .0407. Since the X values were recoded for the ease of computation and are actually in \$1000 denominations, the slope is actually \$40.70. One interpretation of the slope in this problem is that for every unit increase in X (every person added to the flight of the airplane), there is a \$40.70 increase in the cost of the flight. The Y intercept is the point where the line crosses the Y axis (where X is zero). Sometimes in regression analysis, the Y intercept is meaningless in terms of the variables studied. However, in this problem, one interpretation of the Y intercept, which is 1.570 or \$1570, is

TABLE 12.2
Solving for the Slope and the Y Intercept of the Regression Line for the Airline Cost Example

NUMBER OF PASSENGERS X	COST ($1,000) Y	X^2	XY
61	4.280	3,721	261.080
63	4.080	3,969	257.040
67	4.420	4,489	296.140
69	4.170	4,761	287.730
70	4.480	4,900	313.600
74	4.300	5,476	318.200
76	4.820	5,776	366.320
81	4.700	6,561	380.700
86	5.110	7,396	439.460
91	5.130	8,281	466.830
95	5.640	9,025	535.800
97	5.560	9,409	539.320
$\Sigma X = 930$	$\Sigma Y = 56.690$	$\Sigma X^2 = 73,764$	$\Sigma XY = 4462.220$

$$SS_{XY} = \Sigma XY - \frac{\Sigma X \Sigma Y}{n} = 4462.220 - \frac{(930)(56.690)}{12} = 68.745$$

$$SS_{XX} = \Sigma X^2 - \frac{(\Sigma X)^2}{n} = 73,764 - \frac{(930)^2}{12} = 1689$$

$$b_1 = \frac{SS_{XY}}{SS_{XX}} = \frac{68.745}{1689} = .0407$$

$$b_0 = \frac{\Sigma Y}{n} - b_1 \frac{\Sigma X}{n} = \frac{56.690}{12} - (.0407)\frac{930}{12} = 1.570$$

$$\hat{Y} = 1.570 + .0407X$$

that even if there were no passengers on the commercial flight, it would still cost $1570. That is, even when the plane flies empty, there are still costs associated with the flight.

Analysis Using Excel

The equation of the regression line can be obtained in Excel by using the ***Regression*** feature of the **Data Analysis** tool. The dialog box for ***Regression*** is shown in Figure 12.5. This dialog box requires input of the location of the Y variable followed by the location of the X variable. Note that there are several options for types of output given at the bottom of the dialog box, one of which is to include a fitted line plot (scatter plot of the data with a line fit to the data) like the one displayed in Figure 12.3. Residuals will be discussed in Section 12.3 of this chapter.

The resulting output is shown in Figure 12.6. Note that listed under *Coefficients* in the output are: *Intercept* with 1.5655 and *Number of Passengers* with 0.0407. Intercept is the value of the Y intercept in the regression equation. The other coefficient, in this case Number of Passengers, is the value of the slope. From these two figures, we can produce the regression equation of:

$$\hat{Y} = 1.5655 + 0.0407 \text{ Number of Passengers},$$

which is essentially the same as the equation displayed in Table 12.2 (differences due to rounding error).

Figure 12.5 Excel dialog box for **Regression**

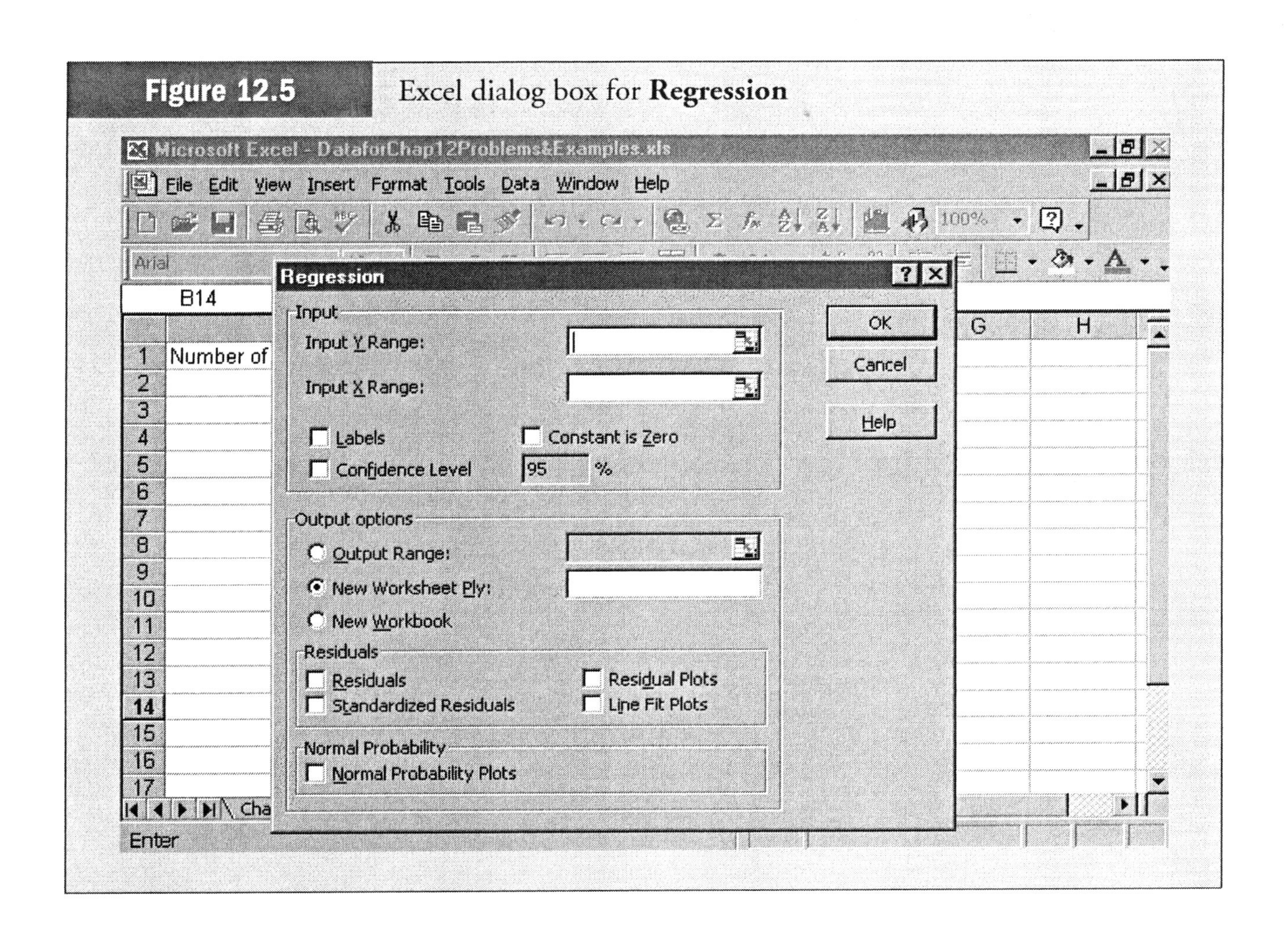

Figure 12.6

Excel Regression output for airline cost problem

SUMMARY OUTPUT

Regression Statistics	
Multiple R	0.948
R Square	0.900
Adjusted R Square	0.890
Standard Error	0.177
Observations	12

ANOVA

	df	SS	MS	F	Significance F
Regression	1	2.8041	2.8041	89.61	2.6E-06
Residual	10	0.3129	0.0313		
Total	11	3.1171			

	Coefficients	Standard Error	t Stat	P-value	Lower 95%	Upper 95%
Intercept	1.5655	0.3375	4.64	0.00092	0.81358	2.31745
Number of Passengers	0.0407	0.0043	9.47	2.6E-06	0.03116	0.05034

DEMONSTRATION PROBLEM 12.1

A specialist in hospital administration stated that the number of FTEs (full-time employees) in a hospital can be estimated by counting the number of beds in the hospital (a common measure of hospital size). A business analyst decided to develop a regression model in an attempt to predict the number of FTEs of a hospital by the number of beds. She surveyed 12 hospitals and obtained the following data. The data are presented in sequence, according to the number of beds.

NUMBER OF BEDS	FTES	NUMBER OF BEDS	FTES
23	69	50	138
29	95	54	178
29	102	64	156
35	118	66	184
42	126	76	176
46	125	78	225

SOLUTION

The following Excel graph is a scatter plot of these data. Note the linear appearance of the data.

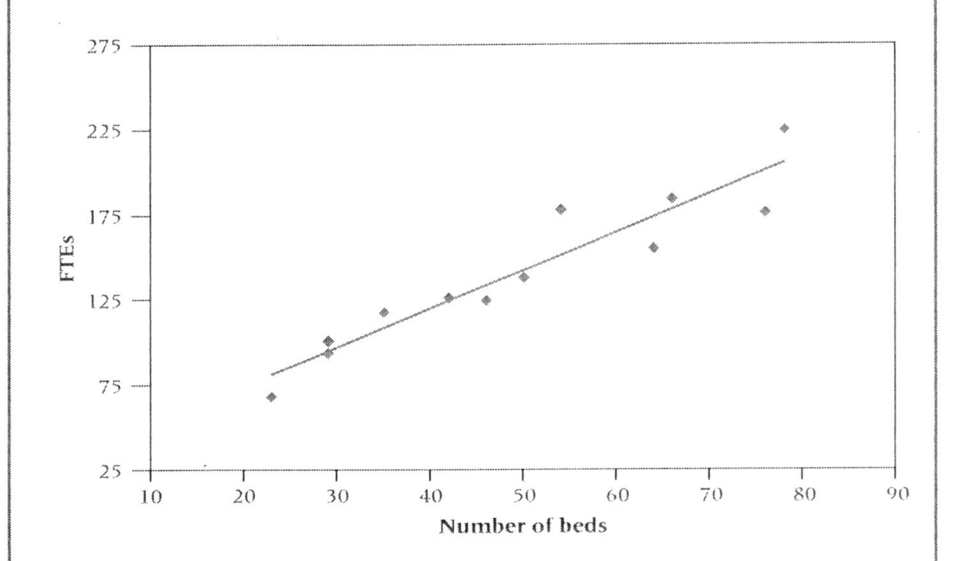

Next, the business analyst determined the values of ΣX, ΣY, ΣX^2, and ΣXY.

HOSPITAL	NUMBER OF BEDS X	FTES Y	X^2	XY
1	23	69	529	1,587
2	29	95	841	2,755
3	29	102	841	2,958
4	35	118	1,225	4,130
5	42	126	1,764	5,292
6	46	125	2,116	5,750
7	50	138	2,500	6,900
8	54	178	2,916	9,612
9	64	156	4,096	9,984
10	66	184	4,356	12,144
11	76	176	5,776	13,376
12	78	225	6,084	17,550
	$\Sigma X = 592$	$\Sigma Y = 1{,}692$	$\Sigma X^2 = 33{,}044$	$\Sigma XY = 92{,}038$

Using these values, the business analyst solved for the sample slope (b_1) and the sample Y intercept (b_0).

$$SS_{XY} = \Sigma XY - \frac{\Sigma X \Sigma Y}{n} = 92{,}038 - \frac{(592)(1692)}{12} = 8566$$

$$SS_{XX} = \Sigma X^2 - \frac{(\Sigma X)^2}{n} = 33{,}044 - \frac{(592)^2}{12} = 3838.667$$

$$b_1 = \frac{SS_{XY}}{SS_{XX}} = \frac{8566}{3838.667} = 2.232$$

$$b_0 = \frac{\Sigma Y}{n} - b_1 \frac{\Sigma X}{n} = \frac{(1692)}{12} - 2.232\left(\frac{592}{12}\right) = 30.888$$

The least squares equation of the regression line is

$$\hat{Y} = 30.888 + 2.23X.$$

The slope of the line, $b_1 = 2.232$, means that for every unit increase of X (every bed), Y (number of FTEs) is predicted to increase by 2.232. Even though the Y intercept helps the business analysts sketch the graph of the line by being one of the points on the line (0, 30.888), it is meaningless information in terms of this solution because $X = 0$ is not in the range of the data.

Shown below is a portion of the Excel output for this problem. Note the coefficients denoting the Y intercept and the slope of the regression line.

	COEFFICIENTS
Intercept	30.912
Number of Beds	2.232

12.2 Problems

12.1 Create a scatter plot for the following data and observe the plot to indicate whether there seems to be a linear trend in the data. Now use Excel's trendline feature to fit a line through the data.

X	6	11	9	14	5	3
Y	5	2	3	1	7	11

12.2 Create a scatter plot for the following data and determine whether there seems to be a linear relationship between X and Y based on your observations. Use Excel's trendline feature to assist you in this decision.

X	36	45	52	20	12	40	63
Y	14	26	35	32	48	18	51

12.3 Create a scatter plot for the following data and determine the equation of the regression line.

X	12	21	28	8	20
Y	17	15	22	19	24

12.4 Create a scatter plot from the following data and determine the equation of the regression line.

X	140	119	103	91	65	29	24
Y	25	29	46	70	88	112	128

12.5 A corporation owns several companies. The strategic planner for the corporation believes dollars spent on advertising can to some extent be a predictor of total sales dollars. As an aid in long-term planning, she gathers the following sales and advertising information from several of the companies for 2001 (in $ millions).

ADVERTISING	SALES
12.5	148
3.7	55
21.6	338
60.0	994
37.6	541
6.1	89
16.8	126
41.2	379

Develop the equation of the simple regression line to predict sales from advertising expenditures using these data.

12.6 Investment analysts generally believe the interest rate on bonds is inversely related to the prime interest rate for loans. That is, bonds perform well when lending rates are down and perform poorly when interest rates are up. Can the bond rate be predicted by the prime interest rate? Use the following data to construct a least squares regression line to predict bond rates by the prime interest rate.

BOND RATE	PRIME INTEREST RATE
5%	16%
12	6
9	8
15	4
7	7

12.7 Is it possible to predict the annual number of business failures in the United States by the number of business starts the previous year? It might seem that the more business starts there are in a given year, the more potential there is for business failure the next year. The following data from Dun & Bradstreet show the number of business failures over a 10-year period and the number of business starts for each of the previous years. Use these data to develop the equation of a regression line to predict the number of business failures from the number of business starts the previous year. Discuss the slope and Y intercept of the model.

NUMBER OF BUSINESS STARTS FOR THE PREVIOUS YEAR	NUMBER OF BUSINESS FAILURES
233,710	57,097
199,091	50,361
181,645	60,747
158,930	88,140
155,672	97,069
164,086	86,133
166,154	71,558
188,387	71,128
168,158	71,931
170,475	83,384

12.8 It appears that over the past 35 years, the number of farms in the United States has declined while the average size of farms has increased. The following data provided by the U.S. Department of Agriculture show five-year interval data for U.S. farms. Use these data to develop the equation of a regression line to predict the average size of a farm by the number of farms. Discuss the slope and Y intercept of the model.

NUMBER OF FARMS (MILLIONS)	AVERAGE SIZE (ACRES)
5.65	213
4.65	258
3.96	297
3.36	340
2.95	374
2.52	420
2.44	426
2.29	441
2.15	460
2.07	469

12.9 Can the annual new orders for manufacturing in the United States be predicted by the raw steel production in the United States? Shown here are the annual new orders for 10 years according to the U.S. Bureau of the Census and the raw steel production for the same 10 years as published by the American Iron & Steel Institute. Use these data to develop a regression model to predict annual new orders by raw steel production. Construct a scatter plot and draw the regression line through the points.

RAW STEEL PRODUCTION (100,000s OF NET TONS)	NEW ORDERS ($ TRILLION)
99.9	2.74
97.9	2.87
98.9	2.93
87.9	2.87
92.9	2.98
97.9	3.09
100.6	3.36
104.9	3.61
105.3	3.75
108.6	3.95

12.3

Analyzing the Fit of the Regression Line: Residuals, r^2, and Standard Error of the Estimate

Simple regression analysis can be performed on data even when the data are not "linear." How do we know that the linear regression analysis "fits" the data well enough to justify the analysis? We now explore three techniques for testing the "fit" of the regression line to the data. These techniques include residual analysis, coefficient of determination (r^2), and standard error of the estimate (S_e).

Residual Analysis

How does a business analyst test a regression line to determine mathematically whether the line is a *good* fit of the data? One type of information available is the *historical data* used to construct the equation of the line. In other words, there are actual Y values that correspond to the X values used in constructing the regression line. Why not insert the historical X values into the equation of the sample regression line and get predicted Y values (denoted $\hat{Y}$) and then compare these predicted values to the actual Y values to determine how much error the equation of the regression line produced? *Each difference between the actual Y values and the predicted Y values is the error of the regression line at a given point,* $Y - \hat{Y}$, and is referred to as the **residual.** It is the sum of squares of these residuals that is minimized to find the least squares line.

Residual
The difference between the actual Y value and the Y value predicted by the regression model; the error of the regression model in predicting each value of the dependent variable.

TABLE 12.3
Predicted Values and Residuals for the Airline Cost Example

NUMBER OF PASSENGERS X	COST ($1,000) Y	PREDICTED VALUE $\hat{Y}$	RESIDUAL $Y-\hat{Y}$
61	4.280	4.053	.227
63	4.080	4.134	−.054
67	4.420	4.297	.123
69	4.170	4.378	−.208
70	4.480	4.419	.061
74	4.300	4.582	−.282
76	4.820	4.663	.157
81	4.700	4.867	−.167
86	5.110	5.070	.040
91	5.130	5.274	−.144
95	5.640	5.436	.204
97	5.560	5.518	.042
			$\Sigma(Y-\hat{Y}) = -.001$

Table 12.3 shows $\hat{Y}$ values and the residuals for each pair of data for the airline cost regression model developed in Section 12.2. The predicted values are calculated by inserting an X value into the equation of the regression line and solving for $\hat{Y}$. For example, when $X = 61$, $\hat{Y} = 1.57 + .0407(61) = 4.053$, as displayed in column 3 of the table. Each of these predicted Y values is subtracted from the actual Y value to determine the error, or residual. For example, the first Y value listed in the table is 4.280 and the first predicted value is 4.053, resulting in a residual of $4.280 - 4.053 = .227$. The residuals for this problem are given in column 4 of the table.

Note that the sum of the residuals is approximately zero. Except for rounding error, the sum of the residuals *always* is *zero*. The reason is that a residual is geometrically the vertical distance from the regression line to a data point. The equations used to solve for the slope and intercept place the line geometrically in the middle of all points. That is, *vertical* distances from the line to the points will cancel each other and sum to zero. Figure 12.7 is an Excel-produced scatter plot of the data and the residuals for the airline cost example.

An examination of the residuals may give the business analyst an idea of how well the regression line fits the historical data points. The largest residual for the airline cost example is −.282, and the smallest is .040. Since the objective of the regression analysis was to predict the cost of flight in $1000s, the regression line produces an error of $282 when there are 74 passengers and an error of only $40 when there are 86 passengers. This result presents the *best* and *worst* cases for the residuals. The business analyst must examine other residuals to determine how well the regression model fits other data points.

Outliers
Data points that lie apart from the rest of the points.

Sometimes residuals are used to locate outliers. **Outliers** are *data points that lie apart from the rest of the points.* Outliers can produce residuals with large magnitudes and are usually easy to identify on scatter plots. Outliers can be the result of misrecorded or miscoded data, or they may simply be data points that do not conform to the general trend. The equation of the regression line is influenced by every data point used in its calculation in a manner similar to the arithmetic mean. Therefore outliers sometimes can unduly influence the regression line by "pulling" the line toward the outliers. The origin of outliers must be investigated to determine whether they should be retained or whether the regression equation should be recomputed without them.

Residuals are usually plotted against the X axis, which reveals a view of the residuals as X increases. Figure 12.8 shows the residuals plotted by Excel against the X axis for the airline cost example.

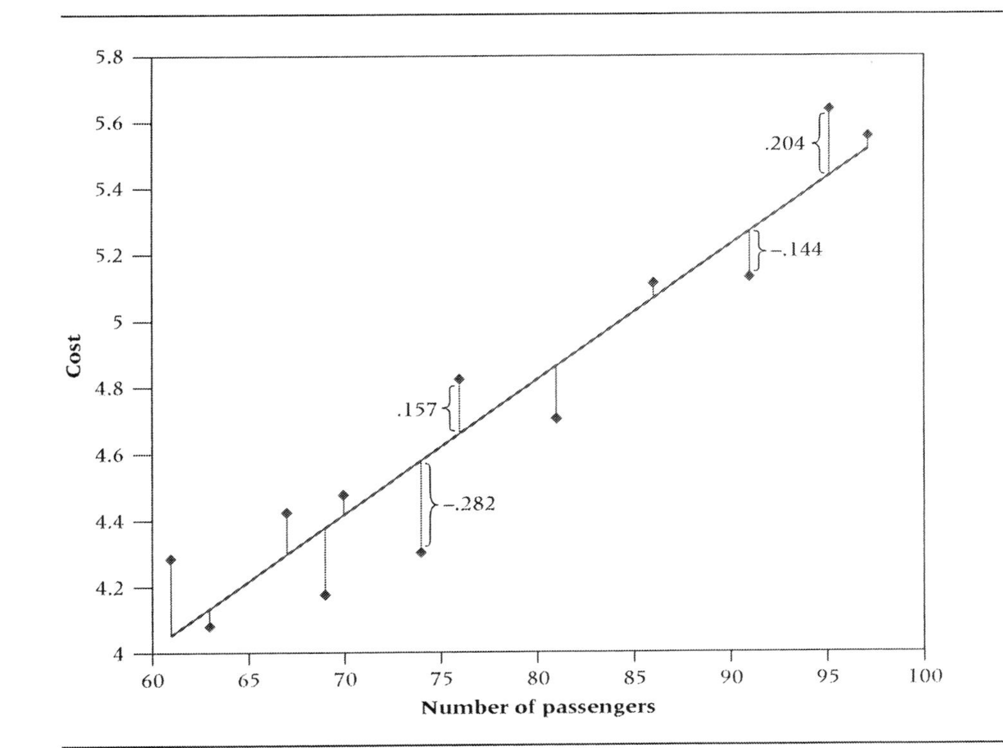

Figure 12.7

Close-up Excel scatter plot with residuals for the airline cost example

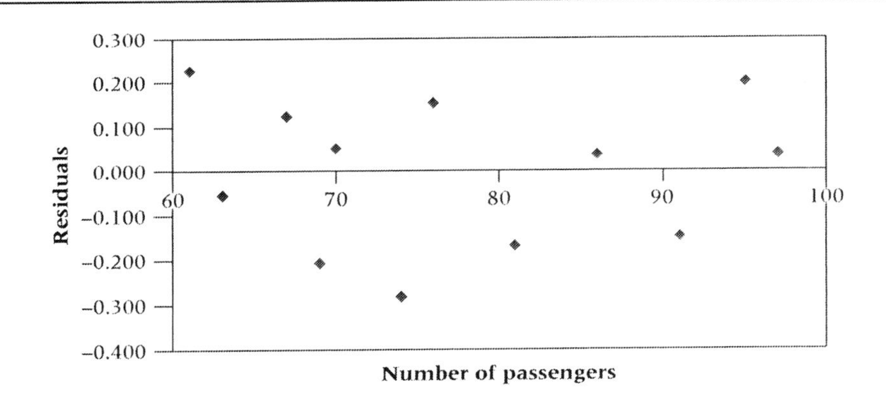

Figure 12.8

Excel graph of residuals for airline cost problem

Using Excel to Compute and Display Residuals

Excel allows you to compute residuals as an option with the **Regression** tool. Note in the Excel dialog box displayed in Figure 12.5 there is a section of **Residuals** optional outputs that can be checked. By selecting ***Residuals,*** you get a printout of all the residuals as shown in Figure 12.9 below; and by selecting **Residual Plots,** you get a plot of the residuals against the X axis like that shown in Figure 12.8.

Figure 12.9

Excel-produced residuals for the airline cost problem

OBSERVATION	PREDICTED COST ($1,000)	RESIDUALS
1	4.051	0.229
2	4.133	−0.053
3	4.296	0.124
4	4.377	−0.207
5	4.418	0.052
6	4.581	−0.281
7	4.662	0.158
8	4.866	−0.166
9	5.070	0.040
10	5.273	−0.143
11	5.436	0.204
12	5.518	0.042

Using Residuals to Test the Assumptions of the Regression Model

One of the major uses of residual analysis is to test some of the assumptions underlying regression. The following are the assumptions of simple regression analysis.

1. The model is linear.
2. The error terms have constant variances.
3. The error terms are independent.
4. The error terms are normally distributed.

Residual plot
A type of graph in which the residuals for a particular regression model are plotted along with their associated values of X.

A particular method for studying the behavior of residuals is the **residual plot.** The residual plot is *a type of graph in which the residuals for a particular regression model are plotted along with their associated value of X* as an ordered pair $(X, Y - \hat{Y})$. Information about how well the regression assumptions are met by the particular regression model can be gleaned by examining the plots. Residual plots are more meaningful with larger sample sizes. For small sample sizes, residual plot analyses can be problematic and subject to over-interpretation. Hence, because the airline cost example is constructed from only 12 pairs of data, one should be cautious in reaching conclusions from Figure 12.8. The residual plots in Figures 12.10, 12.11, and 12.12, however, represent large numbers of data points and therefore are more likely to depict overall trends accurately.

If a residual plot such as the one in Figure 12.10 appears, the assumption that the model is linear does not hold. Note that the residuals are negative for low and high values of X and are positive for middle values of X. The graph of these residuals is parabolic, not linear. The residual plot does not have to be shaped like this for a nonlinear relationship to exist. Any significant deviation from an approximately linear residual plot may mean that a nonlinear relationship exists between the two variables.

Homoscedasticity
The condition that occurs when the error variances produced by a regression model are constant.

Heteroscedasticity
The condition that occurs when the error variances produced by a regression model are not constant.

The assumption of constant error variance sometimes is called **homoscedasticity.** If *the error variances are not constant* (called **heteroscedasticity**), the residual plots might look like one of the two plots in Figure 12.11. Note in Figure 12.11(a) that the error variance is greater for small values of X and smaller for large values of X. The situation is reversed in Figure 12.11(b).

If the error terms are not independent, the residual plots could look like one of the graphs in Figure 12.12. According to these graphs, instead of each error term being independent of the one next to it, the value of the residual is a function of the residual value next to it. For example, a large positive residual is next to a large positive residual and a small negative residual is next to a small negative residual.

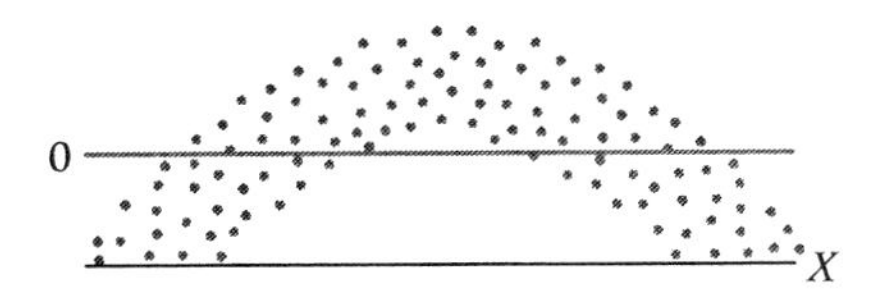

Figure 12.10

Nonlinear residual plot

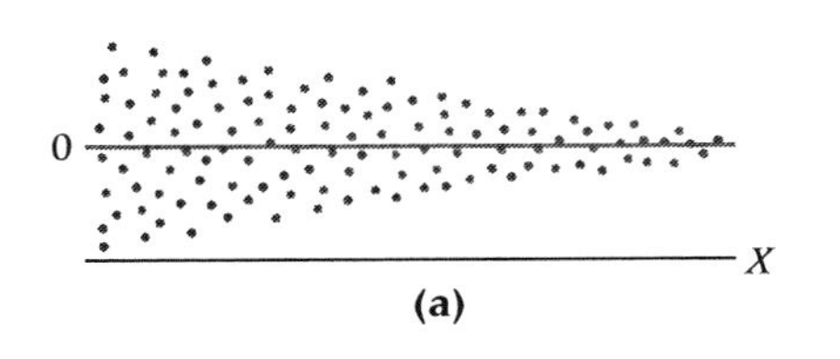

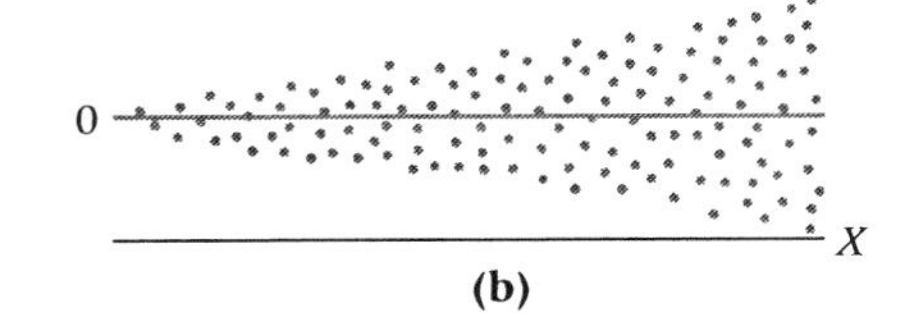

Figure 12.11

Nonconstant error variance

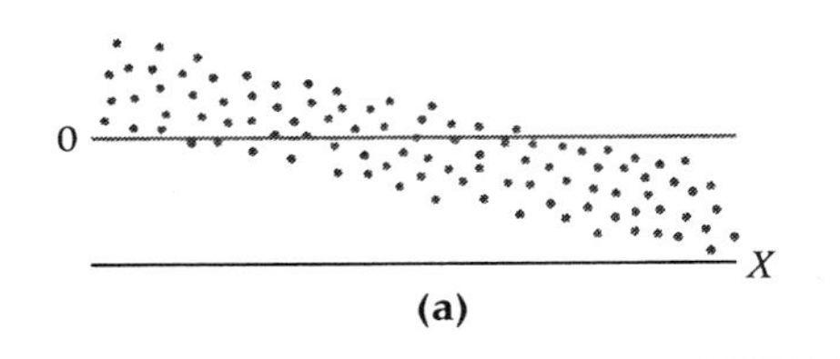

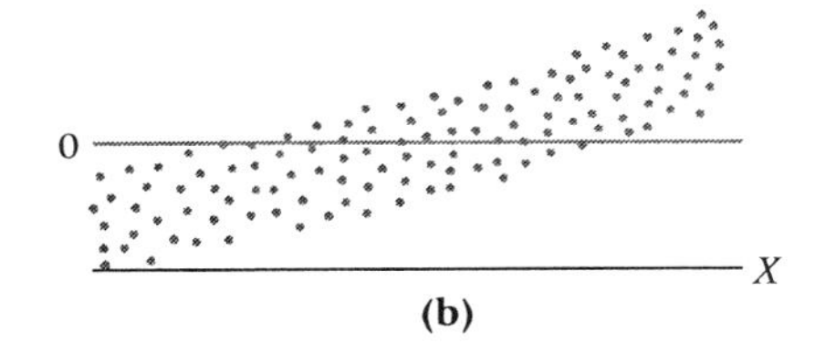

Figure 12.12

Graphs of nonindependent error terms

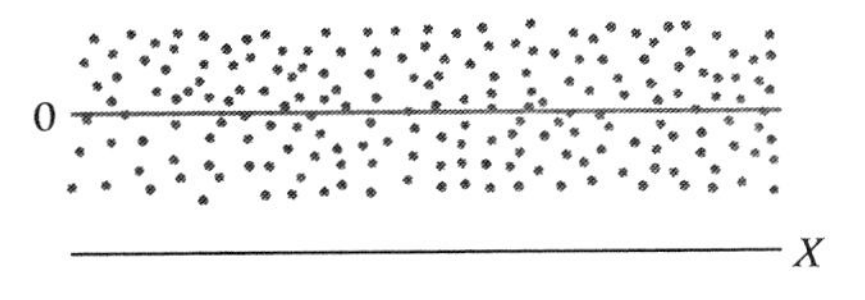

Figure 12.13

Healthy residual graph

The graph of the residuals from a regression analysis that meets the assumptions—a *healthy residual graph*—might look like the graph in Figure 12.13. The plot is relatively linear; the variance of the errors are about equal for each value of X, and the error terms do not appear to be related to adjacent terms.

DEMONSTRATION PROBLEM 12.2

Compute the residuals for Demonstration Problem 12.1 in which a regression model was developed to predict the number of full-time equivalent workers (FTEs) by the number of beds in a hospital. Analyze the residuals.

SOLUTION

The data and computed residuals are shown in the following table.

HOSPITAL	NUMBER OF BEDS X	FTES Y	PREDICTED VALUE $\hat{Y}$	RESIDUALS $Y - \hat{Y}$
1	23	69	82.22	−13.22
2	29	95	95.62	−.62
3	29	102	95.62	6.38
4	35	118	109.01	8.99
5	42	126	124.63	1.37
6	46	125	133.56	−8.56
7	50	138	142.49	−4.49
8	54	178	151.42	26.58
9	64	156	173.74	−17.74
10	66	184	178.20	5.80
11	76	176	200.52	−24.52
12	78	225	204.98	20.02
				$\Sigma(Y - \hat{Y}) = -.01$

Note that the regression model fits these particular data well for hospitals 2 and 5, as indicated by residuals of −.62 and 1.37 FTEs, respectively. For hospitals 1, 8, 9, 11, and 12, the residuals are relatively large, indicating that the regression model does not fit the data for these hospitals well.

Shown below is the Excel-produced residual plot for this problem. An examination of the graph shows that there appears to be greater variability among the residuals towards the higher values of X indicating the potential for heteroscedasticity.

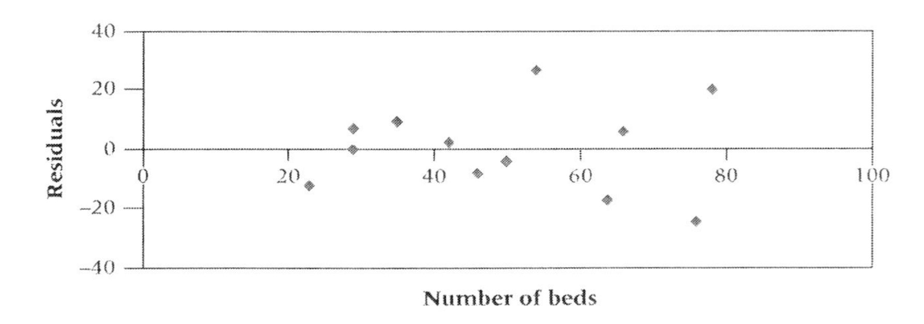

Standard Error of the Estimate

Residuals represent errors of estimation for individual points. With large samples of data, residual computations become laborious. Even with computers, a business analyst sometimes has difficulty working through pages of residuals in an effort to understand the error of the regression model. An alternative way of examining the error of the model is the standard error of the estimate, which provides a single measurement of the regression error.

Because the sum of the residuals is zero, attempting to determine the total amount of error by summing the residuals is fruitless. This zero-sum characteristic of residuals can be avoided by squaring the residuals and then summing them.

Sum of squares of error (SSE)
The sum of the residuals squared for a regression model.

Table 12.4 contains the airline cost data from Table 12.1, along with the residuals and the residuals squared. The *total of the residuals squared* column is called the **sum of squares of error (SSE).**

TABLE 12.4
Determining SSE for the Airline Cost Example

NUMBER OF PASSENGERS X	COST (\$1000) Y	RESIDUAL $Y-\hat{Y}$	$(Y-\hat{Y})^2$
61	4.280	.227	.05153
63	4.080	−.054	.00292
67	4.420	.123	.01513
69	4.170	−.208	.04326
70	4.480	.061	.00372
74	4.300	−.282	.07952
76	4.820	.157	.02465
81	4.700	−.167	.02789
86	5.110	.040	.00160
91	5.130	−.144	.02074
95	5.640	.204	.04162
97	5.560	.042	.00176
		$\Sigma(Y-\hat{Y}) = -.001$	$\Sigma(Y-\hat{Y})^2 = .31434$

Sum of squares of error = SSE = .31434

SUM OF SQUARES OF ERROR

$$SSE = \Sigma(Y-\hat{Y})^2$$

In theory, infinitely many lines can be fit to a sample of points. However, equations 12.1 and 12.3 produce a line of *best fit* for which the SSE is the smallest for any line that can be fit to the sample data. This result is guaranteed, because equations 12.1 and 12.3 are derived from calculus to minimize SSE. For this reason, the regression process used in this chapter is called *least squares* regression.

There is a computational version of the equation for computing SSE. This equation is less meaningful in terms of interpretation than $\Sigma(Y-\hat{Y})^2$, but it is usually easier to compute. The computational formula for SSE follows.

COMPUTATIONAL FORMULA FOR SSE

$$SSE = \Sigma Y^2 - b_0\Sigma Y - b_1\Sigma XY$$

For the airline cost example,

$$\Sigma Y^2 = \Sigma[(4.280)^2 + (4.080)^2 + (4.420)^2 + (4.170)^2 + (4.480)^2 + (4.300)^2 + (4.820)^2 + (4.700)^2 + (5.110)^2 + (5.130)^2 + (5.640)^2 + (5.560)^2 = 270.9251$$

$b_0 = 1.5697928$

$b_1 = .0407016^*$

$\Sigma Y = 56.69$

$\Sigma XY = 4462.22$

$$SSE = \Sigma Y^2 - b_0\Sigma Y - b_1\Sigma XY = 270.9251 - (1.5697928)(56.69) - (.0407016)(4462.22) = .31405$$

The slight discrepancy between this value and the value computed in Table 12.4 is due to rounding error.

*Note: In previous sections, the values of the slope and intercept were rounded off for ease of computation and interpretation. They are shown here with more precision in an effort to reduce rounding error.

The sum of squares error is in part a function of the number of pairs of data being used to compute the sum, which lessens the value of SSE as a measurement of error. A more useful measurement of error is the standard error of the estimate. The **standard error of the estimate,** denoted S_e, is *a standard deviation of the error of the regression model* and has a more practical use than SSE. The standard error of the estimate follows.

Standard error of the estimate (S_e)
A standard deviation of the error of a regression model.

STANDARD ERROR OF THE ESTIMATE

$$S_e = \sqrt{\frac{\text{SSE}}{n-2}}$$

The standard error of the estimate for the airline cost example is

$$S_e = \sqrt{\frac{\text{SSE}}{n-2}} = \sqrt{\frac{.31434}{10}} = .1773.$$

How is the standard error of the estimate used? As previously mentioned, the standard error of the estimate is a standard deviation of error. Recall from Chapter 3 that if data are approximately normally distributed, the empirical rule states that about 68% of all values are within $\mu \pm 1\sigma$ and that about 95% of all values are within $\mu \pm 2\sigma$. One of the assumptions for regression states that for a given X the error terms are normally distributed. Because the error terms are normally distributed, S_e is the standard deviation of error, and the average error is zero, approximately 68% of the error values (residuals) should be within $0 \pm 1S_e$ and 95% of the error values (residuals) should be within $0 \pm 2S_e$. By having knowledge of the variables being studied and by examining the value of S_e, the business analyst can often make a judgment about the fit of the regression model to the data by using S_e. How can the S_e value for the airline cost example be interpreted?

The regression model in that example is used to predict airline cost by number of passengers. Note that the range of the airline cost data in Table 12.1 is from 4.08 to 5.64 ($4080 to $5640). The regression model for the data yields an S_e of .1773. An interpretation of S_e is that the standard deviation of error for the airline cost example is $177.30. If the error terms were normally distributed about the given values of X, approximately 68% of the error terms would be within ±$177.30 and 95% would be within ±2($177.30) = ±$354.60. Examination of the residuals reveals that 100% of the residuals are within $2S_e$. The standard error of the estimate provides a single measure of error, which, if the business analyst has enough background in the area being analyzed, can be used to understand the magnitude of errors in the model. In addition, some business analysts use the standard error of the estimate to identify outliers. They do so by looking for data that are outside $\pm 2S_e$ or $\pm 3S_e$.

DEMONSTRATION PROBLEM 12.3

Compute the sum of squares of error and the standard error of the estimate for Demonstration Problem 12.1, in which a regression model was developed to predict the number of FTEs at a hospital by the number of beds.

SOLUTION

HOSPITAL	NUMBER OF BEDS X	FTES Y	RESIDUALS $Y - \hat{Y}$	$(Y - \hat{Y})^2$
1	23	69	−13.22	174.77
2	29	95	−.62	−0.38
3	29	102	6.38	40.70
4	35	118	8.99	80.82

5	42	126	1.37	1.88
6	46	125	−8.56	73.27
7	50	138	−4.49	20.16
8	54	178	26.58	706.50
9	64	156	−17.74	314.71
10	66	184	5.80	33.64
11	76	176	−24.52	601.23
12	78	225	20.02	400.80
	$\Sigma X = 592$	$\Sigma Y = 1692$	$\Sigma(Y - \hat{Y}) = -.01$	$\Sigma(Y - \hat{Y})^2 = 2448.86$

SSE = 2448.86

$$S_e = \sqrt{\frac{\text{SSE}}{n-2}} = \sqrt{\frac{2448.86}{10}} = 15.65$$

The standard error of the estimate is 15.65 FTEs. An examination of the residuals for this problem reveals that eight of 12 (67%) are within $\pm 1S_e$ and 100% are within $\pm 2S_e$. Is this an acceptable size of error? Hospital administrators probably can best answer that question.

Coefficient of Determination

A widely used measure of fit for regression models is the **coefficient of determination,** or r^2. The coefficient of determination is *the proportion of variability of the dependent variable (Y) accounted for or explained by the independent variable (X).*

Coefficient of determination (r^2)
The proportion of variability of the dependent variable accounted for or explained by the independent variable in a regression model.

The coefficient of determination ranges from 0 to 1. An r^2 of zero means that the predictor accounts for none of the variability of the dependent variable and that there is no regression prediction of Y by X. An r^2 of 1 means that there is perfect prediction of Y by X and that 100% of the variability of Y is accounted for by X. Of course, most r^2 values are between the extremes. The business analyst must interpret whether a particular r^2 is high or low, depending on the use of the model and the context within which the model was developed.

In exploratory research where the variables are less understood, low values of r^2 are likely to be more acceptable than they are in areas of research where the parameters are more developed and understood. One NASA analyst who uses vehicular weight to predict mission cost searches for regression models that have an r^2 of .90 or higher. However, a business analyst who is trying to develop a model to predict the motivation level of employees might be pleased to get an r^2 near .50 in the initial research.

The dependent variable, Y, being predicted in a regression model has a variation that is measured by the sum of squares of $Y(\text{SS}_{YY})$,

$$\text{SS}_{YY} = \Sigma(Y - \bar{Y})^2 = \Sigma Y^2 - \frac{(\Sigma Y)^2}{n},$$

and is the sum of the squared deviations of the Y values from the mean value of Y. This variation can be broken into two additive variations: the *explained variation,* measured by the sum of squares of regression (SSR), and the *unexplained variation,* measured by the sum of squares of error (SSE). This relationship can be expressed in equation form as

$$\text{SS}_{YY} = \text{SSR} + \text{SSE}.$$

If each term in the equation is divided by SS_{YY}, the resulting equation is

$$1 = \frac{\text{SSR}}{\text{SS}_{YY}} + \frac{\text{SSE}}{\text{SS}_{YY}}$$

The term r^2 is the proportion of the Y variability that is explained by the regression model and represented here as

$$r^2 = \frac{\text{SSR}}{\text{SS}_{YY}}.$$

Substituting this into the preceding relationship gives

$$1 = r^2 + \frac{\text{SSE}}{\text{SS}_{YY}}.$$

Solving for r^2 yields Equation 12.4.

COEFFICIENT OF DETERMINATION

$$r^2 = 1 - \frac{\text{SSE}}{\text{SS}_{YY}} = 1 - \frac{SSE}{\Sigma Y^2 - \frac{(\Sigma Y)^2}{n}} \quad (12.4)$$

Note: $0 \le r^2 \le 1$.

The value of r^2 for the airline cost example is solved as follows.

$$\text{SSE} = .31434$$

$$\text{SS}_{YY} = \Sigma Y^2 - \frac{(\Sigma Y)^2}{n} = 270.9251 - \frac{(56.69)^2}{12} = 3.11209$$

$$r^2 = 1 - \frac{\text{SSE}}{\text{SS}_{YY}} = 1 - \frac{.31434}{3.11209} = .899$$

That is, 89.9% of the variability of the cost of flying a Boeing 737 airplane on a commercial flight is accounted for or predicted by the number of passengers. This result also means that 11.1% of the variance in airline flight cost, Y, is unaccounted for by X or unexplained by the regression model.

DEMONSTRATION PROBLEM 12.4

Compute the coefficient of determination (r^2) for Demonstration Problem 12.1, in which a regression model was developed to predict the number of FTEs of a hospital by the number of beds.

SOLUTION

$$\text{SSE} = 2448.6$$

$$\text{SS}_{YY} = 260{,}136 - \frac{1692^2}{12} = 21{,}564$$

$$r^2 = 1 - \frac{\text{SSE}}{\text{SS}_{YY}} = 1 - \frac{2448.6}{21{,}564} = .886$$

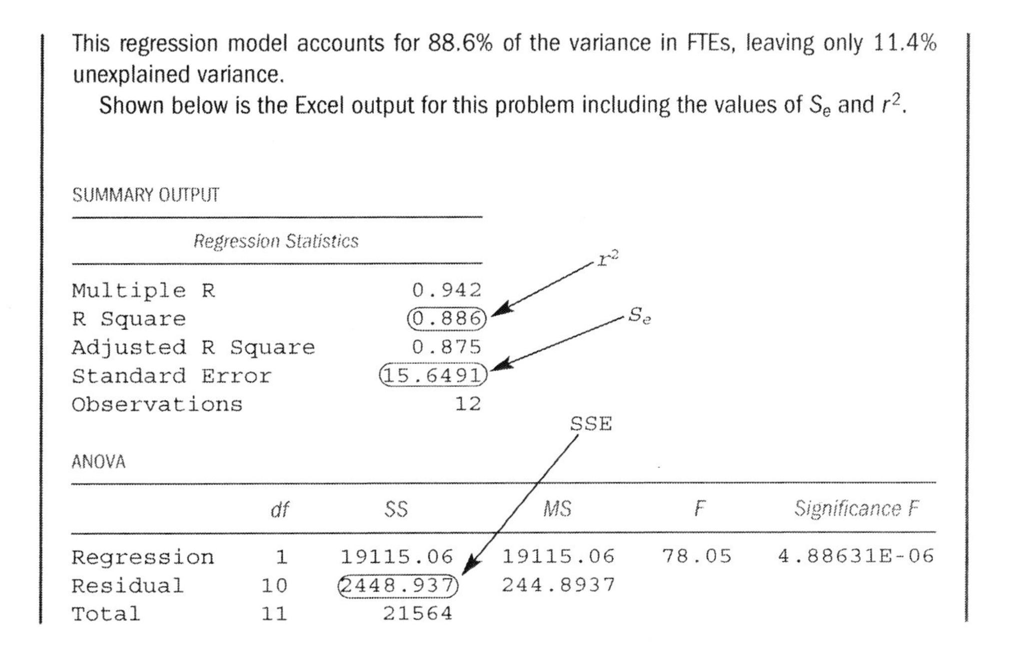

This regression model accounts for 88.6% of the variance in FTEs, leaving only 11.4% unexplained variance.

Shown below is the Excel output for this problem including the values of S_e and r^2.

SUMMARY OUTPUT

Regression Statistics	
Multiple R	0.942
R Square	0.886
Adjusted R Square	0.875
Standard Error	15.6491
Observations	12

ANOVA

	df	*SS*	*MS*	*F*	*Significance F*
Regression	1	19115.06	19115.06	78.05	4.88631E-06
Residual	10	2448.937	244.8937		
Total	11	21564			

Using Excel to Solve for S_e and r^2

Excel's **Regression** tool includes the Standard Error of the Estimate and r^2 in its output. Figure 12.14 displays a portion of the Excel-produced regression output for the airline cost problem. Note the standard error of the estimate, .1769, and the value of the coefficient of determination, $r^2 = .900$ (differences between these values and those calculated before are due to rounding error). In addition, the sum of squares of error, used in the calculation of each of these, is shown in the row beside the word *Residual* under SS (0.31293).

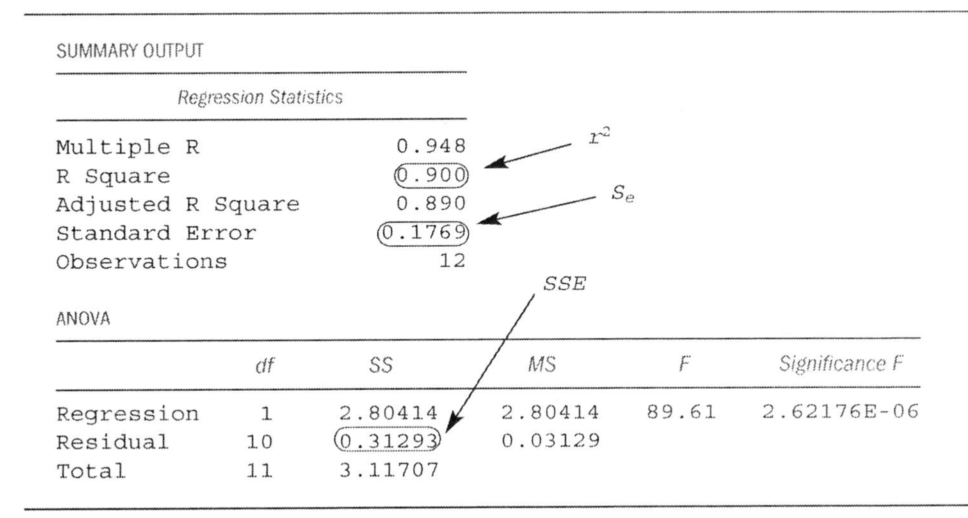

SUMMARY OUTPUT

Regression Statistics	
Multiple R	0.948
R Square	0.900
Adjusted R Square	0.890
Standard Error	0.1769
Observations	12

ANOVA

	df	*SS*	*MS*	*F*	*Significance F*
Regression	1	2.80414	2.80414	89.61	2.62176E-06
Residual	10	0.31293	0.03129		
Total	11	3.11707			

Figure 12.14

Excel Regression output for the airline cost problem including S_e and r^2

12.3
Problems

12.10 Determine the equation of the regression line for the following data. Compute the residuals, the standard error of the estimate, and the coefficient of determination. Study these outputs and comment on the fit of the model.

X	15	8	19	12	5
Y	47	36	56	44	21

12.11 Consider the following data. Develop the simple regression model to predict Y from X. Compute the residuals and develop a residual plot. Comment on the size of the residuals and on any apparent violation of regression assumptions. Compute S_e and r^2 and use these to discuss the strength of the regression model.

X	5	7	11	12	19	25
Y	47	38	32	24	22	10

12.12 Compute the residuals, S_e, and r^2 for Problem 12.5. Comment on the fit of the regression model and on any apparent violation of regression assumptions.

12.13 Compute the residuals, S_e, and r^2 for Problem 12.7. Comment on the fit of the regression model and on any apparent violation of regression assumptions.

12.14 Compute the residuals, S_e, and r^2 for Problem 12.8. Comment on the fit of the regression model and on any apparent violation of regression assumptions.

12.15 Compute the residuals, S_e, and r^2 for Problem 12.9. Comment on the fit of the regression model and on any apparent violation of regression assumptions.

12.16 Wisconsin is an important milk-producing state. Some people might argue that because of transportation costs, the cost of milk increases with the distance of markets from Wisconsin. Suppose the milk prices in eight cities are as follows.

COST OF MILK (PER GALLON)	DISTANCE FROM MADISON (MILES)
\$2.64	1245
2.31	425
2.45	1346
2.52	973
2.19	255
2.55	865
2.40	1080
2.37	296

Use the prices along with the distance of each city from Madison, Wisconsin, to develop a regression line to predict the price of a gallon of milk by the number of miles the city is from Madison. Compute the residuals and construct a residual plot and examine the results for possible violations of regression assumptions. Determine the value of the standard error of the estimate and r^2. Based on the results of this analysis, comment on the strength of the regression model and its fit to the data.

12.17 For each of the following, sketch a graph of the residuals and indicate which of the assumptions underlying regression appear to be in jeopardy on the basis of the graph.

X	$Y-\hat{Y}$
213	−11
216	−5
227	−2
229	−1
237	+6
247	+10
263	+12

X	$Y-\hat{Y}$	X	$Y-\hat{Y}$
5	−21	13	−7
6	+16	14	+5
8	+14	17	−2
9	−11	18	+1
12	−8		

X	$Y-\hat{Y}$	X	$Y-\hat{Y}$
10	+6	14	−3
11	+3	15	+2
12	−1	16	+5
13	−11	17	+8

12.18 Determine the equation of the regression line to predict annual sales of a company from the yearly stock market volume of shares sold in a recent year. Compute the standard error of the estimate and r^2 for this model. Does volume of shares sold appear to be a good predictor of a company's sales? Why or why not?

COMPANY	ANNUAL SALES (BILLIONS)	ANNUAL VOLUME (MILLION SHARES)
Merck	10.5	728.6
Philip Morris	48.1	497.9
IBM	64.8	439.1
Eastman Kodak	20.1	377.9
Bristol-Myers Squibb	11.4	375.5
General Motors	123.8	363.8
Ford Motors	89.0	276.3

12.19 The Conference Board produces a Consumer Confidence Index (CCI) that reflects people's feelings about general business conditions, employment opportunities, and their own income prospects. Some business analysts may feel that consumer confidence is a function of the median household income. Shown here are the CCIs for 9 years and the median household incomes for the same 9 years published by the U.S. Bureau of the Census. Determine the equation of the regression line to predict the CCI from the median household income. Compute the standard error of the estimate for this model. Compute the value of r^2. Does median household income appear to be a good predictor of the CCI? Why or why not?

CCI	MEDIAN HOUSEHOLD INCOME ($1000)
116.8	37.415
91.5	36.770
68.5	35.501
61.6	35.047
65.9	34.700
90.6	34.942
100.0	35.887
104.6	36.306
125.4	37.005

12.4
Hypothesis Tests for the Slope of the Regression Model and Testing the Overall Model

Testing the Slope

Another way to determine how well a regression model fits the data (besides using residual analysis, the standard error of the estimate, and the coefficient of determination) is by conducting a hypothesis test using the sample slope of the regression model to see if the population slope is significantly different from zero.

Suppose a business analyst decided that it is not worth the effort to develop a linear regression model to predict Y from X. An alternative approach might be to average the Y values and use $\overline{Y}$ as the predictor of Y for all values of X. For the airline cost example, instead of using population as a predictor, the business analyst would use the average value of airline cost, $\overline{Y}$, for the sample as the predictor. In this case the average value of Y is

$$\overline{Y} = \frac{56.69}{12} = 4.7242, \text{ or } \$4724.20.$$

Using this result as a model to predict Y, if the number of passengers is 61, 70, or 95—or any other number—the predicted value of Y is still 4.7242. Essentially, this approach fits the line of $\overline{Y} = 4.7242$ through the data, which is a horizontal line with a slope of zero. Would a regression analysis offer anything more than the $\overline{Y}$ model? Using this nonregression model (the $\overline{Y}$ model) as a worst case, the business analyst can analyze the regression line to determine whether it adds a more significant amount of predictability of Y than does the $\overline{Y}$ model. Because the slope of the $\overline{Y}$ line is zero, one way to determine whether the regression line adds significant predictability is to test the *population* slope of the regression line to find out if the slope is different from zero. As the slope of the regression line diverges from zero, the regression model is adding predictability that the $\overline{Y}$ line is not generating. For this reason, testing the slope of the regression line to determine whether the slope is different from zero is important. If the slope is not different from zero, the regression line is doing nothing more than the $\overline{Y}$ line in predicting Y.

How does the business analyst go about testing the slope of the regression line? Why not just examine the calculated slope? For example, the slope of the regression line for the airline cost data is .0407. This value obviously is not zero. The problem is that this slope is a *sample* slope obtained from a sample of 12 data points. If another sample of airline cost and number of passengers were used, a different slope likely would be obtained. Thus the sample slope is a function of the particular sample from which it is obtained. What has to be tested here is the *population* slope. If all the pairs of data points for the population were available, would the slope of that regression line be different from zero? Here the sample slope, b_1, is used as evidence to test whether the population slope is different from zero. The hypotheses for this test follow.

$$H_0: \beta_1 = 0$$
$$H_a: \beta_1 \neq 0$$

Note that this test is two-tailed. The null hypothesis can be rejected if the slope is either negative or positive. A negative slope indicates an inverse relationship between X and Y. That is, larger values of X are related to smaller values of Y and vice versa. Both negative and positive slopes can be different from zero. To determine whether there is a significant positive relationship between two variables, the hypotheses would be one-tailed, or

$$H_0: \beta_1 = 0$$
$$H_a: \beta_1 > 0.$$

To test for a significant negative relationship between two variables, the hypotheses also would be one-tailed, or

$$H_0: \beta_1 = 0$$
$$H_a: \beta_1 < 0.$$

In each case, testing the null hypothesis involves a t test of the slope.

t TEST OF SLOPE

$$t = \frac{b_1 - \beta_1}{S_b}$$

where:

$$S_b = \frac{S_e}{\sqrt{SS_{XX}}}$$

$$S_e = \sqrt{\frac{SSE}{n-2}}$$

$$SS_{XX} = \Sigma X^2 - \frac{(\Sigma X)^2}{n}$$

β_1 = the hypothesized shape

df $= n - 2$

The test of the slope of the regression line for the airline cost regression model using $\alpha = .05$ follows. The regression line derived for the data is

$$\hat{Y} = 1.57 + .0407X.$$

The sample slope is $.0407 = b_1$. The value of S_e is .1773, $\Sigma X = 930$, $\Sigma X^2 = 73{,}764$, and $n = 12$. The hypotheses are

$$H_0: \beta_1 = 0$$
$$H_a: \beta_1 \neq 0.$$

The df $= n - 2 = 12 - 2 = 10$. As this test is two-tailed, $\alpha/2 = .025$. The table t value is $t_{.025,10} = \pm 2.228$. The calculated t value for this sample slope is

$$t = \frac{.0407 - 0}{\dfrac{.1773}{\sqrt{73{,}764 - \dfrac{(930)^2}{12}}}} = 9.43$$

As shown in Figure 12.15, the t value calculated from the sample slope is in the rejection region and the observed $t = 9.43$ is greater than the critical $t = 2.228$. The null hypothesis that the population slope is zero is rejected. This linear regression model is adding significantly more predictive information to the $\overline{Y}$ model (no regression).

It is desirable to reject the null hypothesis in testing the slope of the regression model. In rejecting the null hypothesis of a zero population slope, we are stating that the regression

Figure 12.15

t Test of slope from airline cost example

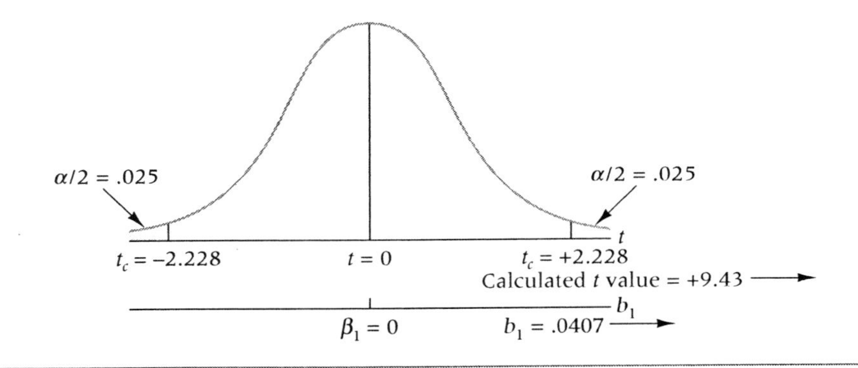

Figure 12.16

Excel Regression output for the airline cost problem including a test of the slope

	COEFFICIENTS	STANDARD ERROR	t STAT	P-VALUE
Intercept	1.5655	0.3375	4.64	0.00092
Number of Beds	0.0407	0.0043	9.47	.0000026

Observed *t* value

p-value of observed *t*

model is adding something to the explanation of the variation of the dependent variable that the average value of *Y* model does not. Failure to reject the null hypothesis in this test causes the business analyst to conclude that the regression model has no predictability of the dependent variable, and the model therefore has little or no use.

Using Excel to Test the Slope of the Regression Model

Excel's **Regression** tool includes a test for the slope of the regression model in its standard output. Figure 12.16 shows a portion of the Excel-produced regression output for the airline cost problem. Observe the value of *t Stat* in the *Number of Beds* row. This value, $t = 9.47$, is the observed (calculated) value of t for the test of the slope, which is essentially the same as the $t = 9.43$ calculated in the section above (with slight differences due to rounding error). The associated p-value is .0000026. Since this is less than $\alpha/2 = .025$ for the two-tailed test of the slope being conducted, the decision is to reject the null hypothesis and conclude that the population slope is significantly different from zero. Most business analysts are not interested in conducting t tests about the *Y* intercept, and we will not discuss such tests in this text.

DEMONSTRATION PROBLEM 12.5

Test the slope of the regression model developed in Demonstration Problem 12.1 to predict the number of FTEs in a hospital from the number of beds to determine whether there is a significant positive slope. Use $\alpha = .01$.

BEDS	FTEs
23	69
29	95
29	102
35	118
42	126
46	125
50	138
54	178
64	156
66	184
76	176
78	225

SOLUTION

The hypotheses for this problem are

$$H_0: \beta_1 = 0$$

$$H_a: \beta_1 > 0.$$

The level of significance is .01. There are 12 pairs of data, so df = 10. The critical table t value is $t_{.01,10} = 2.764$. The regression line equation for this problem is

$$\hat{Y} = 30.888 + 2.232X.$$

The sample slope, b_1, is 2.232, and $S_e = 15.65$, $\Sigma X = 592$, $\Sigma X^2 = 33{,}044$, and $n = 12$. The calculated t value for the sample slope is

$$t = \frac{2.232 - 0}{\dfrac{15.65}{\sqrt{33{,}044 - \dfrac{(592)^2}{12}}}} = 8.84.$$

The calculated t value (8.84) is in the rejection region because it is greater than the critical table t value of 2.764. The null hypothesis is rejected. The population slope for this regression line is significantly different from zero in the positive direction. This regression model is adding significant predictability over the $\bar{Y}$ *model*.

Shown below is the portion of the Excel regression output for this problem containing the t test of the slope. Note that the *t Stat* for number of beds (test of the slope) is essentially the same as the value computed above. The *p*-value of .00000489 is less than $\alpha = .01$ supporting the decision to reject the null hypothesis of the slope.

	COEFFICIENTS	STANDARD ERROR	*t* STAT	P-VALUE
Intercept	30.912	13.2542	2.33	0.041888
Number of Beds	2.232	0.2526	8.83	.00000489

Testing the Overall Model

It is common in regression analysis to compute an F test to determine the overall significance of the model. Most computer software packages include the F text and its associated ANOVA table as standard regression output. In multiple regression (Chapter 13), this is a test to determine whether at least one of the regression coefficients (from multiple predictors) is different from zero. In simple regression, there is only one predictor and only one regression coefficient to test. Because the regression coefficient is the slope of the regression line, the F test for overall significance is testing the same thing as the t test in simple regression. The hypotheses being tested in simple regression by the F test for overall significance are

$$H_0\colon \beta_1 = 0$$
$$H_a\colon \beta_1 \neq 0.$$

In the case of simple regression analysis, $F = t^2$. Thus, for the airline cost example, the F value is

$$F = t^2 = (9.43)^2 = 88.92$$

The F value is computed directly by

$$F = \frac{\dfrac{SS_{reg}}{df_{reg}}}{\dfrac{SS_{err}}{df_{err}}} = \frac{MS_{reg}}{MS_{err}},$$

where:

$df_{reg} = k$,

$df_{err} = n - k - 1$, and

k = the number of independent variables.

The values of the sum of squares (SS), degrees of freedom (df), and mean squares (MS) are obtained from the analysis of variance table, which is produced with other regression statistics as standard output from statistical software packages. Shown here is the analysis of variance table produced by Excel for the airline cost example.

ANOVA

	df	*SS*	*MS*	*F*	*Significance F*
Regression	1	2.80414	2.80414	89.61	.00000262
Residual	10	0.31293	0.03129		
Total	11	3.11707			

The F value for the airline cost example is calculated from this ANOVA table as:

$$F = \frac{\frac{2.80414}{1}}{\frac{0.31293}{10}} = \frac{2.80414}{0.03129} = 89.61$$

The difference between this value (89.61) and the value obtained by squaring the t statistic (88.92) is due to rounding error. The probability of obtaining an F value this large or larger by chance if there is no regression prediction in this model is .00000262 according to the ANOVA output (the p value). This means it is highly unlikely that the population slope is zero and it is highly unlikely that there is no prediction due to regression from this model given the sample statistics obtained. Hence, it is highly likely that this regression model adds significant predictability of the dependent variable.

Note from the ANOVA table that the degrees of freedom due to regression are equal to 1. Simple regression models have only one independent variable; therefore, $k = 1$. The degrees of freedom error in simple regression analysis is always $n - k - 1 = n - 1 - 1 = n - 2$. With the degrees of freedom due to regression (1) as the numerator degrees of freedom and the degrees of freedom due to error ($n - 2$) as the denominator degrees of freedom, Table A.7 can be used to obtain the critical F value ($F_{\alpha,1,n-2}$) to help make the hypothesis-testing decision about the overall regression model if the p value of F is not given in the computer output. This critical F value is always found in the right tail of the distribution. In simple regression, the relationship between the critical t value to test the slope and the critical F value of overall significance is

$$t^2_{\alpha/2,n-2} = F_{\alpha,1,n-2}$$

For the airline cost example with a two-tailed test and $\alpha = .05$, the critical value of $t_{.025,10}$ is ± 2.228 and the critical value of $F_{.05,1,10}$ is 4.96.

$$t^2_{.025,10} = (\pm 2.228)^2 = 4.96 = F_{.05,1,10}$$

12.4 Problems

12.20 Test the slope of the regression line developed in Problem 12.5. Let $\alpha = .05$.

ADVERTISING	SALES
12.5	148
3.7	55
21.6	338
60.0	994
37.6	541
6.1	89
16.8	126
41.2	379

12.21 Test the slope of the regression line developed in Problem 12.7. Let $\alpha = .01$.

STARTS	FAILURES
233,710	57,097
199,091	50,361
181,645	60,747
158,930	88,140
155,672	97,069
164,086	86,133
166,154	71,558
188,387	71,128
168,158	71,931
170,475	83,384

12.22 Test the slope of the regression line developed in Problem 12.8. Let $\alpha = .10$.

FARMS	SIZE
5.65	213
4.65	258
3.96	297
3.36	340
2.95	374
2.52	420
2.44	426
2.29	441
2.15	460
2.07	469

12.23 Test the slope of the regression line developed in Problem 12.9. Let $\alpha = .05$.

PRODUCTION	NEW ORDERS
99.9	2.74
97.9	2.87
98.9	2.93
87.9	2.87
92.9	2.98
97.9	3.09
100.6	3.36
104.9	3.61
105.3	3.75
108.6	3.95

12.24 Test the slope of the regression line developed in Problem 12.16. Let $\alpha = .05$.

COST ($)	DISTANCE
2.64	1245
2.31	425
2.45	1346
2.52	973
2.19	255
2.55	865
2.40	1080
2.37	296

12.25 Test the slope of the regression line developed in Problem 12.18. Let $\alpha = .01$.

SALES	VOLUME
10.5	728.6
48.1	497.9
64.8	439.1
20.1	377.9
11.4	375.5
123.8	363.8
89.0	276.3

12.26 Test the slope of the regression line developed in Problem 12.19. Let $\alpha = .05$.

CCI	INCOME
116.8	37.415
91.5	36.770
68.5	35.501
61.6	35.047
65.9	34.700
90.6	34.942
100.0	35.887
104.6	36.306
125.4	37.005

12.5 Estimation

One of the main uses of regression analysis is as a prediction tool. If the regression function is a good model, the business analyst can use the regression equation to determine values of the dependent variable from various values of the independent variable. For example, financial brokers would like to have a model with which they could predict the selling price of a particular stock on a certain day by some variable, such as the unemployment rate or the producer price index. Marketing managers would like to have a site location model with which they could predict the sales volume of a new location by variables such as population density or number of competitors. The airline cost example presents a regression model that has the potential to predict the cost of flying an airplane by the number of passengers.

A point estimate prediction can be made by taking a particular value of X that is of interest, substituting the value of X into the regression equation, and solving for Y. For example, if the number of passengers is 73, what is the predicted cost of the airline flight? The regression equation for this example was

$$\hat{Y} = 1.57 + .0407X.$$

Substituting $X = 73$ into this equation yields a predicted cost of 4.5411 or $4,541.10.

Confidence Intervals to Estimate the Conditional Mean of $Y: \mu_{Y|X}$

Although a point estimate is often of interest to the business analyst, the regression line is determined by a sample set of points. If a different sample is taken, a different line will result, yielding a different point estimate. Hence computing a confidence interval for the estimating often is useful. Because for any value of X (independent variable) there can be many values of Y (dependent variable), one type of confidence interval is an estimate of the *average* value of Y for a given X. This average value of Y is denoted $E(Y_X)$—the expected value of Y.

$$\hat{Y} \pm t_{\alpha/2,n-2} S_e \sqrt{\frac{1}{n} + \frac{(X_0 - \bar{X})^2}{SS_{XX}}} \quad (12.5)$$

where:

X_0 = a particular value of X

$$SS_{XX} = \Sigma X^2 - \frac{(\Sigma X)^2}{n}$$

CONFIDENCE INTERVAL TO ESTIMATE $E(Y_X)$ FOR A GIVEN VALUE OF X

Use of this formula can be illustrated with construction of a 95% confidence interval to estimate the average value of Y (airline cost) for the airline cost example when X (number of passengers) is 73. This confidence interval utilizes a t value obtained through the degrees of freedom and $\alpha/2$. For a 95% confidence interval, $\alpha = .05$ and $\alpha/2 = .025$. The df $= n - 2 = 12 - 2 = 10$. The table t value is $t_{.025,10} = 2.228$. In addition, other needed values for this problem, which were solved for previously, are

$$S_e = .1773, \quad \Sigma X = 930, \quad \bar{X} = 77.5, \quad \Sigma X^2 = 73{,}764.$$

For $X_0 = 73$, the value of $\hat{Y}$ is 4.5411. The computed confidence interval for the average value of Y, $E(Y_{73})$, is

$$4.5411 \pm (2.228)(.1773)\sqrt{\frac{1}{12} + \frac{(73 - 77.5)^2}{73{,}764 - \frac{(930)^2}{12}}} = 4.5411 \pm .1220,$$

$$4.4191 \le E(Y_{73}) \le 4.6631.$$

That is, the statement can be made with 95% confidence that the average value of Y for $X = 73$ is between 4.4191 and 4.6631.

Table 12.5 shows confidence intervals computed for the airline cost example for several values of X to estimate the average value of Y. Note that as X values get farther from the mean X value (77.5), the confidence intervals get wider; as the X values get closer to the mean, the confidence intervals get narrower. The reason is that the numerator of the second term under the radical sign approaches zero as the value of X nears the mean and increases as X departs from the mean.

TABLE 12.5
Confidence Intervals to Estimate the Average Value of Y for Some X Values in the Airline Cost Example

X	CONFIDENCE INTERVAL	
62	4.0934 ± .1876	3.9058 to 4.2810
68	4.3376 ± .1461	4.1915 to 4.4837
73	4.5411 ± .1220	4.4191 to 4.6631
85	5.0295 ± .1349	4.8946 to 5.1644
90	5.2230 ± .1656	5.0674 to 5.3986

Prediction Intervals to Estimate a Single Value of Y

A second type of interval in regression estimation is a prediction interval to estimate a single value of Y for a given value of X.

PREDICTION INTERVAL TO ESTIMATE Y FOR A GIVEN VALUE OF X

$$\hat{Y} \pm t_{\alpha/2,n-2}S_e\sqrt{1 + \frac{1}{n} + \frac{(X_0 - \bar{X})^2}{SS_{XX}}} \quad (12.6)$$

where:

X_0 = a particular value of X

$$SS_{XX} = \Sigma X^2 - \frac{(\Sigma X)^2}{n}$$

Equation 12.6 is virtually the same as Equation 12.5, except for the additional value of 1 under the radical. This additional value widens the prediction interval to estimate a single value of Y from the confidence interval to estimate the average value of Y. This result seems logical because the average value of Y is toward the middle of a group of Y values. Thus the confidence interval to estimate the average need not be as wide as the prediction interval produced by Equation 12.6, which takes into account all the Y values for a given X.

A 95% prediction interval can be computed to estimate the single value of Y for $X = 73$ from the airline cost example by using Equation 12.6. The same values used to construct the confidence interval to estimate the average value of Y are used here.

$$t_{.025,10} = 2.228, \quad S_e = .1773, \quad \Sigma X = 930, \quad \bar{X} = 77.5, \quad \Sigma X^2 = 73{,}764$$

For $X_0 = 73$, the value of $\hat{Y} = 4.5411$. The computed prediction interval for the single value of Y is

$$4.5411 \pm (2.228)(.1773)\sqrt{1 + \frac{1}{12} + \frac{(73 - 77.5)^2}{73{,}764 - \frac{(930)^2}{12}}} = 4.5411 \pm .4134,$$

$$4.1277 \le Y \le 4.9545.$$

Caution: A regression line is determined from a sample of points. The line, the r^2, the S_e, and the confidence intervals change for different sets of sample points. That is, the linear relationship developed for a set of points does not necessarily hold for values of X outside the domain of those used to establish the model. In the airline cost example, the domain of X values (number of passengers) varied from 61 to 97. The regression model developed from these points may not be valid for flights of say 40, 50, or 100 because the regression model was not constructed with X values of those magnitudes. However, decision makers sometimes extrapolate regression results to values of X beyond the domain of those used to develop the formulas (often in time-series sales forecasting). Understanding the limitations of this type of use of regression analysis is essential.

DEMONSTRATION PROBLEM 12.6

Construct a 95% confidence interval to estimate the average value of Y (FTEs) for Demonstration Problem 12.1 when $X = 40$ beds. Then construct a 95% prediction interval to estimate the single value of Y for $X = 40$ beds.

SOLUTION

For a 95% confidence interval, $\alpha = .05$, $n = 12$, and df = 10. The table t value is $t_{.025,10} = 2.228$; $S_e = 15.65$, $\Sigma X = 592$, $\bar{X} = 49.33$, and $\Sigma X^2 = 33{,}044$. For $X_0 = 40$, $\hat{Y} = 120.17$. The computed confidence interval for the average value of Y is

$$120.17 \pm (2.228)(15.65)\sqrt{\frac{1}{12} + \frac{(40 - 49.33)^2}{33{,}044 - \frac{(592)^2}{12}}} = 120.17 \pm 11.35$$

$$108.82 \le E(Y_{40}) \le 131.52.$$

With 95% confidence, the statement can be made that the average number of FTEs for a hospital with 40 beds is between 108.82 and 131.52.

The computed prediction interval for the single value of Y is

$$120.17 \pm (2.228)(15.65)\sqrt{1 + \frac{1}{12} + \frac{(40 - 49.33)^2}{33{,}044 - \frac{(592)^2}{12}}} = 120.17 \pm 36.67$$

$$83.5 \le Y \le 156.84.$$

Microsoft Excel - 011-CI-PI Macro

Confidence Interval & Prediction Interval for Simple Regression

	A	B	C	D	E	F	G	H
2	*INPUTS*							
3		Cell Range for X Values (independent variable)				Sheet3!$A$2:$A$13		
4		Cell Range for Regression Standard Error				Sheet3!$B$21		
5			Level of Confide	Level of Confidence		95	%	
6	*OUTPUTS*							
7			t Value for Level of Confidence			2.228		
8			Mean of X Values (X-bar)			49.33333		
9			Sum of Squares of X			3838.667		
10		***Values from Regression Results***						
11			Standard Error of Regression			15.64908		
12			Number of Observations			12		
13			Residual Degrees of Freedom			10		
14			Intercept Coefficienct (b_0)			30.91247		
15			Slope Coefficient (b_1)			2.231504		
16			Standard Error of Slope			0.25258		
17	X Values	Y-hat	CI-Half Width	PI-Half Width	CI	CI-Upper	PI	PI-Upper
18	23	82.23706	17.91501093	39.20137581	64.32205	100.1521	43.03569	121.4384
19	29	95.62609	15.24023368	38.05344887	80.38585	110.8663	57.57264	133.6795
20	29	95.62609	15.24023368	38.05344887	80.38585	110.8663	57.57264	133.6795
21	35	109.0151	12.89906979	37.17776553	96.11604	121.9142	71.83734	146.1929
22	42	124.6356	10.87885259	36.52601377	113.7568	135.5145	88.10962	161.1617
23	46	133.5617	10.23893792	36.34055721	123.3227	143.8006	97.2211	169.9022
24	50	142.4877	10.07260909	36.294045	132.4151	152.5603	106.1936	178.7817
25	54	151.4137	10.40260764	36.38700996	141.0111	161.8163	115.0267	187.8007
26	64	173.7287	13.01720679	37.21891886	160.7115	186.7459	136.5098	210.9476
27	66	178.1917	13.75847917	37.48461014	164.4333	191.9502	140.7071	215.6763
28	76	200.5068	18.07050318	39.27267922	182.4363	218.5773	161.2341	239.7795
29	78	204.9698	19.01562366	39.71642219	185.9542	223.9854	165.2534	244.6862

Sheet1 / Sheet2 / CI-PI / Sheet3

With 95% confidence, the statement can be made that a single number of FTEs for a hospital with 40 beds is between 83.5 and 156.84. Obviously this interval is much wider than the 95% confidence interval for the average value of Y for $X = 40$.

Shown on the previous page is a FAST⧹⧹ STAT-produced table showing the computed data for confidence intervals and prediction intervals for this problem, and below is a graph of the 95% interval bands for both the average Y value and the single Y values for all 12 X values in this problem. Note once again the flaring out of the bands near the extreme values of X.

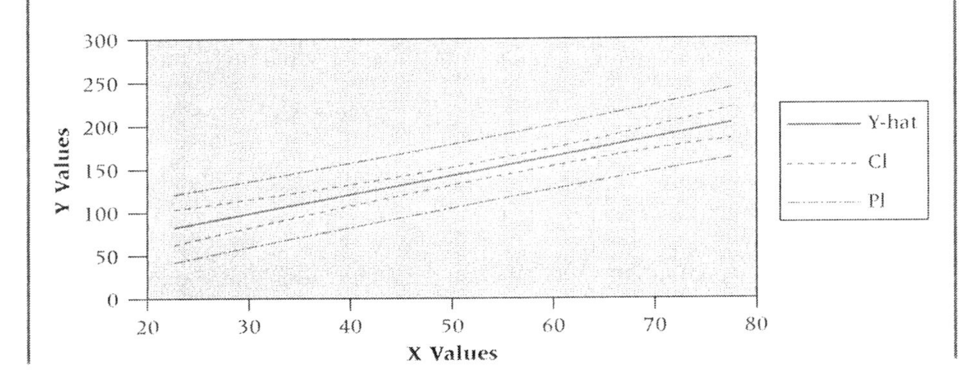

Analysis Using Excel

Excel does not calculate and display confidence and/or prediction intervals for regression analysis. However, **FAST⧹⧹ STAT** can produce confidence and prediction intervals for simple regression analysis utilizing its **Regression C.I. and P.I.** macro procedure. Figure 12.17 displays the dialog box for this macro. Note that this dialog box requires the location of the X variable values, the location of the standard error of the regression model and the level of confidence. Figure 12.18 displays the confidence intervals for various values of X for the average Y value and the prediction intervals for a single Y value for the airline cost problem. Note that the intervals flare out toward the ends, as the values of X depart from the average X value. Note also that the intervals for a single Y value are always wider than the intervals for the average Y value for any given value of X.

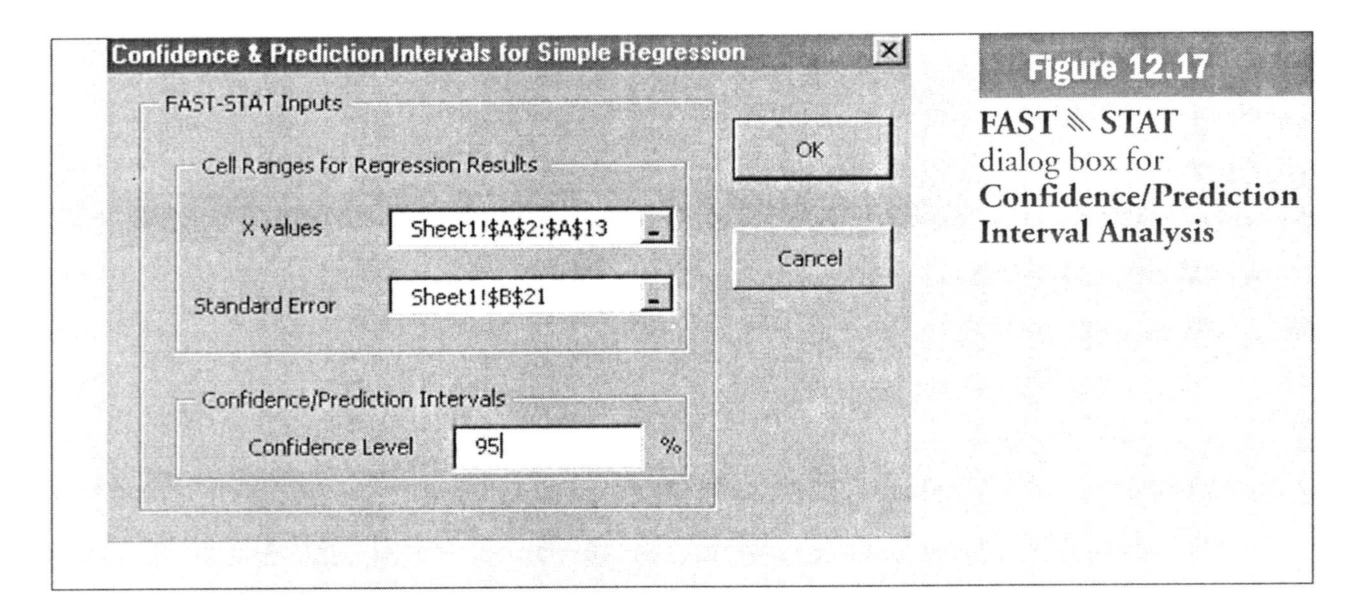

Figure 12.17

FAST⧹⧹ STAT dialog box for **Confidence/Prediction Interval Analysis**

An examination of the prediction interval formula to estimate Y for a given value of X explains why the intervals flare out.

$$\hat{Y} \pm t_{\alpha/2,n-2} S_e \sqrt{1 + \frac{1}{n} + \frac{(X_0 - \overline{X})^2}{\Sigma X^2 - \frac{(\Sigma X)^2}{n}}}$$

Figure 12.18 FAST STAT results for the **Confidence/Prediction Interval Analysis**

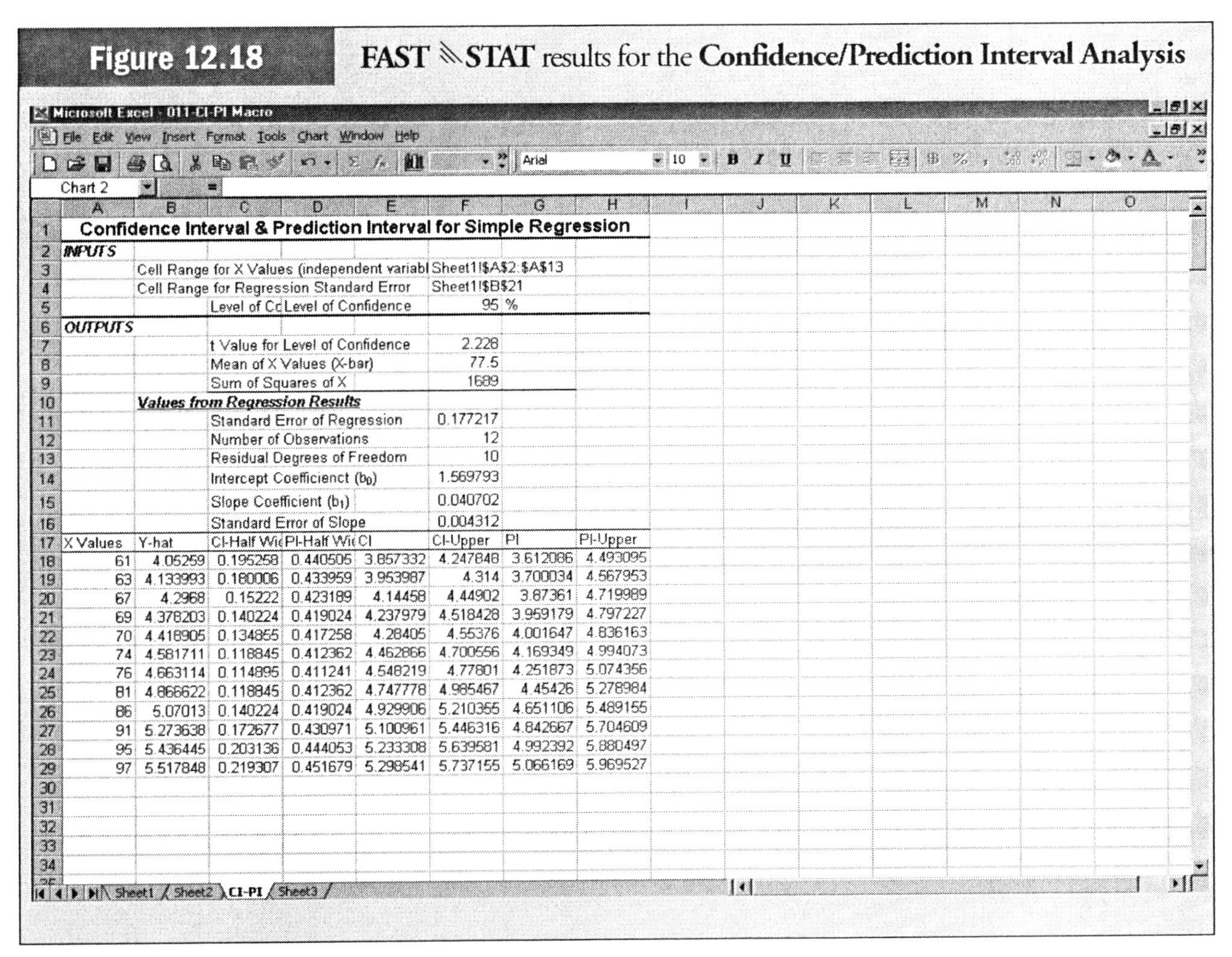

Microsoft Excel - 011-CI-PI Macro

Confidence Interval & Prediction Interval for Simple Regression

INPUTS

Cell Range for X Values (independent variabl	Sheet1!$A$2:$A$13
Cell Range for Regression Standard Error	Sheet1!$B$21
Level of Cc Level of Confidence	95 %

OUTPUTS

t Value for Level of Confidence	2.228
Mean of X Values (X-bar)	77.5
Sum of Squares of X	1689

Values from Regression Results

Standard Error of Regression	0.177217
Number of Observations	12
Residual Degrees of Freedom	10
Intercept Coefficienct (b_0)	1.569793
Slope Coefficient (b_1)	0.040702
Standard Error of Slope	0.004312

X Values	Y-hat	CI-Half Wi	PI-Half Wi	CI	CI-Upper	PI	PI-Upper
61	4.05259	0.195258	0.440505	3.857332	4.247848	3.612086	4.493095
63	4.133993	0.180006	0.433959	3.953987	4.314	3.700034	4.567953
67	4.2968	0.15222	0.423189	4.14458	4.44902	3.87361	4.719989
69	4.378203	0.140224	0.419024	4.237979	4.518428	3.959179	4.797227
70	4.418905	0.134855	0.417258	4.28405	4.55376	4.001647	4.836163
74	4.581711	0.118845	0.412362	4.462866	4.700556	4.169349	4.994073
76	4.663114	0.114895	0.411241	4.548219	4.77801	4.251873	5.074356
81	4.866622	0.118845	0.412362	4.747778	4.985467	4.45426	5.278984
86	5.07013	0.140224	0.419024	4.929906	5.210355	4.651106	5.489155
91	5.273638	0.172677	0.430971	5.100961	5.446316	4.842667	5.704609
95	5.436445	0.203136	0.444053	5.233308	5.639581	4.992392	5.880497
97	5.517848	0.219307	0.451679	5.298541	5.737155	5.066169	5.969527

Sheet1 / Sheet2 / CI-PI / Sheet3

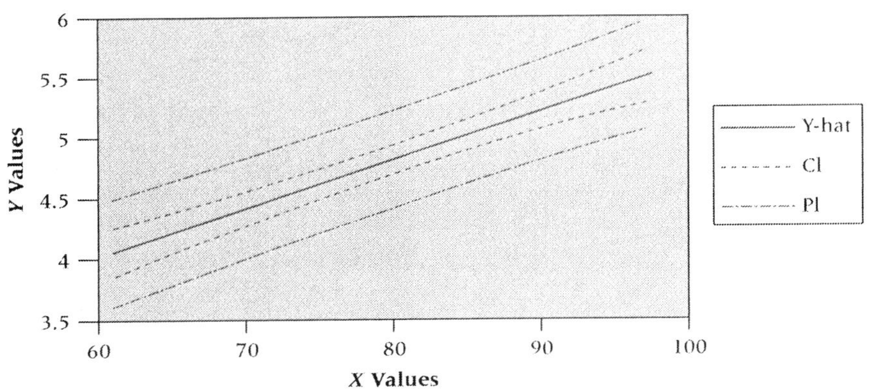

As we enter different values of X_0 from the regression analysis into the equation, the only thing that changes in the equation is $(X_0 - \bar{X})^2$. This expression increases as individual values of X_0 get farther from the mean, resulting in an increase in the width of the interval. The interval is narrower for values of X_0 nearer $\bar{X}$ and wider for values of X_0 farther from $\bar{X}$. A comparison of Equations 12.5 and 12.6 reveals them to be identical except that Equation 12.6 (to compute a prediction interval to estimate Y for a given value of X) contains a 1 under the radical sign and Equation 12.5 does not. This ensures that Equation 12.6 will yield wider intervals than Equation 12.5 for otherwise identical data.

For the optimum use of the **Regression C.I. and P.I.** macro procedure, the X variable values should be sorted either in ascending or descending order. These can either be sorted on the original data worksheet before the macro is initiated, or they can be sorted on the **CI-PI** worksheet after the macro has been run. This requirement stems from Excel's charting feature not from the FAST⧵STAT macro.

Two other suggestions should be considered for the best use of **Regression C.I. and P.I.** If the resulting graph is too small, you may need to adjust the scale for the two axes. To do so place the mouse pointer on the horizontal axis until the words *Value (X) Axis* appears below the pointer. Right click and then click on **Format Axis** from the resulting shortcut menu. Click on the **Scale** tab and change the value for the Minimum, for the Maximum or for both. Click on **OK.** The same process can be used for the vertical axis. If the resulting graph is still too small, you can repeat this process.

The second suggestion is appropriate if the macro is to be run a second time. If so, delete the graph from the first run. Otherwise it will be left on the worksheet and updated during the second run. This slows the computations considerably. You may not be aware the first graph is still on the worksheet since the second graph will cover it exactly. However, if you click and drag the second chart on top, you will see that the first chart has also been re-plotted. To delete the first chart before the second run, click just inside the chart and press the **Del** key. If you are to run a third time, delete the second plot and so on.

12.5 Problems

12.27 Construct a 95% confidence interval for the average value of Y for $X = 40$ in Problem 12.5 shown again below.

ADVERTISING	SALES
12.5	148
3.7	55
21.6	338
60.0	994
37.6	541
6.1	89
16.8	126
41.2	379

12.28 Construct a 90% prediction interval for the single value of Y for 200,000 business starts for Problem 12.7 shown again below. Construct a 90% prediction interval for the single value of Y for 175,000 business starts for Problem 12.7. Compare the results. Which prediction interval is greater? Why do you think this is so?

STARTS	FAILURES
233,710	57,097
199,091	50,361
181,645	60,747
158,930	88,140
155,672	97,069

continued

12.28 *continued*

164,086	86,133
166,154	71,558
188,387	71,128
168,158	71,931
170,475	83,384

12.29 Using FAST\STAT, construct the confidence interval and prediction interval bands for Problem 12.8 shown below. Discuss any "flaring out" that occurs; and if it does occur, explain why. Compare the confidence interval bands to the prediction interval bands. Which is wider and why?

FARMS	SIZE
5.65	213
4.65	258
3.96	297
3.36	340
2.95	374
2.52	420
2.44	426
2.29	441
2.15	460
2.07	469

12.30 Construct a 99% confidence interval for $X = 100$ in Problem 12.9 shown below. Construct a 99% prediction interval for $X = 100$ in Problem 12.9. Explain the difference between the two intervals and why the difference exists. Use FAST\STAT to construct a graph displaying both the confidence interval bands and the prediction interval bands for Problem 12.9. Comment on the graph.

PRODUCTION	NEW ORDERS
99.9	2.74
97.9	2.87
98.9	2.93
87.9	2.87
92.9	2.98
97.9	3.09
100.6	3.36
104.9	3.61
105.3	3.75
108.6	3.95

12.6 Measures of Association

Measures of association are numerical values that yield information about the relatedness of variables. The measures of association discussed in this chapter apply to only two variables. One measure of association is correlation.

Correlation

Whereas regression analysis involves developing a functional relationship between variables, **correlation** is *the process of determining a measure of the strength of relatedness of variables.* For example, do the stocks of two airlines rise and fall in any related manner? Logically, the prices of two stocks in the same industry should be related. For a sample of pairs of data, correlation analysis can yield a numerical value that represents the degree of relatedness of the two stock prices over time. Another example comes from the transportation

Correlation
A measure of the degree of relatedness of two or more variables.

industry. Is there a correlation between the price of transportation and the weight of the object being shipped? Is there a correlation between price and distance? How strong are the correlations? Pricing decisions can be based in part on shipment costs that are correlated with other variables. In economics and finance, how strong is the correlation between the producer price index and the unemployment rate? In retail sales, what variables are related to a particular store's sales? Is sales related to population density, number of competitors, size of the store, amount of advertising, or other variables?

Several measures of correlation are available, the selection of which depends mostly on the level of data being analyzed. Ideally, business analysts would like to solve for ρ, the population coefficient of correlation. However, because business analysts virtually always deal with sample data, this section introduces a widely used sample coefficient of correlation, r. This measure is applicable only if both variables being analyzed have at least an interval level of data.

Pearson product–moment correlation coefficient (r)
A correlation measure used to determine the degree of relatedness of two variables that are at least of interval level.

The term r is called the **Pearson product–moment correlation coefficient,** named after Karl Pearson (1857–1936), an English statistician who developed several coefficients of correlation along with other significant statistical concepts. The term r is *a measure of the linear correlation of two variables.* It is a number that ranges from −1 to 0 to +1, representing the strength of the relationship between the variables. An r value of +1 denotes a perfect positive relationship between two sets of numbers. An r value of −1 denotes a perfect negative correlation, which indicates an inverse relationship between two variables: as one variable gets larger, the other gets smaller. An r value of 0 means that there is no linear relationship between the two variables.

PEARSON PRODUCT–MOMENT CORRELATION COEFFICIENT

$$r = \frac{SS_{XY}}{\sqrt{(SS_{XX})(SS_{YY})}} = \frac{\Sigma(X-\bar{X})(Y-\bar{Y})}{\sqrt{\Sigma(X-\bar{X})^2\Sigma(Y-\bar{Y})^2}} = \frac{\Sigma XY - \frac{(\Sigma X)(\Sigma Y)}{n}}{\sqrt{\left[\Sigma X^2 - \frac{(\Sigma X)^2}{n}\right]\left[\Sigma Y^2 - \frac{(\Sigma Y)^2}{n}\right]}} \quad (12.7)$$

Figure 12.19 depicts five different degrees of correlation: (a) represents strong negative correlation, (b) represents moderate negative correlation, (c) represents moderate positive correlation, (d) represents strong positive correlation, and (e) contains no correlation.

What is the measure of correlation between the interest rate of federal funds and the commodities futures index? With data such as those shown in Table 12.6, which represent the values for interest rates of federal funds and commodities futures indexes for a sample of 12 days, a correlation coefficient, r, can be computed. Examination of Equation 12.7 reveals that the following values must be obtained to compute r: ΣX, ΣX^2, ΣY, ΣY^2, ΣXY, and n. In contrast to regression analysis, in correlation analysis it does not matter which variable is designated X and which is designated Y. For this example, the correlation coefficient is computed as shown in Table 12.7. The r value obtained represents a relatively strong positive relationship between interest rates and commodities futures index over this 12-day period.

Relationship between r and r^2

Is r, the coefficient of correlation, related to r^2, the coefficient of determination in linear regression? The answer is yes: r^2 equals $(r)^2$. That is, the coefficient of determination is the square of the coefficient of correlation. In the preceding economics example, the ob-

Figure 12.19 Five correlations

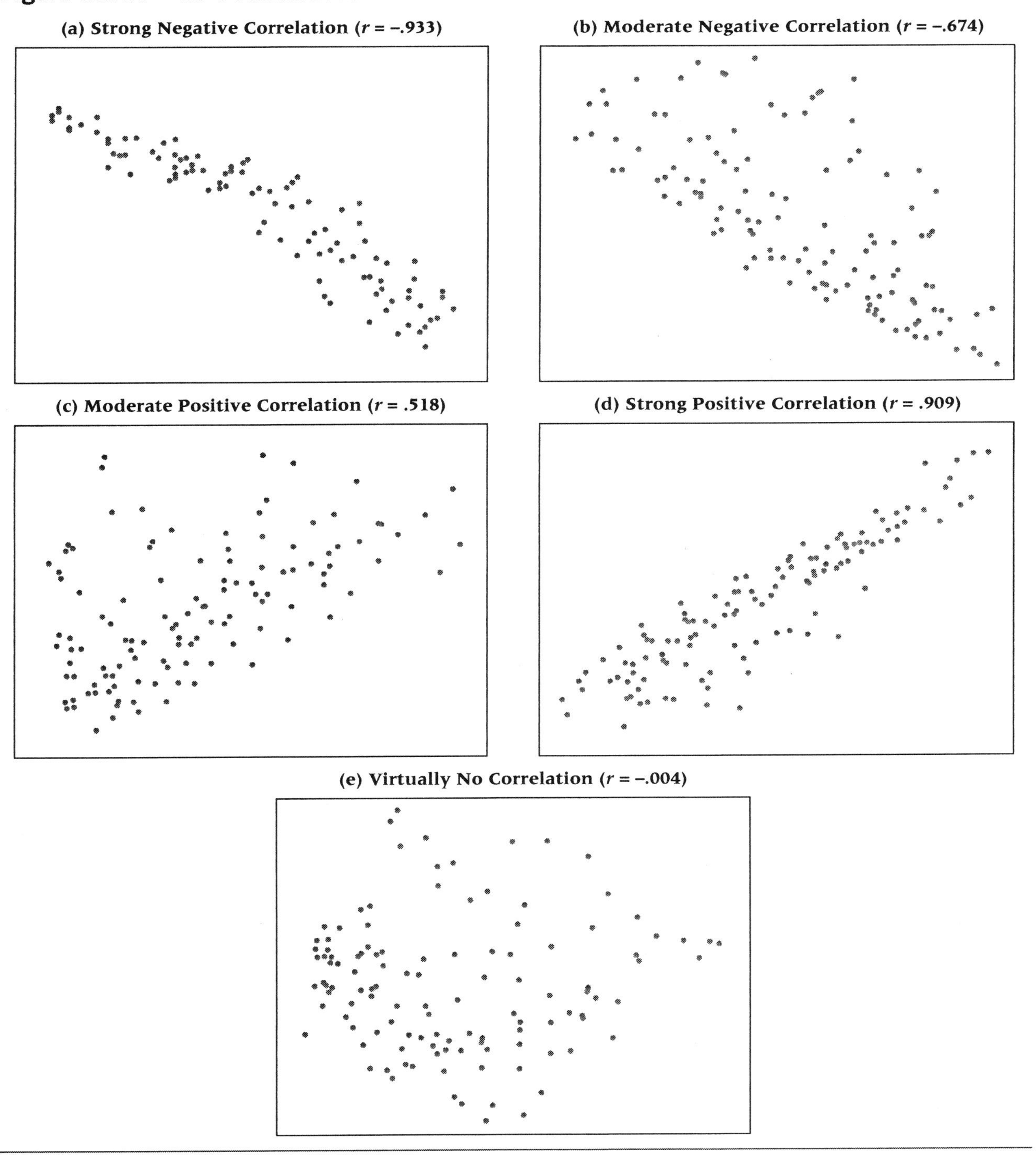

jective was to determine the correlation between interest rates and commodities futures indexes. If a regression model had been developed to predict commodities futures indexes by interest rates, r^2 would be $(r)^2 = (.815)^2 = .66$. In Demonstration Problem 12.1, a regression model was developed to predict FTEs by number of hospital beds. The r^2 value

TABLE 12.6
Data for the Economics Example

DAY	INTEREST RATE	FUTURES INDEX
1	7.43	221
2	7.48	222
3	8.00	226
4	7.75	225
5	7.60	224
6	7.63	223
7	7.68	223
8	7.67	226
9	7.59	226
10	8.07	235
11	8.03	233
12	8.00	241

TABLE 12.7
Computation of r for the Economics Example

DAY	INTEREST X	FUTURES INDEX Y	X^2	Y^2	XY
1	7.43	221	55.205	48,841	1,642.03
2	7.48	222	55.950	49,284	1,660.56
3	8.00	226	64.000	51,076	1,808.00
4	7.75	225	60.063	50,625	1,743.75
5	7.60	224	57.760	50,176	1,702.40
6	7.63	223	58.217	49,729	1,701.49
7	7.68	223	58.982	49,729	1,712.64
8	7.67	226	58.829	51,076	1,733.42
9	7.59	226	57.608	51,076	1,715.34
10	8.07	235	65.125	55,225	1,896.45
11	8.03	233	64.481	54,289	1,870.99
12	8.00	241	64.000	58,081	1,928.00
	$\Sigma X = 92.93$	$\Sigma Y = 2{,}725$	$\Sigma X^2 = 720.220$	$\Sigma Y^2 = 619{,}207$	$\Sigma XY = 21{,}115.07$

$$r = \frac{SS_{XY}}{\sqrt{SS_{XX} \cdot SS_{YY}}} = \frac{\Sigma XY - \frac{(\Sigma X)(\Sigma Y)}{n}}{\sqrt{\left[\Sigma X^2 - \frac{(\Sigma X)^2}{n}\right]\left[\Sigma Y^2 - \frac{(\Sigma Y)^2}{n}\right]}}$$

$$= \frac{(21{,}115.07) - \frac{(92.93)(2725)}{12}}{\sqrt{\left[(720.22) - \frac{(92.93)^2}{12}\right]\left[(619{,}207) - \frac{(2725)^2}{12}\right]}} = .815$$

for the model was .886. Taking the square root of this value yields $r = .941$, which is the correlation between the sample number of beds and FTEs. A word of caution here: Because r^2 is always positive, solving for r by taking $\sqrt{r^2}$ gives the correct magnitude of r but may give the wrong sign. The business analyst must examine the sign of the slope of the regression line to determine whether there is a positive or negative relationship between the variables and then assign the appropriate sign to the correlation value.

Analysis Using Excel

Excel has the capability of computing correlation coefficients. Figure 12.20 shows the Excel dialog box for correlation analysis. Note the *one* box for ***Input Range.*** Place in this box the location of all variables to be correlated. Excel's correlation feature allows for analyzing two or more variables and producing a correlation *matrix* containing multiple correlation coefficients when there are more than two variables.

The Excel output from **Correlation** is in matrix form. Examine Figure 12.21 and find the correlation between interest rates and futures indexes computed in the previous example ($r = .815$).

Figure 12.22 is a correlation matrix produced by Excel for seven variables from the financial database (on the CD-ROM). Observe that the highest correlation ($r = .647$) is between Average Yield and Dividends per Share. The lowest correlation is between Total Revenues and Return on Equity ($r = -.005$). The 1's on the diagonal of the matrix represent the correlation of each variable with itself, which of course is 1.00. The upper right portion (triangle) of the matrix is blank because r is symmetric with X and Y. That is, the correlation of return on equity and gross revenues is the same as the correlation of gross revenues and return on equity.

Figure 12.20 Excel's dialog box for **Correlation**

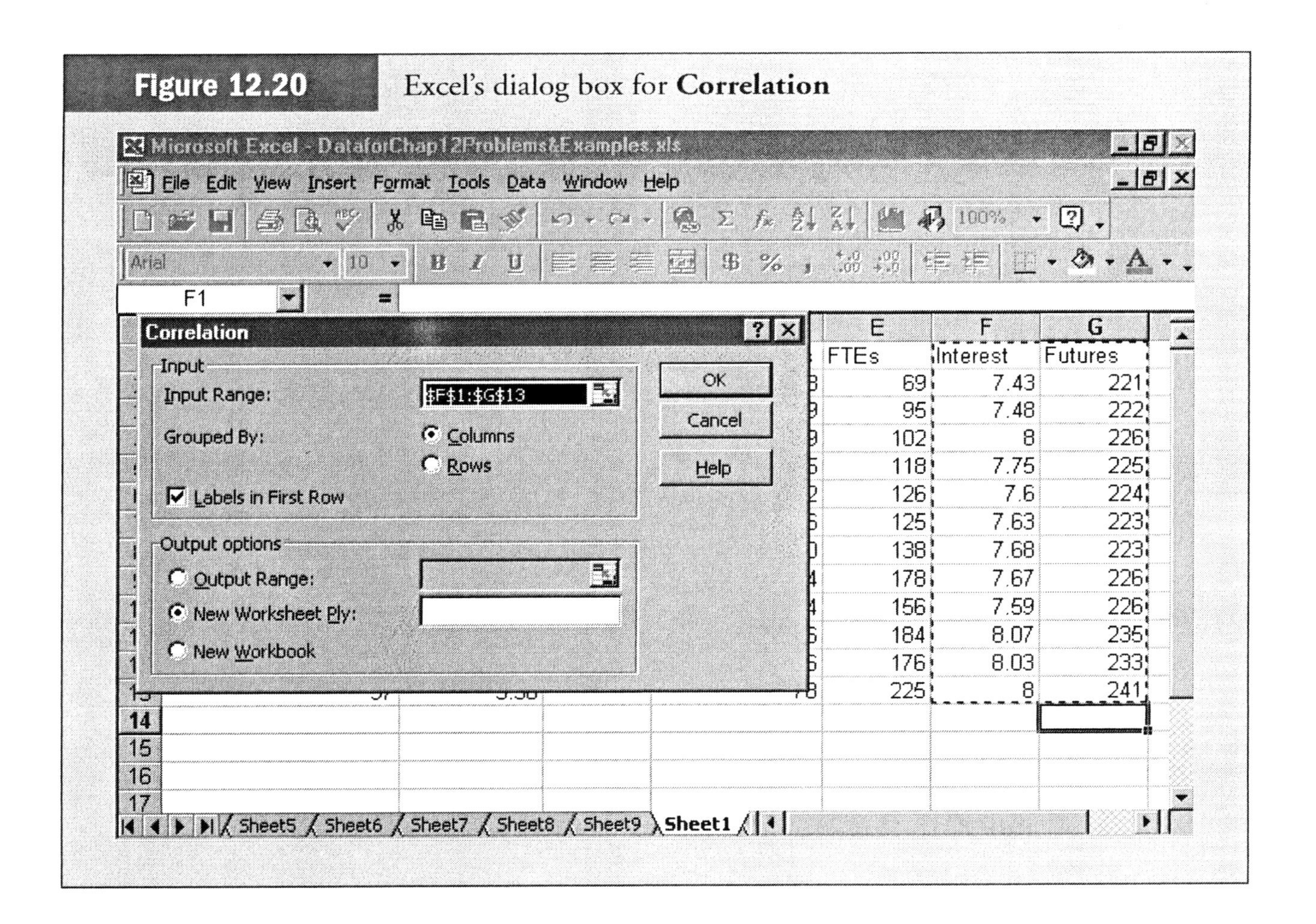

Figure 12.21 Excel computed correlation between interest and futures index

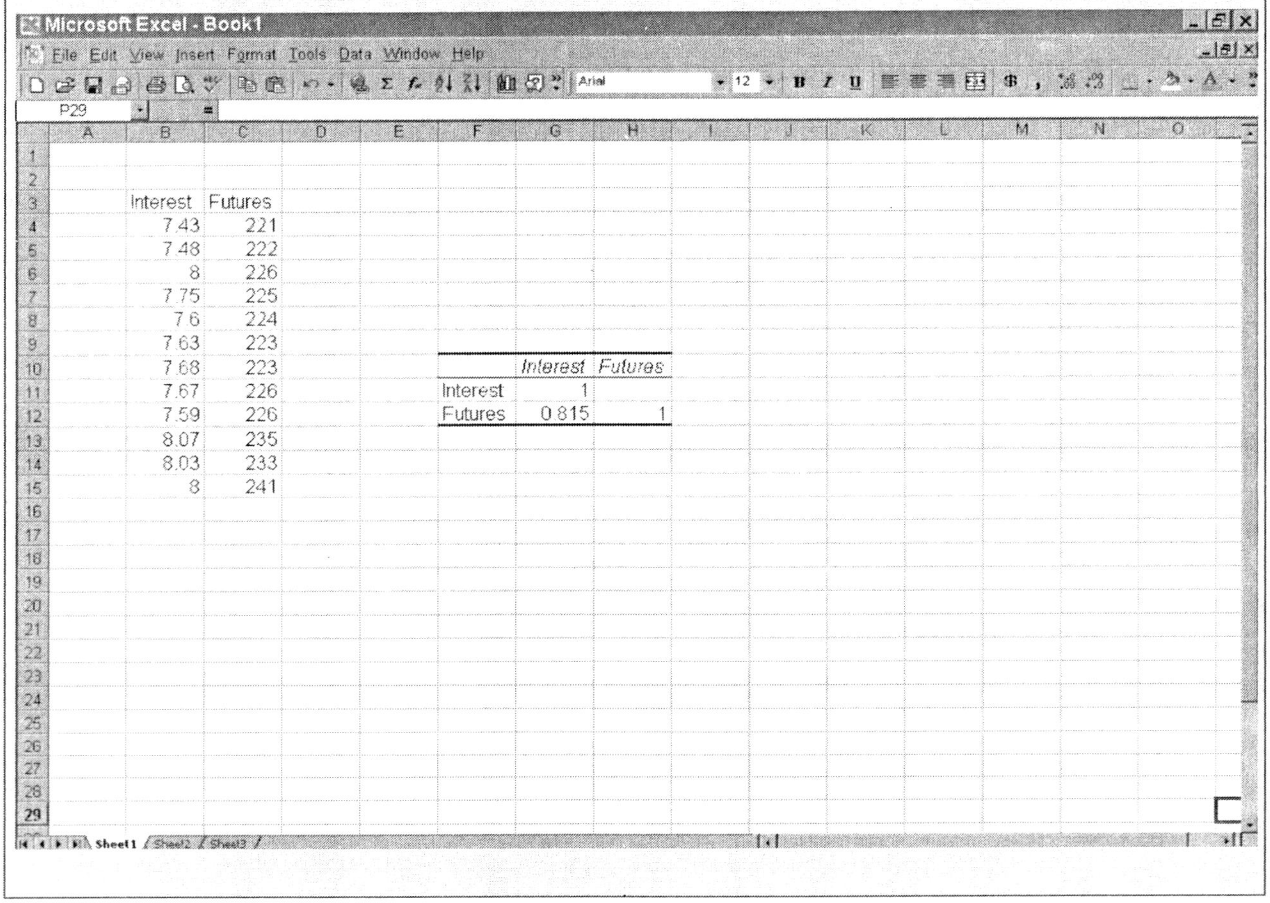
Microsoft Excel - Book1
File Edit View Insert Format Tools Data Window Help
Arial
12
P29
Interest Futures
7.43 221
7.48 222
8 226
7.75 225
7.6 224
7.63 223
7.68 223
7.67 226
7.59 226
8.07 235
8.03 233
8 241
Interest Futures
Interest 1
Futures 0.815 1
Sheet1 Sheet2 Sheet3

Figure 12.22 Excel correlation matrix for the financial database

	TOTAL REVENUES	TOTAL ASSETS	RETURN ON EQUITY	EARNINGS PER SHARE	AVERAGE YIELD	DIVIDENDS PER SHARE	AVERAGE P/E RATIO
Total Revenues	1						
Total Assets	.389	1					
Return on Equity	–.005	–.053	1				
Earnings per Share	.306	.168	.161	1			
Average Yield	–.034	–.105	–.144	–.077	1		
Dividends per Share	.286	.033	–.102	.435	.647	1	
Average P/E Ratio	–.039	.012	–.130	–.294	–.057	–.009	1

12.6
Problems

12.31 Determine the value of the coefficient of correlation, r, for the following data.

X	4	6	7	11	14	17	21
Y	18	12	13	8	7	7	4

12.32 Determine the value of r for the following data.

X	2	6	8	15	19	20	23
Y	5	6	13	16	22	20	21

12.33 Determine the value of r for the following data.

X	158	296	87	110	436
Y	349	510	301	322	550

12.34 In an effort to determine whether there is any correlation between the price of stocks of airlines, an analyst sampled 6 days of activity of the stock market. Using the following prices of Delta stock and Southwest Air stock, compute the coefficient of correlation. Stock prices have been rounded off to the nearest tenth for ease of computation.

DELTA	SOUTHWEST
47.6	15.1
46.3	15.4
50.6	15.9
52.6	15.6
52.4	16.4
52.7	18.1

12.35 During recent years the Dow Jones industrial average (DJIA) has been quite volatile, and in the late 1990s it rose dramatically. Is the DJIA correlated with Treasury Bill rates? Shown here are DJIA for 9 years and the rates of 6-month Treasury Bills for those corresponding years. Compute r for these data. How strong is the correlation? If an analyst wanted to develop a regression model to predict the DJIA by the Treasury Bill rates, how strong would be the model's prediction? Compute r^2 for this model.

DJIA	TREASURY BILL RATE
2200	8.12
2700	7.51
2900	5.42
3200	3.45
3700	3.02
4500	5.51
5600	5.02
7000	5.07

12.36 The following data are the claims (in $ millions) for Blue Cross & Blue Shield benefits for nine states, along with the surplus (in $ millions) that the company had in assets in those states.

STATE	CLAIMS	SURPLUS
Alabama	$1425	$277
Colorado	273	100
Florida	915	120
Illinois	1687	259
Maine	234	40
Montana	142	25
North Dakota	259	57
Oklahoma	258	31
Texas	894	141

Use the data to compute a correlation coefficient, r, to determine the correlation between claims and surplus.

12.37 The National Safety Council released the following data on the incidence rates for fatal or lost-work-time injuries per 100 employees for several industries in three recent years.

INDUSTRY	YEAR 1	YEAR 2	YEAR 3
Textile	.46	.48	.69
Chemical	.52	.62	.63
Communication	.90	.72	.81
Machinery	1.50	1.74	2.10
Services	2.89	2.03	2.46
Nonferrous metals	1.80	1.92	2.00
Food	3.29	3.18	3.17
Government	5.73	4.43	4.00

Compute r for each pair of years and determine which years are most highly correlated.

Summary

Regression is a procedure that produces a mathematical model (function) that can be used to predict one variable by other variables. Correlation is a measure of the relatedness of variables. Simple regression and correlation are bivariate in that the analysis is of two variables.

Simple regression analysis produces a model in which a Y variable, referred to as the dependent variable, is predicted by an X variable, referred to as the independent variable. The resulting regression model is linear. The general form of the equation of the simple regression line is the slope-intercept equation of a line. The equation of the simple regression model consists of a slope of the line as a coefficient of X and a Y intercept value as a constant.

After the equation of the line has been developed, several statistics are available that can be used to determine how well the line fits the data. Using the historical data values of X, predicted values of Y (denoted $\hat{Y}$) can be calculated by inserting values of X into the regression equation. The predicted values can then be compared to the actual values of Y to determine how well the regression equation fits the known data. The difference between a specific Y value and its associated predicted Y value is called the residual or error of prediction. Examination of the residuals can offer insight into the magnitude of the errors produced by a model. In addition, residual analysis can be used to help determine whether the assumptions underlying the regression analysis have been met. Specifically, graphs of the residuals can reveal (1) lack of linearity, (2) lack of homogeneity of error variance, and (3) independence of error terms. Geometrically, the residuals are the vertical distances from the Y values to the regression line. Because the equation that yields the regression line is derived in such a way that the line is in the geometric middle of the points, the sum of the residuals is zero.

A single value of error measurement called the standard error of the estimate, S_e, can be computed. It is the standard deviation of error of a model. The value of S_e can be used as a single guide to the magnitude of the error produced by the regression model.

Another widely used statistic for testing the strength of a regression model is r^2, or the coefficient of determination. The coefficient of determination is the proportion of total variance of the Y variable accounted for or predicted by X. It ranges from 0 to 1. The higher the r^2 is, the stronger the prediction by the model becomes.

Testing to determine whether the slope of the regression line is different from zero is another way to judge the fit of the regression model to the data. If the population slope of the regression line is not different from zero, the regression model is not adding significant predictability to the dependent variable. A t statistic is used to test the significance of the slope. The overall significance of the regression model can be tested by using an F statistic. In simple regression, because there is only one predictor, this test accomplishes the same thing as the t test of the slope and $F = t^2$.

One of the most prevalent uses of a regression model is to predict the values of Y for given values of X. Recognizing that the predicted value is often not the same as the actual value, a confidence interval has been developed to yield a range within which the mean Y value for a given X should be. A prediction interval for a single Y value for a given X value also is given. This second interval is wider because it allows for the wide diversity of individual values, whereas the confidence interval for the mean Y value reflects only the range of average Y values for a given X.

Bivariate correlation can be accomplished with several different measures. In this chapter, only one coefficient of correlation is presented: the Pearson product–moment coefficient of correlation, r. This value ranges from -1 to 0 to $+1$. An r value of $+1$ is perfect positive correlation, and an r value of -1 is a perfect negative correlation. Negative correlation means that as one variable increases in value, the other variable tends to decrease. For r values near zero, there is little or no correlation.

Key Terms

coefficient of determination (r^2)
correlation
dependent variable
deterministic model
heteroscedasticity
homoscedasticity
independent variable
least squares analysis
outliers
Pearson product–moment correlation coefficient (r)
probabilistic model
regression
residual
residual plot
scatter plot
simple regression
standard error of the estimate (S_e)
sum of squares of error (SSE)

SUPPLEMENTARY PROBLEMS

12.38 Use the following data for parts (a) through (f).

X	5	7	3	16	12	9
Y	8	9	11	27	15	13

a. Determine the equation of the least squares regression line to predict Y by X.
b. Using the X values, solve for the predicted values of Y and the residuals.
c. Solve for S_e and r^2.
d. Test the slope of the regression line. Use $\alpha = .01$.
e. Based on the results obtained in parts (b) through (d) make a statement about the fit of the line.

12.39 Use the following data for parts (a) through (h).

X	53	47	41	50	58	62	45	60
Y	5	5	7	4	10	12	3	11

a. Determine the equation of the simple regression line to predict Y from X.
b. Using the X values, solve for the predicted values of Y and the residuals.
c. Solve for SSE.
d. Calculate the standard error of the estimate.
e. Determine the coefficient of determination.
f. Calculate the coefficient of correlation.
g. Test the slope of the regression line. Assume $\alpha = .05$. What do you conclude about the slope?
h. Comment on parts (d) through (f).

12.40 Solve for the value of r for the following data.

X	213	196	184	202	221	247
Y	76	65	62	68	71	75

If you were to develop a regression line to predict Y by X, what value would the coefficient of determination have?

12.41 Determine the equation of the least squares regression line to predict Y from the following data.

X	47	94	68	73	80	49	52	61
Y	14	40	34	31	36	19	20	21

a. Construct a 95% confidence interval to estimate the mean Y value for $X = 60$.
b. Construct a 95% prediction interval to estimate an individual Y value for $X = 70$.
c. Use FAST⋱STAT to produce a graph of the confidence interval and prediction interval bands.
d. Interpret the results obtained in parts (a)–(c).

12.42 Determine the Pearson product–moment correlation coefficient for the following data.

X	1	10	9	6	5	3	2
Y	8	4	4	5	7	7	9

12.43 A manager of a car dealership believes there is a relationship between the number of salespeople on duty and the number of cars sold. Use the sample data collected for five different weeks at the dealership to calculate r. Is there much of a relationship? Solve for r^2. Explain what r^2 means in this problem.

WEEK	NUMBER OF CARS SOLD	NUMBER OF SALESPEOPLE
1	79	6
2	64	6
3	49	4
4	23	2
5	52	3

12.44 Executives of a video rental chain want to predict the success of a potential new store. The company's business analyst begins by gathering information on number of rentals and average family income from several of the chain's present outlets.

RENTALS	AVERAGE FAMILY INCOME ($1000)
710	65
529	43
314	29
504	47
619	52
428	50
317	46
205	29
468	31
545	43
607	49
694	64

Use a computer to develop a regression model to predict the number of rentals per day by the average family income. By examining various statistics in the output, comment on the strength of the model.

12.45 It seems logical that restaurant chains with more units (restaurants) would have greater sales. This is mitigated, however, by several possibilities: some units may be more profitable than others, some units may be larger, some units may serve more meals, some units may serve more expensive meals, and so on. The data shown here was published by Technomic, Inc. Use these data to determine whether there is a correlation between a restaurant chain's sales and its number of units. How strong is the relationship?

CHAIN	SALES ($ BILLIONS)	NUMBER OF UNITS (1000)
McDonald's	17.1	12.4
Burger King	7.9	7.5
Taco Bell	4.8	6.8
Pizza Hut	4.7	8.7
Wendy's	4.6	4.6
KFC	4.0	5.1
Subway	2.9	11.2
Dairy Queen	2.7	5.1
Hardee's	2.7	2.9

12.46 According to the National Marine Fisheries Service, the current landings in millions of pounds of fish by U.S. fleets are almost double what they were in the 1970s. In other words, fishing has not faded as an industry. However, the growth of this industry has varied by region as shown in the following data. Some regions have remained relatively constant, the South Atlantic region has dropped in pounds caught, and the Pacific-Alaska region has grown more than threefold.

FISHERIES	1977	1997
New England	581	642
Mid-Atlantic	213	242
Chesapeake	668	729
South Atlantic	345	269
Gulf of Mexico	1476	1497
Pacific-Alaska	1776	6129

a. Compute the correlation coefficient between the 1977 and 1997 data. What does this tell, if anything, about the industry?
b. Develop a simple regression model to predict the 1997 landings by the 1977 landings. According to the model, if a region had 700 landings in 1977, what would the predicted number be for 1997? Construct a confidence interval for the average Y value for the 700

landings. Use the t statistic to test to determine whether the slope is significantly different from zero. Use $\alpha = .05$. Compute S_e and r^2 and use these along with the t test of the slope to comment on the strength of the regression model.

12.47 People in the aerospace industry believe the cost of a space project is a function of the weight of the major object being sent into space. Use the following data to develop a regression model to predict the cost of a space project by the weight of the space object. Determine r^2 and S_e.

WEIGHT (TONS)	COST (MILLIONS)
1.897	$ 53.6
3.019	184.9
0.453	6.4
0.988	23.5
1.058	33.4
2.100	110.4
2.387	104.6

12.48 The following data represent a breakdown of state banks and all savings organizations in the United States according to the Federal Reserve System.

YEAR	STATE BANKS	ALL SAVINGS
1940	1342	2330
1945	1864	2667
1950	1912	3054
1955	1847	3764
1960	1641	4423
1965	1405	4837
1970	1147	4694
1975	1046	4407
1980	997	4328
1985	1070	3626
1990	1009	2815
1995	1042	2030
1997	992	1779

a. Develop a regression model to predict the total number of state banks by the number of all savings organizations. Compute r^2, S_e, and test the slope of the regression model.

b. Determine the correlation between the number of state banks and the number of all savings organizations.

c. Based on (a) and (b) comment on the relationship between the number of state banks and the number of all savings organizations.

12.49 How strong is the correlation between the inflation rate and 30-year treasury yields? The following data published by Fuji Securities, Inc., are given as pairs of inflation rates and treasury yields for selected years over a 35-year period.

INFLATION RATE	30-YEAR TREASURY YIELD
1.57%	3.05%
2.23	3.93
2.17	4.68
4.53	6.57
7.25	8.27
9.25	12.01
5.00	10.27
4.62	8.45

Compute the Pearson product–moment correlation coefficient to determine the strength of the correlation between these two variables. Comment on the strength and direction of the correlation.

12.50 Is the amount of money spent by companies on advertising a function of the total sales of the company? Shown are sales income and advertising cost data for seven companies, published by *Advertising Age*.

COMPANY	ADVERTISING (MILLIONS)	SALES (BILLIONS)
Procter & Gamble	$1703.1	37.1
Philip Morris	1319.0	56.1
Ford Motor	973.1	153.6
PepsiCo	797.4	20.9
Time Warner	779.1	13.3
Johnson & Johnson	738.7	22.6
MCI	455.4	19.7

Use the data to develop a regression line to predict the amount of advertising by sales. Compute S_e and r^2. Assuming $\alpha = .05$, test the slope of the regression line. Comment on the strength of the regression model.

12.51 Can the consumption of water in a city be predicted by temperature? The following data represent a sample of a day's water consumption and the high temperature for that day.

WATER USE (MILLION GAL)	TEMPERATURE
219	103°
56	39
107	77
129	78
68	50
184	96
150	90
112	75

Develop a least squares regression line to predict the amount of water used in a day in a city by the high temperature for that day. What would be the predicted water usage for a temperature of 100°? Evaluate the regression model by calculating S_e, by calculating r^2, and by testing the slope. Let $\alpha = .01$.

ANALYZING THE DATABASES

1. Use the manufacturing database to correlate the Number of Employees with the Number of Production Workers. Is this a high correlation? What would you expect the correlation to be? Is there a strong correlation between Cost of Materials and Value Added by Manufacture? Why do you think it is this way?
2. Develop a regression model from the manufacturing database to predict New Capital Expenditures from Value Added by Manufacture. Discuss the model and its strength on the basis of indicators presented in this chapter. Does it seem logical that the dollars spent on New Capital Expenditure could be predicted by Value Added by Manufacture?
3. Using the hospital database, develop a regression model to predict the number of Personnel by the number of Births. Now develop a regression model to predict number of Personnel by number of Beds. Examine the regression output. Which model is stronger in predicting number of Personnel? Explain why, using techniques presented in this chapter. Use the second regression model to predict the number of Personnel in a hospital that has 110 beds. Construct a 95% confidence interval around this prediction for the average value of Y.
4. Produce a correlation matrix for the variables Beds, Admissions, Census, Outpatient Visits, Births, Total Expenditures, Payroll Expenditures, and Personnel for the hospital database. Which variables are most highly correlated? Which variables are least correlated?
5. Analyze all the variables except Type in the financial database by using a correlation matrix. The seven variables in this database are capable of producing 21 pairs of correlations. Which are most highly correlated? Select the variable that is most highly correlated with P/E ratio and use it as a predictor to develop a regression model to predict P/E ratio. How did the model do?
6. Use the stock market database to develop a regression model to predict the Utility Index by the Stock Volume. How well did the model perform? Did it perform as you expected? Why or why not? Construct a correlation matrix for the variables of this database (excluding Part of Month) so that you can explore the stock market. Did you discover any apparent relationships between variables?

CASE

DELTA WIRE USES TRAINING AS A WEAPON

The Delta Wire Corporation was founded in 1978 in Clarksdale, Mississippi. The company manufactures high-carbon specialty steel wire for global markets and at present employs around 100 people. For the past few years, sales have increased each year.

A few years ago, however, things did not look as bright for Delta Wire because it was caught in a potentially disastrous bind. With the dollar declining in value, foreign competition was becoming a growing threat to Delta's market position. In addition to the growing foreign competition, industry quality requirements were becoming increasingly tough each year.

Delta officials realized that some conditions, such as the value of the dollar, were beyond their control. However, one area that they could improve upon was employee education. The company worked with training programs developed by the state of Mississippi and a local community college to set up its own school. Delta employees were introduced to statistical process control and other quality assurance techniques. Delta reassured its customers that the company was working hard on improving quality and staying competitive. Customers were invited to sit in on the educational sessions. Because of this effort, Delta has been able to weather the storm and continues to sustain a leadership position in the highly competitive steel wire industry.

DISCUSSION

1. Delta Wire prides itself on its efforts in the area of employee education. Employee education can pay off in many ways. Discuss some of them. One payoff can be the

renewed interest and excitement generated toward the job and the company. Some people theorize that because of a more positive outlook and interest in implementing things learned, the more education received by a worker, the less likely he or she is to miss work days. Suppose the following data represent the number of days of sick leave taken by 20 workers last year along with the number of contact hours of employee education they each received in the past year. Use the techniques learned in this chapter to analyze the data. Include both regression and correlation techniques. Discuss the strength of the relationship and any models that are developed.

EMPLOYEE	HOURS OF EDUCATION	SICK DAYS	EMPLOYEE	HOURS OF EDUCATION	SICK DAYS
1	24	5	11	8	8
2	16	4	12	60	1
3	48	0	13	0	9
4	120	1	14	28	3
5	36	5	15	15	8
6	10	7	16	88	2
7	65	0	17	120	1
8	36	3	18	15	8
9	0	12	19	48	0
10	12	8	20	5	10

2. Many companies have found that the implementation of total quality management has eventually resulted in improved sales. Companies that have failed to adopt quality efforts have lost market share in many cases or have gone out of business. One measure of the effect of a company's quality improvement efforts is customer satisfaction. Suppose Delta Wire hired a research firm to measure customer satisfaction each year. The research firm developed a customer satisfaction scale in which totally satisfied customers can award a score as high as 50 and totally unsatisfied customers can award scores as low as 0. The scores are measured across many different industrial customers and averaged for a yearly mean customer score. Do sales increase with increases in customer satisfaction scores? To study this notion, suppose the average customer satisfaction score each year for Delta Wire is paired with the company's total sales of that year for the last 15 years, and a regression analysis is run on the data. Assume the following Excel output is the result. Suppose you were asked by Delta Wire to analyze the data and summarize the results. What would you find?

Excel Output

SUMMARY OUTPUT

Regression Statistics	
Multiple R	0.949
R Square	0.901
Adjusted R Square	0.894
Standard Error	0.411
Observations	15

ANOVA

	df	*SS*	*MS*	*F*	*Significance F*
Regression	1	20.098	20.098	118.80	0.0000
Residual	13	2.199	0.169		
Total	14	22.297			

	Coefficients	Standard Error	t Stat	P-value
Intercept	1.733	0.436	3.97	0.0016
CustSat	0.162	0.015	10.90	0.0000

3. One of Delta Wire's main concerns over the years has been the value of the U.S. dollar. Foreign exchange rates affect Delta's ability to sell competitively in international markets, and they also help determine the extent to which foreign firms can compete against Delta in the United States. Below is an Excel correlation matrix constructed by using the foreign exchange rates (against the U.S. dollar) for selected years from 1970 through 1997 for five countries: France, Germany, Japan, South Korea, and the United Kingdom. Over this time frame, the Japanese yen has mostly increased in strength in comparison with the dollar (fewer yen to equal a dollar). Examine the correlation matrix and discuss the exchange rates of these countries in relation to each other. If Delta were selling products in all five of these countries, would an unfavorable exchange rate in one country necessarily mean an unfavorable exchange rate in all international markets? Which countries seem to have related exchange rates? What might this mean?

	France	Germany	Japan	S.Korea	U.K.
France	1				
Germany	0.341	1			
Japan	0.005	0.906	1		
S. Korea	0.403	-0.627	-0.792	1	
U.K.	-0.612	0.426	0.710	-0.8699	1

ADAPTED FROM: "Delta Wire Corporation," *Strengthening America's Competitiveness: Resource Management Insights for Small Business Success*. Published by Warner Books on behalf of Connecticut Mutual Life Insurance Company and the U.S. Chamber of Commerce in association with The Blue Chip Enterprise Initiative, 1991; International Monetary Fund.

13

Multiple Regression Analysis

Learning Objectives

This chapter presents the potential of multiple regression analysis as a tool in business decision making and its applications, thereby enabling you to:

1. Develop a multiple regression model.
2. Understand and apply techniques that can be used to determine how well a regression model fits data.
3. Analyze and interpret nonlinear variables in multiple regression analysis.
4. Understand the role of qualitative variables and how to use them in multiple regression analysis.
5. Learn how to build and evaluate multiple regression models.

Dependent variable
In analysis of variance, the measurement that is being analyzed; the response to the different levels of the independent variables. In regression analysis, the variable that is being predicted.

Independent variable
In an analysis of variance, the treatment or factor being analyzed. In regression analysis, the predictor variable.

Simple regression analysis is bivariate linear regression in which one **dependent variable,** Y, is predicted by one **independent variable,** X. Examples of simple regression applications include models to predict retail sales by population density, Dow Jones averages by prime interest rates, crude oil production by energy consumption, and CEO compensation by quarterly sales. However, there are usually other independent variables that, taken in conjunction with these variables, can make the regression model a better fit in predicting the dependent variable. For example, sales could be predicted by the size of store and number of competitors in addition to population density. A model to predict the Dow Jones average of 30 industrials could include, in addition to the prime interest rate, such predictors as yesterday's volume, the bond interest rate, and the producer price index. A model to predict CEO compensation could be developed by using variables such as company earnings per share, age of CEO, and size of company in addition to quarterly sales. A model could perhaps be developed to predict the cost of outsourcing by such variables as unit price, export taxes, cost of money, damage in transit, and other factors. In each of these examples, there is only one dependent variable, Y, as there is with simple regression analysis. However, there are multiple independent variables, X (predictors). *Regression analysis with two or more independent variables or with at least one nonlinear predictor* is called **multiple regression** analysis.

13.1 The Multiple Regression Model

Multiple regression analysis is similar in principle to simple regression analysis. However, it is more complex conceptually and computationally. Recall from Chapter 12 that the equation of the probabilistic simple regression model is

$$Y = \beta_0 + \beta_1 X + \epsilon$$

Multiple regression
Regression analysis with one dependent variable and two or more independent variables or at least one nonlinear independent variable.

where:
Y = the value of the dependent variable,
β_0 = the population Y intercept,
β_1 = the population slope, and
ϵ = the error of prediction.

Extending this notion to multiple regression gives the general equation for the probabilistic multiple regression model.

$$Y = \beta_0 + \beta_1 X_1 + \beta_2 X_2 + \beta_3 X_3 + \ldots + \beta_k X_k + \epsilon$$

Response variable
The dependent variable in a multiple regression model; the variable that the business analyst is trying to predict.

Partial regression coefficient
The coefficient of an independent variable in a multiple regression model that represents the increase that will occur in the value of the dependent variable from a 1-unit increase in the independent variable if all other variables are held constant.

where:
Y = the value of the dependent variable
β_0 = the regression constant
β_1 = the partial regression coefficient for independent variable 1
β_2 = the partial regression coefficient for independent variable 2
β_3 = the partial regression coefficient for independent variable 3
β_k = the partial regression coefficient for independent variable k
k = the number of independent variables

In multiple regression analysis, the dependent variable, Y, is sometimes referred to as the **response variable.** The **partial regression coefficient** of an independent variable, β_i, *represents the increase that will occur in the value of Y from a 1-unit increase in the independent variable if all other variables are held constant.* The "full" (versus partial) regression coefficient of an independent variable is a coefficient obtained from the bivariate model (simple regression) in which the independent variable is the sole predictor of Y, as was the case with the slope in Chapter 12. The partial regression coefficients occur because more than one predictor is included in a model. The partial regression coefficients are analogous to β_1, the slope of the simple regression model in Chapter 12.

In actuality, the partial regression coefficients and the regression constant of a multiple regression model are population values and are unknown. These values are estimated by using sample information. Shown here is the form of the equation for estimating Y with sample information.

$$\hat{Y} = b_0 + b_1X_1 + b_2X_2 + b_3X_3 + \cdots + b_kX_k$$

where:

$\hat{Y}$ = the predicted value of Y
b_0 = the estimate of the regression constant
b_1 = the estimate of regression coefficient 1
b_2 = the estimate of regression coefficient 2
b_3 = the estimate of regression coefficient 3
b_k = the estimate of regression coefficient k
k = the number of independent variables

Multiple Regression Model with Two Independent Variables (First-Order)

The simplest multiple regression model is one constructed with two independent variables, where the highest power of either variable is 1 (first-order regression model). The regression model is

$$Y = \beta_0 + \beta_1X_1 + \beta_2X_2 + \epsilon.$$

The constant and coefficients are estimated from sample information, resulting in the following model.

$$\hat{Y} = b_0 + b_1X_1 + b_2X_2$$

Figure 13.1 is a three-dimensional graph of a series of points (X_1, X_2, Y) representing values from three variables used in a multiple regression model to predict the sales price of a house by the number of square feet in the house and the age of the house. Simple regression models yield a line that is fit through data points in the XY plane. In multiple regression analysis, the resulting model produces a **response surface.** In the multiple regression model shown here with two independent first-order variables, the response surface is a **response plane.** The response plane for such a model is fit in a three-dimensional space (X_1, X_2, Y).

Response surface
The surface defined by a multiple regression model.

Response plane
A plane fit in a three-dimensional space and that represents the response surface defined by a multiple regression model with two independent first-order variables.

If such a response plane is fit into the points shown in Figure 13.1, the result is the graph in Figure 13.2. Notice that most of the points are not on the plane. As in simple regression, there is usually error in the fit of the model in multiple regression. The distances shown in the graph from the points to the response plane are the errors of fit, or residuals ($Y - \hat{Y}$). Multiple regression models with three or more independent variables involve more than three dimensions and are difficult to depict geometrically.

Observe in Figure 13.2 that the regression model attempts to fit a plane into the three-dimensional plot of points. Notice that the plane intercepts the Y axis. Figure 13.2 depicts some values of Y for various values of X_1 and X_2. The error of the response plane (ϵ) in predicting or determining the Y values is the distance from the points to the plane.

Figure 13.1

Points in a sample space

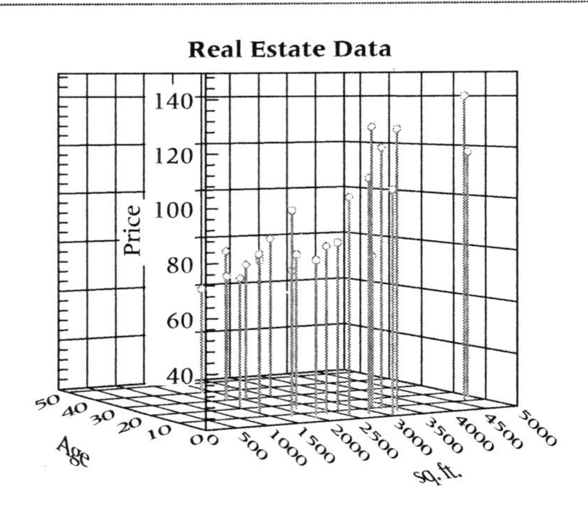

Figure 13.2

Response plane for a first-order two-predictor multiple regression model

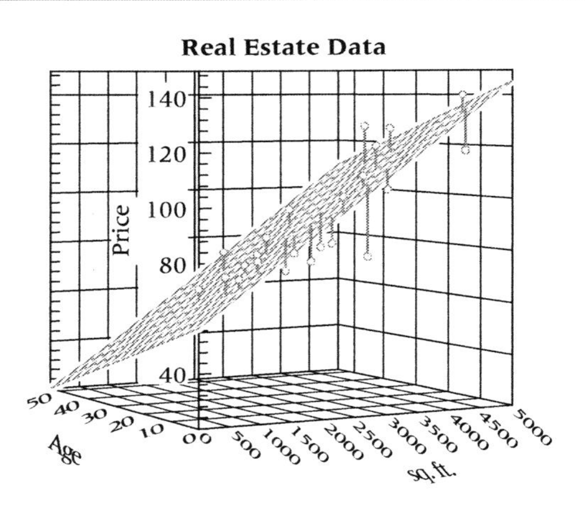

Determining the Multiple Regression Equation

The simple regression equations for determining the sample slope and intercept given in Chapter 12 are the result of using methods of calculus to minimize the sum of squares of error for the regression model. The procedure for developing these equations involves solving two simultaneous equations with two unknowns, b_0 and b_1. Finding the sample slope and intercept from these formulas requires the values of ΣX, ΣY, ΣXY, and ΣX^2.

The procedure for determining formulas to solve for multiple regression coefficients is similar. The formulas are established to *meet an objective of minimizing the sum of squares of error for the model.* Hence, the regression analysis shown here is referred to as **least squares analysis.** Methods of calculus are applied, resulting in $k + 1$ equations with $k + 1$ unknowns (b_0 and k values of b_i) for multiple regression analyses with k independent variables. Thus, a regression model with six independent variables will generate seven simultaneous equations with seven unknowns (b_0, b_1, b_2, b_3, b_4, b_5, b_6).

Least squares analysis The process by which a regression model is developed based on calculus techniques that attempt to produce a minimum sum of the squared error values.

For multiple regression models with two independent variables, the result is three simultaneous equations with three unknowns (b_0, b_1, and b_2).

$$b_0 n + b_1 \Sigma X_1 + b_2 \Sigma X_2 = \Sigma Y$$

$$b_0 \Sigma X_1 + b_1 \Sigma X_1^2 + b_2 \Sigma X_1 X_2 = \Sigma X_1 Y$$

$$b_0 \Sigma X_2 + b_1 \Sigma X_1 X_2 + b_2 \Sigma X_2^2 = \Sigma X_2 Y$$

The process of solving these equations by hand is tedious and time-consuming. Solving for the regression coefficients and regression constant in a multiple regression model with two independent variables requires ΣX_1, ΣX_2, ΣY, ΣX_1^2, ΣX_2^2, $\Sigma X_1 X_2$, $\Sigma X_1 Y$, and $\Sigma X_2 Y$. In actuality, virtually all business analysts use computer statistical software packages to solve for the regression coefficients, the regression constant, and other pertinent information. In this chapter, we will discuss computer output and assume little or no hand calculation. The emphasis will be on the interpretation of the computer output.

A Multiple Regression Model

A real estate study was conducted in a small Louisiana city to determine what variables, if any, are related to the market price of a home. Several variables were explored, including the number of bedrooms, the number of bathrooms, the age of the house, the number of square feet of living space, the total number of square feet of space, and how many garages the house had. Suppose the business analyst wants to develop a regression model to predict the market price of a home by two variables, "total number of square feet in the house" and "the age of the house." Listed in Table 13.1 are the data for these three variables.

Using Excel to perform the multiple regression analysis on the real estate data results in the output given in Figure 13.3.

One of the first items that a business analyst wants to retrieve from regression output is the equation of the regression model. In Excel, the regression equation is found in the column labeled "Coefficients." From Figure 13.3, the coefficient for the number of square feet variable, X_1, is 0.0177, the coefficient for the age variable, X_2, is −0.6663, and the

TABLE 13.1
Real Estate Data

MARKET PRICE ($1000) Y	TOTAL NUMBER OF SQUARE FEET X_1	AGE OF HOUSE (YEARS) X_2
63.0	1605	35
65.1	2489	45
69.9	1553	20
76.8	2404	32
73.9	1884	25
77.9	1558	14
74.9	1748	8
78.0	3105	10
79.0	1682	28
83.4	2470	30
79.5	1820	2
83.9	2143	6
79.7	2121	14
84.5	2485	9
96.0	2300	19
109.5	2714	4
102.5	2463	5
121.0	3076	7
104.9	3048	3
128.0	3267	6
129.0	3069	10
117.9	4765	11
140.0	4540	8

Figure 13.3 Excel output of regression for the real estate example

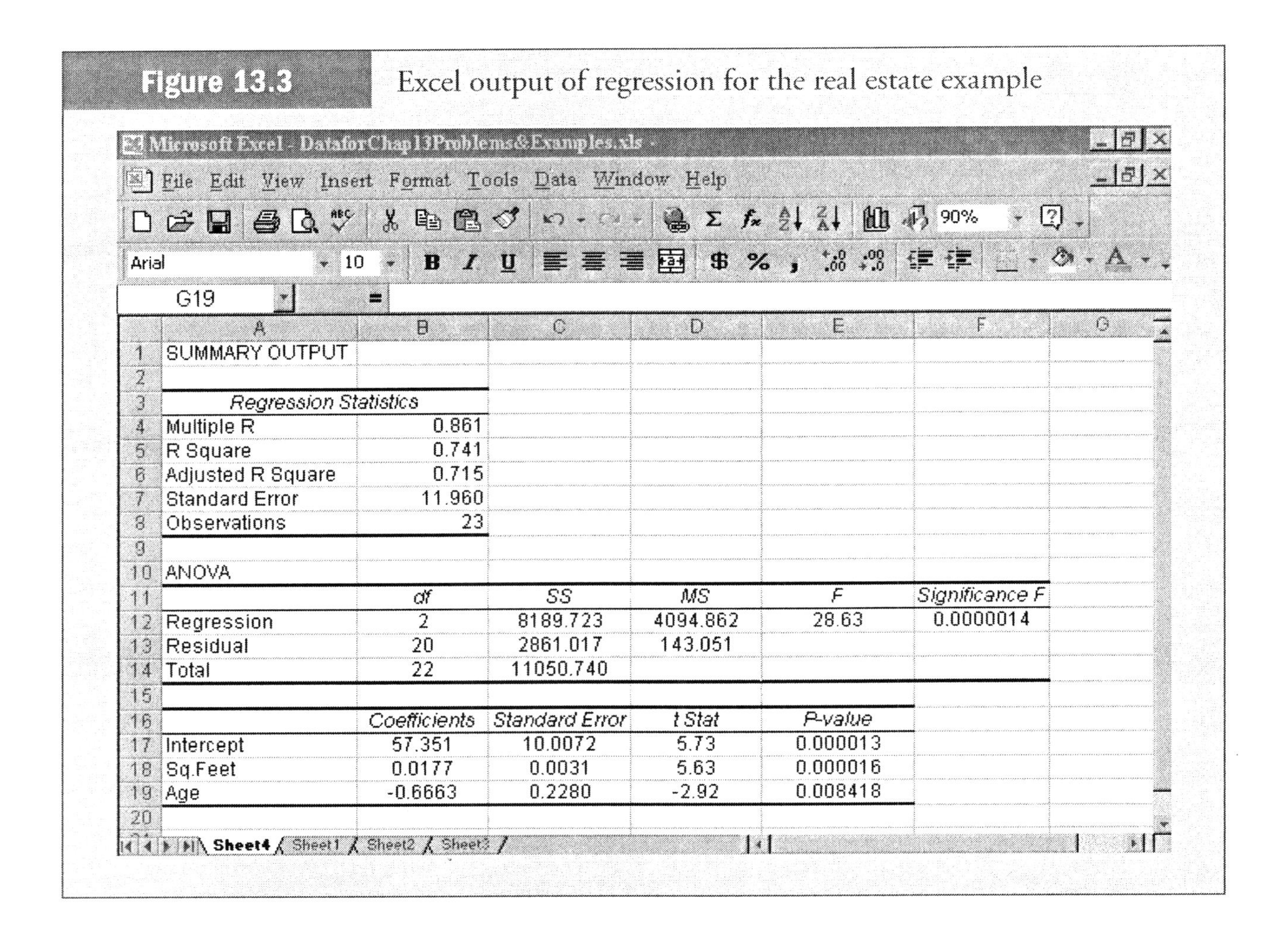

SUMMARY OUTPUT

Regression Statistics	
Multiple R	0.861
R Square	0.741
Adjusted R Square	0.715
Standard Error	11.960
Observations	23

ANOVA

	df	SS	MS	F	Significance F
Regression	2	8189.723	4094.862	28.63	0.0000014
Residual	20	2861.017	143.051		
Total	22	11050.740			

	Coefficients	Standard Error	t Stat	P-value
Intercept	57.351	10.0072	5.73	0.000013
Sq.Feet	0.0177	0.0031	5.63	0.000016
Age	-0.6663	0.2280	-2.92	0.008418

Y intercept is 57.351. From this, the equation of the regression model for the real estate data can be determined:

$$\hat{Y} = 57.351 + .0177\,X_1 - .6663\,X_2$$

The regression constant, 57.351, is the Y intercept. The Y intercept is the value of $\hat{Y}$ if both X_1 (number of square feet) and X_2 (age) are zero. In this example, a practical understanding of the Y intercept is meaningless. It is nonsense to say that if a house contains no square feet ($X_1 = 0$) and is new ($X_2 = 0$) it would cost \$57,351. In addition, the values of $X_1 = 0$ and $X_2 = 0$ are out of the range of values for X_1, X_2 used to construct the model. Note in Figure 13.2, however, that the response plane crosses the Y (price) axis at 57.351.

The coefficient of X_1 (total number of square feet in the house) is .0177. This means that a 1-unit increase in square footage would result in a predicted increase of .0177 (\$1000) = \$17.70 in the price of the home if age were held constant. All other variables being held constant, the addition of 1 square foot of space in the house results in a predicted increase of \$17.70 in the price of the home.

The coefficient of X_2 (age) is −.6663. The negative sign on the coefficient denotes an inverse relationship between the age of a house and the price of the house: the older the house, the lower the price. In this case, if the total number of square feet in the house is kept constant, a 1-unit increase in the age of the house (1 year) will result in $-.6663(\$1000) = -666.30$, a predicted \$666.30 drop in the price.

In examining the regression coefficients, it is important to remember that the independent variables are often measured in different units. It is usually not wise to compare the regression coefficients of predictors in a multiple regression model and decide that the variable with the largest regression coefficient is the best predictor. In this example, the two variables are in different units, square feet and years. Just because X_2 has the larger coefficient (.6663) does not necessarily make X_2 the strongest predictor of Y.

This regression model can be used to predict the price of a house in this small Louisiana city. If the house has 2500 square feet total and is 12 years old, $X_1 = 2500$ and $X_2 = 12$. Substituting these values into the regression model yields

$$\begin{aligned}\hat{Y} &= 57.351 + .0177X_1 - .6663\\ &= 57.351 + .0177(2500) - .6663(12)\\ &= 93.605\end{aligned}$$

The predicted price of the house is \$93,605. Figure 13.2 is a graph of these data with the response plane and the residual distances.

DEMONSTRATION PROBLEM 13.1*

Much of the freight cargo in the world is transported over roads. The volume of freight cargo shipped over roads varies from country to country depending on the size of the country, the amount of commerce, the wealth of the country, and other factors. Shown here are seven of the top 10 countries in which freight cargo is shipped over roads, along with the number of miles of roads and the number of commercial vehicles (trucks and buses) for each country. Use these data to develop a multiple regression model to predict the volume of freight cargo shipped over roads by the length of roads and the number of commercial vehicles. Determine the predicted volume of freight cargo over roads if the length of roads is 600,000 miles and the number of commercial vehicles is 3 million.

COUNTRY	FREIGHT CARGO SHIPPED BY ROAD (MILLION SHORT-TON MILES)	LENGTH OF ROADS (MILES)	NUMBER OF COMMERCIAL VEHICLES
China	278,806	673,239	5,010,000
Brazil	178,359	1,031,693	1,371,127
India	144,000	1,342,000	1,980,000
Germany	138,975	395,367	2,923,000
Italy	125,171	188,597	2,745,500
Spain	105,824	206,271	2,859,438
Mexico	96,049	157,036	3,758,034

*SOURCES: World Data; World Road Statistics; and George Thomas Kurian, *The Illustrated Book of World Rankings*, Armonk, NY, M. E. Sharpe, Inc., 1997.

SOLUTION

The following output shows the results of analyzing the data by using the regression portion of Excel.

SUMMARY OUTPUT

Regression Statistics	
Multiple R	0.812
R Square	0.659
Adjusted R Square	0.488
Standard Error	44273.867
Observations	7

ANOVA

	df	*SS*	*MS*	*F*	*Significance F*
Regression	2	15148592381	7574296191	3.86	0.116
Residual	4	7840701114	1960175278		
Total	6	22989293495			

	Coefficients	*Standard Error*	*t Stat*	*P-value*
Intercept	−26425.45	67624.938	−0.39	0.716
Length of Roads	0.1018	0.0435	2.34	0.079
No. of Comm. Vehicles	0.0410	0.0171	2.39	0.075

The regression equation is

$$\hat{Y} = -26{,}425.45 + .1018X_1 + .0410X_2$$

where:

Y = volume of freight cargo shipped,
X_1 = length of roads, and
X_2 = number of commercial vehicles.

The model indicates that for every 1-unit (1 mile) increase in length of roads, the predicted volume of freight cargo shipped increases by .1018 million short-ton miles, or 101,800 short-ton miles, if the number of commercial vehicles is held constant. If the number of commercial vehicles is increased by 1 unit, the predicted volume of freight cargo shipped increases by .0410 million short-ton miles, or 41,000 short-ton miles, if the length of roads is held constant.

If X_1 (length of roads) is 600,000 and X_2 (number of commercial vehicles) is 3 million, the model predicts that the volume of freight cargo shipped will be 157,655 million short-ton miles:

$$\hat{Y} = -26{,}425.45 + .1018(600{,}000) + .0410(3{,}000{,}000) = 157{,}655$$

Analysis Using Excel

To use Excel for regression analysis, begin by selecting ***Data Analysis*** from the ***Tools*** option on the menu bar. From the ***Data Analysis*** pull-down menu, select **Regression.** The Excel dialog box for **Regression** is shown in Figure 13.4. To use this feature, insert the location of the dependent variable (Y) in the box labeled **Input *Y* Range** and the location of the independent variables (X_1, X_2, . . .) in box labeled **Input *X* Range.** If there are labels

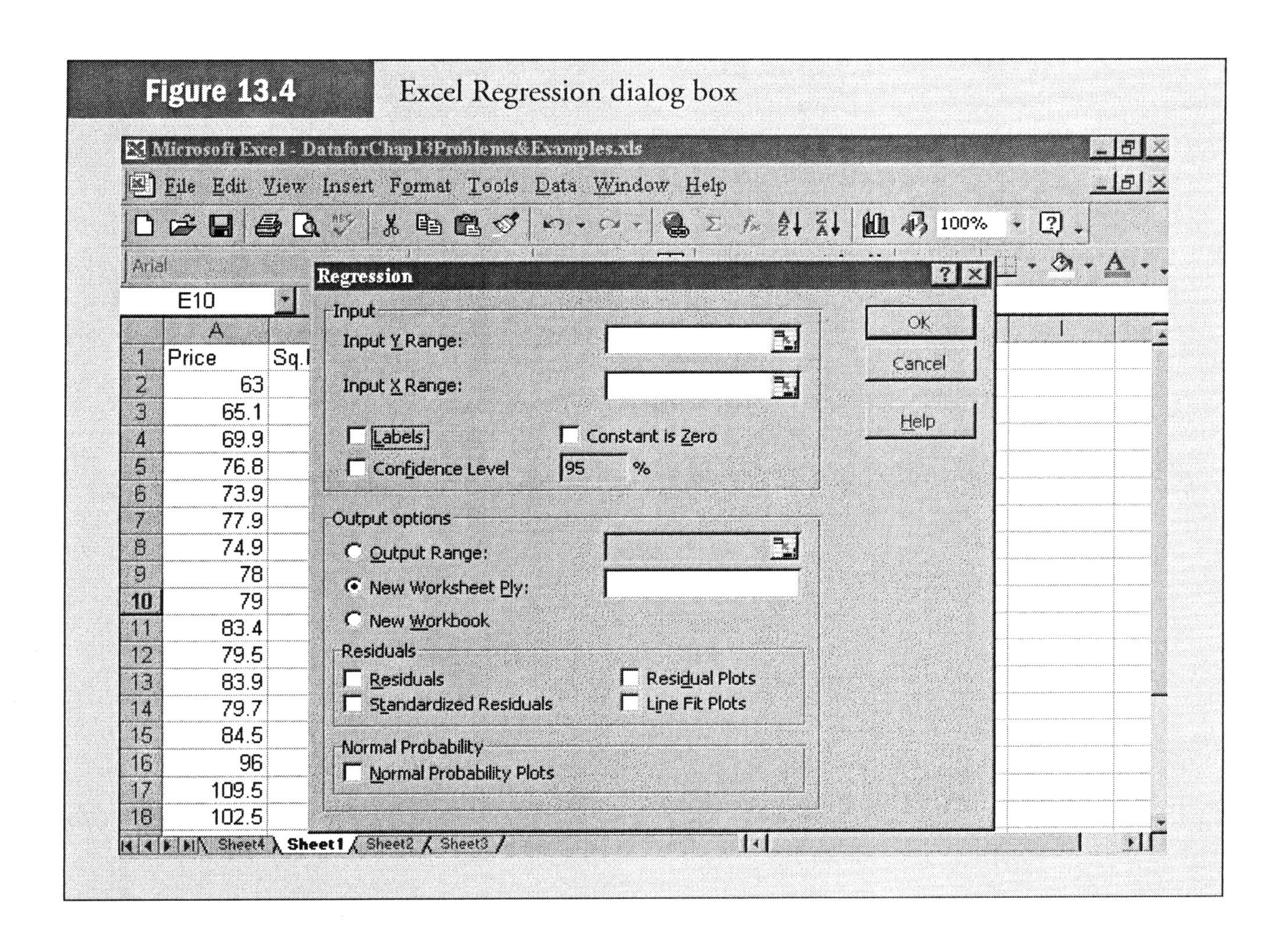

Figure 13.4 Excel Regression dialog box

at the top of the columns, check ***Labels.*** Near the bottom of the dialog box are several residual options. To show the computed residuals, check ***Residuals;*** for a plot of the residuals, check **Residual Plots;** for a line plot, check **Line Fit Plots.** The output for the real estate data problem is shown in Figure 13.3 and will be discussed throughout the chapter.

13.1 Problems

13.1 Use a computer to develop the equation of the regression model for the following data. Comment on the regression coefficients. Determine the predicted value of Y for $X_1 = 200$ and $X_2 = 7$.

Y	X_1	X_2
12	174	3
18	281	9
31	189	4
28	202	8
52	149	9
47	188	12
38	215	5
22	150	11
36	167	8
17	135	5

13.2 Use a computer to develop the equation of the regression model for the following data. Comment on the regression coefficients. Determine the predicted value of Y for $X_1 = 33$, $X_2 = 29$, and $X_3 = 13$.

Y	X_1	X_2	X_3	Y	X_1	X_2	X_3
114	21	6	5	94	40	33	14
94	43	25	8	107	32	14	11
87	56	42	25	119	16	4	7
98	19	27	9	93	18	31	16
101	29	20	12	108	27	12	10
85	34	45	21	117	31	3	8

13.3 Using the following data, determine the equation of the regression model. How many independent variables are there? Comment on the meaning of these regression coefficients.

PREDICTOR	COEFFICIENT
Constant	121.62
X_1	−.174
X_2	6.02
X_3	.00026
X_4	.0041

13.4 Use the following data to determine the equation of the multiple regression model. Comment on the regression coefficients.

PREDICTOR	COEFFICIENT
Constant	31,409.5
X_1	.08425
X_2	289.62
X_3	−.0947

13.5 Is there a particular product that is an indicator of per capita consumption around the world? Shown below are data on per capita consumption, paper consumption, fish consumption, and gasoline consumption for nine countries. Use the data to determine the equation of the multiple regression model to predict per capita consumption by paper consumption, fish consumption, and gasoline consumption. Discuss the impact of increasing paper consumption by 1 unit on the predicted per capita consumption. Discuss the impact of a 1-unit increase in fish consumption on the predicted per capita consumption and the impact of a 1-unit increase in gasoline consumption on the predicted per capita consumption.

COUNTRY	PER CAPITA CONSUMPTION	PAPER CONSUMPTION (KG PER 1000 PEOPLE)	FISH CONSUMPTION (POUNDS)	GASOLINE CONSUMPTION (1000 BARRELS PER DAY)
Japan	$19,700	76,892	158.7	5,454
Portugal	5,570	24,126	132.7	277
United States	16,500	84,579	47.0	17,033
Venezuela	2,090	6,860	31.1	430
Greece	4,490	15,641	42.1	331
Italy	10,790	43,098	44.3	1,936
Norway	13,400	41,575	90.6	183
United Kingdom	9,040	52,335	43.9	1,803
Philippines	640	940	76.3	235

SOURCES: World Development Report; Pulp & Paper Industry; Fishery Statistic Yearbook; Energy Statistics Yearbook; and George Thomas Kurian, *The Illustrated Book of World Rankings*, Armonk, NY, M. E. Sharpe, Inc., 1997.

13.6 Jensen, Solberg, and Zorn investigated the relationship of insider ownership, debt, and dividend policies in companies. One of their findings was that firms with high insider ownership choose lower levels of both debt and dividends. Shown here is a sample of data of these three variables for 11 different industries. Use the data to develop the equation of the regression model to predict insider ownership by debt ratio and dividend payout. Comment on the regression coefficients.

INDUSTRY	INSIDER OWNERSHIP	DEBT RATIO	DIVIDEND PAYOUT
Mining	8.2	14.2	10.4
Food and beverage	18.4	20.8	14.3
Furniture	11.8	18.6	12.1
Publishing	28.0	18.5	11.8
Petroleum refining	7.4	28.2	10.6
Glass and cement	15.4	24.7	12.6
Motor vehicle	15.7	15.6	12.6
Department store	18.4	21.7	7.2
Restaurant	13.4	23.0	11.3
Amusement	18.1	46.7	4.1
Hospital	10.0	35.8	9.0

SOURCE: R. Gerald Jensen, Donald P. Solberg, and Thomas S. Zorn, "Simultaneous Determination of Insider Ownership, Debt, and Dividend Policies," *Journal of Financial and Quantitative Analysis* 27, No. 2, June 1992.

13.2 Evaluating the Multiple Regression Model

Multiple regression models can be developed to fit almost any data set if the level of measurement is adequate and there are enough data points. Once a model has been constructed, it is important to test the model to determine whether it fits the data well and whether the assumptions underlying regression analysis are met. There are several ways to examine the adequacy of the regression model, including testing the overall significance of the model, studying the significance tests of the regression coefficients, computing the residuals, examining the standard error of the estimate, and observing the coefficient of determination.

Testing the Overall Model

With simple regression, a t test of the slope of the regression line is used to determine whether the population slope of the regression line is different from zero—that is, whether the independent variable contributes significantly in linearly predicting the dependent variable. The hypotheses for this test, presented in Chapter 12, are

$$H_0: \beta_1 = 0$$
$$H_a: \beta_1 \neq 0.$$

For multiple regression, an analogous test makes use of the F statistic. The overall significance of the multiple regression model is tested with the following hypotheses.

$$H_0: \beta_1 = \beta_2 = \beta_3 = \cdots = \beta_k = 0$$

H_a: At least one of the regression coefficients is $\neq 0$.

If we fail to reject the null hypothesis, we are stating that the regression model has no significant predictability for the dependent variable. A rejection of the null hypothesis indicates that at least one of the independent variables is adding significant predictability for *Y*.

This *F* test of overall significance is part of the regression output of Excel and appears in the analysis of variance (ANOVA) table. Shown here is the ANOVA table for the real estate example taken from the Excel output in Figure 13.3.

ANOVA

	df	*SS*	*MS*	*F*	*Significance F*
Regression	2	8189.723	4094.862	28.63	0.0000014
Residual	20	2861.017	143.051		
Total	22	11050.740			

The *F* value is 28.63; because $p = .0000014$, the *F* value is significant at $\alpha = .001$. The null hypothesis is rejected, and there is at least one significant predictor of house price in this analysis.

The *F* value is calculated by the following equation.

$$F = \frac{MS_{reg}}{MS_{err}} = \frac{\frac{SS_{reg}}{df_{reg}}}{\frac{SS_{err}}{df_{err}}} = \frac{\frac{SSR}{k}}{\frac{SSE}{N-k-1}}$$

where:

MS = mean square
SS = sum of squares
df = degrees of freedom
k = number of independent variables
N = number of observations

Note that in the ANOVA table for the real estate example, $df_{reg} = 2$. The degrees of freedom formula for regression is the number of regression coefficients plus the regression constant minus 1. The net result is the number of regression coefficients, which equals the number of independent variables, k. In the real estate example, there are two independent variables and so $k = 2$. Degrees of freedom error in multiple regression equals the total number of observations minus the number of regression coefficients minus the regression constant, or $N - k - 1$. For the real estate example, $N = 23$; thus, $df_{err} = 23 - 2 - 1 = 20$.

As shown in Chapter 11, MS = SS/df. The *F* ratio is formed by dividing MS_{reg} by MS_{err}. In using the *F* distribution table to determine a critical value against which to test the calculated *F* value, the degrees of freedom numerator is df_{reg} and the degrees of freedom denominator is df_{err}. The table *F* value is obtained in the usual manner, as presented in Chapter 11. With $\alpha = .01$ for the real estate example, the table value is

$$F_{.01,2,20} = 5.85.$$

Comparing the calculated *F* of 28.63 to this table value shows that the decision is to reject the null hypothesis. This is the same conclusion reached using the *p*-value method from the computer output.

If a regression model has only one linear independent variable, it is a simple regression model. In that case, the F test for the overall model is the same as the t test for significance of the population slope. The F value displayed in the regression ANOVA table is related to the t test for the slope in the simple regression case as follows.

$$F = t^2$$

In simple regression, the F value and the t value give redundant information about the overall test of the model.

Most business analysts who use multiple regression analysis will observe the value of F and its p value rather early in the process. If F is not significant, there is no population regression coefficient that is significantly different from zero, and the regression model has no predictability for the dependent variable.

Significance Tests of the Regression Coefficients

Individual significance tests for each regression coefficient are available by using a t test. This test is analogous to the t test for the slope used in Chapter 12 for simple regression analysis. The hypotheses for testing the regression coefficient of each independent variable take the following form.

$$H_0\colon \beta_1 = 0$$
$$H_a\colon \beta_1 \neq 0$$
$$H_0\colon \beta_2 = 0$$
$$H_a\colon \beta_2 \neq 0$$
$$\vdots$$
$$H_0\colon \beta_k = 0$$
$$H_a\colon \beta_k \neq 0$$

Excel regression output includes observed t values and their associated p-values to test the individual regression coefficients as standard output. Shown here are the t values and their associated probabilities for the real estate example as displayed with the multiple regression output in Figure 13.3.

	Coefficients	*Standard Error*	*t Stat*	*P-value*
Intercept	57.351	10.0072	5.73	0.000013
Square Feet	0.0177	0.0031	5.63	0.000016
Age	-0.6663	0.2280	-2.92	0.008418

At $\alpha = .05$, the null hypothesis is rejected for both variables (p-value for square feet is .000016 and for age is .008418) because the probabilities (p) associated with their t values are less than .05. If the t ratios for any predictor variables are not significant (fail to reject the null hypothesis), the business analyst might decide to drop that variable(s) from the analysis as a nonsignificant predictor(s). Other factors can enter into this decision. In a later section, we will explore techniques for model-building in which there is some variable sorting.

The degrees of freedom for each of these individual tests of regression coefficients are $n - k - 1$. In this particular example, the degrees of freedom are $23 - 2 - 1 = 20$. With $\alpha = .05$ and a two-tailed test, the critical table t value is

$$t_{.025,20} = \pm 2.086.$$

Notice from the t ratios shown here that if this critical table t value had been used as the hypothesis test criterion instead of the p-value method, the results would have been the same. Testing the regression coefficients not only gives the business analyst some insight into the fit of the regression model, but it also helps in the evaluation of how worthwhile individual independent variables are in predicting Y.

Residuals, SSE, and Standard Error of the Estimate

Residual
The difference between the actual Y value and the Y value predicted by the regression model; the error of the regression model in predicting each value of the dependent variable.

The **residual,** or error, of the regression model is *the difference between the Y value and the predicted value of Y,* $(Y - \hat{Y})$. The residuals for a multiple regression model are solved for in the same manner as they are with simple regression. First, a predicted value of Y, $\hat{Y}$, is determined by entering the value for each independent variable for a given set of observations into the multiple regression equation and solving for $\hat{Y}$. Next, the value of $Y - \hat{Y}$ is computed for each set of observations. Shown here are the calculations for the residual of the first set of observations from Table 13.1. The predicted value of Y for $X_1 = 1605$ and $X_2 = 35$ is

$$\hat{Y} = 57.351 + .0177(1605) - .6663(35) = 62.44$$

$$\text{Actual value of } Y = 63.0$$

$$\text{Residual} = Y - \hat{Y} = 63.0 - 62.44 = .56$$

In Table 13.2, all residuals are shown for the real estate example.

An examination of the residuals in Table 13.2 can reveal some information about the fit of the regression model that was used to predict house prices. The business analyst can observe the residuals and decide whether the errors are small enough to support the accuracy of the model. The house price figures are in units of \$1000. Two of the 23 residuals are more than 20.00, or more than \$20,000 off in their prediction. On the other hand, two residuals are less than 1, or \$1000 off in their prediction.

Outliers
Data points that lie apart from the rest of the points.

Residuals are also helpful in locating outliers. **Outliers** are *data points that are apart, or far, from the mainstream of the other data.* They are sometimes data points that were mistakenly recorded or measured. As every data point has an influence on the regression model, outliers can exert an overly important influence on the model because of their distance from other points. An examination of outliers is worth considering. In Table 13.2, the eighth residual listed is –27.702. This error indicates that the regression model was not nearly as successful in predicting house price on this particular house as it was with others (an error of more than \$27,000). For whatever reason, this data point stands somewhat apart from other data points and may be considered an outlier.

Residuals are also useful in testing the assumptions underlying regression analysis. Figure 13.5 contains an Excel-produced plot (using the Chart Wizard and the data from Table 13.2) of the residuals against the fits ($\hat{Y}$). Notice that residual variance seems to increase in the right half of the plot, indicating potential heteroscedasticity. As discussed in Chapter 12, one of the assumptions underlying regression analysis is that the error terms have homoscedasticity or homogeneous variance. That assumption might be violated in

OBSERVATION	PREDICTED PRICE	RESIDUALS
1	62.466	0.534
2	71.465	–6.365
3	71.540	–1.640
4	78.622	–1.822
5	74.073	–0.173
6	75.627	2.273
7	82.991	–8.091
8	105.702	–27.702
9	68.495	10.505
10	81.124	2.276
11	88.265	–8.765
12	91.322	–7.422
13	85.602	–5.902
14	95.383	–10.883
15	85.442	10.558
16	102.772	6.728
17	97.659	4.841
18	107.187	13.813
19	109.356	–4.456
20	111.237	16.763
21	105.064	23.936
22	134.447	–16.547
23	132.460	7.540

TABLE 13.2
Excel-produced Residuals for the Real Estate Regression Model

this example. Figure 13.6 contains an Excel-produced histogram of the residuals (using the histogram feature of data analysis and the fits). Observe that the residuals appear to be somewhat normally distributed indicating that the assumption of normally distributed error terms probably has not been violated.

One of the properties of residuals is that for any given regression model, the residuals add to zero. This zero-sum property can be overcome by *squaring the residuals and then summing the squares.* Such an operation produces the **sum of squares of error (SSE).**

Sum of squares of error (SSE)
The sum of the residuals squared for a regression model.

The formula for computing the sum of squares error (SSE) for multiple regression is the same as it is for simple regression.

$$SSE = \Sigma(Y - \hat{Y})^2$$

For the real estate example, SSE can be computed by squaring and summing the residuals shown in Table 13.2.

$$\begin{aligned} SSE = & [(.534)^2 + (-6.365)^2 + (-1.640)^2 + (-1.822)^2 + (-0.173)^2 + (2.273)^2 \\ & + (-8.091)^2 + (-27.702)^2 + (10.505)^2 + (2.276)^2 + (-8.765)^2 + \\ & (-7.422)^2 + (-5.902)^2 + (-10.883)^2 + (10.558)^2 + (6.728)^2 + (4.841)^2 + \\ & (13.813)^2 + (-4.456)^2 + (16.763)^2 + (23.936)^2 + (-16.547)^2 + (7.540)^2] \\ = & 2861.0 \end{aligned}$$

SSE can also be obtained directly from the Excel regression output by selecting the value of SS (sum of squares) listed beside "Residual." Shown here is the ANOVA portion

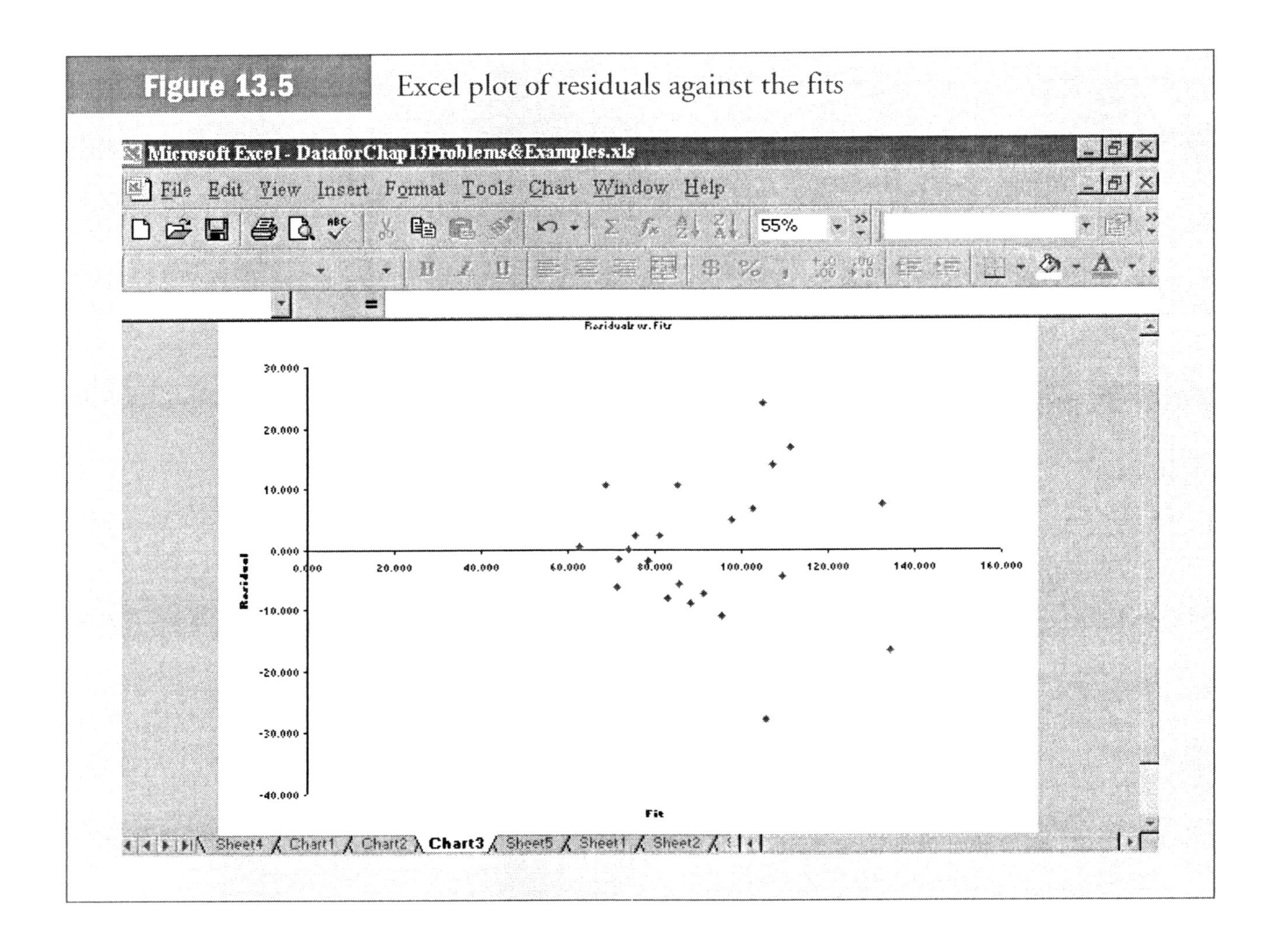

Figure 13.5 Excel plot of residuals against the fits

of the output displayed in Figure 13.3. Note that the SS for "Residual" shown in the ANOVA table equals the value of $\Sigma(Y - \hat{Y})^2$ just computed (2861.0).

ANOVA

	df	*SS*	*MS*	*F*	*Significance F*
Regression	2	8189.723	4094.862	28.63	0.0000014
Residual	20	2861.017 (SSE)	143.051		
Total	22	11050.740			

Standard error of the estimate (S_e) A standard deviation of the error of a regression model.

SSE has limited usage as a measure of error. However, it is a tool that is used to solve for other, more useful measures. One of those is the **standard error of the estimate, S_e,** which is essentially *the standard deviation of residuals (error) for the regression model.* As explained in Chapter 12, an assumption underlying regression analysis is that the error terms are approximately normally distributed with a mean of zero. With this information and by the empirical rule, approximately 68% of the residuals should be within $\pm 1S_e$ and 95% should be within $\pm 2S_e$. This makes the standard error of the estimate a very useful tool in estimating how accurately a regression model is fitting the data.

The standard error of the estimate is computed by dividing SSE by the degrees of freedom of error for the model and taking the square root.

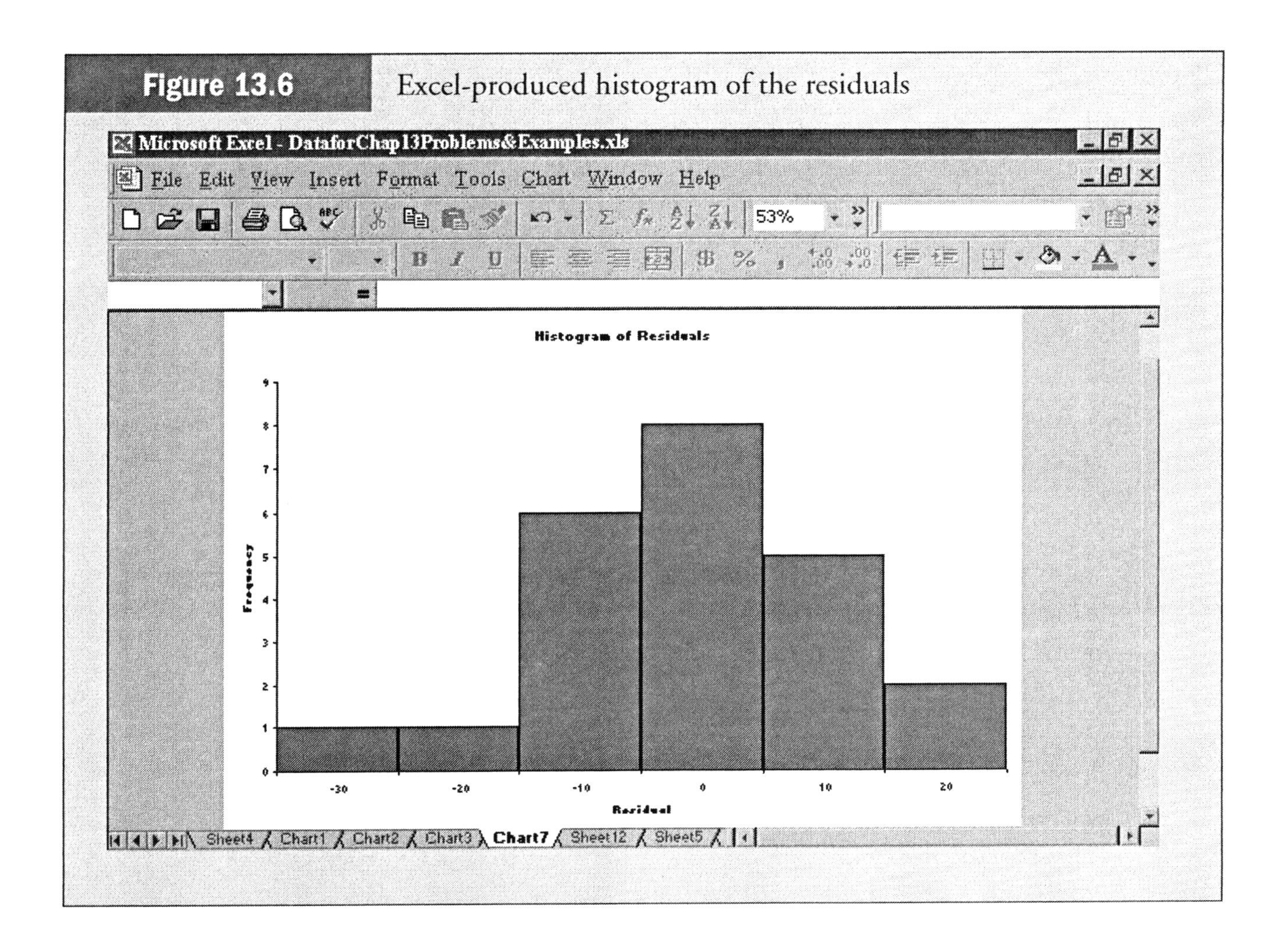

Figure 13.6 Excel-produced histogram of the residuals

$$S_e = \sqrt{\frac{\text{SSE}}{n - k - 1}}$$

where:

n = number of observations

k = number of independent variables

The value of S_e can be computed for the real estate example as follows.

$$S_e = \sqrt{\frac{\text{SSE}}{n - k - 1}} = \sqrt{\frac{2861}{23 - 2 - 1}} = 11.96$$

The standard error of the estimate, S_e, is usually given as standard output from regression analysis by computer software packages. The Excel output displayed in Figure 13.3 contains

Standard Error = 11.960.

This is the standard error of the estimate for the real estate example. By the empirical rule, approximately 68% of the residuals should be within $\pm 1S_e = \pm 1(11.96) = \pm 11.96$. Since house prices are in units of \$1000, approximately 68% of the predictions are within $\pm 11.96(\$1000)$, or $\pm$ \$11,960.

The residuals for this example, presented in Table 13.2, show that 18/23, or about 78%, of the residuals are within this span. According to the empirical rule, approximately 95% of the residuals should be within $\pm 2S_e$, or $\pm 2(11.96) = \pm 23.92$. Further examination of the residual values in Table 13.2 shows that 21 of 23, or 91%, are within this range. The business analyst can study the standard error of the estimate and these empirical-rule–related ranges and decide whether the error of the regression model is sufficiently small to justify further use of the model.

Coefficient of Multiple Determination (R^2)

Coefficient of multiple determination (R^2)
The proportion of variation of the dependent variable accounted for by the independent variables in the regression model.

The **coefficient of multiple determination (R^2)** is analogous to coefficient of determination (r^2) discussed in Chapter 12. R^2 represents *the proportion of variation of the dependent variable, Y, accounted for by the independent variables in the regression model.* As with r^2, the range of possible values for R^2 is from 0 to 1. An R^2 of 0 indicates no relationship between the predictor variables in the model and Y. An R^2 of 1 indicates that 100% of the variability of Y has been accounted for by the predictors. Of course, it is desirable for R^2 to be high, indicating the strong predictability of a regression model. The coefficient of multiple determination can be calculated by the following formula.

$$R^2 = \frac{\text{SSR}}{\text{SS}_{YY}} = 1 - \frac{\text{SSE}}{\text{SS}_{YY}}$$

R^2 can be calculated in the real estate example by using the SS regression (SSR), the SS error (SSE), and SS total (SS_{YY}) from the ANOVA portion of Figure 13.3.

ANOVA

	df	*SS*	*MS*	*F*	*Significance F*
Regression	2	8189.723 (SSR)	4094.862	28.63	0.0000014
Residual	20	2861.017 (SSE)	143.051		
Total	22	11050.740 (SS_{YY})			

$$R^2 = \frac{\text{SSR}}{SS_{YY}} = \frac{8189.723}{11050.740} = .741$$

or

$$R^2 = 1 - \frac{\text{SSE}}{\text{SS}_{YY}} = 1 - \frac{2861.017}{11050.740} = .741$$

In addition, Excel prints out R^2 as standard output with regression analysis. A reexamination of Figure 13.3 reveals that R^2 is given as

$$R \text{ Square} = 0.741$$

This result indicates that a relatively high proportion of the variation of the dependent variable, house price, is accounted for by the independent variables in this regression model.

Adjusted R^2

As additional independent variables are added to a regression model, the value of R^2 cannot decrease, and in most cases it will increase. In the formulas for determining R^2,

$$R^2 = \frac{\text{SSR}}{\text{SS}_{YY}} = 1 - \frac{\text{SSE}}{\text{SS}_{YY}}$$

The value of SS_{YY} for a given set of observations will remain the same as independent variables are added to the regression analysis because SS_{YY} is the sum of squares for the dependent variable. Because additional independent variables are likely to increase SSR at least by some amount, the value of R^2 will probably increase for any additional independent variables.

However, sometimes additional independent variables add no *significant* information to the regression model, yet R^2 increases. R^2 therefore may yield an inflated figure. Statisticians have developed an **adjusted R^2** to take into consideration both the additional information each new independent variable brings to the regression model and the changed degrees of freedom of regression. Many standard statistical computer packages now compute and report adjusted R^2 as part of the output. The formula for computing adjusted R^2 is

Adjusted R^2
A modified value of R^2 in which the degrees of freedom are taken into account, thereby allowing the business analyst to determine whether the value of R^2 is inflated for a particular multiple regression model.

$$\text{Adjusted } R^2 = 1 - \frac{\dfrac{\text{SSE}}{n-k-1}}{\dfrac{\text{SS}_{YY}}{n-1}}.$$

The value of adjusted R^2 for the real estate example can be solved by using information from the ANOVA portion of the computer output in Figure 13.3.

ANOVA (annotations: $n-k-1$ → Residual df; $n-1$ → Total df; SSE → Residual SS; SS_{YY} → Total SS)

	df	*SS*	*MS*	*F*	*Significance F*
Regression	2	8189.723	4094.862	28.63	0.0000014
Residual	20	2861.017	143.051		
Total	22	11050.740			

$$\text{Adj. } R^2 = 1 - \frac{\dfrac{2861.017}{20}}{\dfrac{11050.740}{22}} = 1 - .285 = .715$$

The Excel regression output in Figure 13.3 contains the value of the adjusted R^2 already computed. For the real estate example, this value is shown as

Adjusted R Square = 0.715

A comparison of R^2 (.741) with the adjusted R^2 (.715) for this example shows that the adjusted R^2 reduces the overall proportion of variation of the dependent variable accounted for by the independent variables by a factor of .026, or 2.6%. The gap between the R^2 and adjusted R^2 tends to increase as nonsignificant independent variables are added to the regression model. As n increases, the difference between R^2 and adjusted R^2 becomes less.

Figure 13.7

Annotated version of the Excel output of regression for the real estate problem

SUMMARY OUTPUT

Regression Statistics		
Multiple R	0.861	
R Square	0.741	← Coefficient of multiple determination (R^2)
Adjusted R Square	0.715	← Adjusted R^2
Standard Error	11.960	← Standard error of estimate (S_e)
Observations	23	

ANOVA table and F test for overall model

ANOVA

	df	*SS*	*MS*	*F*	*Significance F*
Regression	2	8189.723	4094.862	28.63	0.0000014
Residual	20	2861.017	143.051		
Total	22	11050.740			

	Coefficients	*Standard Error*	*t Stat*	*P-value*
Intercept	-57.351	10.0072	-5.73	0.000013
Sq. Feet	0.0177	0.0031	5.63	.0.000016
Age	-0.6663	0.2280	-2.92	0.008418

Components of regression equation

t tests of regression coefficients

A Reexamination of the Excel Regression Output

Figure 13.7 shows again the Excel multiple regression output for the real estate example. Many of the concepts discussed thus far in the chapter are highlighted. Note the following items.

1. The components of equation of the regression model
2. The ANOVA table with the F value for the overall test of the model
3. The t ratios, which test the significance of the regression coefficients
4. The value of SSE
5. The value of S_e
6. The value of R^2
7. The value of adjusted R^2

DEMONSTRATION PROBLEM 13.2

Discuss the Excel multiple regression output for Demonstration Problem 13.1. Comment on the F test for the overall significance of the model, the t tests of the regression coefficients, and the values of S_e, R^2, and adjusted R^2.

SOLUTION

This regression analysis was done to predict the volume of freight cargo shipped annually in a country by road using the predictors "length of roads" and "number of commercial vehicles." The equation of the regression model was presented in the solution of

Demonstration Problem 13.1. Shown here is the complete multiple regression output from the Excel analysis of the data.

SUMMARY OUTPUT

Regression Statistics	
Multiple R	0.812
R Square	0.659
Adjusted R Square	0.488
Standard Error	44273.87
Observations	7

ANOVA

	df	SS	MS	F	Significance F
Regression	2	15148592381	7574296191	3.86	0.116
Residual	4	7840701114	1960175278		
Total	6	22989293495			

	Coefficients	Standard Error	t Stat	P-value
Intercept	-26425.45	67624.94	-0.39	0.716
Length of Roads	0.1018	0.0435	2.34	0.079
No. of Comm. Veh.	0.0409	0.0171	2.39	0.075

RESIDUAL OUTPUT

Observation	Predicted Freight Cargo	Residuals
1	247276.61	31529.39
2	134768.10	43590.90
3	191296.29	−47296.29
4	133523.80	5451.20
5	105201.93	19969.07
6	111667.11	−5843.11
7	143450.17	−47401.17

The value of F for this problem is 3.86, with a p value of .116, which is not significant at $\alpha = .05$. On the basis of this information, the null hypothesis would not be rejected for the overall test of significance. None of the regression coefficients are significantly different from zero and there is no significant predictability of the volume of freight cargo shipped by road from this regression model.

An examination of the t ratios support this conclusion using $\alpha = .05$. The t ratio for length of roads is 2.34 with an associated p value of .079, and the t ratio for number of commercial vehicles is 2.39 with an associated p value of .075. Neither p value is less than .05.

The standard error of the estimate is $S_e = 44{,}273.87$, indicating that approximately 68% of the residuals are within $\pm 44{,}273.87$. An examination of the Excel-produced residuals shows that actually five out of seven, or 71.4%, of the residuals fall in this interval. Approximately 95% of the residuals should be within $\pm 2(44{,}273.87) = \pm 88{,}547.74$, and an examination of the Excel-produced residuals shows that seven out of seven, or 100%, of the residuals are within this interval. Shipping industry analysts could examine the value of the standard error of the estimate to determine whether this model produces results with small enough error to suit their needs.

R^2 for this regression analysis is .659 or 65.9%. That is, 65.9% of the variation in the volume of freight cargo is accounted for by these two independent variables. Conversely, 34.1% of the variation is unaccounted for by this model. The adjusted R^2 is only .488 or 48.8%, indicating that the value of R^2 is considerably inflated. Thus, it could be that the two predictors of the regression model actually account for less than half of the variation of the dependent variable when R^2 is adjusted.

This problem highlights the notion that a regression model can be developed for data and not really fit the data in a significant way. By examining the values of F, t, S_e, R^2, and adjusted R^2, the business analyst can begin to understand whether the regression model is providing any significant predictability for Y.

13.2 Problems

13.7 Examine the Excel output shown here for a multiple regression analysis. How many predictors were analyzed? Determine the equation of the regression model. Comment on the overall significance of the regression model. What is the value of the standard error of the estimate? Find R^2 and compare it with the adjusted value of R^2. Discuss the t ratios of the variables and their significance.

SUMMARY OUTPUT

Regression Statistics	
Multiple R	0.664
R Square	0.440
Adjusted R Square	0.268
Standard Error	10.258
Observations	35

ANOVA

	df	*SS*	*MS*	*F*	*Significance F*
Regression	8	2153.051	269.131	2.56	0.0334
Residual	26	2736.044	105.232		
Total	34	4889.096			

	Coefficients	*Standard Error*	*t Stat*	*P-value*
Intercept	-56.594	19.6515	2.88	0.008
X1	0.208	0.1608	1.29	0.208
X2	-0.368	0.1434	-2.56	0.016
X3	-0.219	0.1357	-1.61	0.119
X4	0.351	0.1779	1.97	0.059
X5	0.260	0.1370	1.90	0.068
X6	-0.131	0.1308	-1.00	0.327
X7	0.044	0.1477	0.30	0.767
X8	-0.048	0.1804	-0.27	0.793

13.8 Following is Excel output for a multiple regression analysis. Study the ANOVA table, the Standard Error of the Estimate, R^2, adjusted R^2, the t ratios, and discuss the strengths and weaknesses of the regression model. Does this model appear to fit the data well? From the information here, what recommendations would you make about the predictor variables in the model?

SUMMARY OUTPUT

Regression Statistics	
Multiple R	0.788
R Square	0.621
Adjusted R Square	0.518
Standard Error	26.373
Observations	15

ANOVA

	df	*SS*	*MS*	*F*	*Significance F*
Regression	3	12550.193	4183.40	6.01	0.0111
Residual	11	7650.740	695.52		
Total	14	20200.933			

	Coefficients	*Standard Error*	*t Stat*	*P-value*
Intercept	116.294	37.317	3.12	0.010
X1	-1.255	0.301	-4.17	0.002
X2	0.249	0.558	0.45	0.664
X3	0.491	0.306	1.61	0.137

13.9 Using the data in Problem 13.5, develop a multiple regression model to predict per capita consumption by the consumption of paper, fish, and gasoline. Discuss the output and pay particular attention to the F test, the t tests, and the values of S_e, R^2, and the adjusted R^2.

13.10 Using the data from Problem 13.6, develop a multiple regression model to predict insider ownership from debt ratio and dividend payout. Comment on the strength of the model and the predictors by examining the ANOVA table, the t tests, and the values of S_e, R^2, and the adjusted R^2.

13.11 Develop a multiple regression model to predict Y from X_1, X_2, and X_3 using the following data. Discuss the values of F, t, S_e, R^2, and adjusted R^2. Compute the residuals. Plot a graph of the residuals against the fits. Construct a histogram of the residuals. By observing the residuals, the residual plot, and the histogram, comment on any possible violations of regression assumptions.

Y	X_1	X_2	X_1
5.3	44	11	401
3.6	24	40	219
5.1	46	13	394
4.9	38	18	362
7.0	61	3	453
6.4	58	5	468
5.2	47	14	386
4.6	36	24	357
2.9	19	52	206
4.0	31	29	301
3.8	24	37	243
3.8	27	36	228
4.8	36	21	342
5.4	50	11	421
5.8	55	9	445

13.12 Use the following data to develop a regression model to predict Y from X_1 and X_2. Comment on the output. Develop a regression model to predict Y from X_1 only. Compare the results of this model with those of the model using both predictors. How do the values of R^2 compare? What might you conclude by examining the output from both regression models? Using the residuals, a plot of the residuals against the fits, and a histogram of the residuals, discuss any possible violations of regression assumptions.

Y	X_1	X_2
28	12.6	134
43	11.4	126
45	11.5	143
49	11.1	152
57	10.4	143
68	9.6	147
74	9.8	128
81	8.4	119
82	8.8	130
86	8.9	135
101	8.1	141
112	7.6	123
114	7.8	121
119	7.4	129
124	6.4	135

13.13 Study the following Excel multiple regression output. How many predictors are there in this model? How many observations? What is the equation of the regression line? Discuss the strength of the model in terms of R^2, adjusted R^2, S_e, and F. Which predictors if any are significant? Why or why not? Comment on the overall effectiveness of the model.

SUMMARY OUTPUT

Regression Statistics	
Multiple R	0.842407116
R Square	0.709649749
Adjusted R Square	0.630463317
Standard Error	109.4295947
Observations	15

ANOVA

	df	*SS*	*MS*	*F*	*Significance F*
Regression	3	321946.8018	107315.6	8.961759	0.00272447
Residual	11	131723.1982	11974.84		
Total	14	453670			

	Coefficients	*Standard Error*	*t Stat*	*P-value*
Intercept	657.0534435	167.4595388	3.923655	0.002378
X Variable 1	5.710310868	1.791835982	3.186849	0.008655
X Variable 2	−0.416916682	0.322192459	−1.294	0.222174
X Variable 3	−3.471481072	1.442934778	−2.40585	0.03487

13.3
Indicator (Dummy) Variables

Some variables are referred to as **qualitative variables** (as opposed to *quantitative* variables) because qualitative variables do not yield quantifiable outcomes. Instead, qualitative variables yield nominal or ordinal level information, which is used more to categorize items. These variables have a role in multiple regression and are referred to as **indicator,** or **dummy, variables.** In this section, we will examine the role of indicator, or dummy, variables as predictors or independent variables in multiple regression analysis.

Qualitative variable, or Indicator variable, or Dummy variable
Represents whether or not a given item or person possesses a certain characteristic and is usually coded as 0 or 1.

Indicator variables arise in many ways in business research. Mail questionnaire or personal interview demographic questions are prime candidates because they tend to generate qualitative measures on such items as gender, geographic region, occupation, marital status, level of education, economic class, political affiliation, religion, management/nonmanagement status, buying/leasing a home, method of transportation, or type of broker. In one business study, business analysts were attempting to develop a multiple regression model to predict the distances shoppers drive to malls in the greater Cleveland area. One independent variable was whether or not the mall was located on the shore of Lake Erie. In a second study, a site-location model for pizza restaurants included indicator variables for (1) whether or not the restaurant served beer and (2) whether or not the restaurant had a salad bar.

These indicator variables are qualitative in that no interval or ratio level measurement is assigned to a response. For example, if a mall is located on the shore of Lake Erie, awarding it a score of 20 or 30 or 75 because of its location makes no sense. In terms of gender, what value would you assign to a man or a woman in a regression study? Yet these types of indicator, or dummy, variables are often useful in multiple regression studies and can be included if they are coded in the proper format.

Most business analysts code indicator variables by using 0 or 1. For example, in the shopping mall study, malls located on the shore of Lake Erie could be assigned a 1, and all other malls would then be assigned a 0. The assignment of 0 or 1 is arbitrary, with the number merely holding a place for the category. For this reason, the coding is referred to as "dummy" coding; the number represents a category by holding a place and is not a measurement.

Many indicator, or dummy, variables are dichotomous, such as male/female, salad bar/no salad bar, employed/not employed, and rent/own. For these variables, a value of 1 is arbitrarily assigned to one category and a value of 0 is assigned to the other category. Some qualitative variables contain several categories, such as the variable "type of job," which might have the categories assembler, painter, and inspector. In this case, using a coding of 1, 2, and 3, respectively, is tempting. However, that type of coding creates problems for multiple regression analysis. For one thing, the category "inspector" would receive a value that is three times that of "painter." In addition, the values of 1, 2, and 3 indicate a hierarchy of job types: assembler < painter < inspector.

The proper way to code such indicator variables is with the 0, 1 coding. Two separate independent variables should be used to code the three categories of type of job. The first variable is assembler, where a 1 is recorded if the person's job is assembler and a 0 is recorded if it is not. The second variable is painter, where a 1 is recorded if the person's job is painter and a 0 is recorded if it is not. A variable should not be assigned to inspector, because all workers in the study for whom a 1 was not recorded either for the assembler variable or the painter variable must be inspectors. Thus, coding the inspector variable would result in redundant information and is not necessary. This reasoning holds for all indicator variables with more than two categories. If an indicator variable has c categories, then $c - 1$ dummy variables must be created and inserted into the regression analysis in order to include the indicator variable in the multiple regression.*

*If c indicator variables are included in the analysis, no unique estimators of the regression coefficients can be found. [J. Neter, M. H. Kutner, W. Wasserman, and C. Nachtsheim. *Applied Linear Regression Models,* 3d ed. Chicago, Richard D. Irwin, Inc., 1996.]

An example of an indicator variable with more than two categories is the result of the following question taken from a typical questionnaire.

Your office is located in which region of the country?

____ Northeast ____ Midwest ____ South ____ West

Suppose a business analyst is using a multiple regression analysis to predict the cost of doing business and believes geographic location of the office is a potential predictor. How does the business analyst insert this qualitative variable into the analysis? Because $c = 4$ for this question, three dummy variables are inserted into the analysis. Table 13.3 shows one possible way this may have occurred with 13 respondents. Note that rows 2, 7, and 11 contain all zeros, which indicate that those respondents have offices in the West. Thus, a fourth dummy variable for the West region is not necessary and, indeed, should not be included because the information contained in such a fourth variable is contained in the other three variables.

A word of caution is in order. Because of degrees of freedom and interpretation considerations, it is important that a multiple regression analysis have enough observations to handle adequately the number of independent variables entered. Some business analysts recommend as a rule of thumb that there be at least three observations per independent variable. If a qualitative variable has multiple categories, resulting in several dummy independent variables, and if several qualitative variables are being included in an analysis, the number of predictors can rather quickly exceed the limit of recommended number of variables per number of observations. Nevertheless, dummy variables can be very useful and are a way in which nominal or ordinal information can be recoded and incorporated into a multiple regression model.

As an example, consider the issue of gender discrimination in the salary earnings of workers in some industries. In examining this issue, suppose a random sample of 15 workers is drawn from a pool of employed laborers in a particular industry and the workers' average monthly salaries are determined, along with their age and gender. The data are shown in Table 13.4. As gender can be only male or female, this variable is a dummy variable requiring 0, 1 coding. Suppose we arbitrarily let 1 denote male and 0 denote female. Figure 13.8 is the multiple regression model developed from the data of Table 13.4 by using Excel to predict the dependent variable, monthly salary, by two independent variables, age and gender.

The computer output in Figure 13.8 results in the regression equation for this model.

$$\text{Salary} = 0.7321 + 0.1112\ \text{Age} + 0.4587\ \text{Gender}$$

TABLE 13.3
Coding for the Indicator Variable of Geographic Location for Regression Analysis

NORTHEAST X_1	MIDWEST X_2	SOUTH X_3
1	0	0
0	0	0
1	0	0
0	0	1
0	1	0
0	1	0
0	0	0
0	0	1
1	0	0
1	0	0
0	0	0
0	1	0
0	0	1

An examination of the t ratios reveals that the dummy variable "gender" has a regression coefficient that is significant at $\alpha = .001$ ($t = 8.58$, $p = .000$). The overall model is significant at $\alpha = .001$ ($F = 48.54$, $p = .000002$). The standard error of the estimate, $S_e = .0968$, indicates that approximately 68% of the errors of prediction are within ±$96.8 (.0968 × $1000). The R^2 is relatively high at 89.0%, and the adjusted R^2 is 87.2%.

The t value for gender indicates that gender is a significant predictor of monthly salary in this model. This is apparent when one looks at the effects of this dummy variable another way. Figure 13.9 shows the graph of the regression equation when gender = 1 (male) and the graph of the regression equation when gender = 0 (female). When gender = 1 (male), the regression equation becomes

$$.7321 + .1112(\text{age}) + .4587(1) = 1.1908 + .1112(\text{age}).$$

TABLE 13.4
Data for the Monthly Salary Example

MONTHLY SALARY ($1000)	AGE (10 YEARS)	GENDER (1 = MALE, 0 = FEMALE)
1.548	3.2	1
1.629	3.8	1
1.011	2.7	0
1.229	3.4	0
1.746	3.6	1
1.528	4.1	1
1.018	3.8	0
1.190	3.4	0
1.551	3.3	1
0.985	3.2	0
1.610	3.5	1
1.432	2.9	1
1.215	3.3	0
.990	2.8	0
1.585	3.5	1

Figure 13.8

Excel regression output for the monthly salary example

Regression Statistics

Multiple R	0.943
R Square	0.890
Adjusted R Square	0.872
Standard Error	0.0968
Observations	15

ANOVA

	df	*SS*	*MS*	*F*	*Significance F*
Regression	2	0.9095	0.4547	48.54	0.000002
Residual	12	0.1124	0.0094		
Total	14	1.0219			

	Coefficients	*Standard Error*	*t Stat*	*P-value*
Intercept	0.7321	0.2356	3.11	0.0091
Age	0.1112	0.0721	1.54	0.1488
Gender	0.4587	0.0535	8.58	0.0000

Figure 13.9

Regression model for male and female gender

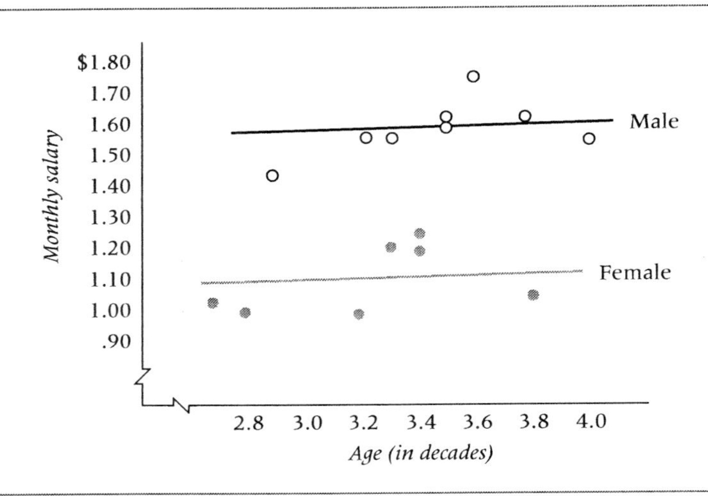

When gender = 0 (female), the regression equation becomes

$$.7321 + .1112(\text{age}) + .4587(0) = .7321 + .1112(\text{age}).$$

The full regression model (with both predictors) has a response surface that is a plane in a three-dimensional space. However, if a value of 1 is entered for gender into the full regression model, as just shown, the regression model is reduced to a line passing through the plane formed by monthly salary and age. If a value of 0 is entered for gender, as shown, the full regression model also reduces to a line passing through the plane formed by monthly salary and age. Figure 13.9 displays these two lines. Notice that the only difference in the two lines is the Y intercept. Observe the monthly salary with male gender, as depicted by ○, versus the monthly salary with female gender, depicted by ●. The difference in the Y intercepts of these two lines is .4587, which is the value of the regression coefficient for gender. This signifies that, on average, men earn $458.70 per month more than women for this population.

13.3
Problems

13.14 Analyze the following data by using a multiple regression computer software package to predict Y using X_1 and X_2. Notice that X_2 is a dummy variable. Discuss the output from the regression analysis; in particular, comment on the predictability of the dummy variable.

Y	X_1	X_2
16.8	27	1
13.2	16	0
14.7	13	0
15.4	11	1
11.1	17	0
16.2	19	1
14.9	24	1
13.3	21	0
17.8	16	1
17.1	23	1
14.3	18	0
13.9	16	0

13.15 Given here are the data from a dependent variable and two independent variables. The second independent variable is an indicator variable with several categories. Hence, this variable is represented by X_2, X_3, and X_4. How many categories are there in total for this independent variable? Use a computer to perform a multiple regression analysis on this data to predict Y from the X values. Discuss the output and pay particular attention to the dummy variables.

Y	X_1	X_2	X_3	X_4
11	1.9	1	0	0
3	1.6	0	1	0
2	2.3	0	1	0
5	2.0	0	0	1
9	1.8	0	0	0
14	1.9	1	0	0
10	2.4	1	0	0
8	2.6	0	0	0
4	2.0	0	1	0
9	1.4	0	0	0
11	1.7	1	0	0
4	2.5	0	0	1
6	1.0	1	0	0
10	1.4	0	0	0
3	1.9	0	1	0
4	2.3	0	1	0
9	2.2	0	0	0
6	1.7	0	0	1

13.16 Given here is Excel output for a multiple regression model that was developed to predict Y from two independent variables, X_1 and X_2. Variable X_2 is a dummy variable. Discuss the strength of the multiple regression model on the basis of the output. Focus on the contribution of the dummy variable. Plot X_1 and Y with X_2 as 0, and then plot X_1 and Y with X_2 as 1. Compare the two lines and discuss the differences.

Regression Statistics	
Multiple R	0.623
R Square	0.388
Adjusted R Square	0.341
Standard Error	11.744
Observations	29

ANOVA

	df	*SS*	*MS*	*F*	*Significance F*
Regression	2	2270.11	1135.05	8.23	0.0017
Residual	26	3585.75	137.91		
Total	28	5855.86			

	Coefficients	*Standard Error*	*t Stat*	*P-value*
Intercept	41.225	6.380	6.46	0.0000008
X_1	1.081	1.353	0.80	0.4316
X_2	-18.404	4.547	-4.05	0.0004

13.17 Falvey, Fried, and Richards* developed a multiple regression model to predict the average price of a meal at New Orleans restaurants. The variables explored included such indicator variables as the following.

Accepts reservations

Accepts credit cards

Has its own parking lot

Has a separate bar or lounge

Has a maitre d'

Has a dress code

Is candlelit

Has live entertainment

Serves alcoholic beverages

Is a steakhouse

Is in the French Quarter

Suppose a relatively simple model is developed to predict the average price of a meal at a restaurant in New Orleans from the number of hours the restaurant is open per week, the probability of being seated upon arrival, and whether the restaurant is located in the French Quarter. Use the following data and a computer to develop such a model. Comment on the output.

PRICE	HOURS	PROBABILITY OF BEING SEATED	FRENCH QUARTER
$ 8.52	65	.62	0
21.45	45	.43	1
16.18	52	.58	1
6.21	66	.74	0
12.19	53	.19	1
25.62	55	.49	1
13.90	60	.80	0
18.66	72	.75	1
5.25	70	.37	0
7.98	55	.64	0
12.57	48	.51	1
14.85	60	.32	1
8.80	52	.62	0
6.27	64	.83	0

13.18 A business analyst has gathered 155 observations on four variables: job satisfaction, occupation, industry, marital status. He or she wants to develop a multiple regression model to predict job satisfaction by the other three variables. All three predictor variables are qualitative variables with the following categories.

1. Occupation: accounting, management, marketing, finance
2. Industry: manufacturing, healthcare, transportation
3. Marital status: married, single

How many variables will be in the regression model? Delineate the number of predictors needed in each category and discuss the total number of predictors.

*ADAPTED FROM: Rodney E. Falvey, Harold O. Fried, and Bruce Richards, "An Hedonic Guide to New Orleans Restaurants," *Quarterly Review of Economics and Finance*, 32, No. 1, Spring 1992.

13.4 More Complex Regression Models

The regression models presented thus far, along with many others, are based on the **general linear regression model,** which has the form

$$Y = \beta_0 + \beta_1 X_1 + \beta_2 X_2 + \cdots + \beta_k X_k + \epsilon \qquad (13.1)$$

where:

β_0 = the regression constant,
$\beta_1, \beta_2, \ldots, \beta_k$ are the partial regression coefficients for the k independent variables,
$X_1, \ldots, X_k$ are the independent variables, and
k = the number of independent variables.

General linear regression model
Regression models that take the form of $Y = \beta_0 + \beta_1 X_1 + \beta_2 X_2 + \ldots + \beta_k X_k + \epsilon$, where the parameters, β_i, are linear.

In this general linear model, the parameters, β_i, are linear. This does not mean, however, that the dependent variable, Y, is necessarily linearly related to the predictor variables. Scatter plots sometimes reveal a curvilinear relationship between X and Y. Multiple regression response surfaces are not restricted to linear surfaces and may be curvilinear.

To this point, the variables, X_i, have represented different predictors. For example, in the real estate example presented previously, the variables, X_1, X_2, represented two predictors: number of square feet in the house and the age of the house, respectively. Certainly, regression models can be developed for more than two predictors. For example, a marketing site-location model could be developed in which sales, as the response variable, is predicted by population density, number of competitors, size of the store, and number of salespeople. Such a model could take the form

$$Y = \beta_0 + \beta_1 X_1 + \beta_2 X_2 + \beta_3 X_3 + \beta_4 X_4 + \epsilon.$$

This regression model has four X_i variables, each of which represents a different predictor.

The general linear model also applies to situations in which some X_i represent recoded data from a predictor variable already represented in the model by another independent variable. In some models, X_i represents variables that have undergone a mathematical transformation to allow the model to follow the form of the general linear model.

This section explores some of these other linear models, including polynomial regression models, regression models with interaction, and models with transformed variables, along with some **nonlinear regression models.**

Nonlinear regression model
Multiple regression models in which the models are nonlinear, such as polynomial models, logarithmic models, and exponential models.

Polynomial Regression

Regression models in which the highest power of any predictor variable is 1 and in which there are no interaction terms—cross products $(X_i \cdot X_j)$—are referred to as *first-order models*. Simple regression models like those presented in Chapter 12 are *first-order models with one independent variable.* The general model for simple regression is

$$Y = \beta_0 + \beta_1 X_1 + \epsilon.$$

If a second independent variable is added, the model is referred to as a *first-order model with two independent variables* and appears as

$$Y = \beta_0 + \beta_1 X_1 + \beta_2 X_2 + \epsilon.$$

Polynomial regression models are regression models that are second- or higher-order models. They contain squared, cubed, or higher powers of the predictor variable(s) and contain response surfaces that are curvilinear. Yet, they are still special cases of the general linear model.

Consider a regression model with one independent variable where the model includes a second predictor, which is the independent variable squared. Such a model is referred to as a *second-order model with one independent variable* because the highest power among the predictors is 2, but there is still only one independent variable. This model takes the following form.

$$Y = \beta_0 + \beta_1 X_1 + \beta_2 X_1^2 + \epsilon$$

This model can be used to explore the possible fit of a quadratic model in predicting a dependent variable. How can this be a special case of the general linear model? Let X_2 of the general linear model be equal to X_1^2; then $Y = \beta_0 + \beta_1 X_1 + \beta_2 X_1^2 + \epsilon$ becomes $Y = \beta_0 + \beta_1 X_1 + \beta_2 X_2 + \epsilon$. Through what process does a business analyst go to develop the regression constant and coefficients for a curvilinear model such as this?

The process of multiple regression analysis assumes a linear fit of the regression coefficients and regression constant, but not necessarily a linear relationship of the independent variable values (Xs). Hence, a business analyst can often accomplish curvilinear regression by recoding the data *before* the multiple regression analysis is attempted.

As an example, consider the data given in Table 13.5. This table contains sales volumes (in \$1,000,000) for 13 manufacturing companies along with the number of manufacturer's representatives associated with each firm. A simple regression analysis to predict sales by the number of manufacturer's representatives results in the Excel output in Figure 13.10. This regression output shows a regression model with an r^2 of 87.0%, a standard error of the estimate equal to 51.10, a significant overall F test for the model, and a significant t ratio for the predictor number of manufacturer's representatives.

Figure 13.11(a) is a scatter plot for the data in Table 13.5. Notice that the plot of number of representatives and sales is not a straight line and is an indication that the relationship between the two variables may be curvilinear. To explore the possibility that there may be a quadratic relationship between sales and number of representatives, the business analyst creates a second predictor variable, (number of manufacturer's representatives)^2, to use in the regression analysis to predict sales along with number of manufacturer's representatives, as shown in Table 13.6. Thus, a variable can be created to explore second-order parabolic relationships by squaring the data from the independent variable of the linear model and entering it into the analysis. Figure 13.11(b) is a scatter plot of sales with (number of manufacturer's reps)^2. Note that this graph, with the squared term, more closely approaches a

TABLE 13.5
Sales Data for
13 Manufacturing Companies

MANUFACTURER	SALES (\$1,000,000)	NUMBER OF MANUFACTURING REPRESENTATIVES
1	2.1	2
2	3.6	1
3	6.2	2
4	10.4	3
5	22.8	4
6	35.6	4
7	57.1	5
8	83.5	5
9	109.4	6
10	128.6	7
11	196.8	8
12	280.0	10
13	462.3	11

Regression Statistics	
Multiple R	0.933
R Square	0.870
Adjusted R Square	0.858
Standard Error	51.10
Observations	13

Figure 13.10

Excel simple regression output for manufacturing example

ANOVA

	df	*SS*	*MS*	*F*	*Significance F*
Regression	1	192395	192395	73.69	0.000
Residual	11	28721	2611		
Total	12	221117			

	Coefficients	*Standard Error*	*t Stat*	*P-value*
Intercept	-107.03	28.737	-3.72	0.003
MfgrRp	41.026	4.779	1.54	0.000

Figure 13.11 Scatter plots of manufacturing data

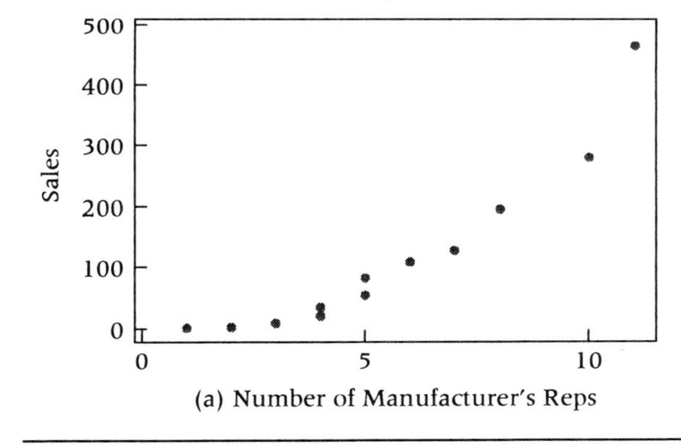

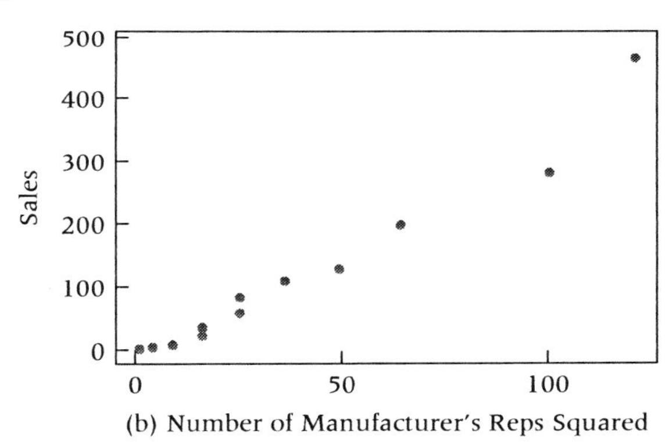

MANUFACTURER	SALES ($1,000,000) Y	NUMBER OF MGFR. REPS X_1	(NO. MGFR. REPS)^2 $X_2 = (X_1)^2$
1	2.1	2	4
2	3.6	1	1
3	6.2	2	4
4	10.4	3	9
5	22.8	4	16
6	35.6	4	16
7	57.1	5	25
8	83.5	5	25
9	109.4	6	36
10	128.6	7	49
11	196.8	8	64
12	280.0	10	100
13	462.3	11	121

TABLE 13.6
Display of Manufacturing Data with Newly Created Variable

straight line than does the graph in Figure 13.11(a). By recoding the predictor variable, the business analyst has potentially created a better regression fit.

With these data, a multiple regression model can be developed. Figure 13.12 shows the Excel output for the regression analysis to predict sales by number of manufacturer's representatives and (number of manufacturer's representatives)^2.

Examine the output in Figure 13.12 and compare it with the output in Figure 13.10 for the simple regression model. The R^2 for this model is 97.3%, which is an increase from the r^2 of 87.0% for the single linear predictor model. The standard error of the estimate for this model is 24.59, which is considerably lower than the 51.10 value obtained from the simple regression model. Remember, the sales figures were in units of \$1,000,000. The quadratic model reduced the standard error of the estimate by 26.51 (\$1,000,000), or \$26,510,000. It appears that the quadratic model is a better model for predicting sales.

An examination of the t statistic for the squared term and its associated probability in Figure 13.12 shows that it is statistically significant at $\alpha = .001$ ($t = 6.12$ with a probability of .000). If this t statistic were not significant, the business analyst would most likely drop the squared term and revert to the first-order model (simple regression model).

In theory, third- and higher-order models can be explored. Generally, business analysts tend to utilize first- and second-order regression models more than higher-order models. Remember that most regression analysis is used in business to aid decision making. Higher-power models (third, fourth, etc.) become difficult to interpret and difficult to explain to decision makers. In addition, the business analyst is usually looking for trends and general directions. The higher the order in regression modeling, the more the model tends to follow irregular fluctuations rather than meaningful directions.

Regression Models with Interaction

Often when two different independent variables are used in a regression analysis, there is an *interaction* between the two variables. This is the same interaction discussed in Chap-

Figure 13.12

Excel output for quadratic model of manufacturing example

Regression Statistics	
Multiple R	0.986
R Square	0.973
Adjusted R Square	0.967
Standard Error	24.59
Observations	13

ANOVA

	df	*SS*	*MS*	*F*	*Significance F*
Regression	2	215069	107534	177.79	0.000
Residual	10	6048	605		
Total	12	221117			

	Coefficients	*Standard Error*	*t Stat*	*P-value*
Intercept	18.067	24.673	0.73	0.481
MfgrRp	-15.723	9.550	-1.65	0.131
MfgrRpSq	4.750	0.776	6.12	0.000

ter 11 in two-way analysis of variance, where one variable will act differently over a given range of values for the second variable than it does over another range of values for the second variable. For example, in a manufacturing plant, temperature and humidity might interact in such a way as to have an effect on the hardness of the raw material. The air humidity may affect the raw material differently at different temperatures.

In regression analysis, interaction can be examined as a separate independent variable. An interaction predictor variable can be designed by multiplying the data values of one variable by the values of another variable, thereby creating a new variable. A model that includes an interaction variable is

$$Y = \beta_0 + \beta_1 X_1 + \beta_2 X_2 + \beta_3 X_1 X_2 + \epsilon.$$

The X_1X_2 term is the interaction term. Even though this model has 1 as the highest power of any one variable, it is considered to be a second-order equation because of the X_1X_2 term.

Suppose the data in Table 13.7 represent the closing stock prices for three corporations over a period of 15 months. An investment firm wants to use the prices for stocks 2 and 3 to develop a regression model to predict the price of stock 1. The form of the general linear regression equation for this model is

$$Y = \beta_0 + \beta_1 X_1 + \beta_2 X_2 + \epsilon.$$

where:

Y = price of stock 1,
X_1 = price of stock 2, and
X_2 = price of stock 3.

Using Excel to develop this regression model, the firm's business analyst obtains the first output displayed in Figure 13.13(a). This regression model is a first-order model with two predictors, X_1 and X_2. This model produced a modest R^2 of .472. Both of the t ratios are small and statistically nonsignificant ($t = -.62$ with a p value of .549 and $t = -.36$ with a p value of .728). Although the overall model is statistically significant, $F = 5.37$ with probability of .022, neither predictor is significant.

TABLE 13.7
Prices of Three Stocks over a 15-month Period

STOCK 1	STOCK 2	STOCK 3
41	36	35
39	36	35
38	38	32
45	51	41
41	52	39
43	55	55
47	57	52
49	58	54
41	62	65
35	70	77
36	72	75
39	74	74
33	83	81
28	101	92
31	107	91

Sometimes the effects of two variables are not additive because there are interacting effects between the two variables. In such a case, the business analyst can use multiple regression analysis to explore the interaction effects by including an interaction term in the equation.

$$Y = \beta_0 + \beta_1 X_1 + \beta_2 X_2 + \beta_3 X_1 X_2 + \epsilon$$

Figure 13.13

Two Excel Regression outputs—without and with interaction

(a) First regression analysis with 2 predictors without interaction

SUMMARY OUTPUT

Regression Statistics	
Multiple R	0.687
R Square	0.472
Adjusted R Square	0.384
Standard Error	4.570
Observations	15

ANOVA

	df	*SS*	*MS*	*F*	*Significance F*
Regression	2	224.29	112.15	5.37	0.022
Residual	12	250.64	20.89		
Total	14	474.93			

	Coefficients	*Standard Error*	*t Stat*	*P-value*
Intercept	50.8555	3.791	13.41	0.000
Stock 2	-0.1190	0.193	-0.62	0.549
Stock 3	-0.0708	0.199	-0.36	0.728

(b) Second regression analysis with the interaction variable included

SUMMARY OUTPUT

Regression Statistics	
Multiple R	0.897
R Square	0.804
Adjusted R Square	0.751
Standard Error	2.909
Observations	15

ANOVA

	df	*SS*	*MS*	*F*	*Significance F*
Regression	3	381.85	127.28	15.04	0.0003
Residual	11	93.09	8.46		
Total	14	474.93			

	Coefficients	*Standard Error*	*t Stat*	*P-value*
Intercept	12.046	9.312	1.29	0.222
Stock 2	0.879	0.262	3.36	0.006
Stock 3	0.220	0.144	1.54	0.153
Interaction	-0.010	0.002	-4.32	0.001

The equation fits the form of the general linear model,

$$Y = \beta_0 + \beta_1 X_1 + \beta_2 X_2 + \beta_3 X_3 + \epsilon,$$

where $X_3 = X_1X_2$. Each individual observation of X_3 is obtained through a recoding process by multiplying the associated observations of X_1 and X_2.

Applying this procedure to the stock example, the business analyst uses the interaction term and Excel to obtain the second regression output shown in Figure 13.13(b). This output contains X_1, X_2, and the interaction term, X_1X_2. Observe the R^2, which equals .804 for this model. The introduction of the interaction term has caused the R^2 to increase from 47.2% to 80.4%. In addition, the standard error of the estimate has decreased from 4.57 in the first model to 2.909 in the second model. The t ratios for both the X_1 term and the interaction term are statistically significant in the second model ($t = 3.36$ with a p value of .006 for X_1 and $t = -4.32$ with a probability of .001 for X_1X_2). The inclusion of the interaction term has helped the regression model account for a substantially greater amount of the dependent variable and is a significant contributor to the model.

Figure 13.14(a) is the response surface for the first regression model presented in Figure 13.13(a) (the model without interaction). As you observe the response plane with stock 3 as the point of reference, you see the plane moving upward with increasing values of stock 1 as the plane moves away from you toward smaller values of stock 2. Now examine Figure 13.14(b), the response surface for the second regression model presented in Figure 13.13(b) (the model with interaction). Note how the response plane is twisted, with its slope changing as it moves along stock 2. This pattern is caused by the interaction effects of stock 2 price and stock 3 prices. A cross section of the plane taken from left to right at any given stock 2 price produces a line that attempts to predict the price of stock 3 from the price of stock 1. As you more back through different prices of stock 2, the slope of that line changes, indicating that the relationship between stock 1 and stock 3 varies according to stock 2.

A business analyst also could develop a model using two independent variables with their squares and interaction. Such a model would be a *second-order model with two independent variables.* The model would look like this.

$$Y = \beta_0 + \beta_1 X_1 + \beta_2 X_2 + \beta_3 X_1^2 + \beta_4 X_2^2 + \beta_5 X_1 X_2 + \epsilon$$

This is sometimes referred to as the "full" quadratic model for two predictors.

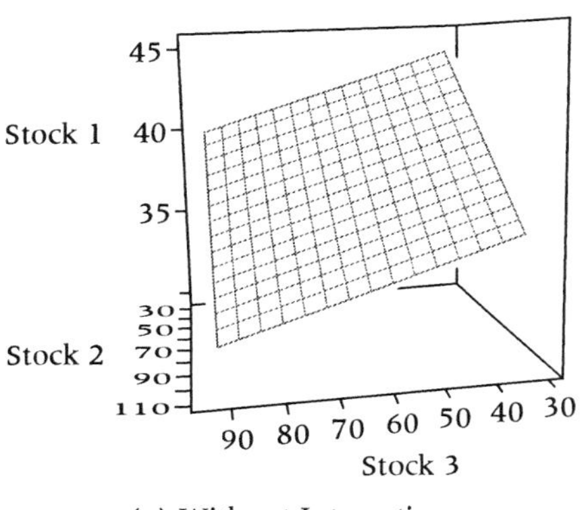

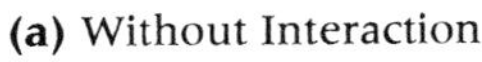

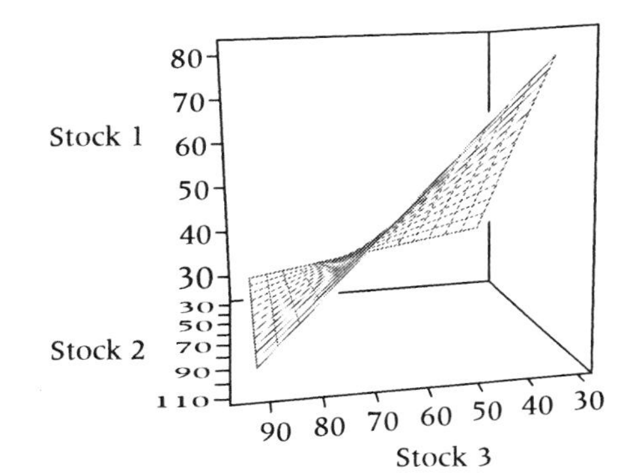

(b) With Interaction

Figure 13.14

Response surfaces for the stock example—without and with interaction

Model Transformation

To this point in examining polynomial and interaction models, the focus has been on recoding values of X variables. Some multiple regression situations require that the dependent variable, Y, be recoded. Two such transformations include log Y and $1/Y$.

Suppose the following data represent the annual sales and annual advertising expenditures for seven companies. Can a regression model be developed from these figures that can be used to predict annual sales by annual advertising expenditures?

COMPANY	SALES ($ MILLION/YEAR)	ADVERTISING ($ MILLION/YEAR)
1	2,580	1.2
2	11,942	2.6
3	9,845	2.2
4	27,800	3.2
5	18,926	2.9
6	4,800	1.5
7	14,550	2.7

One mathematical model that is a good candidate for fitting these data is an exponential model of the form

$$Y = \beta_0 \beta_1^X \epsilon.$$

This model can be transformed (by taking the log of each side) to get it in the form of the general linear equation.

$$\log Y = \log \beta_0 + X \log \beta_1$$

This transformed model requires a recoding of the Y data through the use of logarithms. Notice that X is not recoded but that the regression constant and coefficient are in logarithmic scale. If we let $Y' = \log Y$, $\beta_0' = \log \beta_0$, and $\beta_1' = \log \beta_1$, the exponential model is in the form of the general linear model.

$$Y' = \beta_0' + \beta_1' X$$

The process begins by taking the log of the Y values. The data used to build the regression model and the Excel regression output for these data follow.

LOG SALES (Y)	ADVERTISING (X)
3.4116	1.2
4.0771	2.6
3.9932	2.2
4.4440	3.2
4.2771	2.9
3.6812	1.5
4.1629	2.7

Regression Statistics	
Multiple R	0.990
R Square	0.980
Adjusted R Square	0.977
Standard Error	0.054
Observations	7

ANOVA

	df	*SS*	*MS*	*F*	*Significance F*
Regression	1	0.7392	0.7392	250.36	0.000
Residual	5	0.0148	0.0030		
Total	6	0.7540			

	Coefficients	*Standard Error*	*t Stat*	*P-value*
Intercept	2.9003	0.0729	39.80	0.000
Advertising (X)	0.4751	0.0300	15.82	0.000

A simple regression model (without the log recoding of the Y variable) yields an R^2 of 87% whereas the exponential model R^2 is 98%. The t statistic for advertising is 15.82 with a p value of 0.000 in the exponential model and 5.774 with a p value of 0.002 in the simple regression model. Thus the exponential model gives a better fit than does the simple regression model. An examination of (X^2, Y) and (X^3, Y) models reveals R^2 of .930 and .969, respectively, which are quite high but still not as good as the R^2 yielded by the exponential model.

The resulting equation of the exponential regression model is

$$Y = 2.9003 + .4751X.$$

In using this regression equation to determine predicted values of Y for X, remember that the resulting predicted Y value is in logarithmic form and the antilog of the predicted Y must be taken to get the predicted Y value in raw units. For example, to get the predicted Y value (sales) for an advertising figure of 2.0 ($ million), substitute $X = 2.0$ into the regression equation.

$$Y = 2.9003 + .4751X = 2.9003 + .4751(2.0) = 3.8505$$

The log of sales is 3.8505. Taking the antilog of 3.8505 results in the predicted sales in raw units.

$$\text{antilog}(3.8505) = 7087.61 \text{ (\$ million)}$$

Thus, the exponential regression model predicts that $2.0 million of advertising will result in $7,089.61 million of sales.

There are other ways to transform mathematical models so that they can be treated like the general linear model. One example is an inverse model such as

$$Y = \frac{1}{\beta_0 + \beta_1 X_1 + \beta_2 X_2 + \epsilon}.$$

Such a model can be manipulated algebraically into the form

$$\frac{1}{Y} = \beta_0 + \beta_1 X_1 + \beta_2 X_2 + \epsilon.$$

Substituting $Y' = 1/Y$ into this equation results in an equation that is in the form of the general linear model.

$$Y' = \beta_0 + \beta_1 X_1 + \beta_2 X_2 + \epsilon$$

To use this "inverse" model, recode the data values for Y by using $1/Y$. The regression analysis is done on the $1/Y$, X_1, and X_2 data. To get predicted values of Y from this model, enter the raw values of X_1 and X_2. The resulting predicted value of Y from the regression equation will be the inverse of the actual predicted Y value.

DEMONSTRATION PROBLEM 13.3

In the aerospace and defense industry, some cost estimators predict the cost of new space projects by using mathematical models that take the form

$$Y = \beta_0 X^{\beta_1} \epsilon.$$

These cost estimators often use the weight of the object being sent into space as the predictor (X) and the cost of the object as the dependent variable (Y). Quite often β_1 turns out to be a value between 0 and 1, resulting in the predicted value of Y equaling some root of X.

Use the sample cost data given here to develop a cost regression model in the form just shown to determine the equation for the predicted value of Y. Use this regression equation to predict the value of Y for $X = 3000$.

Y (COST IN BILLIONS)	X (WEIGHT IN TONS)
1.2	450
9.0	20,200
4.5	9,060
3.2	3,500
13.0	75,600
0.6	175
1.8	800
2.7	2,100

SOLUTION

The equation

$$Y = \beta_0 X^{\beta_1} \epsilon$$

is not in the form of the general linear model, but it can be transformed by using logarithms,

$$\log Y = \log \beta_0 + \beta_1 \log X + \epsilon,$$

which takes on the general linear form

$$Y' = \beta_0' + \beta_1 X',$$

where:

$Y' = \log Y$,

$\beta_0' = \log \beta_0$, and

$X' = \log X$.

This equation requires that both X and Y be recoded by taking the logarithm of each.

LOG Y	LOG X
.0792	2.6532
.9542	4.3054
.6532	3.9571
.5051	3.5441
1.1139	4.8785
−.2218	2.2430
.2553	2.9031
.4314	3.3222

Using these data, the computer produces the following regression constant and coefficient.

$$b'_0 = -1.25292 \quad b_1 = .49606$$

From these values, the equation of the predicted Y value is determined to be

$$\log \hat{Y} = -1.25292 + .49606 \log X.$$

If $X = 3000$, $\log X = 3.47712$, and

$$\log \hat{Y} = -1.25292 + .49606(3.47712) = .47194,$$

then

$$\hat{Y} = \text{antilog}(\log \hat{Y}) = \text{antilog}(.47194) = 2.9644.$$

The predicted value of Y is \$2.9644 billion for $X = 3000$ tons of weight.

Taking the antilog of $b_0' = -1.25292$ yields .055857. From this and $b_1 = .49606$, the model can be written in the original form:

$$Y = (.055857)X^{.49606}.$$

Substituting $X = 3000$ into this formula also yields \$2.9645 billion for the predicted value of Y.

13.4 Problems

13.19 Use the following data to develop a quadratic model to predict Y from X. Develop a simple regression model from the data and compare the results of the two models. Does the quadratic model seem to provide any better predictability? Why or why not?

X	Y	X	Y
14	200	15	247
9	74	8	82
6	29	5	21
21	456	10	94
17	320		

13.20 Use the following data to develop a curvilinear model to predict Y. Include both X_1 and X_2 in the model in addition to X_1^2, X_2^2, and the interaction term X_1X_2. Comment on the overall strength of the model and the significance of each predictor. Use a computer software package to graph the response surface of the "full" quadratic model. Develop a regression model with the same independent variables as the first model but without the interaction variable. Compare this model to the "full" quadratic model. Graph the response surface of this model. How does it compare to the response surface of the "full" model?

Y	X_1	X_2
47.8	6	7.1
29.1	1	4.2
81.8	11	10.0
54.3	5	8.0
29.7	3	5.7
64.0	9	8.8
37.4	3	7.1
44.5	4	5.4
42.1	4	6.5
31.6	2	4.9
78.4	11	9.1
71.9	9	8.5
17.4	2	4.2
28.8	1	5.8
34.7	2	5.9
57.6	6	7.8
84.2	12	10.2
63.2	8	9.4
39.0	3	5.7
47.3	5	7.0

13.21 Develop a multiple regression model of the form

$$Y = b_0 b_1^X \epsilon$$

using the following data to predict Y from X.

Y	X	Y	X
2485	3.87	740	2.83
1790	3.22	4010	3.62
874	2.91	3629	3.52
2190	3.42	8010	3.92
3610	3.55	7047	3.86
2847	3.61	5680	3.75
1350	3.13	1740	3.19

13.22 The Publishers Information Bureau, Inc., in New York City released magazine advertising expenditure data compiled by leading national advertisers. The data were organized by product type over several years in time. Shown here are data on total magazine advertising expenditures and household equipment and supplies advertising expenditures. Using these data, develop a regression model to predict total magazine advertising expenditures by household equipment and supplies advertising expenditures and by (household equipment and supplies advertising expenditures)^2. Compare this model to a regression model to predict total magazine advertising expenditures by only household equipment and supplies advertising expenditures. Construct a scatter plot of the data. Does the shape of the plot suggest some alternative models. If so, develop at least one other model and compare the model to the other two previously developed.

TOTAL MAGAZINE ADVERTISING EXPENDITURES (MILLIONS $)	HOUSEHOLD EQUIPMENT AND SUPPLIES EXPENDITURES (MILLIONS $)
1193	34
2846	65
4668	98
5120	93
5943	102
6644	103

13.23 Dun & Bradstreet Corporation reports, among other things, information about new business incorporations and number of business failures over the years. Shown here are data on business failures since 1970 and current liabilities of the failing companies. Use these data and the following model to predict current liabilities of the failing companies by the number of business failures. Discuss the strength of the model.

$$Y = b_0 b_1^X \epsilon$$

Now develop a different regression model by recoding *X*. Compare your models.

RATE OF BUSINESS FAILURES SINCE 1970 (10,000)	CURRENT LIABILITIES OF FAILING COMPANIES (MILLIONS $)
44	1,888
43	4,380
42	4,635
61	6,955
88	15,611
110	16,073
107	29,269
115	36,937
120	44,724
102	34,724
98	39,126
65	44,261

13.24 Shown here is Excel output for two regression analyses. The first regression analysis is done with the predictor variables X_1 and X_2. The second regression analysis is done with X_1 and X_2 along with an interaction term, X_1X_2. Study the output for each model and compare the models. Did the inclusion of the interaction term make much of a difference in the model?

Model without Interaction

Regression Statistics	
Multiple R	0.943
R Square	0.890
Adjusted R Square	0.882
Standard Error	4.199
Observations	30

ANOVA

	df	*SS*	*MS*	*F*	*Significance F*
Regression	2	3851.544	1925.722	109.24	0.0000
Residual	27	475.976	17.629		
Total	29	4327.521			

	Coefficients	*Standard Error*	*t Stat*	*P-value*
Intercept	-15.0805	9.6281	-1.57	0.1289
X1	0.5450	0.0615	8.86	0.0000
X2	0.6070	0.0556	10.92	0.0000

SUMMARY OUTPUT

Model with Interaction

Regression Statistics	
Multiple R	0.956
R Square	0.914
Adjusted R Square	0.904
Standard Error	3.778
Observations	30

ANOVA

	df	*SS*	*MS*	*F*	*Significance F*
Regression	3	3956.371	1318.79	92.38	0.0000
Residual	26	371.149	14.27		
Total	29	4327.521			

	Coefficients	*Standard Error*	*t Stat*	*P-value*
Intercept	103.398	44.571	2.32	0.0285
X1	-0.436	0.366	-1.19	0.2447
X2	-0.408	0.378	-1.08	0.2899
X1X2	0.008	0.003	2.71	0.0118

13.5 Model-Building: Search Procedures

To this point in the chapter, we have explored various types of multiple regression models, we have evaluated the strengths of regression models, and we have learned how to understand more about the output from Excel's regression analysis tool. In this section we examine procedures for developing several multiple regression model options to aid in the decision-making process.

Suppose a business analyst wants to develop a multiple regression model to predict the world production of crude oil. The business analyst realizes that much of the world crude oil market is driven by variables related to usage and production in the United States. She decides to use as predictors the following four independent variables.

1. U.S. energy consumption
2. Gross U.S. nuclear electricity generation
3. U.S. coal production
4. Fuel rate of U.S.-owned automobiles

The business analyst measured data for each of these variables for the year preceding each data point of world crude oil production, figuring that the world production is driven by the previous year's activities in the United States. It would seem that as the energy consumption of the United States increases, so would world production of crude oil. In addition, it makes sense that as nuclear electricity generation, coal production, and fuel rates increase, world crude oil production would decrease if energy consumption stays approximately constant.

In Table 13.8 are data for the four independent variables along with the dependent variable, world crude oil production. Using the data presented in Table 13.8, the business analyst attempted to develop a multiple regression model using four different independent variables. The result of this process was the Excel output in Figure 13.15. Examining the output, the business analyst can reach some conclusions about that particular model and its variables.

The output contains an R^2 value of 92.1%, a standard error of the estimate of 1.188, and an overall significant F value of 60.85. Notice from Figure 13.15 that the t ratios indicate that the regression coefficients of three of the predictor variables, nuclear, coal, and fuel rate, are not significant at $\alpha = .05$. If the business analyst were to drop these three variables out of the regression analysis and rerun the model with the other predictor only, what would happen to the model? What if the business analyst ran a regression model with only two or three predictors? How would these models compare to the full model with all four predictors? Are all the predictors necessary?

TABLE 13.8 Data for Multiple Regression Model to Predict Crude Oil Production

WORLD CRUDE OIL PRODUCTION (MILLION BARRELS PER DAY)	U.S. ENERGY CONSUMPTION (QUADRILLION BTUS PER YEAR)	U.S. NUCLEAR ELECTRICITY GROSS GENERATION (BILLION KILOWATT-HOURS)	U.S. COAL PRODUCTION (MILLION SHORT-TONS)	U.S. FUEL RATE FOR AUTOMOBILES (MILES PER GALLON)
55.7	74.3	83.5	598.6	13.4
55.7	72.5	114.0	610.0	13.6
52.8	70.5	172.5	654.6	14.0
57.3	74.4	191.1	684.9	13.8
59.7	76.3	250.9	697.2	14.1
60.2	78.1	276.4	670.2	14.3
62.7	78.9	255.2	781.1	14.6
59.6	76.0	251.1	829.7	16.0
56.1	74.0	272.7	823.8	16.5
53.5	70.8	282.8	838.1	16.9
53.3	70.5	293.7	782.1	17.1
54.5	74.1	327.6	895.9	17.4
54.0	74.0	383.7	883.6	17.5
56.2	74.3	414.0	890.3	17.4
56.7	76.9	455.3	918.8	18.0
58.7	80.2	527.0	950.3	18.8
59.9	81.4	529.4	980.7	19.0
60.6	81.3	576.9	1029.1	20.3
60.2	81.1	612.6	996.0	21.2
60.2	82.2	618.8	997.5	21.0
60.2	83.9	610.3	945.4	20.6
61.0	85.6	640.4	1033.5	20.8
62.3	87.2	673.4	1033.0	21.1
64.1	90.0	674.7	1063.9	21.2
66.3	90.6	628.6	1089.9	21.5
67.0	89.7	666.8	1109.8	21.6

Figure 13.15

Regression results for oil production example—model 15 (4 independent variables)

SUMMARY OUTPUT

Regression Statistics	
Multiple R	0.959
R Square	0.921
Adjusted R Square	0.905
Standard Error	1.1884
Observations	26

ANOVA

	df	*SS*	*MS*	*F*	*Significance F*
Regression	4	343.877	85.941	60.85	0.00000
Residual	21	29.661	1.412		
Total	25	373.427			

	Coefficients	*Standard Error*	*t Stat*	*P-value*
Intercept	3.8260	8.016	0.48	0.63807
USEnCons	0.7843	0.080	9.85	0.00000
USNucGen	-0.0043	0.007	-0.64	0.52768
USCoalPr	0.0109	0.006	1.74	0.09580
FuelRate	-0.8253	0.459	-1.80	0.08629

In developing regression models for business decision making, there are at least two considerations. The first is to develop a regression model that accounts for the most variation of the dependent variable—that is, develop models that maximize the explained proportion of the deviation of the Y values. At the same time, the regression model should be as parsimonious (simple and economic) as possible. The reason is that the more complicated a quantitative model becomes, the harder it is for managers to understand and implement the model. In addition, the more variables there are in a model, the more expensive it is to gather historical data or update present data for the model. These two considerations (dependent variable explanation and parsimony of the model) are quite often in opposition to each other. Hence the business analyst, as the model builder, often needs to explore many model options.

Search procedures
Processes whereby more than one multiple regression model is developed for a given database, and the models are compared and sorted by different criteria, depending on the given procedure.

All possible regressions
A multiple regression search procedure in which all possible multiple linear regression models are determined from the data using all variables.

In the world crude oil production regression model, if three variables explain the deviation of world crude oil production nearly as well as four variables, the simpler model is more attractive. Is there some way to conduct regression analysis so that the business analyst can examine several models and then choose the most attractive one? The answer is to use search procedures.

Search procedures are *processes whereby more than one multiple regression model is developed for a given data base, and the models are compared and sorted by different criteria, depending on the given procedure.* Virtually all search procedures are done on a computer. Several search procedures are discussed in this section, including all possible regressions, stepwise regression, forward selection, and backward elimination.

All Possible Regressions

The **all possible regressions** search procedure computes all the possible linear multiple regression models from the data using all the independent variables. If a data set contains k independent variables, this approach will compute $2^k - 1$ different regression models.

ONE PREDICTOR	TWO PREDICTORS	THREE PREDICTORS	FOUR PREDICTORS
X_1	X_1, X_2	X_1, X_2, X_3	X_1, X_2, X_3, X_4
X_2	X_1, X_3	X_1, X_2, X_4	
X_3	X_1, X_4	X_1, X_3, X_4	
X_4	X_2, X_3	X_2, X_3, X_4	
	X_2, X_4		
	X_3, X_4		

TABLE 13.9
Predictors for All Possible Regressions with Four Independent Variables

For the crude oil production example, the procedure of all possible regressions would produce $2^4 - 1 = 15$ different models for the $k = 4$ independent variables. It produces all the single-predictor models. The number of these equals the combination of four items taken one at a time, ${}_4C_1$. As discussed in Chapter 4, ${}_4C_1 = 4!/1!3! = 4$. In like manner, the all possible regressions procedure produces all the models with two predictors. The number of these equals the combination of four items taken two at a time, ${}_4C_2$. The value of ${}_4C_2 = 4!/2!2! = 6$. In like manner, the procedure produces four models with three predictors and one model with four predictors for a total of 15 different models. Table 13.9 presents the 15 possible combinations of predictors.

Once all the possible models have been determined, they are evaluated according to criteria that measure the adequacy of the model to fit the data. As discussed in Section 13.2, four possible measures of fit include the coefficient of determination, R^2; the adjusted R^2; the standard error of the estimate; and a test of the overall model with the F statistic.

The first of these four criteria, R^2, will always increase as more predictor variables are added to a model. The randomness of each added variable, even irrelevant variables, will improve the fit of the model. As a consequence, the model with all k variables will have the greatest R^2 value. The second of the four criteria, the adjusted R^2, modifies R^2 to account for the relationship of the sample size to the number of variables in the model. For that reason, the adjusted R^2 is used instead of R^2.

The third of these criteria, the standard error of the estimate, always yields equivalent results to the adjusted R^2. The model with the largest adjusted R^2 will also have the smallest standard error and vice versa.

The fourth criterion, the F statistic, measures the overall fit of a model. However, it is not useful for comparing models with differing degrees of freedom. To use it for such a comparison requires the consideration of the p-values for the corresponding F statistic values.

A criterion not discussed in Section 13.2 that is frequently used for comparing alternative regression models is the C_p statistic. It provides a measure of the difference between the estimated model and the true model. It is computed through the following equation.

$$C_p = \frac{(1 - R_p^2)(n - T)}{(1 - R_T^2)} - (n - 2p) + 2$$

where:

n = sample size
p = the number of independent variables included in a specific regression model
T = 1 + the number of independent variables in the full regression model (= $k + 1$)
R_p^2 = coefficient of determination for the regression model with p independent variables
R_T^2 = coefficient of determination for the full regression model

Figure 13.16 All possible regressions criteria values for oil production example

Regr. No.	Dependent Variable	Independents Variables Included				R Squared	Adjusted R Squared	Overall Model		Cp Computations			
		En Cons	Nuc Gen	Coal Pr	Fuel Rate			F Statistic	p Value	p	Rp-sqrd	Cp	Cp - p - 1
1	Cr Oil Prd	yes				0.8524	0.8462	138.6	1.86E-11	1	0.8524	17.04	15.04
2	Cr Oil Prd		yes			0.4500	0.4271	19.6	0.000176	1	0.4500	123.47	121.47
3	Cr Oil Prd			yes		0.3891	0.3637	15.3	0.000662	1	0.3691	139.57	137.57
4	Cr Oil Prd				yes	0.3425	0.3151	12.5	0.001686	1	0.3425	151.90	149.90
5	Cr Oil Prd	yes	yes			0.9055	0.8973	110.2	1.64E-12	2	0.9055	4.99	1.99
6	Cr Oil Prd	yes		yes		0.8828	0.8726	86.6	1.97E-11	2	0.8828	11.00	8.00
7	Cr Oil Prd	yes			yes	0.9083	0.9003	113.9	1.17E-12	2	0.9083	4.25	1.25
8	Cr Oil Prd		yes	yes		0.4524	0.4048	9.5	0.000983	2	0.4524	124.83	121.83
9	Cr Oil Prd		yes		yes	0.5313	0.4905	13.0	0.000164	2	0.5313	103.96	100.96
10	Cr Oil Prd			yes	yes	0.3946	0.3419	7.5	0.003118	2	0.3946	140.12	137.12
11	Cr Oil Prd	yes	yes	yes		0.9083	0.8958	72.7	1.42E-11	3	0.9083	6.25	2.25
12	Cr Oil Prd	yes	yes		yes	0.9091	0.8967	73.3	1.3E-11	3	0.9091	6.04	2.04
13	Cr Oil Prd	yes		yes	yes	0.9190	0.9080	83.2	3.66E-12	3	0.9190	3.42	-0.58
14	Cr Oil Prd		yes	yes	yes	0.5533	0.4924	9.1	0.00042	3	0.5533	100.14	96.14
15	Cr Oil Prd	yes	yes	yes	yes	0.9206	0.9054	60.8	3E-11	4	0.9206	5.00	0.00
		Maximum or Minimum Values =				***0.9206***	***0.9080***	***138.6***	***1.17E-12***				***-0.58***

For the crude oil production example of Figure 13.15, we note that the value for n is 26, the value of T is 5 and the value for R_T^2 is 0.92057. These three values are combined with the values for R_p^2 and p for each of the 15 possible models to compute a value for C_p for each of them.

If a model only has random differences from the true model, the average value of C_p is equal to $p + 1$. Furthermore, a regression model with a good fit will have a value of C_p that is less than $p + 1$. Therefore in evaluating alternative regression models with this statistic, the objective is to identify a model such that the value of the expression $(C_p - p - 1)$ is negative.

To demonstrate the use of all these criteria, we have run all 15 of the possible regressions for the crude oil production example. The values for each of the criteria for evaluating the adequacy of the model fit for all the regressions are summarized in Figure 13.16

Figure 13.16 presents the results for the 15 models beginning with the models with only one independent variable and ending with the one with all four independent variables. The regression results for the last model, designated as Model 15 in Figure 13.16, were previously presented in Figure 13.15.

The *values shown in the* R^2 *column* of Figure 13.16 are as expected. In particular as independent variables are added to a model, the R^2 value increases. Accordingly, the model with all four independent variables, Model 15, has the highest R^2 value.

SUMMARY OUTPUT

Regression Statistics	
Multiple R	0.959
R Square	0.919
Adjusted R Square	0.908
Standard Error	1.1725
Observations	26

ANOVA

	df	*SS*	*MS*	*F*	*Significance F*
Regression	3	343.183	114.394	83.21	0.0000
Residual	22	30.243	1.375		
Total	25	373.427			

	Coefficients	*Standard Error*	*t Stat*	*P-value*
Intercept	8.454	3.463	2.44	0.0231
USEnCons	0.754	0.063	11.94	0.0000
USCoalPr	0.010	0.006	1.71	0.1022
FuelRate	-1.028	0.328	-3.14	0.0048

Figure 13.17

Regression results for oil production example—Model 13 (3 independent variables)

The *adjusted R^2 value* takes into consideration both the additional information each new independent variable brings to a regression model and the changed degrees of freedom. As indicated in Figure 13.16, the best value for it is 0.9080 for Model 13. It has the three independent variables of "energy consumption," "coal production," and "fuel rate." The regression results for this model are shown in Figure 13.17.

As shown in Figure 13.17, the F value for the overall model is 83.21 with a corresponding p value (labeled as *Significant F*) of 0.00000000000366. Accordingly, the overall model is extremely significant. However an examination of the t ratios (labeled as *t Stat*) and their corresponding p values suggests that only the two variables, "energy consumption" and "fuel rate," are significant at $\alpha = .05$. This indicates it would be best to eliminate the variable, "coal production," from the model. The removal of it yields Model 7 of Figure 13.16. The regression results for Model 7 are shown in Figure 13.18.

The F value for the overall model in Figure 13.18 is 113.92 with a corresponding p value of 0.00000000000117. This is a slight improvement over Model 13. A comparison of the p values for the independent variables t ratios shows that both of them have improved (decreased).

To summarize these considerations, the adjusted R^2 criterion identified the three-variable Model 13 as the potentially best model. However, our further consideration of the individual independent variables suggests that actually the two-variable Model 7 is preferred.

The next criterion shown in Figure 13.16 is the *F statistic* value for the overall model. The highest value for it is for Model 1. However, the F statistic isn't meaningful in comparing models with different numbers of variables since it doesn't account for the differing degrees of freedom for finding the critical F value. The corresponding *p-value* for each F statistic value does take into consideration the degrees of freedom. The best p-value as shown in Figure 13.16 is for Model 7.

The final criterion of Figure 13.16 is the *C_p statistic.* As previously indicated, the goal for it is to identify a model with a C_p value greater than $p + 1$. The last column of

Figure 13.18

Regression results for oil production example—Model 7 (2 independent variables)

SUMMARY OUTPUT

Regression Statistics	
Multiple R	0.953
R Square	0.908
Adjusted R Square	0.900
Standard Error	1.2201
Observations	26

ANOVA

	df	*SS*	*MS*	*F*	*Significance F*
Regression	2	339.186	169.593	113.92	0.0000
Residual	23	34.240	1.489		
Total	25	373.427			

	Coefficients	*Standard Error*	*t Stat*	*P-value*
Intercept	7.1403	3.513	2.03	0.0538
USEnCons	0.7720	0.065	11.91	0.0000
FuelRate	-0.5173	0.138	-3.75	0.0011

Figure 13.16 identifies only one model with such a condition. It is Model 13 again. The regression results for it were given in Figure 13.17. As before a further consideration of these results would lead to the conclusion that it would be best to delete the "coal production" variable. Thus, we again conclude that Model 7 is better.

In passing, we should point out that the C_p *minus* $p + 1$ column shows a value of zero for the full model, Model 15. This will always be true for the full model. Through manipulation of the algebraic expression for C_p *minus* $p + 1$, it can be shown that it will always be zero for the full model.

We have considered five separate criteria in our discussion of Figure 13.16. As we have shown, two of these—R^2 and the F statistic—are not useful in comparing alternative regression models with varying number of variables. The use of the other three, the adjusted R^2, the p-value for the overall model, and the C_p statistic, have been demonstrated. For the crude oil production example, all three of these criteria resulted in identifying Model 7 as the preferred relationship. This consistency among the three criteria will not always occur. Particularly for problems with a larger number of potential independent variables, it may well be that these criteria identify different preferred models. It may then be necessary for the business analyst to use other considerations to select among these preferred models.

As previously mentioned, the all possible regressions search procedure requires considering a total of $2^k - 1$ models where k is the total number of independent variables. Accordingly, the possible number of models to be considered for various values of k is as given in column two of Table 13.10. However, this number can be reduced slightly by noting that the best *one* independent variable model will always be the model produced using the independent variable that has the highest correlation coefficient value with the dependent variable. For the oil production example, Excel provides the correlation coefficients given in Figure 13.19. From these values, we can conclude the best one variable model will be that with "energy consumption" as the independent variable. This conclusion is consistent with all five criteria for the four one independent variable models given in Figure 13.16.

TABLE 13.10
Number of Regressions to be Evaluated

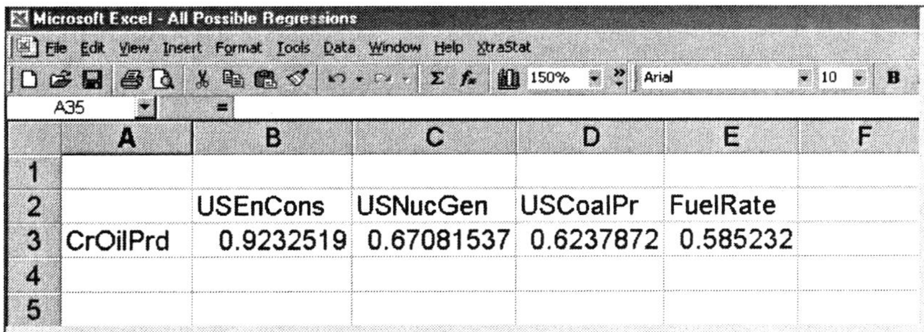

k	$2^k - 1$	$2^k - k$
1	1	1
2	3	2
3	7	3
4	15	12
5	31	27
6	63	58
7	127	121

Microsoft Excel - All Possible Regressions

	A	B	C	D	E	F
1						
2		USEnCons	USNucGen	USCoalPr	FuelRate	
3	CrOilPrd	0.9232519	0.67081537	0.6237872	0.585232	
4						
5						

Figure 13.19
Oil production example correlation coefficients

By incorporating the use of the simple correlation coefficients for the one independent variable models into the all possible regressions procedure, the number of models to be considered is reduced by $k - 1$. Thus, the total number of models to be evaluated is computed as $(2^k - 1) - (k - 1) = (2^k - k)$. Values for this expression are given in the third column of Table 13.10.

The all possible regressions search procedure enables the business analyst to consider every possible model. In theory, this eliminates the chance that the analyst will never consider some models, as can be the case with the search procedures given below. On the other hand, the search through all the possible models may require more time and effort than is reasonable. This may particularly become an issue for problems with a large number of potential independent variables. As a result, a number of search procedures have been suggested for identifying the *best* model without the need to evaluate all possible models. Three such procedures that are frequently used are the forward selection, the backward elimination, and the stepwise regression procedures. All three of these procedures use a stepwise approach for attempting to identify the *best* model without evaluating all possible models. All three of these search procedures are oftentimes included in specialized statistical software packages.

Other Search Procedures

FORWARD SELECTION The **forward selection** search procedure starts with a model with no independent variables. It then considers all k models with one independent variable. It chooses the model with the highest simple correlation coefficient (or r^2) with the dependent variable. Suppose this variable is designated as X_1. Next the procedure examines the $k - 1$ two-variable models that include X_1 and each of the remaining $k - 1$ variables individually. It selects the two-variable model with the highest R^2 (or F) and designates this second variable as X_2. The procedure next considers the $k - 2$ three-variable models that include X_1, X_2, and each of the remaining $k - 2$ variables individually. The

Forward selection
A multiple regression search procedure that is essentially the same as stepwise regression analysis except that once a variable is entered into the process, it is never deleted.

procedure selects the three-variable model with the highest R^2 (or F). Forward selection continues adding variables in this manner until the addition of a variable results in an insignificant increase in R^2 as determined by an F test. As you will note from this description, once a variable is added to the model it doesn't leave.

Backward elimination A step-by-step multiple regression search procedure that continues until only variables with significant t values remain in the model.

BACKWARD ELIMINATION The **backward elimination** search procedure is the opposite of the forward selection procedure. It starts with a model that includes all the independent variables. It then considers all k models in which one of the variables is removed. These models have $k - 1$ independent variables. It selects the variable that causes the smallest decrease in R^2 to be eliminated from the model. Next the procedure considers the $k - 1$ models in which one additional variable is removed. These models have $k - 2$ independent variables. The variable that causes the smallest decrease in R^2 is eliminated from the model. The procedure continues eliminating variables in this manner until the deletion of a variable results in a significant decrease in R^2 as evaluated by an F test. For this procedure once a variable leaves the model it is not considered for re-entry later.

Stepwise regression A step-by-step multiple regression search procedure that begins by developing a regression model with a single predictor variable and adds and deletes predictors one step at a time, examining the fit of the model at each step until there are no more significant predictors remaining outside the model.

STEPWISE REGRESSION The **stepwise regression** search procedure is the most flexible of these three procedures. It is similar to the forward selection procedure. However at the end of each step in the process of adding variables, it considers all the variables in the model for possible removal. If the contribution of a previously added variable becomes insignificant with the addition of the latest variable, that previously added variable is removed. Thus, the procedure is a combination of the forward selection and the backward elimination procedures. The stepwise regression procedure continues adding variables and then considering the elimination of prior variables in this manner until the addition of a variable results in an insignificant increase in R^2 as determined by an F test. Each variable that is deleted from the model at some step is considering for possible re-entry at the later steps in the process.

13.5 Problems

13.25 Use Excel and the following data to develop all possible regression models to predict Y. Use adjusted R^2 and the C_p statistic to select the strongest model.

Y	X_1	X_2	X_3
21	5	108	57
17	11	135	34
14	14	113	21
13	9	160	25
19	16	122	43
15	18	142	40
24	7	93	52
17	9	128	38
22	13	105	51
20	10	111	43
16	20	140	20
13	19	150	14
18	14	126	29
12	21	175	22
23	6	98	38
18	15	129	40

13.26 Given here are the data for a dependent variable and four potential predictors. Use these data and Excel to develop all possible regression models to predict Y. Use adjusted R^2 and the C_p statistic to select the strongest model.

Y	X_1	X_2	X_3	X_4
101	2	77	1.2	42
127	4	72	1.7	26
98	9	69	2.4	47
79	5	53	2.6	65
118	3	88	2.9	37
114	1	53	2.7	28
110	3	82	2.8	29
94	2	61	2.6	22
96	8	60	2.4	48
73	6	64	2.1	42
108	2	76	1.8	34
124	5	74	2.2	11
82	6	50	1.5	61
89	9	57	1.6	53
76	1	72	2.0	72
109	3	74	2.8	36
123	2	99	2.6	17
125	6	81	2.5	48

13.27 The National Underwriter Company in Cincinnati, Ohio, publishes property and casualty insurance data. Given here is a portion of the data published. These data include information from the U.S. insurance industry about (1) net income after taxes, (2) dividends to policyholders, (3) net underwriting gain/loss, and (4) premiums earned. Use the data and all possible regressions to predict premiums earned from the other three variables. Compute the C_p statistic on each model and use it along with the adjusted R^2 to select the "best" model.

PREMIUMS EARNED	NET INCOME	DIVIDENDS	UNDERWRITING GAIN/LOSS
30.2	1.6	.6	.1
47.2	.6	.7	−3.6
92.8	8.4	1.8	−1.5
95.4	7.6	2.0	−4.9
100.4	6.3	2.2	−8.1
104.9	6.3	2.4	−10.8
113.2	2.2	2.3	−18.2
130.3	3.0	2.4	−21.4
161.9	13.5	2.3	−12.8
182.5	14.9	2.9	−5.9
193.3	11.7	2.9	−7.6

13.28 The U.S. Energy Information Administration releases figures in their publication, *Monthly Energy Review*, about the cost of various fuels and electricity. Following are the figures for four different items over a 12-year period. Use the data and all possible regressions to predict the cost of residential electricity from the cost of residential natural gas, residual fuel oil, and leaded regular gasoline. Examine the data and discuss the output in light of C_p and adjusted R^2.

RESIDENTIAL ELECTRICITY (kWh)	RESIDENTIAL NATURAL GAS (1000 FT³)	RESIDUAL FUEL OIL (GAL)	LEADED REGULAR GASOLINE (GAL)
2.54	1.29	.21	.39
3.51	1.71	.31	.57
4.64	2.98	.44	.86
5.36	3.68	.61	1.19
6.20	4.29	.76	1.31
6.86	5.17	.68	1.22
7.18	6.06	.65	1.16
7.54	6.12	.69	1.13
7.79	6.12	.61	1.12
7.41	5.83	.34	.86
7.41	5.54	.42	.90
7.49	4.49	.33	.90

13.6 Multicollinearity

Multicollinearity
A problematic condition that occurs when two or more of the independent variables of a multiple regression model are highly correlated.

One problem that can arise in multiple regression analysis is multicollinearity. **Multicollinearity** is *when two or more of the independent variables of a multiple regression model are highly correlated.* Technically, if two of the independent variables are correlated, we have *collinearity;* when three or more independent variables are correlated, we have multicollinearity, However, the two terms are frequently used interchangeably.

The reality of business research is that most of the time there is some correlation between predictors (independent variables). The problem of multicollinearity arises when the intercorrelation between predictor variables is high. This causes several other problems, particularly in the interpretation of the analysis.

1. It is difficult, if not impossible, to interpret the estimates of the regression coefficients.
2. Inordinately small t values for the regression coefficients may result.
3. The standard deviations of regression coefficients are overestimated.
4. The algebraic sign of estimated regression coefficients may be the opposite of what would be expected for a particular predictor variable.

There are many situations in business research where the problem of multicollinearity can arise in regression analysis. For example, suppose a model is being developed to predict salaries in a given industry. Independent variables such as years of education, age, years in management, experience on the job, and years of tenure with the firm might be considered as predictors. It is obvious that several of these variables are correlated and yield redundant information. Suppose a financial regression model is being developed to predict bond market rates by such independent variables as Dow Jones average, prime interest rates, GNP, producer price index, and consumer price index. Several of these predictors are likely to be intercorrelated.

In the world crude oil production example used in Section 13.5, several of the independent variables are intercorrelated, leading to the potential of multicollinearity problems. Table 13.11 gives the correlations of the predictor variables for this example. Note that r values are quite high ($r > .90$) for fuel rate and nuclear (.972), fuel rate and coal (.968), and coal and nuclear (.952).

Table 13.11 shows that fuel rate and coal production are highly correlated. Using fuel rate as a single predictor of crude oil production produces the following simple regression model.

$$\hat{Y} = 44.869 + .7838(\text{fuel rate}).$$

TABLE 13.11
Correlations among Oil Production Predictor Variables

	ENERGY CONSUMPTION	NUCLEAR	COAL	FUEL RATE
Energy consumption	1	.856	.791	.791
Nuclear	.856	1	.952	.972
Coal	.791	.952	1	.968
Fuel rate	.796	.972	.968	1

Notice that the estimate of the regression coefficient, .7838, is positive, indicating that as fuel rate increases, oil production increases. Using coal as a single predictor of crude oil production yields the following simple regression model.

$$\hat{Y} = 45.072 + .0157(\text{coal})$$

The multiple regression model developed using both fuel rate and coal to predict crude oil production is

$$\hat{Y} = 45.806 + .02278(\text{coal}) - .3934(\text{fuel rate}).$$

Observe that this regression model indicates a *negative* relationship between fuel rate and oil production (–.3934), which is in opposition to the *positive* relationship shown in the regression equation for fuel rate as a single predictor. Because of the multicollinearity between coal and fuel rate, these two independent variables interact in the regression analysis in such a way as to produce regression coefficient estimates that are difficult to interpret. Extreme caution should be exercised before interpreting these regression coefficient estimates.

The problem of multicollinearity can also affect the t values that are used to evaluate the regression coefficients. Because the problems of multicollinearity among predictors can result in an overestimation of the standard deviation of the regression coefficients, the t values tend to be underrepresentative when multicollinearity is present. There are regression models containing multicollinearity in which all t values are nonsignificant but the overall F value for the model is highly significant.

This collinearity may explain the fact that the overall model is significant but none of the predictors are significant. It also underscores one of the problems with multicollinearity: underrepresented t values. The t values test the strength of the predictor given the other variables in the model. If a predictor is highly correlated with other independent variables, it will appear not to add much to the explanation of Y and produce a low t value. However, had the predictor not been in the presence of these other variables, the predictor might have explained a high proportion of variation of Y.

Many of the problems created by multicollinearity are interpretation problems. The business analyst should be alert to and aware of multicollinearity potential with the predictors in the model and view the model outcome in light of such potential.

The problem of multicollinearity is not a simple one to overcome. However, there are several ways to make inroads into the problem. One way is to examine a correlation matrix like the one in Table 13.11 to search for possible intercorrelations among potential predictor variables. If several variables are highly correlated, the business analyst can select the variable that is most correlated to the dependent variable and use that variable to represent the others in the analysis. One problem with this idea is that correlations can be more complex than simple correlation among variables. That is, simple correlation values do not always reveal multiple correlation between variables. In some instances, variables may not appear to be correlated as pairs, but one variable is a linear combination of several other variables. This situation is also an example of multicollinearity, and a cursory observation of the correlation matrix will probably not reveal the problem.

Stepwise regression is another way to prevent the problem of multicollinearity. The search process enters the variables one at a time and compares the new variable to those in solution. If a new variable is entered and the t values on old variables become nonsignificant, the old variables are dropped out of solution. In this manner, it is more difficult for the problem of multicollinearity to affect the regression analysis. Of course, because of multicollinearity, some important predictors may not enter in to the analysis.

Variance inflation factor A statistic computed using the R^2 value of a regression model developed by predicting one independent variable of a regression analysis by other independent variables; used to determine whether there is multicollinearity among the variables.

Other techniques are available to attempt to control for the problem of multicollinearity. One is called a **variance inflation factor,** in which a regression analysis is done to predict an independent variable by the other independent variables. In this case, the independent variable being predicted becomes the dependent variable. As this process is done for each of the independent variables, it is possible to determine whether any of the independent variables are a function of the other independent variables, yielding evidence of multicollinearity. By using the R_i^2 from such a model, a variance inflation factor (VIF) can be computed to determine whether the standard errors of the estimates are inflated:

$$\text{VIF} = \frac{1}{1 - R_i^2}$$

where R_i^2 is the coefficient of determination for any of the models to predict an independent variable by the other $k - 1$ independent variables. Some business analysts follow a guideline that if the variance inflation factor is greater than 10 or the R_i^2 value is more than .90 for the largest variance inflation factors, a severe multicollinearity problem is present.*

13.6

Problems

13.29 Develop a correlation matrix for the independent variables in Problem 13.25. Study the matrix and make a judgment as to whether or not substantial multicollinearity is present among the predictors. Why or why not?

13.30 Construct a correlation matrix for the four independent variables for Problem 13.26 and search for possible multicollinearity. What did you find and why?

13.31 In Problem 13.27, you were asked to compute all possible regressions to predict premiums earned by net income, dividends, and underwriting gain or loss. Study the results, including the regression coefficients, to determine whether there may be a problem with multicollinearity. Construct a correlation matrix of the three variables to aid you in this task.

13.32 Study the three predictor variables in Problem 13.28 and attempt to determine whether substantial multicollinearity is present between the predictor variables. If there is a problem of multicollinearity, how could that affect the outcome of the multiple regression analysis?

*William Mendenhall and Terry Sincich, *A Second Course in Business Statistics: Regression Analysis.* San Francisco, Dellen Publishing Company, 1989. John Neter, William Wasserman, Michael H. Kutner, *Applied Linear Regression Models,* 2d ed., Homewood, IL, Richard D. Irwin, Inc., 1989.

Summary

Multiple regression analysis is a statistical tool in which a mathematical model is developed in an attempt to predict a dependent variable by two or more independent variables or in which at least one predictor is nonlinear. Because doing multiple regression analysis by hand is extremely tedious and time-consuming, it is almost always done on a computer.

The standard output from a multiple regression analysis is similar to that of simple regression analysis. A regression equation is produced with a constant that is analogous to the Y intercept in simple regression and with estimates of the regression coefficients that are analogous to the estimate of the slope in simple regression. An F test for the overall model is computed to test to determine whether at least one of the regression coefficients is significantly different from zero. This F value is usually displayed in an ANOVA table, which is part of the regression output. The ANOVA table also contains the sum of squares of error and sum of squares of regression, which are used to compute other statistics in the model.

Computer regression output contains t values, which are used to determine the significance of the regression coefficients. Using these t values, statisticians can make decisions about including or excluding variables from the model.

Residuals, standard error of the estimate, and R^2 are also standard multiple regression computer output. The coefficient of determination for simple regression models is denoted r^2, whereas for multiple regression it is R^2. The interpretation of residuals, standard error of the estimate, and R^2 in multiple regression is very similar to that in simple regression. Because R^2 can be inflated with nonsignificant variables in the mix, an adjusted R^2 is often computed. Unlike R^2, adjusted R^2 takes into account the degrees of freedom and the number of observations.

Indicator, or dummy, variables are qualitative variables that are used to represent categorical data in the multiple regression model. These variables are coded as 0, 1 and are often used to represent nominal or ordinal classification data that the business analyst wants to use in the regression analysis. If a qualitative variable contains more than two categories, it generates multiple dummy variables. In general, if a qualitative variable contains c categories, $c - 1$ dummy variables should be created.

Multiple regression analysis can handle nonlinear independent variables. One way to do this is to recode the data and enter the variables into the analysis in the normal way.

However, some nonlinear regression models, such as exponential models, require that the entire model be transformed. Often the transformation involves the use of logarithms. In some cases, the resulting value of the regression model is in logarithmic form and the antilogarithm of the answer must be taken to determine the predicted value of Y.

Search procedures are used to help sort through the independent variables as predictors in the examination of various possible models. Several search procedures are available, including *all possible regressions, stepwise regression, forward selection,* and *backward elimination.* The *all possible regressions* procedure computes every possible regression model for a set of data. The drawbacks of this procedure include the time and energy required to compute all possible regressions and the difficulty of deciding which models are most appropriate. The *stepwise regression* procedure involves selecting and adding one independent variable at a time to the regression process after beginning with a one-predictor model. Variables are added to the model at each step if they contain the most significant t value associated with the remaining variables. If no additional t value is statistically significant at any given step, the procedure stops. With stepwise regression, at each step the process examines the variables already in the model to determine whether their t values are still significant. If not, they are dropped from the model, and the process searches for other independent variables with large, significant t values to replace the variable(s) dropped. The *forward selection procedure* is the same as stepwise regression but does not drop variables out of the model once they have been included. The *backward elimination* procedure begins with a "full" model, a model that contains all the independent variables. The sample size must be large enough to justify a full model, which can be a limiting factor. Backward elimination starts dropping out the least important predictors one at a time until only significant predictors are left in the regression model.

One of the problems in using multiple regression is multicollinearity, or correlations among the predictor variables. This problem can cause overinflated estimates of the standard deviations of regression coefficients, misinterpretation of regression coefficients, undersized t values, and misleading signs on the regression coefficients. It can be lessened by using an intercorrelation matrix of independent variables to help recognize bivariate correlation; by using stepwise regression to sort the variables one at a time; and/or by using statistics such as a variance inflation factor.

Key Terms

adjusted R^2
all possible regressions
backward elimination
coefficient of multiple determination (R^2)
dependent variable
dummy variable
forward selection
general linear regression model
independent variable
indicator variable
least squares analysis
multicollinearity
multiple regression
nonlinear regression model
outliers
partial regression coefficient
qualitative variable
R^2
residual
response plane
response surface
response variable
search procedures
standard error of the estimate (S_e)
stepwise regression
sum of squares of error (SSE)
variance inflation factor

SUPPLEMENTARY PROBLEMS

13.33 Use the following data to develop a multiple regression model to predict Y from X_1 and X_2. Discuss the output, including comments about the overall strength of the model, the significance of the regression coefficients, and other indicators of model fit.

X_1	X_2	Y
29	1.64	198
71	2.81	214
54	2.22	211
73	2.70	219
67	1.57	184
32	1.63	167
47	1.99	201
43	2.14	204
60	2.04	190
32	2.93	222
34	2.15	197

13.34 Given here are the data for a dependent variable, Y, and independent variables. Use these data to develop a regression model to predict Y. Discuss the output. Which variable is an indicator variable? Was it a significant predictor of Y?

X_1	X_2	X_3	Y
0	51	16.4	14
0	48	17.1	17
1	29	18.2	29
0	36	17.9	32
0	40	16.5	54
1	27	17.1	86
1	14	17.8	117
0	17	18.2	120
1	16	16.9	194
1	9	18.0	203
1	14	18.9	217
0	11	18.5	235

13.35 Use the following data and an all possible regression analysis to predict Y. In addition to the two independent variables given here, include three other predictors in your analysis: the square of each X as a predictor and an interaction predictor. Discuss the results of the process.

X_1	X_2	Y	X_1	X_2	Y
10	3	2002	5	12	1750
5	14	1747	6	8	1832
8	4	1980	5	18	1795
7	4	1902	7	4	1917
6	7	1842	8	5	1943
7	6	1883	6	9	1830
4	21	1697	5	12	1786
11	4	2021			

13.36 Use the X_1 values and the log of the X_1 values given here to predict the Y values by using an all possible regressions procedure. Discuss the output. Were either or both of the predictors significant?

Y	X_1	Y	X_1
20.4	850	13.2	204
11.6	146	17.5	487
17.8	521	12.4	192
15.3	304	10.6	98
22.4	1029	19.8	703
21.9	910	17.4	394
16.4	242	19.4	647

13.37 The U.S. Commodities Futures Trading Commission reports on the volume of trading in the U.S. commodity futures exchanges. Shown here are the figures for grain, oilseeds, and livestock products over a period of several years. Use these data to develop a multiple regression model to predict grain futures volume of trading from oilseeds volume and livestock products volume. All figures are given in units of millions. Graph each of these predictors separately with the response variable and use these to explore possible recoding schemes for nonlinear relationships. Include any of these in the regression model. Comment on the results.

GRAIN	OILSEEDS	LIVESTOCK
2.2	3.7	3.4
18.3	15.7	11.8
19.8	20.3	9.8
14.9	15.8	11.0
17.8	19.8	11.1
15.9	23.5	8.4
10.7	14.9	7.9
10.3	13.8	8.6
10.9	14.2	8.8
15.9	22.5	9.6
15.9	21.1	8.2

13.38 The U.S. Bureau of Mines produces data on the price of minerals. Shown here are the average prices per year for several minerals over a decade. Use these data and an all possible regressions procedure to produce a model to predict the average price of gold from the other variables. Comment on the results of the process.

GOLD ($ PER OZ)	COPPER (CENTS PER LB)	SILVER ($ PER OZ)	ALUMINUM (CENTS PER LB)
161.1	64.2	4.4	39.8
308.0	93.3	11.1	61.0
613.0	101.3	20.6	71.6
460.0	84.2	10.5	76.0
376.0	72.8	8.0	76.0
424.0	76.5	11.4	77.8
361.0	66.8	8.1	81.0
318.0	67.0	6.1	81.0
368.0	66.1	5.5	81.0
448.0	82.5	7.0	72.3
438.0	120.5	6.5	110.1
382.6	130.9	5.5	87.8

13.39 The Shipbuilders Council of America in Washington, DC, publishes data about private shipyards. Among the variables reported by this organization are the employment figures (per 1000), the number of naval vessels under construction, and the number of repairs or conversions done to commercial ships (in millions of dollars). Shown here are the data for these three variables over a 7-year period. Use the data to develop a regression model to predict private shipyard employment from number of naval vessels under construction and repairs or conversions of commercial ships. Graph each of these predictors separately with the response variable and use these graphs to explore possible recoding schemes for nonlinear relationships. Include any of these in the regression model. Comment on the regression model and its strengths and/or its weaknesses.

EMPLOYMENT	NAVAL VESSELS	COMMERCIAL SHIP REPAIRS OR CONVERSIONS
133.4	108	431
177.3	99	1335
143.0	105	1419
142.0	111	1631
130.3	100	852
120.6	85	847
120.4	79	806

13.40 The U.S. Bureau of Labor Statistics produces consumer price indexes for several different categories. Shown here are the percentage changes in consumer price indexes over a period of 20 years for food, shelter, apparel, and fuel oil. Also displayed are the percentage changes in consumer price indexes for all commodities. Use these data and on all possible regression procedure to develop a model that attempts to predict all commodities by the other four variables. Construct scatter plots of each of these with all commodities. Examine the graphs and use the information to develop any other appropriate predictor variables by recoding data and include them in the analysis. Comment on the result of this analysis.

ALL COMMODITIES	FOOD	SHELTER	APPAREL	FUEL OIL
.9	1.0	2.0	1.6	3.7
.6	1.3	.8	.9	2.7
.9	.7	1.6	.4	2.6
.9	1.6	1.2	1.3	2.6
1.2	1.3	1.5	.9	2.1
1.1	2.2	1.9	1.1	2.4
2.6	5.0	3.0	2.5	4.4
1.9	.9	3.6	4.1	7.2
3.5	3.5	4.5	5.3	6.0
4.7	5.1	8.3	5.8	6.7
4.5	5.7	8.9	4.2	6.6
3.6	3.1	4.2	3.2	6.2
3.0	4.2	4.6	2.0	3.3
7.4	14.5	4.7	3.7	4.0
11.9	14.3	9.6	7.4	9.3
8.8	8.5	9.9	4.5	12.0
4.3	3.0	5.5	3.7	9.5
5.8	6.3	6.6	4.5	9.6
7.2	9.9	10.2	3.6	8.4
11.3	11.0	13.9	4.3	9.2

13.41 The U.S. Department of Agriculture publishes data annually on various selected farm products. Shown here are the unit production figures for three farm products for 10 years during a 20-year period. Use these data and an all possible regression analysis to predict corn production by the production of soybeans and wheat. Comment on the results.

CORN (MILLION BUSHELS)	SOYBEANS (MILLION BUSHELS)	WHEAT (MILLION BUSHELS)
4152	1127	1352
6639	1798	2381
4175	1636	2420
7672	1861	2595
8876	2099	2424
8226	1940	2091
7131	1938	2108
4929	1549	1812
7525	1924	2037
7933	1922	2739

13.42 Cost-of-living indexes for selected metropolitan areas have been accumulated by the American Chamber of Commerce Business analysts Association. Shown here are cost-of-living indexes for 25 different cities on five different items for a recent year. Use the data to develop a regression model to predict the grocery cost-of-living index by the indexes of housing, utilities, transportation, and healthcare. Discuss the results, highlighting both the significant and nonsignificant predictors.

CITY	GROCERY ITEMS	HOUSING	UTILITIES	TRANSPORTATION	HEALTHCARE
Albany	108.3	106.8	127.4	89.1	107.5
Albuquerque	96.3	105.2	98.8	100.9	102.1
Augusta, GA	96.2	88.8	115.6	102.3	94.0
Austin	98.0	83.9	87.7	97.4	94.9
Baltimore	106.0	114.1	108.1	112.8	111.5
Buffalo	103.1	117.3	127.6	107.8	100.8
Colorado Springs	94.5	88.5	74.6	93.3	102.4
Dallas	105.4	98.9	108.9	110.0	106.8
Denver	91.5	108.3	97.2	105.9	114.3
Des Moines	94.3	95.1	111.4	105.7	96.2
El Paso	102.9	94.6	90.9	104.2	91.4
Indianapolis	96.0	99.7	92.1	102.7	97.4
Jacksonville, FL	96.1	90.4	96.0	106.0	96.1
Kansas City	89.8	92.4	96.3	95.6	93.6
Knoxville	93.2	88.0	91.7	91.6	82.3
Los Angeles	103.3	211.3	75.6	102.1	128.5
Louisville	94.6	91.0	79.4	102.4	88.4
Memphis	99.1	86.2	91.1	101.1	85.5
Miami	100.3	123.0	125.6	104.3	137.8
Minneapolis	92.8	112.3	105.2	106.0	107.5
Mobile	99.9	81.1	104.9	102.8	92.2
Nashville	95.8	107.7	91.6	98.1	90.9
New Orleans	104.0	83.4	122.2	98.2	87.0
Oklahoma City	98.2	79.4	103.4	97.3	97.1
Phoenix	95.7	98.7	96.3	104.6	115.2

13.43 Shown here is output from two Excel regression analyses on the same problem. The first output was done on a "full" model. In the second output, the variable with the smallest absolute t value has been removed, and the regression has been rerun like a second step of a backward elimination process. Examine the two outputs. Explain what happened, what the results mean, and what might happen in a third step.

Regression Statistics	
Multiple R	0.567
R Square	0.321
Adjusted R Square	0.208
Standard Error	159.681
Observations	29

ANOVA

	df	*SS*	*MS*	*F*	*Significance F*
Regression	4	289856.08	72464.02	2.84	0.046
Residual	24	611955.23	25498.13		
Total	28	901811.31			

	Coefficients	*Standard Error*	*t Stat*	*P-value*
Intercept	336.79	124.08	2.71	0.012
X1	1.65	1.78	0.93	0.363
X2	-5.63	13.47	-0.42	0.680
X3	0.26	1.68	0.16	0.878
X4	185.50	66.22	2.80	0.010

Regression Statistics	
Multiple R	0.566
R Square	0.321
Adjusted R Square	0.239
Standard Error	156.534
Observations	29

ANOVA

	df	*SS*	*MS*	*F*	*Significance F*
Regression	3	289238.1	96412.7	3.93	0.020
Residual	25	612573.2	24502.9		
Total	28	901811.3			

	Coefficients	*Standard Error*	*t Stat*	*P-value*
Intercept	342.919	115.34	2.97	0.006
X1	1.834	1.31	1.40	0.174
X2	-5.749	13.18	-0.44	0.667
X4	181.220	59.05	3.07	0.005

ANALYZING THE DATABASES

1. Use the manufacturing database to develop a multiple regression model to predict Cost of Materials by Number of Employees, New Capital Expenditures, Value Added by Manufacture, Value of Industry Shipments, and End-of-Year Inventories. Create indicator variables for values of industry shipments that have been coded from 1 to 4. Use all possible regressions procedure. Does there appear to be a problem of multicollinearity in this analysis? Discuss the results of the analysis.
2. Construct a correlation matrix for the hospital database variables. Are some of the variables highly correlated? Which ones and why? Perform all possible regressions analysis to predict Personnel by Control, Service, Beds, Admissions, Census, Outpatients, and Births. The variables Region, Control, and Service will need to be coded as indicator variables. Control has two subcategories, and Service has three.
3. Develop a regression model using the financial database. Use Total Revenues, Total Assets, Return on Equity, Earnings Per Share, Average Yield, and Dividends Per Share to predict the average P/E ratio for a company. How strong is the model? Use all possible regressions to help sort out the variables. Several of these variables may be measuring similar things. Construct a correlation matrix to explore the possibility of multicollinearity among the predictors.
4. Use the stock market database to develop a regression model to predict the composite index from Part of the Month, Stock Volume, Reported Trades, Dollar Value, and Warrants Volume. You will need to treat Part of the Month as a qualitative variable with three subcategories. Drop out the least significant variable if there is one that is not significant at $\alpha = .05$ and rerun the model. How much did R^2 drop? Continue to do this until there are only significant predictors left. Describe the final model.

CASE

VIRGINIA SEMICONDUCTOR

Virginia Semiconductor, Inc., is a producer of silicon wafers used in the manufacture of microelectronic products. The company, situated in Fredericksburg, Virginia, was founded in 1978 by two brothers, Thomas and Robert Digges. Virginia Semiconductor was growing and prospering in the early 1980s by selling a high volume of low-profit-margin wafers. However, in 1985, without notice, Virginia Semiconductor lost two major customers that represented 65% of its business. Left with only 35% of its sales base, the company desperately needed customers.

Thomas Digges, Jr., CEO of Virginia Semiconductor, decided to seek markets where his company's market share would be small but profit margin would be high because of the value of its engineering research and its expertise. This turned out to be a wise decision for the small, versatile company.

Virginia Semiconductor developed a silicon wafer that was two inches in diameter, 75 microns thick, and polished on both sides. Such wafers were needed by several customers, but had never been produced before. The company produced a number of these wafers and sold them for more than 10 times the price of conventional wafers.

Soon the company was making wafers from two to four microns thick (extremely thin), wafers with textured surfaces for infrared applications, and wafers with micromachined holes or shapes and selling them in specialized markets. It was able to deliver these products faster than competitors were able to deliver standard wafers.

Having made inroads at replacing lost sales, Virginia Semiconductor still had to streamline operations and control inventory and expenses. There were no layoffs, but the average workweek dropped to 32 hours and the president took an 80% pay reduction for a time. Expenses were cut as far as seemed possible.

The company had virtually no long-term debt and fortunately was able to make it through this period without incurring any additional significant debt. The absence of large monthly debt payments enabled the company to respond quickly to new production needs.

Virginia Semiconductor improved production quality by cross-training employees. In addition, the company participated in the State of Virginia's economic development efforts to find markets in Europe, Japan, Korea, and Israel. Exports, which were 1% of the company's business in 1985, now represent 40%.

The company continues to find new customers because of new products. One new ultramachining wafer has become a key component in auto airbags. Today the company has more than 300 active customers, whereas it had fewer than 50 in 1985.

DISCUSSION

1. It is often useful to decision makers at a company to determine what factors enter into the size of a customer's purchase. Suppose decision makers at Virginia Semiconductor want to determine from past data what variables might be predictors of size of purchase and are able to gather some data on various customer companies. Assume the following data represent information gathered on 16 companies on five variables: the total amount of purchases made during a one-year period (size of purchase), the size of the purchasing company (in total sales volume), the percentage of all purchases made by the customer company that were imports, the distance of the customer company from Virginia Semiconductor, and whether or not the customer company had a single central purchasing agent. Use these data to generate a multiple regression model to predict size of purchase by the other variables. Summarize your findings in terms of the strength of the model, significant predictor variables, and any new variables generated by recoding.

SIZE OF PURCHASE ($1000)	COMPANY SIZE ($ MILLION SALES)	% CUSTOMER IMPORTS	DISTANCE FROM VA SEMICONDUCTOR	CENTRAL PURCHASER?
27.9	25.6	41	18	1
89.6	109.8	16	75	0
12.8	39.4	29	14	0
34.9	16.7	31	117	0
408.6	278.4	14	209	1
173.5	98.4	8	114	1
105.2	101.6	20	75	0
510.6	139.3	17	50	1
382.7	207.4	53	35	1
84.6	26.8	27	15	1
101.4	13.9	31	19	0
27.6	6.8	22	7	0
234.8	84.7	5	89	1
464.3	180.3	27	306	1
309.8	132.6	18	73	1
294.6	118.9	16	11	1

2. Suppose that the next set of data is Virginia Semiconductor's sales figures for the past 11 years, along with the average number hours worked per week by a full-time employee and the number of different customers the company has for its unique wafers. How did the average workweek length and/or number of customers relate to total sales figures? Use scatter plots to examine possible relationships between sales and hours per week and sales and number of customers. Use these plots to explore possible ways to recode the data. Use an all possible regressions analysis to explore the relationships. Let the response variable be "sales" and the predictors be "average

number hours worked per week," "number of customers," and any new variables created by recoding. Explore quadratic relationships, interaction, and other relationships that seem appropriate by using stepwise regression. Summarize your findings in terms of model strength and significant predictors.

SALES ($ MILLION)	AVERAGE HOURS WORKED PER WEEK	NUMBER OF CUSTOMERS
15.6	44	54
15.7	43	52
15.4	41	55
14.3	41	55
11.8	40	39
9.7	40	28
9.6	40	37
10.2	38	58
11.3	38	67
14.3	32	186
14.8	37	226

As Virginia Semiconductor continues to grow and prosper, there is always the danger that the company will slip back into inefficient ways. Suppose that after a few years the company's sales begin to level off, but it continues hiring employees. Such figures over a 10-year period of time may look like the data given here. Graph these data, using sales as the response variable and number of employees as the predictor. Study the graph and using the information learned, develop a regression model to predict sales by the number of employees. On the basis of what you find, what would you recommend to management about the trend if it were to continue? What do you see in these data that management ought to be concerned about?

SALES ($ MILLION)	NUMBER OF EMPLOYEES
20.2	120
24.3	122
28.6	127
33.7	135
35.2	142
35.9	156
36.3	155
36.2	167
36.5	183
36.6	210

ADAPTED FROM: "Virginia Semiconductor: A New Beginning," *Real-World Lessons for America's Small Businesses: Insights from the Blue Chip Enterprise Initiative 1994*. Published by *Nation's Business* magazine on behalf of Connecticut Mutual Life Insurance Company and the U.S. Chamber of Commerce in association with The Blue Chip Enterprise Initiative, 1994.

14

ETHICAL ISSUES IN BUSINESS RESEARCH

What you will learn in this chapter

- To explain why ethical questions are philosophical questions.
- To define *societal norms.*
- To describe the three parties involved in most research situations and discuss how the interaction among these parties may identify a series of ethical questions.
- To discuss the rights and obligations of the respondent.
- To discuss the rights and obligations of the researcher.
- To discuss the rights and obligations of the client/sponsor.
- To discuss selected issues such as deception, privacy, and advocacy research from the perspective of each of the three parties.
- To discuss the role of codes of ethics.

Executives of a firm interested in acquiring information concerning union members' attitudes toward management put a hidden microphone (attached to a tape recorder) in the employees' coffee room so that the union members' conversations might be observed unobtrusively. Is there a moral question involved here?

An accounting researcher who has sampled 100 organizations in a survey on CPA firms' accounting practices believes that a particular CPA firm in the sample is inefficiently managed. He discards its questionnaires, eliminating the firm from the analysis. Is this proper?

A number of West Coast residents believe that national television news networks making early projections about presidential races before local polls close has an impact on voting behavior, especially turnout. Is early projection of election returns an ethical practice?

The personnel manager of a large bank tries to persuade a researcher to undertake a project with "political purposes." Is this in the organization's best interest?

Each of these situations illustrates an ethical issue in business research. Just as there are ethical aspects to all human interaction, there are some ethical questions about business research. This book considers various ethical and moral issues concerning fair business dealings, proper research techniques, and appropriate utilization of research results in other chapters. This chapter addresses the growing concern in recent years about the ethical implications of business research. ■

ETHICAL QUESTIONS ARE PHILOSOPHICAL QUESTIONS

societal norms
Codes of behavior adopted by a group, suggesting what a member of the group ought to do under given circumstances.

Ethical questions are philosophical questions. There is no general agreement among philosophers about the answers to such questions. However, the rights and obligations of individuals are generally dictated by the norms of society. **Societal norms** are codes of behavior adopted by a group; they suggest what a member of a group ought to do under given circumstances.[1] This chapter reflects the author's perceptions of the norms of our society (and undoubtedly his own values to some extent).[2]

GENERAL RIGHTS AND OBLIGATIONS OF CONCERNED PARTIES

In most research situations, three parties are involved: the *researcher,* the *sponsoring client (user),* and the *respondent (subject).* The interaction of each of these parties with one or both of the other two identifies a series of ethical questions. Consciously or unconsciously, each party expects certain rights and feels certain obligations toward the other parties. Exhibit 5.1 diagrams this relationship. Within any society there is a set of normatively prescribed expectations of behavior (including rights and obligations) associated with a social role, such as researcher, and another, reciprocal role, such as respondent. Certain ethical behaviors may be expected only in certain specific situations, while other expectations may be more generalized. If there are conflicting perspectives about behavioral expectations, ethical problems may arise. For instance, several ethical issues concern the researcher's expected rights versus those of the respondent/subject. A number of questions arise because researchers believe they have the right to seek information, but subjects believe they have a certain right to privacy. A respondent who says "I don't care to answer your question about my income" believes that he or she has the right to refuse to participate. Yet some researchers will persist in trying to get that information. In general, a fieldworker is not expected to overstep the boundary society places on individuals' privacy.

EXHIBIT 5.1 INTERACTION OF RIGHTS AND OBLIGATIONS OF PARTIES IN RESEARCH

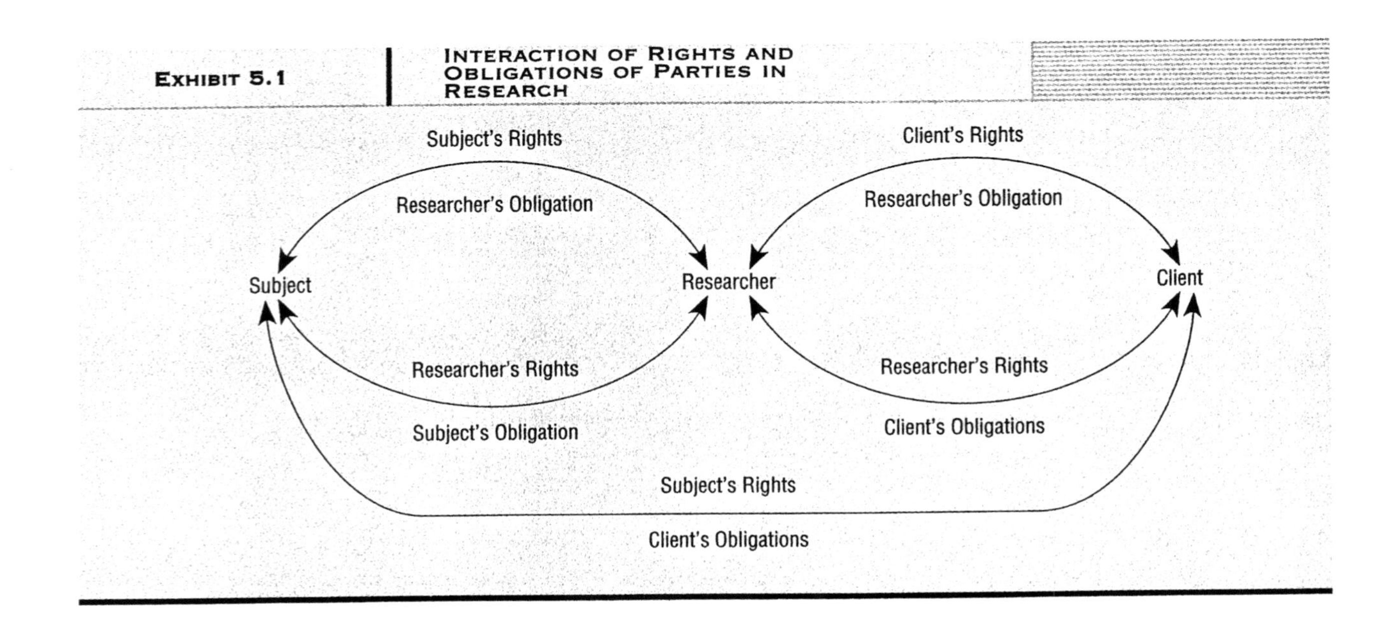

For each of the subject's rights there is a corresponding obligation on the part of the researcher. For example, the individual's right to privacy dictates that the researcher has an obligation to protect the anonymity of the respondent. When a respondent discloses information about personal matters, it is assumed that such information will be guarded from all people other than the researcher.

Rights and Obligations of the Respondent

informed consent
The expressed or implied acknowledgment waiving an individual's right to privacy when he or she agrees to participate in a research study.

The ethical issues vary somewhat, depending on whether the participant has given willing and informed consent. The notion of **informed consent** means that an individual understands the reason for the research and waives his or her right to privacy when he or she agrees to participate in the research study. (The rights of a participant in an unobtrusive observation study differ from a survey respondent's rights because he or she has not willingly consented to be a subject of the research.) In return for being truthful, the survey respondent has the right to expect confidentiality and anonymity. (*Privacy* refers to the issue of whether a respondent chooses to answer a researcher's questions; a person may choose to protect her privacy by not answering. *Confidentiality* refers to the obligation on the part of the researcher not to reveal the identity of an individual research subject. A person who waives her right to privacy by agreeing to answer a researcher's questions nonetheless has a right to expect that her answers and her identity will remain confidential.) Privacy and confidentiality are profound ethical issues in business research.

The Obligation to Be Truthful

When a subject willingly consents to participate, it is generally expected that he or she will provide truthful answers. Honest cooperation is the main obligation of the respondent or subject.

Privacy

Americans relish their privacy. A major polling organization indicated that almost 80 percent of Americans believe that collecting and giving out personal information without their knowledge is a serious violation of their privacy.[3] Hence, the right to privacy is an important question in business research. This issue involves the subject's freedom to choose whether to comply with an investigator's request.[4] Traditionally, researchers have assumed that individuals make an informed choice. However, critics have argued that the old, the poor, the poorly educated, and other underprivileged individuals may not be aware of their right to choose. Further, they have argued that an interviewer may begin with some vague explanation of a survey's purpose, initially ask questions that are relatively innocuous, and then move to questions of a highly personal nature. It has been suggested that subjects be informed of their right to be left alone or to break off the interview at any given time. Researchers should not follow the tendency to "hold on" to busy respondents. However, this view is definitely not universally accepted in the research community.[5]

Another aspect of the privacy issue is illustrated by the question "Is the telephone call that interrupts someone's favorite television program an invasion of privacy?" The answer to this issue—and to most privacy questions—lies in the dilemma of determining where the rights of the individual end and the needs of society for better scientific information on citizen preference take over.[6] Generally, certain standards of common courtesy have been set by interviewing firms—for example, not to interview late in the evening and at

New technologies are making it easier to compile computerized databases that combine survey results with personal records. There is growing public concern about privacy issues as better technology makes it easier for business researchers to link survey respondents' answers to Social Security, tax, and other government records.

other inconvenient times. However, there are several critics who may never be appeased. The computerized interview ("junk phone call") has stimulated increased debate over this aspect of the privacy issue. As a practical matter, respondents may feel more relaxed about privacy issues if they know who is conducting a survey. Thus, it is generally recommended that field interviewers indicate that they are legitimate researchers by passing out business cards, wearing name tags, or in other ways identifying the name of their company.

In an observation study, the major ethical issues concern whether the observed behavior is public or private. Generally it is believed that unobtrusive observation of public behavior in such places as stores, airports, and museums is not a serious invasion of privacy. However, recording private behavior with hidden cameras and the like does represent a violation of this right. For example, in a survey of research directors and executives, the practice of observing women through a one-way mirror as they tried on bras was disapproved of by approximately 80 percent of the executives.[7]

Deception

In a number of situations the researcher creates a false impression by disguising the purpose of the research. The researcher, at least at the outset of the research, is not open and honest. Bluntly stated, to avoid possible biased reactions, the subject is lied to. Deception or concealment may be used if a researcher would otherwise be unable to observe or straightforwardly ask about the phenomena of interest and still hold all other factors constant. Generally, researchers who use deception argue that it is justified under two conditions: (1) No physical danger or psychological harm will be caused by the deception, and (2) the researcher takes personal responsibility for informing the respondent of the concealment or deception after the research project ends.

The issue of deception is interrelated with the subject's right to be informed and with the means-to-an-end philosophical issue. The major question is, Does a small deception substantially increase the value of the research?

Suppose a survey research project must contact busy executives. Pretending to be calling long distance might improve the response rate—but is this a justifiable means to this end?

A distinction has been made between deception and discreet silence. The ethical question concerning the manifest content of a questionnaire versus the true purpose of the research has been cleverly stated as follows:

> Must we really explain, when we ask the respondent to agree or disagree with the statement, "prison is too good for sex criminals; they should be publicly whipped or worse," it is really the authoritarianism of his personality we are investigating, and not the public opinion on crime and punishment?[8]

The Right to Be Informed

It has been argued that subjects have a right to be informed of all aspects of the research, including information about its purpose and sponsorship. The argument for the researcher's obligation to protect this right is based on the academic tradition of informing and enlightening the public.

A pragmatic argument for providing respondents with information about the nature of the study concerns the long-run ability of researchers to gain cooperation from respondents. If the public understands why survey or experimental information has been collected and that the researchers may be trusted with private information, it may be easier in the long run to conduct research. Several research suppliers have suggested that public relations work is needed to sell the public on the benefits of the research industry.

Rights and Obligations of the Researcher

General business ethics should be a standard for business research firms and business research departments. Our concern is not with issues such as bribery or the welfare and safety of one's employees but with ethical issues that are specifically germane to business research practices.

More has been written about the ethics of researchers than about those of the other two parties because this group's purpose is clearly identifiable. Exhibit 5.1 illustrated that researchers have obligations to both subjects and clients as well as corresponding rights. A number of professional associations have developed standards and operating procedures for ethical practice by researchers. Exhibit 5.2 is the **code of ethics** for the American Association for Public Opinion Research. This code touches on several major issues that will be further explored in this book. Students contemplating entering business research should check for codes of ethics set out by professional associations.

code of ethics
A statement of principles and operating procedures for ethical practice.

The Purpose of Research Is Research

It is considered unacceptable to misrepresent a sales tactic as business research. The Federal Trade Commission has indicated that it is illegal to use any plan, scheme, or ruse that misrepresents the true status of the person making the call as a door-opener to gain admission to a prospect's home, office, or other establishment.[9] This sales ploy is considered to be unethical as well as illegal. No research firm should engage in any practice other than scientific investigation.

Objectivity

Ensuring accuracy via objectivity and scientific investigation is stressed throughout this book. Researchers should maintain high standards to ensure

Exhibit 5.2 | **Code of Professional Ethics and Practices: American Association for Public Opinion Research**

We, the members of the American Association for Public Opinion Research, subscribe to the principles expressed in the following Code. Our goals are to support sound and ethical practice in the conduct of public opinion research and in the use of such research for policy and decision making in the public and private sectors, as well as to improve public understanding of opinion research methods and the proper use of opinion research results.

We pledge ourselves to maintain high standards of scientific competence and integrity in conducting, analyzing, and reporting our work and in our relations with survey respondents, with our clients, with those who eventually use the research for decision-making purposes, and with the general public. We further pledge ourselves to reject all tasks or assignments that would require activities inconsistent with the principles of this code.

The Code

I. Principles of Professional Practice in the Conduct of Our Work

A. We shall exercise due care in developing research designs and survey instruments, and in collecting, processing, and analyzing data, taking all reasonable steps to assure the reliability and validity of results.

1. We shall recommend and employ only those tools and methods of analysis which, in our professional judgment, are well suited to the research problem at hand.
2. We shall not select research tools and methods of analysis because of their capacity to yield misleading conclusions.
3. We shall not knowingly make interpretations of research results, nor shall we tacitly permit interpretations that are inconsistent with the data available.
4. We shall not knowingly imply that interpretations should be accorded greater confidence than the data actually warrant.

B. We shall describe our methods and findings accurately and in appropriate detail in all research reports, adhering to the standards for minimal disclosure specified in Section III, below.

C. If any of our work becomes the subject of a formal investigation of an alleged violation of this Code, undertaken with the approval of the AAPOR Executive Council, we shall provide additional information on the survey in such detail that a fellow survey practitioner would be able to conduct a professional evaluation of the survey.

II. Principles of Professional Responsibility in Our Dealings with People

A. *The Public:*

1. If we become aware of the appearance in public of serious distortions of our research, we shall publicly disclose what is required to correct these distortions, including, as appropriate, a statement to the public media, legislative body, regulatory agency, or other appropriate group, in or before which the distorted findings were presented.

B. *Clients or Sponsors:*

1. When undertaking work for a private client, we shall hold confidential all proprietary information obtained about the client and about the conduct and findings of the research undertaken for the client, except when the dissemination of the information is expressly authorized by the client, or when disclosure becomes necessary under terms of Section I-C or II-A of this Code.
2. We shall be mindful of the limitations of our techniques and capabilities and shall accept only those research assignments which we can reasonably expect to accomplish within these limitations.

C. *The Profession:*

1. We recognize our responsibility to contribute to the science of public opinion research and to disseminate as freely as possible the ideas and findings which emerge from our research.
2. We shall not cite our membership in the Association as evidence of professional competence, since the Association does not so certify any persons or organizations.

D. *The Respondent:*

1. We shall strive to avoid the use of practices or methods that may harm, humiliate, or seriously mislead survey respondents.

EXHIBIT 5.2 | **CODE OF PROFESSIONAL ETHICS AND PRACTICES *(CONTINUED)***

2. Unless the respondent waives confidentiality for specified uses, we shall hold as privileged and confidential all information that might identify a respondent with his or her responses. We shall also not disclose or use the names of respondents for nonresearch purposes unless the respondents grant us permission to do so.

III. *Standards for Minimal Disclosure*

Good professional practice imposes the obligation upon all public opinion researchers to include, in any report of research results, or to make available when that report is released, certain essential information about how the research was conducted. At a minimum, the following items should be disclosed:

1. Who sponsored the survey, and who conducted it.
2. The exact wording of questions asked, including the text of any preceding instruction or explanation to the interviewer or respondent that might reasonably be expected to affect the response.
3. A definition of the population under study, and a description of the sampling frame used to identify this population.
4. A description of the sample selection procedure, giving a clear indication of the method by which the respondents were selected by the researcher, or whether the respondents were entirely self-selected.
5. Size of sample and, if applicable, completion rates and information on eligibility criteria and screening procedures.
6. A discussion of the precision of the findings, including, if appropriate, estimates of sampling error, and a description of any weighting or estimating procedures used.
7. Which results are based on parts of the sample, rather than on the total sample.
8. Method, location, and dates of data collection.

that the data they collect are accurate. Further, they must not intentionally try to prove a particular point for political purposes.

Misrepresentation of Research

Research companies (and clients) should not misrepresent the statistical accuracy of their data, nor should they overstate the significance of the results by altering the findings. Basically, it is assumed that the researcher has the obligation to both the client and the subjects to analyze the data honestly and to report correctly the actual data collection methods. For example, the failure to report a variation from the technically correct probability sampling procedure is ethically questionable. Similarly, any major error that has occurred during the course of the study should not be kept secret from management or the client sponsor. Hiding errors or allowing variations from the proper procedures tends to distort or shade the results. A more blatant breach of the researcher's responsibilities would be the outright distortion of data.

Protecting the Right to Confidentiality of Both Subjects and Clients

A number of clients might be very desirous of a list of favorable organizational prospects generated from a research survey. It is the researcher's responsibility to ensure that the privacy and anonymity of the respondents are preserved. If the respondent's name and address are known, this information should not be forwarded to the sponsoring organization under any circumstances.

Information that a research supplier obtains about a client's general business affairs should not be disseminated to other clients or third parties. The clients (users of business research) have a number of rights and obligations. Their primary right is to expect objective and accurate data from the research supplier. They should also expect that their instructions relating to confidentiality have been carried out.

Dissemination of Faulty Conclusions

Another ethical issue concerns the dissemination of faulty conclusions. After conducting a research project, the researcher or decision maker may disseminate conclusions from the research that are inconsistent with or not warranted by the data. Most research professionals consider this to be improper.

TO THE POINT

He uses statistics as a drunken man uses a lampost—for support rather than illumination.

ANDREW LANG

A dramatic example of violation of this principle is an advertisement for cigarettes that cited a study of smokers. The advertisement compared two brands and stated that "of those expressing a preference, over 65 percent preferred" the advertised brand to a competitive brand. The misleading portion of this reported result was that most of the respondents did *not* express a preference; they indicated that both brands tasted about the same. Thus, only a very small percentage of those studied actually revealed a preference, and the results were somewhat misleading. Such shading of the results falls short of the obligation to report accurate findings.

Competing Research Proposals

Consider a client who has solicited several bids for a business research project. The research supplier that wins the bid is asked by the client to appropriate ideas from the proposal of a competing research supplier and include them in the research study to be done for the client. This is generally regarded as unethical.[10]

Rights and Obligations of the Sponsoring Client (User)

Ethics between Buyer and Seller

The general business ethics expected to exist between a purchasing agent and a sales representative should apply in the business research situation. For example, if the purchasing agent has already decided to purchase a product (or research proposal) from a friend, it is generally considered unethical for him to solicit competitive bids that have no chance of being accepted just to fulfill a corporate purchasing policy stating that a bid must be put out to three competitors.

An Open Relationship with Research Suppliers

The sponsoring client has the obligation to encourage the research supplier to seek out the truth objectively. To encourage this objectivity, a full and open statement of the problem, explication of time and money constraints, and any

DILBERT Reprinted by permission of United Features Syndicate, Inc.

Business researchers have certain obligations. The purpose of research should be research.

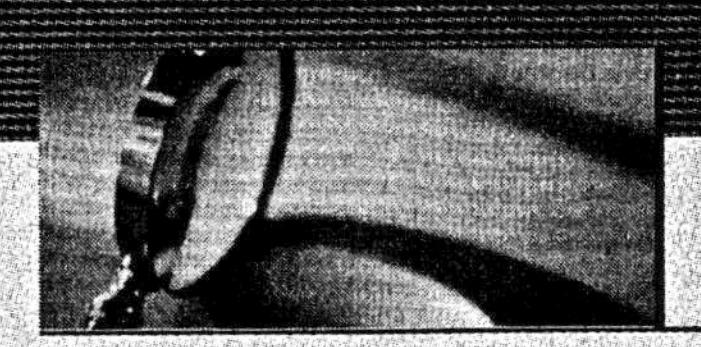

RESEARCH INSIGHT

HERTZ WAS NOT AMUSED

A few years ago, a magazine called *Corporate Travel* published the results of a consumer survey of the travel industry.[11] In the category of rental cars, the magazine declared Avis the winner of what was to be its first annual Alfred Award, named for Alfred Kahn, former chairman of the Civil Aviation Board. Avis, not surprisingly, quickly launched an advertising campaign touting its standing in the poll.

Joseph Russo, vice president for government and public affairs at Avis's archrival, Hertz, was not amused. He called the magazine's editor and asked if he could see a press release and any other material that might explain the survey's results and methodology. "We've won virtually every other poll that's ever been done," said Russo. (Indeed, surveys like these are popularity contests that tend to favor bigger competitors over smaller ones, and they are almost impossible to duplicate or verify.) "So we wanted to see if we were missing the boat."

But Russo said he could not get much information about the survey. "I said, How many people voted in this, was it bigger than a bread basket?"

It turned out that the survey responses had disappeared under mysterious circumstances. The magazine's marketing manager, who had overseen the poll, had left the magazine. "A search of their files has also failed to turn up any statistical tabulation or record of the responses for any category," wrote the president of *Corporate Travel's* parent to Hertz. Meanwhile, said Russo, "We had corporate accounts saying, I see you guys came in after Avis."

Eventually Hertz filed suit against the publisher of the magazine and Avis, charging false advertising. "We said if we allow this to go on, anyone will be able to do anything on the basis of a survey," Russo said. The parties settled, with Avis agreeing to stop calling itself the car rental company of choice among business travelers.

other insights that may help the supplier anticipate costs and problems should be provided.[12] In other words, the research sponsor should encourage efforts to reduce bias and to listen to the voice of the public.

An Open Relationship with Interested Parties

Conclusions should be based on the data. A user of research should not knowingly disseminate conclusions from a given research project or service that are inconsistent with the data or are not warranted by them.[13] Violation of this principle is perhaps the greatest transgression that a client can commit. Justifying a self-serving, political position that is not supported by the data poses serious ethical questions. Indicating that data show something so that a sale can be made is also ethically questionable.

Privacy

The privacy rights of subjects create a privacy obligation on the part of the client. Suppose a database marketing company is offering a mailing list compiled by screening millions of households to obtain brand usage information. The information would be extremely valuable to your firm, but you suspect those individuals who filled out the information forms were misled into thinking they were participating in a survey. Would it be ethical to purchase

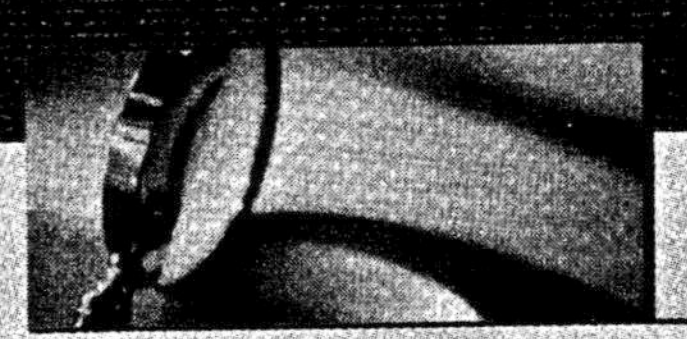

RESEARCH INSIGHT

PUSH POLLING

The question, in the midst of a telephone poll, was as shocking as it was designed to be: Would you still favor Rudy Silbaugh, a Republican candidate for the Wisconsin state assembly, if you knew he voted to give guns back to juveniles who had used them in crimes?[14]

Mr. Silbaugh and other Wisconsin Republicans filed a lawsuit because of that damaging assertion, which the Republican Party said was made recently by a telemarketing firm calling on behalf of Democratic candidates. But they recognized the campaign tactic, having used it themselves.

It's known as "push polling," and it has increasingly become implemented at the last minute of political campaigns when the airwaves have grown saturated with political messages.

For years, campaign pollsters have conducted surveys of a few hundred voters to test the potency of negative information for later use in broad attacks, such as television advertising. What's different about push polling, though not easy to trace, is the use of phone calls as the means of disseminating attacks to thousands of voters at a time. But unlike the case with TV ads or direct-mail brochures, federal law doesn't require congressional campaigns to identify who's paying for the calls.

"If people want to lie, cheat, and steal, they should be held accountable," said Rep. Tom Petri, Republican of Wisconsin, who complains that during an election campaign, anonymous callers told constituents that he was a tool of Japanese auto dealers and responsible for the savings and loan mess.

In Colorado, the campaign of Democratic governor Roy Romer, who was reelected, complained to the state attorney general that opponent Bruce Benson's campaign used push polling in violation of a Colorado statute forbidding anonymous campaigning.

The advocacy in question, according to a script obtained by the governor's aides, asked voters if they'd be more or less likely to support Mr. Romer if they knew that "there have been nearly 1,300 murders in Colorado since Romer was first elected and not one murderer has been put to death." Follow-up questions informed voters that the state parole board "has granted early release to an average of four convicted felons per day every day since Romer took office," that Mr. Romer spent "one out of every four days outside of Colorado" during his four-year term, and that he "is being sued for mismanaging the state's foster-care system."

The attorney general declined to prosecute, but Romer campaign manager Alan Salazar complained that the lack of accountability of push polling, as well as the enhanced credibility of an attack delivered personally to voters, makes the practice worrisome.

the mailing list? If respondents have been deceived about the purpose of a survey and their names subsequently are sold as part of a user mailing list, this practice is certainly unethical. The client as well as the research supplier has the obligation to maintain respondents' privacy.

Consider another example. Sales managers know that a survey of their business-to-business customers' buying intentions includes a means to attach a customer name to each questionnaire. This confidential information could be of benefit to a sales representative calling on a specific customer. A client wishing to be ethical must resist the temptation to identify those accounts (i.e., those respondents) who are the hottest prospects.

Privacy on the Internet

Privacy on the Internet is a controversial issue. A number of groups question whether Web site questionnaires, registration forms, and other means of collecting personal information are legitimate. Many managers argue that their organizations don't need to know who the user is because the individual's name is not important for their purposes. However, they do want to know certain information (such as demographic characteristics or product usage) associated with an anonymous profile. For instance, a Web advertiser could reach a targeted audience without having access to identifying information. Of course, unethical companies may violate the anonymity guideline.

America Online's privacy policy states that AOL will not read customers' e-mail, collect any information about Web site visits, or give key data to other organizations without authorization. AOL will seek parents' written approval to get data from children at sites targeting kids.[15] Research shows that people are more willing to disclose sensitive information if they know a Web site's privacy policy.[16]

For this reason, many high-traffic Web sites such as Yahoo and Lycos have privacy statements that visitors can easily access. Organizations such as the

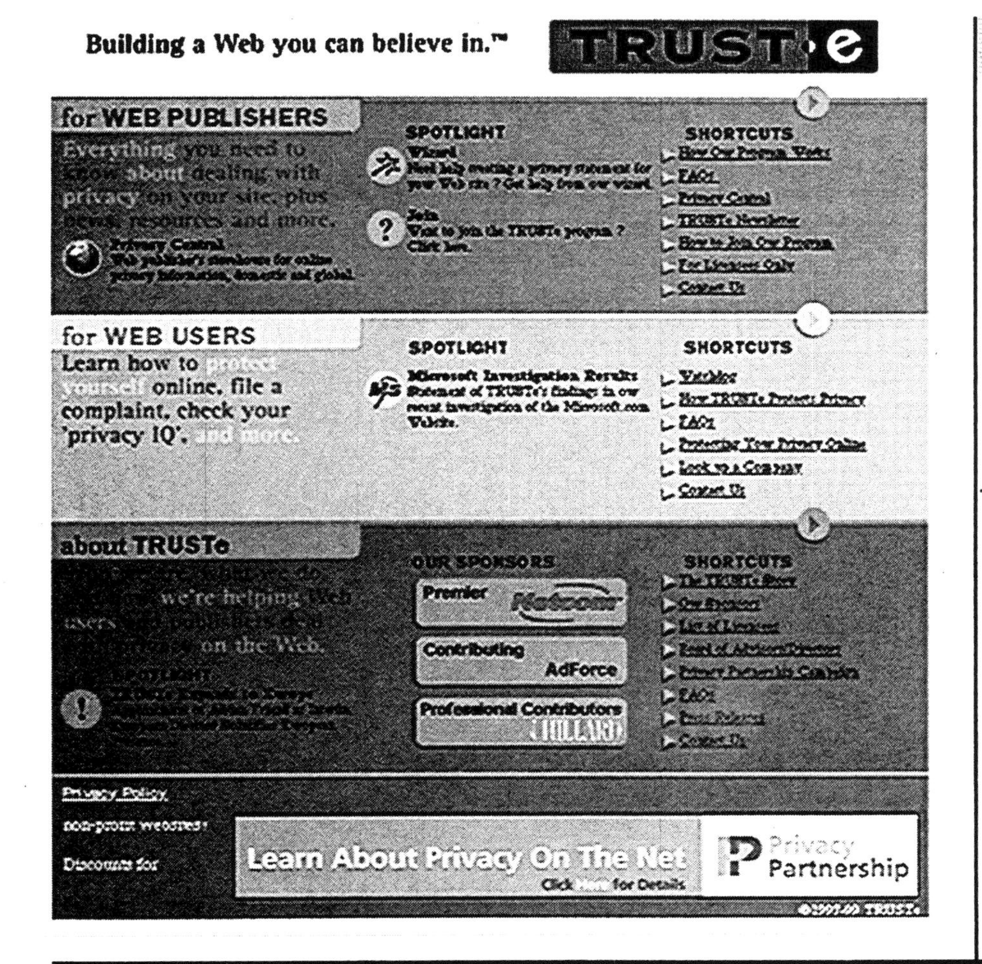

TRUSTe (http://www.Truste.org) is a third-party organization that evaluates Web sites' privacy policies, certifies Web sites, and issues a Seal of Trust to organizations that meet its privacy standards.[17] TRUSTe classifies sites into three categories: "no exchange," sites where no personal user data are collected; "1to1 exchange," sites that collect user data for their own purposes but do not share them with third parties; and "3rd party exchange," sites that share the information with others. "1to1 exchange" sites are permitted to share user data—such as credit card numbers, names, and addresses—with business partners in order to complete transactions as long as the business partners agree not to collect the user data themselves.[18]

Electronic Frontier Foundation and the Online Privacy Alliance are involved in developing privacy guidelines.

Commitment to Research

Some potential clients have been known to request research proposals from a research supplier when there is a low probability that the research will be conducted. A research consultant's opinion may be solicited even though management is not really planning research and funds have not been allocated for the project. For example, obtaining an outsider's opinion of a company problem via a research proposal provides an inexpensive consultation. If the information supports a given manager's position in an ongoing debate within the company, it could be used politically rather than as a basis for research. Because the research supplier must spend considerable effort planning a custom-designed study, most research practitioners believe that the client has the obligation to be serious about considering a project before soliciting proposals.

Pseudo-Pilot Studies

As noted, it is important for clients to be open about the business problem to be investigated. However, there is a special case of this problem that should be explained. Sometimes a client will suggest that a more comprehensive study is in the planning stages and that the proposal the research supplier is bidding on is a pilot study. The client might say something like "I don't want to promise anything, but you should know that this is the first in a very ambitious series of studies we are planning to undertake, and if you sharpen your pencil in estimating cost . . . ."[19] The research consultant is told that if his or her company does a good job during the pilot study stages, there will be an additional major contract down the line. Too often these pilot studies are "come-ons"—the comprehensive study never materializes, and the consultant must absorb a loss.

Advocacy Research

advocacy research
Research undertaken to support a specific claim in a legal action.

Advocacy research—research undertaken to support a specific claim in a legal action—puts a client in a unique situation. Advocacy research, such as a survey conducted to show that a brand name is not a generic name, differs from research that is intended for internal use only.[20] The traditional factors, such as

Many lawyers hire jury consultants who use business research methods to help determine what type of person would make a favorable juror. Lawyers also conduct advocacy research to provide evidence from survey findings that support their viewpoints.

sample size, people to be interviewed, and questions to be asked, are weighed against cost when making an internal decision. A court's opinion of the value of advocacy research may be based exclusively on sampling design and validity of the questions asked. Thus, the slightest variation from technically correct sampling procedures may be magnified by an attorney until a standard business research project no longer appears adequate in the judge's eye.

The ethics of advocacy research present a number of serious questions. Consider the following quote:

> Almost never do you see a researcher who appears as an independent witness, quite unbiased. You almost always see a witness appearing either for the FTC or for the industry. You can almost predict what is going to be concluded by the witness for the FTC. And you can almost predict what will be concluded by the witness for industry. That says that research in this setting is not after full truth and it is not dispassionate in nature. And for those of us who consider ourselves to be researchers, that is a serious quandary.[21]

Researchers doing advocacy research do not necessarily bias results intentionally. However, attorneys in an advocacy research trial rarely submit research evidence that does not support the client's position.

The question of advocacy research is one of objectivity: Can the researcher search out the truth when the sponsoring client wishes to support its position at a trial? The ethical question stems from a conflict between legal ethics and research ethics, and perhaps only the individual researcher can resolve this question.

A FINAL NOTE ON ETHICS

There is no question that there are unethical researchers in the world and that shady dealings do occur. But business researchers are no different from other business people—or from people in general, for that matter. One may occasionally run across the case of a researcher who produces a report on fabricated findings, just as there are occasional cases of interviewers who cheat by filling out the questionnaires themselves. (In pre-Castro Cuba there was at least one firm that, for a fee, would provide a handsomely engraved certificate attesting that the Court of Public Opinion held the client or the client's products in whatever kind of high esteem might be desired—with no extra charge for percentages.)[22] Under some circumstances even good researchers take shortcuts, some of which may be ethically questionable. However, like most business people, researchers are generally ethical. Of course, the answer to the question "What is ethical?" is not easy—only one's conscience operates to inhibit any questionable practice.[23]

SUMMARY

There is no general agreement about the answers to ethical questions that surround business research. However, societal norms suggest codes of conduct that are appropriate in given circumstances. There are three concerned parties in business research situations: the researcher, the sponsoring client (user), and the respondent (subject). Each party has certain rights and obligations. The respondent's rights include the right to privacy and the right to be informed about all aspects of the research; his or her main obligation is to give honest answers to research questions. The researcher is expected to adhere to the purpose of the research; maintain objectivity; avoid misrepresenting research findings; protect subjects' and clients' right to confidentiality; and avoid shading research conclusions. The client is obligated to observe general business ethics when dealing with research suppliers; avoid misusing the research findings to support its aims; respect research respondents' privacy; and be open about its intentions to conduct research and about the business problem to be investigated. A serious challenge to objectivity occurs when advocacy research—research conducted to support a specific legal claim—is undertaken.

Key Terms

societal norms
informed consent
code of ethics
advocacy research

Questions for Review and Critical Thinking

1. Why are ethical questions philosophical questions?
2. Identify the rights and obligations of researchers, clients, and subjects of business research.
3. Name some business research practices that are ethically questionable.
4. How might the business research industry take action to ensure that the public believes that research is a legitimate activity and that firms that misrepresent and deceive the public using business research as a sales ploy are not true business researchers?
5. Comment on the ethics of the following situations:
   (a) A researcher plans to code questionnaires in an employee survey using invisible ink.
   (b) A researcher is planning to videotape users' reactions to a new product in a simulated kitchen environment from behind a one-way mirror.
   (c) A food warehouse club advertises "savings up to 30 percent" after a survey showed a range of savings from 2 percent to 30 percent below that of an average shopping trip for selected items.
   (d) A radio station broadcasts the following message during a syndicated rating service's rating period: "Please fill out your diary."
   (e) A researcher pretends to be a member of a business firm's secretarial pool and observes workers without the workers realizing that they are part of a research study.
   (f) A researcher tells a potential respondent that an interview will last 10 minutes rather than the 30 minutes the researcher actually anticipates.
   (g) When you visit your favorite sports team's home page on the Web, you are asked to fill out a registration questionnaire before you enter the site. The team then sells your information (team allegiance, age, address, etc.) to a company that markets sports memorabilia via catalogs and direct mail.
   (h) A regional telephone company contemplates a proposal to telemarket services to its customers with unlisted telephone numbers.
   (i) A drug store chain stopped providing transaction information to a Massachusetts marketing firm that reminded customers to refill prescriptions.
6. Page through your local newspaper to find a story derived from survey research results. Does the newspaper article outline the study's methodology? Could the research have been termed advocacy research?

Exploring the Internet

1. ESOMAR is the World Association of Opinion and Marketing Research Professionals. The organization was founded in 1948 as the European Society for Opinion and Marketing Research. Check out its online ESOMAR Directory of Research Organizations, listing over 1,500 research organizations in 100 countries at http://www.esomar.nl/directory.html.
2. One purpose of the United Kingdom's Market Research Society is to set and enforce the ethical standards to be observed by research practitioners. Go to its Web site at http://www.marketresearch.org.uk/fr-code.htm to view its code of conduct. Visit the Web sites of the Council of American Survey Research Organizations (www.casro.org), the American Marketing Association (www.marketingpower.com), and the Marketing Research Association (www.mra-net.org), and compare their codes of ethics to that of the United Kingdom's Market Research Society.

Tables

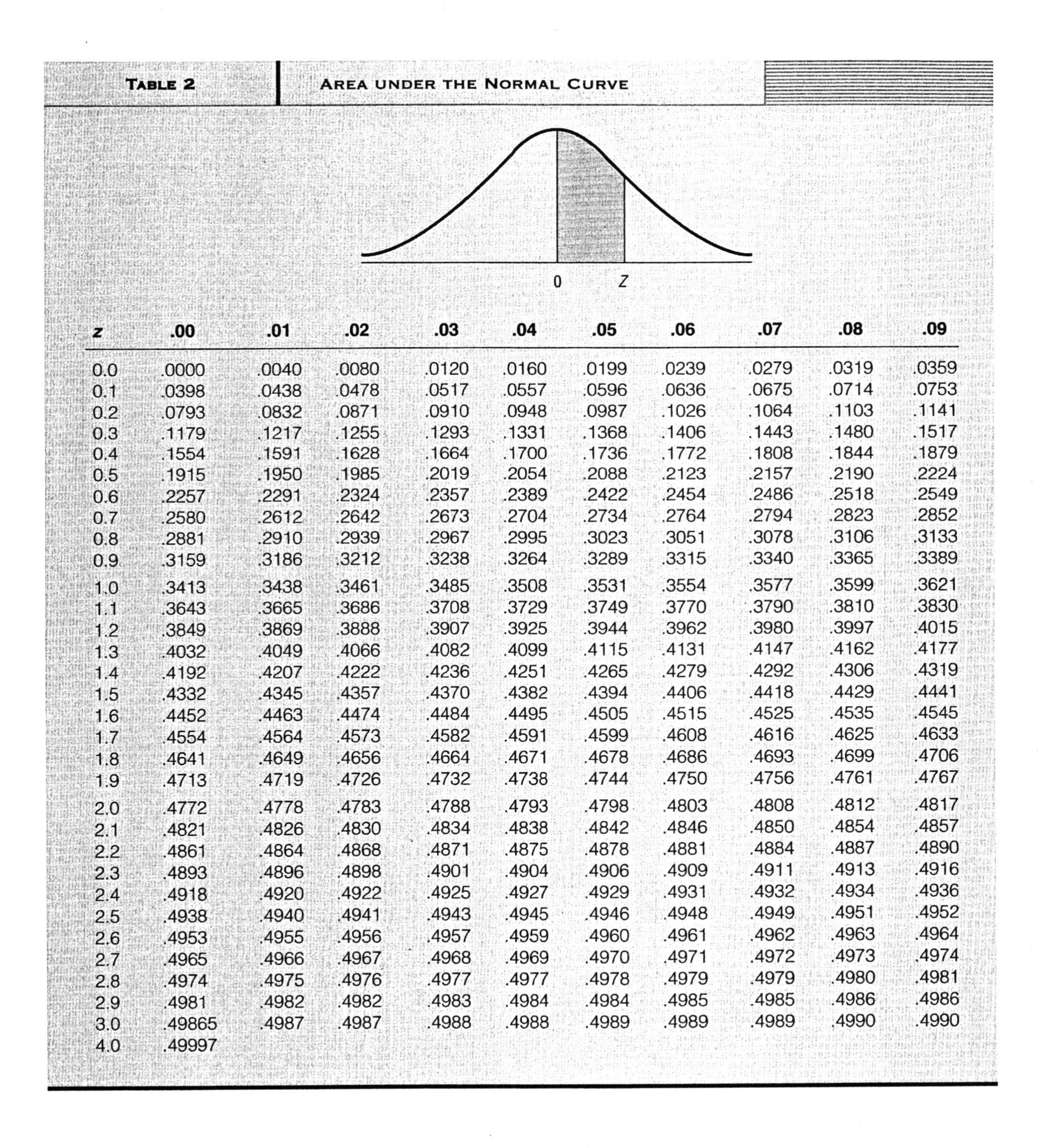

TABLE 2 AREA UNDER THE NORMAL CURVE

z	.00	.01	.02	.03	.04	.05	.06	.07	.08	.09
0.0	.0000	.0040	.0080	.0120	.0160	.0199	.0239	.0279	.0319	.0359
0.1	.0398	.0438	.0478	.0517	.0557	.0596	.0636	.0675	.0714	.0753
0.2	.0793	.0832	.0871	.0910	.0948	.0987	.1026	.1064	.1103	.1141
0.3	.1179	.1217	.1255	.1293	.1331	.1368	.1406	.1443	.1480	.1517
0.4	.1554	.1591	.1628	.1664	.1700	.1736	.1772	.1808	.1844	.1879
0.5	.1915	.1950	.1985	.2019	.2054	.2088	.2123	.2157	.2190	.2224
0.6	.2257	.2291	.2324	.2357	.2389	.2422	.2454	.2486	.2518	.2549
0.7	.2580	.2612	.2642	.2673	.2704	.2734	.2764	.2794	.2823	.2852
0.8	.2881	.2910	.2939	.2967	.2995	.3023	.3051	.3078	.3106	.3133
0.9	.3159	.3186	.3212	.3238	.3264	.3289	.3315	.3340	.3365	.3389
1.0	.3413	.3438	.3461	.3485	.3508	.3531	.3554	.3577	.3599	.3621
1.1	.3643	.3665	.3686	.3708	.3729	.3749	.3770	.3790	.3810	.3830
1.2	.3849	.3869	.3888	.3907	.3925	.3944	.3962	.3980	.3997	.4015
1.3	.4032	.4049	.4066	.4082	.4099	.4115	.4131	.4147	.4162	.4177
1.4	.4192	.4207	.4222	.4236	.4251	.4265	.4279	.4292	.4306	.4319
1.5	.4332	.4345	.4357	.4370	.4382	.4394	.4406	.4418	.4429	.4441
1.6	.4452	.4463	.4474	.4484	.4495	.4505	.4515	.4525	.4535	.4545
1.7	.4554	.4564	.4573	.4582	.4591	.4599	.4608	.4616	.4625	.4633
1.8	.4641	.4649	.4656	.4664	.4671	.4678	.4686	.4693	.4699	.4706
1.9	.4713	.4719	.4726	.4732	.4738	.4744	.4750	.4756	.4761	.4767
2.0	.4772	.4778	.4783	.4788	.4793	.4798	.4803	.4808	.4812	.4817
2.1	.4821	.4826	.4830	.4834	.4838	.4842	.4846	.4850	.4854	.4857
2.2	.4861	.4864	.4868	.4871	.4875	.4878	.4881	.4884	.4887	.4890
2.3	.4893	.4896	.4898	.4901	.4904	.4906	.4909	.4911	.4913	.4916
2.4	.4918	.4920	.4922	.4925	.4927	.4929	.4931	.4932	.4934	.4936
2.5	.4938	.4940	.4941	.4943	.4945	.4946	.4948	.4949	.4951	.4952
2.6	.4953	.4955	.4956	.4957	.4959	.4960	.4961	.4962	.4963	.4964
2.7	.4965	.4966	.4967	.4968	.4969	.4970	.4971	.4972	.4973	.4974
2.8	.4974	.4975	.4976	.4977	.4977	.4978	.4979	.4979	.4980	.4981
2.9	.4981	.4982	.4982	.4983	.4984	.4984	.4985	.4985	.4986	.4986
3.0	.49865	.4987	.4987	.4988	.4988	.4989	.4989	.4989	.4990	.4990
4.0	.49997									

TABLE 3 DISTRIBUTION OF t FOR GIVEN PROBABILITY LEVELS

	LEVEL OF SIGNIFICANCE FOR ONE-TAILED TEST					
	.10	.05	.025	.01	.005	.0005
	LEVEL OF SIGNIFICANCE FOR TWO-TAILED TEST					
d.f.	.20	.10	.05	.02	.01	.001
1	3.078	6.314	12.706	31.821	63.657	636.619
2	1.886	2.920	4.303	6.965	9.925	31.598
3	1.638	2.353	3.182	4.541	5.841	12.941
4	1.533	2.132	2.776	3.747	4.604	8.610
5	1.476	2.015	2.571	3.365	4.032	6.859
6	1.440	1.943	2.447	3.143	3.707	5.959
7	1.415	1.895	2.365	2.998	3.499	5.405
8	1.397	1.860	2.306	2.896	3.355	5.041
9	1.383	1.833	2.262	2.821	3.250	4.781
10	1.372	1.812	2.228	2.764	3.169	4.587
11	1.363	1.796	2.201	2.718	3.106	4.437
12	1.356	1.782	2.179	2.681	3.055	4.318
13	1.350	1.771	2.160	2.650	3.012	4.221
14	1.345	1.761	2.145	2.624	2.977	4.140
15	1.341	1.753	2.131	2.602	2.947	4.073
16	1.337	1.746	2.120	2.583	2.921	4.015
17	1.333	1.740	2.110	2.567	2.898	3.965
18	1.330	1.734	2.101	2.552	2.878	3.922
19	1.328	1.729	2.093	2.539	2.861	3.883
20	1.325	1.725	2.086	2.528	2.845	3.850
21	1.323	1.721	2.080	2.518	2.831	3.819
22	1.321	1.717	2.074	2.508	2.819	3.792
23	1.319	1.714	2.069	2.500	2.807	3.767
24	1.318	1.711	2.064	2.492	2.797	3.745
25	1.316	1.708	2.060	2.485	2.787	3.725
26	1.315	1.706	2.056	2.479	2.779	3.707
27	1.314	1.703	2.052	2.473	2.771	3.690
28	1.313	1.701	2.048	2.467	2.763	3.674
29	1.311	1.699	2.045	2.462	2.756	3.659
30	1.310	1.697	2.042	2.457	2.750	3.646
40	1.303	1.684	2.021	2.423	2.704	3.551
60	1.296	1.671	2.000	2.390	2.660	3.460
120	1.289	1.658	1.980	2.358	2.617	3.373
∞	1.282	1.645	1.960	2.326	2.576	3.291

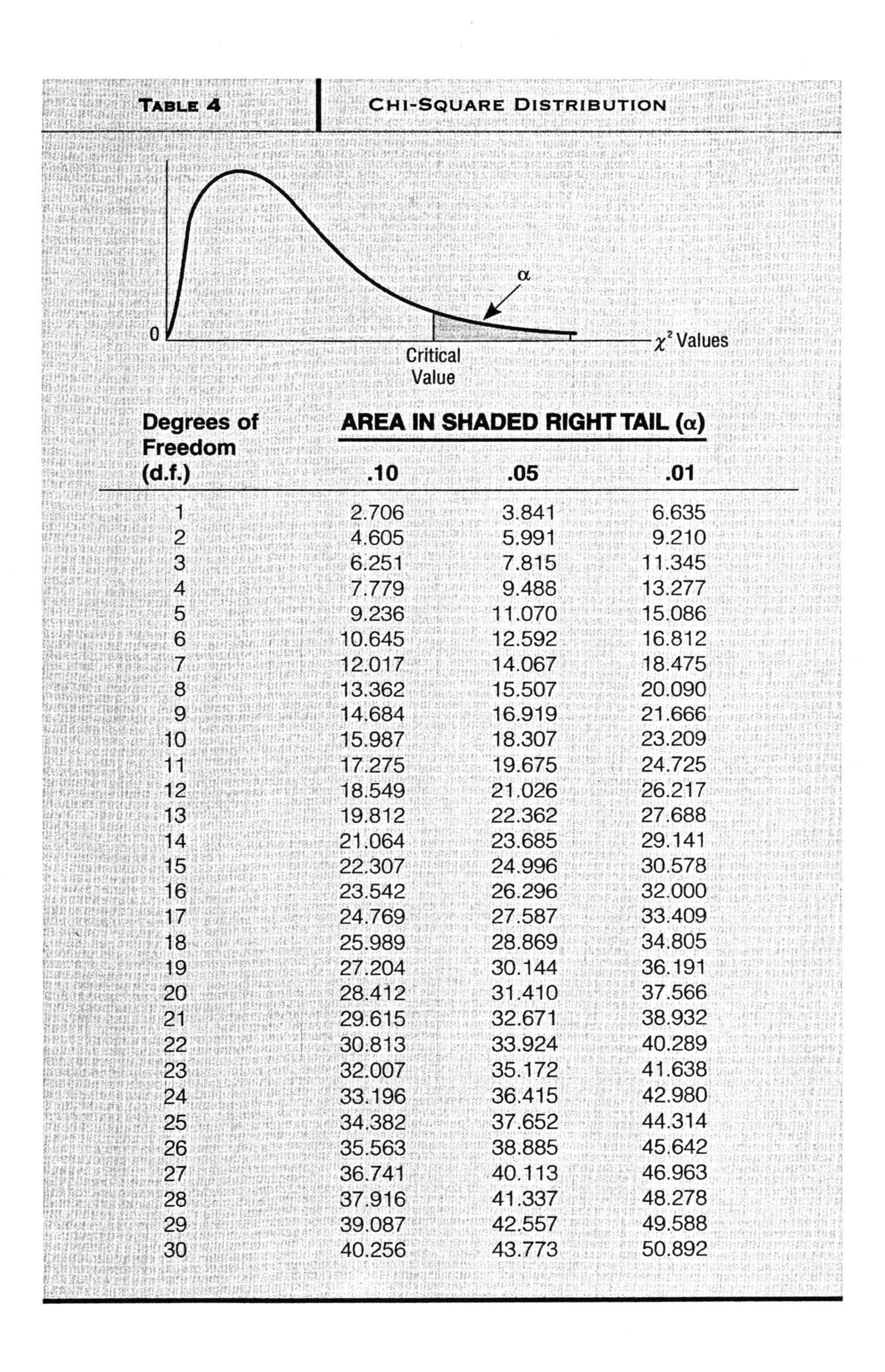

TABLE 4 CHI-SQUARE DISTRIBUTION

Degrees of Freedom (d.f.)	AREA IN SHADED RIGHT TAIL (α)		
	.10	.05	.01
1	2.706	3.841	6.635
2	4.605	5.991	9.210
3	6.251	7.815	11.345
4	7.779	9.488	13.277
5	9.236	11.070	15.086
6	10.645	12.592	16.812
7	12.017	14.067	18.475
8	13.362	15.507	20.090
9	14.684	16.919	21.666
10	15.987	18.307	23.209
11	17.275	19.675	24.725
12	18.549	21.026	26.217
13	19.812	22.362	27.688
14	21.064	23.685	29.141
15	22.307	24.996	30.578
16	23.542	26.296	32.000
17	24.769	27.587	33.409
18	25.989	28.869	34.805
19	27.204	30.144	36.191
20	28.412	31.410	37.566
21	29.615	32.671	38.932
22	30.813	33.924	40.289
23	32.007	35.172	41.638
24	33.196	36.415	42.980
25	34.382	37.652	44.314
26	35.563	38.885	45.642
27	36.741	40.113	46.963
28	37.916	41.337	48.278
29	39.087	42.557	49.588
30	40.256	43.773	50.892

TABLE 5 CRITICAL VALUES OF F_{ν_1, ν_2} FOR $\alpha = .05$

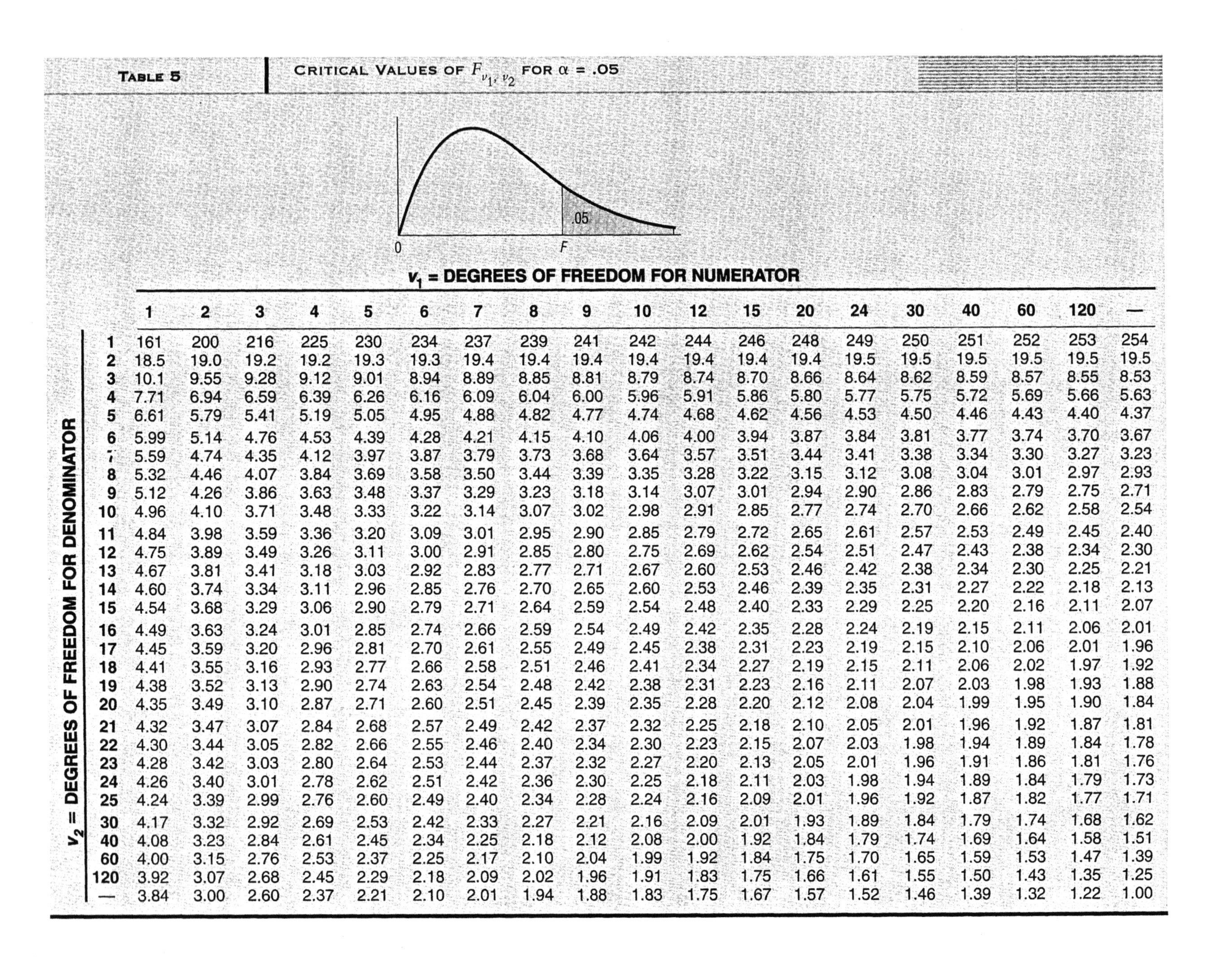

v_1 = DEGREES OF FREEDOM FOR NUMERATOR

v_2 = DEGREES OF FREEDOM FOR DENOMINATOR	1	2	3	4	5	6	7	8	9	10	12	15	20	24	30	40	60	120	—
1	161	200	216	225	230	234	237	239	241	242	244	246	248	249	250	251	252	253	254
2	18.5	19.0	19.2	19.2	19.3	19.3	19.4	19.4	19.4	19.4	19.4	19.4	19.4	19.5	19.5	19.5	19.5	19.5	19.5
3	10.1	9.55	9.28	9.12	9.01	8.94	8.89	8.85	8.81	8.79	8.74	8.70	8.66	8.64	8.62	8.59	8.57	8.55	8.53
4	7.71	6.94	6.59	6.39	6.26	6.16	6.09	6.04	6.00	5.96	5.91	5.86	5.80	5.77	5.75	5.72	5.69	5.66	5.63
5	6.61	5.79	5.41	5.19	5.05	4.95	4.88	4.82	4.77	4.74	4.68	4.62	4.56	4.53	4.50	4.46	4.43	4.40	4.37
6	5.99	5.14	4.76	4.53	4.39	4.28	4.21	4.15	4.10	4.06	4.00	3.94	3.87	3.84	3.81	3.77	3.74	3.70	3.67
7	5.59	4.74	4.35	4.12	3.97	3.87	3.79	3.73	3.68	3.64	3.57	3.51	3.44	3.41	3.38	3.34	3.30	3.27	3.23
8	5.32	4.46	4.07	3.84	3.69	3.58	3.50	3.44	3.39	3.35	3.28	3.22	3.15	3.12	3.08	3.04	3.01	2.97	2.93
9	5.12	4.26	3.86	3.63	3.48	3.37	3.29	3.23	3.18	3.14	3.07	3.01	2.94	2.90	2.86	2.83	2.79	2.75	2.71
10	4.96	4.10	3.71	3.48	3.33	3.22	3.14	3.07	3.02	2.98	2.91	2.85	2.77	2.74	2.70	2.66	2.62	2.58	2.54
11	4.84	3.98	3.59	3.36	3.20	3.09	3.01	2.95	2.90	2.85	2.79	2.72	2.65	2.61	2.57	2.53	2.49	2.45	2.40
12	4.75	3.89	3.49	3.26	3.11	3.00	2.91	2.85	2.80	2.75	2.69	2.62	2.54	2.51	2.47	2.43	2.38	2.34	2.30
13	4.67	3.81	3.41	3.18	3.03	2.92	2.83	2.77	2.71	2.67	2.60	2.53	2.46	2.42	2.38	2.34	2.30	2.25	2.21
14	4.60	3.74	3.34	3.11	2.96	2.85	2.76	2.70	2.65	2.60	2.53	2.46	2.39	2.35	2.31	2.27	2.22	2.18	2.13
15	4.54	3.68	3.29	3.06	2.90	2.79	2.71	2.64	2.59	2.54	2.48	2.40	2.33	2.29	2.25	2.20	2.16	2.11	2.07
16	4.49	3.63	3.24	3.01	2.85	2.74	2.66	2.59	2.54	2.49	2.42	2.35	2.28	2.24	2.19	2.15	2.11	2.06	2.01
17	4.45	3.59	3.20	2.96	2.81	2.70	2.61	2.55	2.49	2.45	2.38	2.31	2.23	2.19	2.15	2.10	2.06	2.01	1.96
18	4.41	3.55	3.16	2.93	2.77	2.66	2.58	2.51	2.46	2.41	2.34	2.27	2.19	2.15	2.11	2.06	2.02	1.97	1.92
19	4.38	3.52	3.13	2.90	2.74	2.63	2.54	2.48	2.42	2.38	2.31	2.23	2.16	2.11	2.07	2.03	1.98	1.93	1.88
20	4.35	3.49	3.10	2.87	2.71	2.60	2.51	2.45	2.39	2.35	2.28	2.20	2.12	2.08	2.04	1.99	1.95	1.90	1.84
21	4.32	3.47	3.07	2.84	2.68	2.57	2.49	2.42	2.37	2.32	2.25	2.18	2.10	2.05	2.01	1.96	1.92	1.87	1.81
22	4.30	3.44	3.05	2.82	2.66	2.55	2.46	2.40	2.34	2.30	2.23	2.15	2.07	2.03	1.98	1.94	1.89	1.84	1.78
23	4.28	3.42	3.03	2.80	2.64	2.53	2.44	2.37	2.32	2.27	2.20	2.13	2.05	2.01	1.96	1.91	1.86	1.81	1.76
24	4.26	3.40	3.01	2.78	2.62	2.51	2.42	2.36	2.30	2.25	2.18	2.11	2.03	1.98	1.94	1.89	1.84	1.79	1.73
25	4.24	3.39	2.99	2.76	2.60	2.49	2.40	2.34	2.28	2.24	2.16	2.09	2.01	1.96	1.92	1.87	1.82	1.77	1.71
30	4.17	3.32	2.92	2.69	2.53	2.42	2.33	2.27	2.21	2.16	2.09	2.01	1.93	1.89	1.84	1.79	1.74	1.68	1.62
40	4.08	3.23	2.84	2.61	2.45	2.34	2.25	2.18	2.12	2.08	2.00	1.92	1.84	1.79	1.74	1.69	1.64	1.58	1.51
60	4.00	3.15	2.76	2.53	2.37	2.25	2.17	2.10	2.04	1.99	1.92	1.84	1.75	1.70	1.65	1.59	1.53	1.47	1.39
120	3.92	3.07	2.68	2.45	2.29	2.18	2.09	2.02	1.96	1.91	1.83	1.75	1.66	1.61	1.55	1.50	1.43	1.35	1.25
—	3.84	3.00	2.60	2.37	2.21	2.10	2.01	1.94	1.88	1.83	1.75	1.67	1.57	1.52	1.46	1.39	1.32	1.22	1.00

TABLE 6 CRITICAL VALUES OF F_{ν_1, ν_2} FOR $\alpha = .01$

0 F .01

ν_1 = DEGREES OF FREEDOM FOR NUMERATOR

ν_2 = DEGREES OF FREEDOM FOR DENOMINATOR	1	2	3	4	5	6	7	8	9	10	12	15	20	24	30	40	60	120	—
1	4,052	5,000	5,403	5,625	5,764	5,859	5,928	5,982	6,023	6,056	6,106	6,157	6,209	6,235	6,261	6,287	6,313	6,339	6,366
2	98.5	99.0	99.2	99.2	99.3	99.3	99.4	99.4	99.4	99.4	99.4	99.4	99.4	99.5	99.5	99.5	99.5	99.5	99.5
3	34.1	30.8	29.5	28.7	28.2	27.9	27.7	27.5	27.3	27.2	27.1	26.9	26.7	26.6	26.5	26.4	26.3	26.2	26.1
4	21.2	18.0	16.7	16.0	15.5	15.2	15.0	14.8	14.7	14.5	14.4	14.2	14.0	13.9	13.8	13.7	13.7	13.6	13.5
5	16.3	13.3	12.1	11.4	11.0	10.7	10.5	10.3	10.2	10.1	9.89	9.72	9.55	9.47	9.38	9.29	9.20	9.11	9.02
6	13.7	10.9	9.78	9.15	8.75	8.47	8.26	8.10	7.98	7.87	7.72	7.56	7.40	7.31	7.23	7.14	7.06	6.97	6.88
7	12.2	9.55	8.45	7.85	7.46	7.19	6.99	6.84	6.72	6.62	6.47	6.31	6.16	6.07	5.99	5.91	5.82	5.74	5.65
8	11.3	8.65	7.59	7.01	6.63	6.37	6.18	6.03	5.91	5.81	5.67	5.52	5.36	5.28	5.20	5.12	5.03	4.95	4.86
9	10.6	8.02	6.99	6.42	6.06	5.80	5.61	5.47	5.35	5.26	5.11	4.96	4.81	4.73	4.65	4.57	4.48	4.40	4.31
10	10.0	7.56	6.55	5.99	5.64	5.39	5.20	5.06	4.94	4.85	4.71	4.56	4.41	4.33	4.25	4.17	4.08	4.00	3.91
11	9.65	7.21	6.22	5.67	5.32	5.07	4.89	4.74	4.63	4.54	4.40	4.25	4.10	4.02	3.94	3.86	3.78	3.69	3.60
12	9.33	6.93	5.95	5.41	5.06	4.82	4.64	4.50	4.39	4.30	4.16	4.01	3.86	3.78	3.70	3.62	3.54	3.45	3.36
13	9.07	6.70	5.74	5.21	4.86	4.62	4.44	4.30	4.19	4.10	3.96	3.82	3.66	3.59	3.51	3.43	3.34	3.25	3.17
14	8.86	6.51	5.56	5.04	4.70	4.46	4.28	4.14	4.03	3.94	3.80	3.66	3.51	3.43	3.35	3.27	3.18	3.09	3.00
15	8.68	6.36	5.42	4.89	4.56	4.32	4.14	4.00	3.89	3.80	3.67	3.52	3.37	3.29	3.21	3.13	3.05	2.96	2.87
16	8.53	6.23	5.29	4.77	4.44	4.20	4.03	3.89	3.78	3.69	3.55	3.41	3.26	3.18	3.10	3.02	2.93	2.84	2.75
17	8.40	6.11	5.19	4.67	4.34	4.10	3.93	3.79	3.68	3.59	3.46	3.31	3.16	3.08	3.00	2.92	2.83	2.75	2.65
18	8.29	6.01	5.09	4.58	4.25	4.01	3.84	3.71	3.60	3.51	3.37	3.23	3.08	3.00	2.92	2.84	2.75	2.66	2.57
19	8.19	5.93	5.01	4.50	4.17	3.94	3.77	3.63	3.52	3.43	3.30	3.15	3.00	2.92	2.84	2.76	2.67	2.58	2.49
20	8.10	5.85	4.94	4.43	4.10	3.87	3.70	3.56	3.46	3.37	3.23	3.09	2.94	2.86	2.78	2.69	2.61	2.52	2.42
21	8.02	5.78	4.87	4.37	4.04	3.81	3.64	3.51	3.40	3.31	3.17	3.03	2.88	2.80	2.72	2.64	2.55	2.46	2.36
22	7.96	5.72	4.82	4.31	3.99	3.76	3.59	3.45	3.35	3.26	3.12	2.98	2.83	2.75	2.67	2.58	2.50	2.40	2.31
23	7.88	5.66	4.76	4.26	3.94	3.71	3.54	3.41	3.30	3.21	3.07	2.93	2.78	2.70	2.62	2.54	2.45	2.35	2.26
24	7.82	5.61	4.72	4.22	3.90	3.67	3.50	3.36	3.26	3.17	3.03	2.89	2.74	2.66	2.58	2.49	2.40	2.31	2.21
25	7.77	5.57	4.68	4.18	3.86	3.63	3.46	3.32	3.22	3.13	2.99	2.85	2.70	2.62	2.53	2.45	2.36	2.27	2.17
30	7.58	5.39	4.51	4.02	3.70	3.47	3.30	3.17	3.07	2.98	2.84	2.70	2.55	2.47	2.39	2.30	2.21	2.11	2.01
40	7.31	5.18	4.31	3.83	3.51	3.29	3.12	2.99	2.89	2.80	2.66	2.52	2.37	2.29	2.20	2.11	2.02	1.92	1.80
60	7.08	4.98	4.13	3.65	3.34	3.12	2.95	2.82	2.72	2.63	2.50	2.35	2.20	2.12	2.03	1.94	1.84	1.73	1.60
120	6.85	4.79	3.95	3.48	3.17	2.96	2.79	2.66	2.56	2.47	2.34	2.19	2.03	1.95	1.86	1.76	1.66	1.53	1.38
—	6.63	4.61	3.78	3.32	3.02	2.80	2.64	2.51	2.41	2.32	2.18	2.04	1.88	1.79	1.70	1.59	1.47	1.32	1.00

GLOSSARY OF TERMS

abstract level In theory development, the level of knowledge expressing a concept that exists only as an idea or a quality apart from an object.
acquiescence bias A category of response bias in which individuals have a tendency to agree with all questions or to indicate a positive connotation to a new idea.
administrative error An error caused by the improper administration or execution of a research task.
advocacy research Research undertaken to support a specific claim in a legal action.
affective component The component of attitude that reflects one's general feelings or emotions toward an object.
alternative hypothesis A statement indicating the opposite of the null hypothesis.
analysis of dependence A collective term to describe any multivariate statistical technique that attempts to explain or predict the dependent variable on the basis of two or more independent variables.
analysis of interdependence A collective term to describe any multivariate statistical technique that attempts to give meaning to a set of variables or seeks to group things together.
analysis of variance (ANOVA) Analysis of the effects of one treatment variable on an interval-scaled or ratio-scaled dependent variable; a technique to determine if statistically significant differences in means occur between two or more groups.
analysis of variance summary table A table that presents the results of a regression calculation.
applied research Research undertaken to answer questions about specific problems or to make decisions about a particular course of action or policy decision.
area sample A cluster sample in which the primary sampling unit is a geographic area.
attitude An enduring disposition to consistently respond in a given manner to various aspects of the world; composed of affective, cognitive, and behavioral components.
attitude rating scale Measures used to rate attitudes, such as the Likert scale, semantic differential, and Stapel scale.
attribute A single characteristic or fundamental feature of an object, person, situation, or issue.
auspices bias Bias in the responses of subjects caused by their being influenced by the organization conducting the study.
automatic interaction detection See *Chi-square automatic interaction detection (CHAID)*.
average deviation A measure of dispersion that is computed by calculating the deviation score of each observation value, summing up the deviation scores, and dividing by the sample size.

back translation Taking a questionnaire that has previously been translated into another language and then having a second, independent translator translate it back into the original language.
backward linkage A term implying that the late stages of the research process will have an influence on the early stages.
balanced rating scale A fixed-alternative rating scale that has an equal number of positive and negative categories; a neutral or indifference point is at the center of the scale.
bar chart A graphic aid that shows changes in a variable at discrete intervals.
base (base number) The number of respondents or observations that indicate a total; used as a basis for computing percentages in each column or row in a cross-tabulation table.
basic experimental design An experimental design in which a single independent variable is manipulated in order to observe its effect on a single dependent variable.
basic (pure) research Research that is intended to expand the boundaries of knowledge itself; or to verify the acceptability of a given theory.
behavioral component The component of attitude that includes buying intentions and behavioral expectations; reflects a predisposition to action.
behavioral differential An instrument developed to measure the behavioral intentions of subjects toward an object or category of objects.
between-group variance Variation of scores between groups due either to the manipulation of an independent variable or to characteristics of the independent variable.
bivariate data analysis A type of data analysis and hypothesis used in the testing when the investigation concerns simultaneous investigation of two variables using tests of differences or measures of association between two variables at a time.
bivariate linear regression A measure of linear association that investigates straight-line relationships of the type $Y = \alpha + \beta X$, where Y is the dependent variable, X is the independent variable, and a and b are two constants to be estimated.
bivariate statistics Tests of differences or measures of association between two variables at a time.
blinding A technique used to control subjects' knowledge of whether or not they have been given a particular experimental treatment.
box and whisker plot A graphic device that represents central tendencies, percentiles, variability, and frequency distributions.
briefing session A training session to ensure that all interviewers are provided with common information.
business intelligence software Computer programs that permit managers to restructure and analyze data in extensive data warehouses to discover significant patterns and relationships.
business research The systematic and objective process of gathering, recording, and analyzing data for aid in making business decisions.

callback An attempt to recontact an individual selected for the sample.
canonical correlation analysis A technique used to determine the degree of linear association between two sets of variables, each consisting of several variables.
case study method An exploratory research technique that intensively investigates one or a few situations similar to the researcher's problem situation.
categorical variable Any variable that has a limited number of distinct values.
category scale An attitude scale consisting of several response categories to provide the respondent with alternative ratings.
causal research Research conducted to identify cause-and-effect relationships among variables when the research problem has already been narrowly defined.
cell Section of a table representing a specific combination of two variables or a specific value of a variable.
census An investigation of all the individual elements making up a population.
central-limit theorem The theory stating that as a sample size increases, the distribution of sample means of size n, randomly selected, approaches a normal distribution.
central location interviewing The practice of conducting telephone interviews from a central location, which allows effective supervision and control of the quality of interviewing.
chart A graphic aid used to translate numerical information into visual form so that relationships may be easily understood.

check box In an Internet questionnaire, a small graphic box, next to an answer, that a respondent clicks on to choose that answer; typically, a check mark or an X appears in the box when the respondent clicks on it.
checklist question A type of fixed-alternative question that allows the respondent to provide multiple answers to a single question.
chi-square automatic interaction detection (CHAID) A clustering method used to investigate the interaction of a large set of independent variables; a method of breaking a large heterogeneous group into various homogeneous subgroups.
chi-square (χ^2) test A test that statistically determines significance in the analysis of frequency distributions.
choice technique A measurement task that identifies preferences by requiring respondents to choose between two or more alternatives.
classificatory variable See *Categorical variable.*
cluster analysis An analysis that classifies individuals or objects into a small number of mutually exclusive groups, ensuring that there will be as much likeness within groups and as much difference among groups as possible.
cluster sampling An economically efficient sampling technique in which the primary sampling unit is not the individual element in the population but a large cluster of elements.
code A rule used for interpreting, classifying, and recording data in the coding processes; the actual numerical or other character symbol assigned to raw data.
code book A book identifying each variable in a study and its position in the data matrix. The book is used to identify a variable's description, code name, and field.
code of ethics A statement of principles and operating procedures for ethical practice.
coding The process of identifying and classifying each answer with a numerical score or other character symbol.
coding sheet A ruled sheet of paper used to transfer data from questionnaires or data collection forms after data have been collected.
coefficient of correlation See *Simple correlation coefficient.*
coefficient of determination (r^2) A measure of that portion of the total variance of a variable that is accounted for by knowing the value of another variable.
coefficient of multiple determination In multiple regression, the percentage of the variance in the dependent variable that is explained by the variation in the independent variables.
coefficient of partial regression The percentage of the variance in the dependent variable that is explained by a single independent variable, with the other independent variables held constant.
cognitive component The component of attitude that represents one's awareness of and knowledge about an object.
cohort effect A change in the dependent variable resulting from subjects in one experimental condition experiencing historical situations different from those of subjects in other experimental conditions.
communality In factor analysis, a measure of the percentage of a variable's variation that is explained by the factors.
communication process The process by which one person or source sends a message to an audience or receiver and then receives feedback about the message.
comparative rating scale Any measure of attitudes that asks respondents to rate a concept in comparison with a benchmark explicitly used as a frame of reference.
completely randomized design (CRD) An experimental design that uses a random process to assign experimental units to treatments in order to investigate the effects of a single independent variable.
complex experimental design An experimental design that uses statistical methods to isolate the effects of extraneous variables or to allow for manipulation of multiple independent variables.
compromise design An approximation of an experimental design, which may fall short of the requirements of random assignment of subjects or treatments to groups.
computer-assisted telephone interviewing (CATI) A type of telephone interviewing in which the interviewer reads questions from a computer screen and enters the respondent's answers directly into a computer.
computer interactive survey A survey in which a respondent completes a self-administered questionnaire displayed on a computer monitor. The computer is programmed to ask questions in a sequence determined by respondents' previous answers.
computer map A computer-generated map that portrays a variable, such as demographic data, in two or three dimensions.
computerized, voice-activated telephone interviewing A form of computer-assisted interviewing in which a voice-synthesized module records a respondent's single-word response in a computer file.
concept A generalized idea about a class of objects, attributes, occurrences, or processes; an abstraction of reality that is the basic unit for theory development.
concept testing A form of research that tests something that acts as a proxy for a new or revised program, product, or service.
conceptual definition A verbal explanation of the meaning of a concept. It defines the domain of the concept, and it may explain what the concept is not.
concomitant variation The variation of two phenomena or events together.
concurrent validity A type of criterion validity whereby a new measure correlates with a criterion measure taken at the same time.
confidence interval estimate A specified range of numbers within which a population mean is expected to lie; the set of acceptable hypotheses or the level of probability associated with an interval estimate.
confidence level A percentage or decimal value that tells how confident a researcher can be about being correct. It states the long-run percentage of the time that a confidence interval will include the true population mean.
constancy of conditions A procedure in which subjects in experimental groups are exposed to situations identical except for differing conditions of the independent variable.
constant error An error that occurs in the same experimental condition every time the basic experiment is repeated.
constant-sum scale A measure of attitudes in which respondents are asked to divide a constant sum to indicate the relative importance of attributes.
construct validity The ability of a measure to confirm a network of related hypotheses generated from a theory based on the concepts.
consumer panel A sample of individuals or households that record their attitudes, behavior, or purchasing habits in a diary over time.
content analysis A research technique for the objective, systematic, and quantitative description of the manifest content of communication.
contingency table The results of a cross-tabulation of two variables, such as answers to two survey questions.
continuous variable Any variable that has an infinite number of possible values.
contrived observation Observation in which the investigator creates an artificial environment in order to test a hypothesis.
control group A group of subjects who are exposed to the control condition in an experiment—that is, they are subjects not exposed to the experimental treatment.
convenience sampling The sampling procedure used to obtain those units or people most conveniently available.
cookies Small computer files inserted by a content provider into the computer of a visitor to a Web site; a cookie allows the content provider to track the user's visits to other Web sites and store that information.
correlation coefficient See *Simple correlation coefficient.*
correlation matrix The standard form for reporting correlational results.
counterbalancing A technique to reduce error caused by order of presentation by varying the order of experimental treatments for different groups.
counterbiasing statement An introductory statement or preface to a question that reduces a respondent's reluctance to answer potentially embarrassing questions.
cover letter A letter that accompanies the questionnaire in a mail survey. Its purpose is to induce the reader to complete and return the questionnaire.

criterion validity The ability of some measure to correlate with other measures of the same construct.
critical values The values that lie exactly on the boundary of the region of rejection.
cross-check Comparison of data from one organization with data from another source.
cross-functional teams Teams of people from various departments within a company, who work together to accomplish a common goal.
cross-sectional study A study in which various segments of a population are sampled at a single point in time.
cross-tabulation Organizing data by groups, categories, or classes to facilitate comparisons; a joint frequency distribution of observations on two or more sets of variables.
cumulative percentage A percentage (or percentage distribution) that has increased by successive additions.
customer relationship management (CRM) A decision support system that brings together numerous pieces of information about customers and their relationship with the company.

data Recorded measures of certain phenomena.
data conversion The process of changing the original form of the data to a format suitable to achieve the research objective.
data entry The process of transferring data from a research project to computers.
data matrix A rectangular arrangement of data into rows and columns.
data mining The use of powerful computers to dig through and analyze volumes of data to discover patterns about an organization's customers, products, and activities.
data-processing error A category of administrative error that occurs because of incorrect data entry, incorrect computer programming, or other error during data analysis.
data transformation The process of changing data from their original form to a format that better supports data analysis to achieve research objectives. Also called data conversion.
database A collection of raw data or information arranged in a logical manner and organized in a form that can be stored and processed by a computer.
database search and retrieval system A computerized system that allows a user to find and retrieve data.
debriefing Providing subjects with all pertinent facts about the nature and purpose of an experiment after its completion.
decision support system A computer-based system that helps decision makers confront problems through direct interaction with databases and analytical software.
deductive reasoning The logical process of deriving a conclusion about a specific instance based on a known general premise or something known to be true.
degrees of freedom (d.f.) The number of constraints or assumptions needed to calculate a statistical term.
demand characteristics Experimental design procedures that unintentionally hint to subjects about the experimenter's hypothesis; situational aspects of an experiment that demand that the participant respond in a particular way.
dependence method Any multivariate statistical technique used to explain the behavior of one or more dependent variables on the basis of two or more independent variables. Multiple regression analysis is a dependence method.
dependent variable A criterion or a variable that is to be predicted or explained. The criterion or standard by which the results of an experiment are judged. It is so named because it is expected to be dependent on the experimenter's manipulation of the independent variable.
depth interview A relatively unstructured, extensive interview used in the primary stages of the research process.
descriptive analysis The transformation of raw data into a form that will make them easy to understand and interpret; rearranging, ordering, manipulating data to provide descriptive information.
descriptive research Research designed to describe characteristics of a population or a phenomenon.
descriptive statistics Statistics used to describe or summarize information about a population or sample.
determinant-choice question A type of fixed-alternative question that requires a respondent to choose one (and only one) response from among several possible alternatives.
diagnostic analysis Analysis used to clarify research findings, such as explanations respondents give for a behavior or attitude.
dialog box A window that opens on a computer screen to prompt the user to enter information.
direct data entry The use of a computer terminal as an input device for data storage.
direct observation A straightforward attempt to observe and record what naturally occurs; the investigator does not create an artificial situation.
discriminant analysis A statistical tool for determining linear combinations of independent variables that show large differences in group means. The intent is to predict the probability of objects belonging in two or more mutually exclusive categories based on several independent variables.
discriminant validity The ability of some measure to have a low correlation with measures of dissimilar concepts.
discussion guide Written prefatory remarks and an outline of topics/questions that will be addressed in a focus group.
disguised question An indirect type of question that assumes that the purpose of the study must be hidden from respondents.
disproportional stratified sample A stratified sample in which the sample size for each stratum is allocated according to analytical considerations.
door-in-the-face compliance technique A two-step method for securing a high response rate. In step 1 an initial request, so large that nearly everyone refuses it, is made. In step 2 a second request is made for a smaller favor; respondents are expected to comply with this more reasonable request.
door-to-door interview Personal interview conducted at the respondent's home or place of business.
double-barreled question A question that may induce bias because it covers two issues at once.
double-blind design A technique in which neither the subjects nor the experimenter knows which are the experimental and which are the controlled conditions.
drop-down box In an Internet questionnaire, a space-saving device that reveals responses when they are needed but otherwise hides them from view.
drop-off method A survey method that requires the interviewer to travel to the respondent's location to drop off questionnaires that will be picked up later.
dummy table Representation of an actual table that will be in the findings section of the final report; used to provide a better understanding of what the actual outcome of the research will be.

e-mail survey A survey that uses questionnaires distributed and returned by e-mail.
editing The process of making data ready for coding and transfer to data storage. Its purpose is to ensure the completeness, consistency, and reliability of data.
elaboration analysis An analysis of the basic cross-tabulation for each level of a variable not previously considered, perhaps subgroups of the sample.
electronic data exchange (EDI) The linking of two or more companies' computer systems.
electronic interactive media Communication media that allow an organization and an audience to interact using digital technology (for example, through the Internet).
empirical level Level of knowledge that is verifiable by experience or observation.
environmental scanning Information gathering designed to detect indications of environmental changes in their initial stages of development.
equivalent-form method A method of measuring the correlation between alternative instruments, designed to be as equivalent as possible, administered to the same group of subjects.
error checking The final stage of the coding process, during which codes are verified and corrected as necessary.
error trapping Using software to control the flow of an Internet questionnaire—for

example, to prevent respondents from backing up or failing to answer a question.
evaluation research The formal, objective measurement and appraisal of the extent to which a given activity, project, or program has achieved its objectives.
experience survey An exploratory research technique in which individuals who are knowledgeable about a particular research problem are surveyed.
experiment A research method in which conditions are controlled so that one or more variable can be manipulated in order to test a hypothesis and experimentation is a research method that, by manipulating only one variable, allows evaluation of causal relationships among the variables.
experimental group The group of subjects exposed to an experimental treatment.
experimental treatment An alternative manipulation of the independent variable being investigated.
experimenter bias An effect on an experiment's results caused by the experimenter's presence, actions, or comments.
exploratory research Initial research conducted to clarify and define the nature of a problem.
external validity The ability of an experiment to generalize the results to the external environment.
extremity bias A category of response bias that results because some individuals tend to use extremes when responding to questions.
eye-tracking equipment Any of a number of devices that record how a subject views a stimulus, such as an advertisement, and how much time is spent looking at the various parts of the stimulus.

***F*-statistic** A test statistic that measures the ratio of one sample variance to another sample variance, such as the variance between groups to the variance within groups.
***F*-test** A procedure used to determine if there is more variability in the scores of one sample than in the scores of another sample.
face (content) validity Professional agreement that a scale logically appears to accurately measure what it is intended to measure.
fact finding A secondary data research objective aimed at collecting descriptive information to support decision making.
factor analysis A type of analysis used to discern the underlying dimensions or regularity in phenomena. Its general purpose is to summarize the information contained in a large number of variables into a smaller number of factors. There are a number of factor-analytical techniques.
factor loading A measure of the importance of a variable in measuring a factor; a means for interpreting and labeling a factor.
factor score A number that represents each observation's calculated value on each factor in a factor analysis.
factorial design An experimental design that investigates the interaction of two or more independent variables.
fax survey A survey that uses questionnaires distributed and/or returned via fax machines.
feedback A reverse flow of communication that may be used to modify subsequent communication.
field A collection of characters that represent a single type of data.
field editing Preliminary editing by a field supervisor on the same day as the interview; its purpose is to catch technical omissions, check legibility of handwriting, and clarify responses that are logically or conceptually inconsistent.
field experiment An experiment conducted in a natural setting, often for a long period of time.
field interviewing service A research supplier that specializes in gathering data.
fieldworker An individual responsible for gathering data in the field; for example, a personal interviewer administering a door-to-door questionnaire.
file A collection of related records.
file server An Internet server that contains documents and programs that can be accessed and downloaded via the host to a user's own computer.
file transfer protocol (ftp) A software program that allows users to establish an interactive file transfer session with a remote host's computer system so that the user can read and download full-text versions of files from the remote system.
filter question A question in a questionnaire that screens out respondents not qualified to answer a second question.
fixed-alternative question A question in which the respondent is given specific limited alternative responses and asked to choose the one closest to his or her own viewpoint.
focus group interview An unstructured, free-flowing interview with a small group of people.
follow-up A letter or postcard reminding a respondent to return a questionnaire.
foot-in-the-door compliance technique Based on foot-in-the-door theory, which attempts to explain compliance with a large or difficult task on the basis of the respondent's prior compliance with a smaller request.
forced answering software Software that prevents respondents from continuing with an Internet questionnaire if they fail to answer a question.
forced-choice scale A fixed-alternative rating scale that requires respondents to choose one of the fixed alternatives.
forecasting An effort to predict future business activity using secondary data and statistical techniques.
forward linkage A term implying that the early stages of the research process will influence the design of the later stages.
frequency-determination question A type of fixed-alternative question that asks for an answer about general frequency of occurrence.
frequency distribution A set of data organized by summarizing the number of times a particular value of a variable occurs.
frequency table A simple tabulation that indicates the frequency with which respondents give a particular answer.
funnel technique Asking general questions before specific questions in order to obtain unbiased responses.

global information system An organized collection of computer hardware and software, data, and personnel designed to capture, store, update, manipulate, analyze, and immediately display information about worldwide business activity.
graphic (visual) aid A picture or diagram used to clarify a complex point or to emphasize a message.
graphic rating scale A measure of attitude consisting of a graphic continuum that allows respondents to rate an object by choosing any point on the continuum.
guinea pig effect An effect on the results of an experiment caused by subjects changing their normal behavior or attitudes in order to cooperate with an experimenter.

Hawthorne effect An unintended effect on the results of a research experiment caused by the subjects knowing that they are participants.
hidden observation Situation in which the subject is unaware that observation is taking place.
history effect A specific event in the external environment occurring between the first and second measurements that is beyond the control of the experimenter and that affects the validity of an experiment.
host Any computer that has access to other computers on the Internet. One or more people may log on to a host computer through their personal computers.
human interactive media Personal forms of communication in which a message is directed at an individual (or small group), who then has the opportunity to interact with the communicator.
hypothesis An unproven proposition or supposition that tentatively explains certain facts or phenomena; a proposition that is empirically testable.
hypothesis test of a proportion A statistical test of a hypothesis about a proportion of a population based on data for a sample from the population.
hypothetical construct A variable that is not directly observable but is measured through an indirect indicators, such as verbal expression or overt behavior.

iceberg principle The idea that the dangerous part of many business problems is neither visible to nor understood by business managers.
in-house editing A rigorous editing job performed by centralized office staff.
in-house interviewer A fieldworker who is employed by the company that will be

using the survey data rather than by a research supplier.
independent variable A variable that is expected to influence the dependent variable. Its value may be changed or altered independently of any other variable. In an experimental design, the variable that can be manipulated to be whatever the experimenter wishes.
index (composite) measure Multi-item instrument constructed to measure a single concept; also called a composite measure.
index number Data summary values based on data for some base period to facilitate comparisons over time.
inductive reasoning The logical process of establishing a general proposition on the basis of observation of particular facts.
inferential statistics Statistics used to make inferences or judgments about a population on the basis of a sample.
information A body of facts that are in a format suitable for decision making.
informed consent The expressed or implied acknowledgment waiving an individual's right to privacy when he or she agrees to participate in a research study.
instrument A data collection form such as a questionnaire or other measuring device.
instrumentation effect An effect on the results of an experiment caused by a change in the wording of questions, a change in interviewers, or other changes in procedures to measure the dependent variable.
interaction effect The influence on a dependent variable by combinations of two or more independent variables.
interactive help desk In an Internet questionnaire, a live, real-time support feature that solves problems or answers questions respondents may encounter in completing the questionnaire.
intercept An intercepted segment of a line. The point at which a regression line intersects the *Y*-axis.
internal and proprietary data Secondary data that are created, recorded, or generated by the organization.
internal records and reports system A data collection and retrieval system that establishes orderly procedures to ensure that data on costs, shipments, inventory, sales, and other recurrent data are routinely collected, entered, and stored in a computer.
internal source Source of secondary data that is found inside the organization. The data are often referred to as internal and proprietary.
internal validity Validity determined by whether an experimental treatment was the sole cause of changes in a dependent variable.
Internet A worldwide network of computers that allows access to information and documents from distant sources; a combination of a worldwide communication system and the world's largest public library, containing seemingly endless range of information.
Internet survey A self-administered questionnaire posted on a Web site.
interpretation The process of making inferences and drawing conclusions concerning the meaning and implications of a research investigation.
interquartile range The part of a data distribution between the 25th and 75th percentiles; also called the midspread.
interval scale A scale that not only arranges objects or alternatives according to their magnitudes but also distinguishes this ordered arrangement in units of equal intervals.
interviewer bias Bias in the responses of subjects due to the influence of the interviewer.
interviewer cheating The practice of filling in fake answers or falsifying questionnaires while working as an interviewer.
interviewer error Administrative error caused by failure of an interviewer to record response correctly.
intranet A company's private data network that uses Internet standards and technology.
intuitive decision making Decision making based on impressions or experience, without evident rational thought or inference.
item nonresponse The technical term for an unanswered question on an otherwise complete questionnaire.

judgment (purposive) sampling A nonprobability sampling technique in which an experienced researcher selects the sample based upon some appropriate characteristic of the sample members.

knowledge A blend of information, experience, and insights that provides a framework that can be thoughtfully applied when assessing new information or evaluating relevant situations.
knowledge management The process of creating an inclusive, comprehensive, easily accessible organizational memory, which is often called the organization's intellectual capital.

laboratory experiment An experiment conducted in a laboratory or artificial setting to obtain almost complete control over the research setting.
ladder of abstraction Organization of concepts in sequence from the most concrete and individual to the most general.
Latin square design A balanced, two-way classification scheme that attempts to control or block out the effect of two or more extraneous factors by restricting randomization with respect to row and column effects.
leading question A question that suggests or implies certain answers.
least-squares method A mathematical technique for ensuring that the regression line will best represent the linear relationship between *X* and *Y*.
Likert scale A measure of attitudes designed to allow respondents to indicate how strongly they agree or disagree with carefully constructed statements that range from very positive to very negative toward an attitudinal object.
line graph A graphic aid showing the relationship of one variable to another. The dependent variable is generally shown on the vertical axis and the independent variable on the horizontal axis.
list server An Internet server that permits subscribers to join a mailing list and communicate with others around the globe.
loaded question A question that suggests a socially desirable answer or is emotionally charged.
longitudinal study A survey of respondents at different points in time, thus allowing analysis of response continuity and changes over time.

magnitude of error A value from a confidence interval that indicates how precise an estimate must be.
mail survey A self-administered questionnaire sent through the mail to respondents.
mailing list A list of the names, addresses, and phone numbers of specific populations.
main effect The influence on a dependent variable by each independent variable (separately).
mall intercept interviews Personal interviews conducted in shopping malls.
marginals Row and column totals in a contingency table.
market potential An estimate based on secondary data of likely sales volume of a given product within a market.
market tracking The observation and analysis of trends in industry volume and brand share over time.
matching A procedure for the assignment of subjects to groups; it ensures each group of respondents is matched on the basis of pertinent characteristics.
maturation effect An effect on the results of a research experiment caused by changes in the experimental subjects over time.
mean A measure of central tendency; the arithmetic average.
measures of association Statistical values designed to represent covariation between variables.
mechanical observation Observation technique that uses video cameras, traffic counters, and other machines to record behavior.
median A measure of central tendency that is the midpoint; the value below which half the values in a sample fall.
mode A measure of central tendency; the value that occurs most often.
model A representation of a system or a process.
model building An attempt to specify relationships between variables based on secondary data, sometimes using descriptive or predictive equations.
moderator variable A third variable that, when introduced into an analysis, alters or

has a contingent effect on the relationship between an independent variable and a dependent variable.
monadic rating scale Any measure of attitudes that asks respondents about a single concept in isolation.
mortality effect Sample attrition that occurs when some subjects withdraw from an experiment before it is completed, thus affecting the validity of the experiment.
multidimensional scaling A technique that measures attitudes about objects in multidimensional space on the basis of respondents' judgments of similarity of objects.
multiple discriminant analysis A statistical technique for predicting the probability that an object will belong in one of two or more mutually exclusive categories (dependent variable), based on several independent variables.
multiple regression analysis An analysis of association in which the effects of two or more independent variables on a single, interval-scaled or ratio-scaled dependent variable are investigated simultaneously.
multistage area sampling Sampling that involves using a combination of other probability sampling techniques.
multivariate analysis of variance (MANOVA) A statistical technique that provides a simultaneous significance test of mean difference between groups, made for two or more dependent variables.
multivariate data analysis Statistical methods that allow the simultaneous investigation of more than two variables.

nominal scale A scale in which the numbers or letters assigned to objects serve as labels for identification or classification; a measurement scale of the simplest type.
nonforced-choice scale A fixed-alternative rating scale that provides a no-opinion category or that allows respondents to indicate that they cannot say which alternative is their choice.
nonparametric statistics Statistical procedures that use nominal- or ordinal-scaled data and make no assumptions about the distribution of the population (or sampling distribution).
nonprobability sampling A sampling technique in which units of the sample are selected on the basis of personal judgment or convenience.
nonrespondent A person who is not contacted or who refuses to cooperate in a research project.
nonresponse error The statistical difference between a survey that includes only those who responded and a perfect survey that would also include those who failed to respond.
normal distribution A symmetrical, bell-shaped distribution that describes the expected probability distribution of many chance occurrences.
not-at-home contact A potential respondent who is not at home or who is otherwise inaccessible on the first and second attempts at contact.
null hypothesis A statement about a status quo asserting that any change from what has been thought to be true will be due entirely to random error.
numerical scale An attitude rating scale similar to a semantic differential except that it uses numbers instead of verbal descriptions as response options to identify response positions.

observation The systematic recording of nonverbal as well as verbal behavior and communication.
observer bias A distortion of measurement resulting from the cognitive behavior or actions of the witnessing observer.
one-group pretest–posttest design A quasi-experimental design in which the subjects in the experimental group are measured before and after the treatment is administered but in which there is no control group.
one-shot design A quasi-experimental design in which a single measure is recorded after the treatment is administered and there is no control group. Also known as an after-only design.
online focus group A focus group whose members carry on their discussion through an Internet chat room.
open-ended box In an Internet questionnaire, a box where respondents can type in their own answers to open-ended questions.
open-ended response question A question that poses some problem and asks the respondent to answer in his or her own words.
operational definition A definition that gives meaning to a concept by specifying the activities or operations necessary in order to measure it.
opt in To give permission to receive selected e-mail, such as questionnaires, from a company with an Internet presence.
optical scanning system A data processing input device that reads material directly from mark sensed questionnaires.
optimal allocation stratified sample A sampling procedure in which both the size and the variation of each stratum are considered when determining sample size for each stratum.
oral presentation A spoken summary of the major findings, conclusions, and recommendations, given to clients or line managers to provide them with the opportunity to clarify any ambiguous issues by asking questions.
order bias Bias caused by the influence of earlier questions in a questionnaire or by an answer's position in a set of answers.
order of presentation bias An error in an experiment caused by subjects accumulating experience in the course of responding to multiple experimental treatments.
ordinal scale A scale that arranges objects or alternatives according to their magnitudes.
outlier A value that lies outside the normal range of a set of data.

paired comparison A measurement technique that involves presenting the respondent with two objects and asking the respondent to pick the preferred object. More than two objects may be presented, but comparisons are made in pairs.
panel study A longitudinal study that involves collecting data from the same sample of individuals or households over time.
parametric statistical procedures Statistical procedures that use interval-scaled or ratio-scaled data and assume populations or sampling distributions with normal distributions.
participant observation Situation in which an observer gains firsthand knowledge by being in or around the social setting being investigated.
percentage A part of a whole expressed in hundredths.
percentage distribution A frequency distribution into a table (or graph) that summarizes percentage values associated with particular values of a variable.
performance-monitoring research Research that regularly provides feedback for evaluation and control of business activity.
periodicity A problem that occurs in systematic sampling when the original list has a systematic pattern.
personal interview The gathering of information through face-to-face contact with an individual.
physical-trace evidence A visible mark of some past event or occurrence.
picture frustration A version of the Thematic Apperception Test that uses a cartoon drawing for which the respondent suggests dialogue that the cartoon characters might speak.
pie chart A graphic aid that shows the composition of some total quantity at a particular time; each angle, or "slice," is proportional to its percentage of the whole.
pilot study Any small-scale exploratory research technique that uses sampling but does not apply rigorous standards.
pivot question A filter question used to determine which version of a second question will be asked.
plug value An answer inserted according to a predetermined decision rule, if an editor finds a missing answer where there can be no missing values.
point estimate An estimate of the population mean in the form of a single value, usually the sample mean.
pooled estimate of the standard error An estimate of the standard error based on the assumption that variances of both groups (populations) are equal.
pop-up boxes In an Internet questionnaire, boxes that appear at selected points and contain information or instructions for respondents.
population (universe) A complete group of entities sharing some common set of characteristics.
population distribution A frequency distribution of the elements of a population.

population element An individual member of a specific population.
population parameter Variables in a population or measured characteristics of the population.
postcoding Determination of a framework for classifying responses to questions after editing, because coded categories cannot be established before data collection.
posttest-only control group design An after-only design in which the experimental group is tested after exposure to the treatment, and the control group is tested at the same time without having been exposed to the treatment; no premeasure is taken.
predictive validity A type of criterion validity whereby a new measure predicts a future event or correlates with a criterion measure administered at a later time.
preliminary tabulation Tabulation of the results of a pretest.
pretest A trial run with a group of respondents used to screen out problems in the instructions or design of a questionnaire.
pretest–posttest control-group design A true experimental design in which the experimental group is tested before and after exposure to the treatment, and the control group is tested at the same two times without being exposed to the experimental treatment.
pretesting The administration of a questionnaire to a small group of respondents in order to detect ambiguity or bias in the questions.
primary data Data gathered and assembled specifically for the research project at hand.
primary sampling unit (PSU) A unit selected in the first stage of sampling.
probability distribution The organization of probability values associated with particular values of a variable into a table (or graph).
probability sampling A sampling technique in which every member of the population has a known, nonzero probability of selection.
probing The verbal prompts made by a fieldworker when the respondent must be motivated to communicate his or her answer more fully. Probing encourages respondents to enlarge on, clarify, or explain answers.
problem definition The crucial first stage in the research process—determining the problem to be solved and the objectives of the research. The indication of a specific business decision area that will be clarified by answering some research questions.
production coding The physical activity of transferring the data from the questionnaire or data collection form after the data have been collected.
program strategy The overall plan to utilize a series of business research projects; a planning activity that places each project into the company's business plan.
projective technique An indirect means of questioning that enables a respondent to "project" beliefs and feelings onto a third party, an inanimate object, or a task situation.
proportion The percentage of population elements that successfully meet some criterion.
proportional stratified sample A stratified sample in which the number of sampling units drawn from each stratum is in proportion to the population size of that stratum.
proposition A statement concerned with the relationships among concepts; an assertion of a universal connection between events that have certain properties.
pseudo-research Research conducted for the purpose of organizational politics rather than to gather objective information for business decisions.
psychogalvanometer A device that measures galvanic skin response (GSR), involuntary changes in the electrical resistance of the skin.
psychographics A basis for market segmentation stressing consumer life-style characteristics and buying patterns in pursuit of life goals.
pupilometer A device used to observe and record changes in the diameter of the pupils of the eyes.
push button In a dialog box on an Internet questionnaire, a small outlined area, such as a rectangle or an arrow, that the respondent clicks on to select an option or perform a function, such as Submit.
push technology An information technology that delivers content to the viewer's desktop (using computer software known as smart agents or intelligent agents to find information) without the user's having to do the searching, or that stores entire Web sites on a user's computer for later viewing.

quadrant analysis A variation of the cross-tabulation table in which responses to two rating scale questions are plotted in four quadrants on a two-dimensional table.
quasi-experimental design An experimental design that fails to control adequately for loss of external or internal validity.
quota sampling A nonprobability sampling procedure that ensures that certain characteristics of a population sample will be represented to the exact extent that the investigator desires.

radio button In an Internet questionnaire, a circular icon, resembling a button, that activates one response choice and deactivates others when a respondent clicks on it.
random digit dialing A method of obtaining a representative sample for a telephone interview by using a table of random numbers to generate telephone numbers.
random error An error in which repetitions of the basic experiment sometimes favor one experimental condition and sometimes the other on a chance basis. See also *Random sampling error.*
random sampling error The difference between the result of a sample and the result of a census conducted using identical procedures; a statistical fluctuation that occurs because of chance variation in the elements selected for a sample.
randomization A procedure in which the assignment of subjects and treatments of groups is based on chance.
randomized block design (RBD) An extension of the completely randomized design in which a single extraneous variable that might affect test units' response to the treatment has been identified and the effects of this variable are isolated by being blocked out.
randomized response questions A research procedure for dealing with sensitive topics that uses a random procedure to determine which of two questions a respondent will be asked.
range The distance between the smallest and largest values of a frequency distribution.
range of possible random error The potential difference between a population mean and an observed value.
ranking A measurement task that requires that the respondents rank order a small number of activities, events, or objects on the basis of overall preference or some characteristic of the stimulus.
rating A measurement task that requires the respondent to estimate the magnitude of a characteristic or quality that an object possesses.
ratio scale A scale having absolute rather than relative quantities and possessing an absolute zero, where there is an absence of a given attribute.
recoding Changing codes to facilitate analysis.
record A collection of related fields.
refusal A person who is unwilling to participate in a research project.
region of rejection An area under a curve with values that are very unlikely to occur if the null hypothesis is true but relatively probable if the alternative hypothesis is true.
regression (bivariate) analysis A technique that attempts to predict the values of a continuous, interval-scaled or ratio-scaled dependent variable from the specific values of the independent variable.
reliability The degree to which measures are free from error and therefore yield consistent results.
repeat purchase rate Percentage of purchasers making a second or repeat purchase.
repeated measures Experimental technique in which the same subjects are exposed to all experimental treatments in order to eliminate any problems due to subject differences.
report format The general plan of organization for the parts of a written or oral research report.
research design A master plan specifying the methods and procedures for collecting and analyzing the needed information.
research follow-up Recontacting of decision makers and/or clients after they have had a chance to read a research report.

research methodology A discussion within the body of a research report of the research design, data collection methods, sampling techniques, fieldwork procedures, and data analysis efforts.
research objective The purpose of the research, expressed in measurable terms; the definition of what the research should accomplish.
research program Planning activity that identifies an ongoing series of research projects designed to supply an organization's continuing information needs.
research project A specific research investigation; a study that completes or is planned to follow the stages in the research process.
research proposal A written statement of the research design that includes a statement explaining the purpose of the study and a detailed, systematic outline of a particular research methodology.
research report A presentation of research findings directed to a specific audience to accomplish a specific purpose.
research supplier A commercial business research service that conducts business research activity for clients. The research supplier may be thought of as a business research consulting company.
residual The difference between the actual value of the dependent variable and the estimated value of the dependent variable in the regression equation.
respondent The person who answers an interviewer's questions or provides answers to written questions in a self-administered survey.
respondent error A classification of sample biases resulting from some respondent action or inaction, such as nonresponse or response bias.
response bias Survey error that occurs when respondents tend to answer questions in a certain direction. Examples of response bias are acquiescence bias, extremity bias, interviewer bias, auspices bias, and social desirability bias.
response latency The time it takes to decide between two alternatives; used as a measure of the strength of preference.
response rate The number of questionnaires returned or completed, divided by the total number of eligible people who were contacted or asked to participate in the survey.
reverse directory A directory similar to a telephone directory in which listings are by city and street address or by telephone numbers rather than alphabetical by last name.
role playing A projective research technique that requires the subject to act out someone else's behavior in a particular setting.
rotation In factor analysis, changing of geometric axes that represent the factors so as to contemplate a new problem solution having fewer or more factors.
rule of measurement An instruction to guide assignment of a number or other measurement designation.
sample A subset, or some part, of a larger population.
sample bias A persistent tendency for the results of a sample to deviate in one direction from the true value of the population parameter.
sample distribution A frequency distribution of the elements of a sample.
sample selection error An administrative procedural error caused by improper selection of a sample, thus introducing bias.
sample size The size of a sample; the number of observations or cases specified by (1) the estimated variance of the population, (2) the magnitude of acceptable error, and (3) the confidence level.
sample statistics Variables in a sample or measures computed from sample data.
sample survey Formal term for survey; it indicates that the purpose of contacting respondents is to obtain a representative sample of the target population.
sampling The process of using a small number of items or parts of a larger population to make conclusions about the whole population.
sampling distribution A theoretical probability distribution of all possible samples of a certain size drawn from a particular population.
sampling error See *Random sampling error.*
sampling frame The list of elements from which a sample may be drawn; also called working population.
sampling frame error Error that occurs when certain sample elements are not listed or available and are not represented in the sampling frame.
sampling interval The number of population elements between units selected for the sample.
sampling unit A single element or group of elements subject to selection in the sample.
sampling verification A fieldwork supervision task that requires checking to assure that samples conform to a project's sampling plan.
scale Any series of items that are progressively arranged according to value or magnitude; a series into which an item can be placed according to its quantification.
scanner data Product and brand sales data collected through optical character-recognition systems.
scientific method Techniques or procedures used to analyze empirical evidence in an attempt to confirm or disprove prior conceptions.
scientific observation The systematic process of recording the behavioral patterns of people, objects, and occurrences as they are witnessed.
search engine A computerized directory that allows anyone to search the World Wide Web for information in a particular way. Some search titles or headers of documents, others search the documents themselves, and still others search other indexes or directories.
secondary data Data that have been previously collected for some purpose other than the one at hand.
secondary data analysis Preliminary review of data collected for another purpose to clarify issues in the early stages of a research effort.
secondary sampling unit A unit selected in the second stage of sampling.
selection effect A sample bias resulting in differential selection of respondents for the comparison groups.
self-administered questionnaire A questionnaire that is filled in by the respondent rather than by an interviewer.
self-selection bias A bias that occurs because people who feel strongly about a subject are more likely to respond to survey questions than people who feel indifferent about that subject.
semantic differential An attitude measure consisting of a series of seven-point bipolar rating scales allowing response to a concept.
sensitivity A measurement instrument's ability to accurately measure variability in stimuli or responses.
sentence completion A projective technique in which respondents are required to complete a number of partial sentences with the first word or phrase that comes to mind.
server A computer that provides services on the Internet. A *file server* is an Internet server containing documents and programs that can be accessed and downloaded via the host to the user's own computer. A *list server* is an Internet server that admits subscribers to a mailing list to communicate with each other around the globe.
significance level The critical probability in choosing between the null and alternative hypotheses; the probability level that is too low to warrant support of the null hypothesis.
simple correlation coefficient A statistical measure of the covariation, or association, between two variables.
simple-dichotomy question A fixed-alternative question that requires the respondent to choose one of two alternatives.
simple random sampling A sampling procedure that assures each element in the population an equal chance of being included in the sample.
simple tabulation Counting the number of different responses to a question and arranging them in a frequency distribution.
situation analysis A preliminary investigation or informal gathering of background information to familiarize researchers or managers with the decision area.
slope The inclination of a regression line as compared to a base line, rise (vertical distance) over run (horizontal difference).
smart agent software Software that learns preferences and finds information without the user's having to search for it.
snowball sampling A sampling procedure in which initial respondents are selected by probability methods and additional respondents are obtained from information provided by the initial respondents.
social desirability bias Bias in the responses of subjects caused by their desire,

either conscious or unconscious, to gain prestige or to appear in a different social role.
societal norms Codes of behavior adopted by a group, suggesting what a member of the group ought to do under given circumstances.
Solomon four-group design A true experimental design that combines both the pretest-posttest with control group and the posttest-only with control group designs, thereby providing a means for controlling the interactive testing effect and other sources of extraneous variation.
sorting technique A measurement technique that presents a respondent with several concepts printed on cards and requires the respondent to arrange the cards into a number of piles to classify the concepts.
split-ballot technique A technique used to control for response bias. Two alternative phrasings of the same questions are utilized for respective halves of the sample to yield a more accurate total response than would be possible if only a single phrasing were utilized.
split-half method A method of measuring the degree of internal consistency by checking one half of the results of a set of scaled items against the other half.
spurious relationship An apparent relationship between two variables that is not authentic, but appears authentic because an elaboration analysis with a third variable has not yet been conducted.
standard deviation A quantitative index of a distribution's spread or variability; the square root of the variance.
standard error of the mean The standard deviation of the sampling distribution of the mean.
standard error of the proportion The standard deviation of the sampling distribution of the proportion.
standardized normal distribution A normal curve with a mean of zero and a standard deviation of one. It is a theoretical probability distribution.
Stapel scale An attitude measure that places a single adjective in the center of an even number of numerical values.
static group design An after-only design in which subjects in the experimental group are measured after being exposed to the experimental treatment, and the control group is measured without having been exposed to the experimental treatment; no pretreatment measure is taken.
status bar In an Internet questionnaire, a visual indicator that tells the respondent what portion of the survey he or she has completed.
stratified sampling A probability sampling procedure in which subsamples are drawn from simple random within different strata that are more or less equal on some characteristic.
streaming media Multimedia content, such as audio or video, that can be accessed on the Internet without being downloaded first.
structured question A question that imposes a limit on the number of allowable responses.
survey A research technique in which information is gathered from a sample of people by use of a questionnaire or interview; a method of data collection based on communication with a representative sample of individuals.
syndicated service A business research supplier that provides standardized information for many clients, such as, for example, the A. C. Nielsen Retail Index.
systematic (nonsampling) error Error resulting from some imperfect aspect of the research design that causes response error or from a mistake in the execution of the research; error arising from sample bias, mistakes in recording responses, or nonresponses from persons who were not contacted or who refused to participate.
systematic sampling A sampling procedure in which an initial starting point is selected by a random process, and then every nth number on the list is selected.

***t*-distribution** A family of symmetrical, bell-shaped distributions with a mean of 0 and a standard deviation of 1, used when the population standard deviation is unknown or when testing a hypothesis with a small sample size.
***t*-test** A univariate hypothesis test using the t-distribution rather than the *Z*-distribution. It is used when the population standard deviation is unknown and the sample size is small.
***t*-test for difference of means** A technique used to test the hypothesis that the mean scores on some interval-scaled variable are significantly different for two independent samples or groups.
table A graphic aid generally used for presenting numerical information, especially when such information can be arranged in rows and columns.
tabulation The orderly arrangement of data in a frequency table or other summary format.
tachistoscope A device that controls the amount of time a subject is exposed to a visual image.
target population The specific, complete group relevant to the research project.
telephone interviewing Contacting respondents by telephone to gather responses to survey questions.
telephone survey The data collection method that uses telephone interviewing to collect the data.
test of differences Investigation of a hypothesis that states that two (or more) groups differ with respect to measures on a variable.
test marketing The scientific testing and controlled experimental procedure that provides an opportunity to test a new product or a new marketing plan under realistic marketing conditions to obtain a measure of sales or profit potentials.
test-retest method The administering of the same scale or measure to the same respondents at two separate points in time in order to test for reliability.
test tabulation Tallying of a small sample of the total number of replies to a particular question during the coding process in order to construct coding categories.
test unit A subject or entity whose responses to experimental treatments are observed and measured.
testing effect In a before-and-after study the effect of pretesting, which may sensitize subjects when taking a test for the second time, thus affecting the validity of the experiment.
thematic apperception test (TAT) A test consisting of a series of pictures shown to research subjects who are then asked to provide a description of the pictures. The researcher analyzes the content of these descriptions in an effort to clarify a research problem.
theory A coherent set of general propositions used to explain the apparent relationships among certain observed phenomena. Theories allow generalizations beyond individual facts or situations.
third-person technique A projective technique in which the respondent is asked why a third person does what he or she does or what he or she thinks about an object, event, person, or activity. The respondent is expected to transfer his or her attitudes to the third person.
Thurstone scale An attitude measure in which judges assign scale values to attitudinal statements and then subjects are asked to respond to these statements.
time-series design An experimental design utilized when experiments are conducted over long periods of time. It allows researchers to distinguish between temporary and permanent changes in dependent variables.
total quality management (TQM) A business philosophy that focuses on integrating customer-driven quality throughout the organization.
total variance In analysis of variance, the sum of within-group variance and between-group variance.
training interview A practice session during which an inexperienced fieldworker records answers on a questionnaire to develop skills and clarify project requirements.
Type I error An error caused by rejecting the null hypothesis when it is true.
Type II error An error caused by failing to reject the null hypothesis when the alternative hypothesis is true.

unbalanced rating scale A fixed-alternative rating scale that has more response categories piled up at one end of the scale and an unequal number of positive and negative categories.

undisguised question A straightforward question that assumes the respondent is willing to reveal the answer.
univariate data analysis A type of analysis that assesses the statistical significance of a hypothesis about a single variable.
universal product code (UPC) A system that records product and brand sales information in bar codes that can be read by optical scanners.
unstructured question A question that does not restrict the respondent's answers.
user interaction system Computer software that manages the interface between the user and the system.

validity The ability of a scale or measuring instrument to measure what it is intended to measure.
variable Anything that may assume different numerical or categorical values.
variable piping software Software that allows variables to be inserted into an Internet questionnaire as a respondent is completing it.
variance A measure of variability or dispersion. The square root is the standard deviation.
verification The quality control procedures used in fieldwork to ensure that interviewers are following the sampling procedures; the method used to determine if interviewers are falsifying interviews.
verification by reinterviewing A fieldwork supervision task that requires recontacting respondents to assure that interviews were properly conducted.
visible observation Situation in which the observer's presence is known to the subject.
voice pitch analysis A physiological measurement technique that records abnormal frequencies in the voice that are supposed to reflect emotional reactions to various stimuli.

welcome screen The first Web page in an Internet survey, which introduces the survey and requests that the respondent enter a password or PIN.
within-group variance Variation of scores within a group due to random error or individual difference.
word association test A projective research technique in which the subject is presented with a list of words, one at a time, and asked to respond with the first word that comes to mind.
World Wide Web (WWW) A portion of the Internet that is a system of computer servers that organize information into documents called Web pages.

***Z*-test** A univariate hypothesis test using the standardized normal distribution, which is the distribution of Z.
***Z*-test for differences of proportions** A technique is used to test the hypothesis that proportions are significantly different for two independent samples or groups.

INDEX

A

B

C

D